EIGHTH EDITION

Sewerage and sewage treatment

Harold E. Babbitt

Professor Emeritus of Sanitary Engineering
University of Illinois

E. Robert Baumann

Professor of Civil Engineering
Iowa State College

NEW YORK · JOHN WILEY & SONS, INC.

London · Chapman & Hall, Ltd.

Preface

A new edition of a book is expected to emphasize the advance of knowledge in the field covered. However, insofar as sewerage and sewage treatment are concerned, in the words of the Committee on Sewerage and Sewage Treatment of the American Society of Civil Engineers: [1] "Changes in sewer design and construction rarely occur with suddenness and almost never with the fanfare that sometimes accompanies new developments in sewage treatment processes and in sludge disposal methods. Sewerage changes are evolutionary. . . ." The eighth edition marks a signal development in the life of this book, which first appeared in 1922. This development is the association of a new author in its preparation. The advent of the younger man should revitalize the text, eliminate deadwood, and assist in maintaining a close sympathy with the needs of the student and the younger engineer.

Changes from the seventh edition are scattered throughout the text. Each paragraph has been reviewed and where change has not been justified none has been made. All chapters show effects of review and reconsideration. Although new methods, new processes, and new standards continue to develop, their inclusion cannot be permitted to increase the size of the book. Hence, additions are balanced by deletions, as much as feasible. Easily observable additions include copious references to the literature. The book thus becomes somewhat of a review of literature and provides an open sesame to the researcher in any particular corner of the field. An attempt has been made to use the units of expression recommended by the Committee of the Federation of Sewage and Industrial Wastes Associations [2] as far as current practice will permit. Time will be required to make

---

[1] American Society of Civil Engineers, *Jour. San. Eng. Div.*, Paper 1013, June, 1956.

[2] See *Sewage and Industrial Wastes*, February, 1957, p. 134.

the complete adoption of such units general in practice. Answers to about one-half of the problems have been included. If experience follows that of a previous edition in which answers were included, there will be an increase of correspondence with users unable to check the published answer. The chapter on industrial wastes has been revamped by placing industrial processes in alphabetical order, and by the addition of some processes. The growing emphasis on oxidation ponds is recognized by devoting added space to the subject, and the increased attention in practice to sludge treatment and disposal has been recognized by increased emphasis in the book.

Deletions, to provide space, have been made by limiting the references to dates subsequent to 1940, insofar as may have been considered reasonable. References given will lead to earlier publications so that the field is open to the searcher wishing to pursue the subject more deeply. Some of the discussion on construction has been shortened, as, for example, explosives and blasting. Despite its importance in sewerage this subject can be dealt with more thoroughly in a text devoted to general civil engineering construction.

Illustrations have been changed so that almost half differ from the previous edition. Pertinent data have been placed in the tables to aid in the preparation and solution of problems in the book and to aid in the design of sewers and of sewage treatment plants.

It is noted that the preface of the previous edition was dated February, 1953. The closing words to that preface are equally applicable today. It said: "Frequent revision of this book is necessary, therefore, to keep the student and the practitioner informed of the latest practices in the field."

H. E. BABBITT
E. R. BAUMANN

August, 1958

Contents

Chapter 1

Introduction

1-1. Sewers. A sewer is a channel or conduit intended for the conveyance of liquid wastes. The water carriage of wastes in a comprehensive system of conduits, commonly called a sewer system, is a relatively recent development historically. Modern cities could not exist on a high plane of sanitation without the protection to health and the convenience that are afforded by a comprehensive sewer system. Although practically all cities in the United States are sewered, changing populations, increasing loads, depreciation, and other conditions will continue to demand the maintenance and improvement of old sewer facilities and also the design and construction of additional utilities. It was estimated by the United States Public Health Service, in 1955,[1] that an annual expenditure of a quarter of a billion dollars would be necessary to keep pace with sewerage needs in the United States.

1-2. Sewage treatment and disposal. The collection and concentration of the liquid wastes from a community, known as *sewage*, create a problem of its disposal requiring solution for the protection of the health and comfort of the public. The ultimate disposal of sewage can be only onto land or into water.

The land disposal of sewage includes spreading it on the ground surface; distributing it just beneath the ground surface through a system of subsurface distribution pipes; discharging it, under favorable conditions, into leaching pits or drainage wells; or discharging it into dry stream beds from which it may soak into the ground or flow ultimately into a body of water. Some form of treatment to prepare sewage for ultimate disposal is commonly required. The solid matters removed by treatment may be buried, burned, dumped into water, or used for commercial purposes such as fertilizer filler.

---

[1] See *Sewage and Industrial Wastes,* hereinafter abbreviated as *S. and I.W.,* December, 1955, p. 1382.

1

If the volume of diluting water or the area and nature of land used for disposal are not as they should be, a nuisance will be created. The aim of all methods of sewage treatment has so far been to produce an effluent which could be disposed of without nuisance and, in certain exceptional cases, to protect public water supplies from pollution. Financial returns have been sought only as a secondary consideration. A few sewage farms and irrigation projects might be considered exceptions to this, because the value of the water in the sewage as an irrigant has been the primary incentive in the promotion of such farms.

It is to be remembered that, since the aim of all sewage treatment is to produce an effluent that can be disposed of without causing a nuisance, the simplest process by which this result can be attained under the conditions presented is the process to be adopted. Sewage cannot be *purified*. Drinking water cannot be made from it in a practical manner and on a large scale.

In the treatment of sewage highly specialized knowledge is needed for the design, construction, maintenance, and operation of the equipment and structures required. The art of sewage treatment is in a state of flux owing to the ever-changing and increasing knowledge of the chemical and biological activities involved. The engineer in sewage treatment must, therefore, be constantly alert to the changing conditions in order that treatment plants may be designed and operated so as to give the required services with greatest satisfaction at lowest cost.

1–3. Methods of collection. The so-called *dry method* for the collection of human excreta preceded the modern *water-carriage method* of collection. The dry method, still practiced in unsewered areas throughout the world, consists of the accumulation of night soil in privies, midden heaps, and cesspools, and its removal by manual methods and its transportation in vehicles to points of ultimate disposal.

The mixing of human excreta with sufficient water to act as a vehicle to create *sewage*, together with the collection of sewage in a system of pipes through which it is conducted by the buoyant effect and scouring velocity of water, is known as the *water-carriage system*. The dilution of the solid matter in water to form sewage is normally so great that the mixture flows according to the laws of hydraulics as applied to water. It will flow through properly designed and maintained conduits and will be conveyed to the point of treatment or of ultimate disposal.

1–4. Sewer, sewage, and sewerage. Three terms in common use in sanitary engineering are sewer, sewage, and sewerage. They require definition.

The word *sewer*, as a noun, refers to a conduit or channel intended to convey sewage; the verb *sewer* means to supply or equip with sewers; and as an adjective *sewer* means pertaining to sewers as, for example, a sewer system.

Sewage, as a noun, means used water together with such organic and inorganic solids, liquid industrial wastes, ground water, and dry-weather runoff as may be mixed with it. *Sewage*, as an adjective, pertains to sewers or sewerage as, for example, sewage works or sewage association. It is preferable to use the term sewer system rather than sewage system. The word sewage cannot be used correctly as a verb.

Sewerage, as a noun, may mean: (1) the structures, devices, equipment, and appurtenances intended for the collection, transportation, and pumping of sewage and other liquid wastes, but excluding works for the treatment of sewage; or (2) the plan or idea for the collection of and the removal of sewage from a community. *Sewerage* may be used as an adjective, but not as a noun, synonymously with sewage. The word sewerage is also used correctly as a noun or an adjective to include everything in connection with the problems of a community and its sewage as, for example, in the titles Milwaukee Sewerage Commission or the Seattle Metropolitan Sewerage Survey. In these cases everything encompassed within the problem is included, as collection, pumping, conveyance, treatment, and financing.

It is to be emphasized that the preceding are definitions of the words as used *technically*, and they do not agree in all aspects with the standard dictionary definitions. For example, it is technically incorrect to use the word sewerage to mean used water, although certain dictionaries permit such use of the term.

1–5. Types of sewers. The special uses to which sewers are put necessitate names to differentiate them. Among these special names are:

Branch sewer, a sewer which receives sewage from a relatively small area, usually a few laterals, and discharges into a main sewer. *Combined sewer*, a sewer that receives storm water, surface runoff, and sewage. *Common sewer*, a sewer in which all abutters have equal rights. *Depressed sewer*, synonymous with siphon or inverted siphon, a section of a sewer constructed lower than adjacent sections, to pass beneath an obstacle or obstruction. It runs full under the force of gravity and at greater than atmospheric pressure, the sewage entering and leaving at atmospheric pressure. *Intercepting sewer,* "a sewer which receives dry-weather flow from a number of transverse sewers or outlets and frequently additional predetermined quantities of storm water (if from a combined system), and conducts such waters to a point for treatment and disposal." [2] An intercepting sewer is usually a large sewer, flowing parallel to a natural drainage channel, into which a number of main or outfall sewers discharge. *Lateral* or *lateral sewer,* a sewer discharging into another sewer and having no other common sewer tributary to it. *Main* or *trunk sewer,* a sewer that receives sewage from many tributary branches and sewers, serving as an outlet for a large territory. *Outfall* sewer, a sewer that receives the sewage from the collection system and conducts it to a point of final discharge or to a disposal plant. It may, in general, be considered as that portion of a main or trunk sewer below the lowest branch. *Relief sewer* or *overflow sewer,* a sewer built to carry the flows in excess of the capacity of an existing sewer. *Sanitary sewer,* a sewer intended to carry sanitary sewage. *Separate sewer,* a sewer intended to carry only sanitary sewage and dry-weather flow. *Storm sewer, storm-water drain,* or *storm-water channel,* "a sewer which carries storm water and surface water, street wash, and other wash waters, or drainage, but excludes sewage and industrial wastes." [2] *Storm overflow* or *storm-water overflow,* "a sewer used to carry the excess of storm flow from a main or intercepting sewer to an independent outlet." [2] *Trunk sewer,* "a sewer which receives many tributary branches and serves a large territory." [2]

1–6. Types of sewage. Among the different types of sewage may be included:

Combined sewage, a combination of sanitary sewage and surface or storm water, with or without industrial wastes. *Crude sewage* or *raw sewage,* untreated sewage. *Dilute* or *weak sewage,* "sewage containing less than 150 ppm (parts per million) of suspended solids and BOD (biochemical oxygen demand)." [2] *Domestic sewage,* "sewage derived principally from dwellings, business buildings, institutions, and the like. (It may or may not contain ground water, surface water, or storm water.)" [2] *Dry-weather flow,* the normal flow in a sewer during dry weather. *Fresh sewage,* "sewage of recent origin containing dissolved oxygen at the point of examination." [2]. *Ground water* or *infiltration water,* water that has leached from the ground into the sewer. *House sewage,* "sewage from dwellings . . . and loosely used for domestic sewage." [2] *Industrial sewage,* "sewage in which industrial wastes predominate." [2] *Sanitary sewage,* sewage containing human excrement: "(1) domestic sewage with storm and surface water excluded; (2) sewage

[2] From *Glossary of Water and Sewage Control Engineering,* prepared by a Joint Committee and published about 1949 by the American Public Health Assoc., American Water Works Assoc., American Society Civil Engineers, and Federation of Sewage Works Association.

discharging from the sanitary conveniences of dwellings (including apartment houses and hotels), office buildings, factories, or institutions; and (3) the water supply of a community after it has been used and discharged into a sewer." [2] *Septic sewage*, "sewage undergoing putrefaction under anaerobic conditions." [2] *Stale sewage*, "a sewage containing little or no oxygen, but as yet free from putrefaction." [2] *Storm water* or *storm sewage* is the excess water from rainfall that runs off on the surface of the ground. It is to be distinguished from *surface water*, which is water other than storm water flowing on or over the surface of the ground.

1-7. Physical characteristics of sewage. Sewage contains a small amount of solids in a proportionally tremendous weight of water. In normal, domestic sewage it may be expected that 1 ton or more of water will carry 1 lb of solids,[3] of which ½ lb is in solution, ¼ lb will settle, and ¼ lb is in suspension.

Ordinary fresh sewage is gray, somewhat of the appearance of soapy dishwater. It contains particles of suspended matter that are visible to the naked eye. If the sewage is fresh, some of the suspended matter can be distinguished as matches, bits of paper, fecal matter, rags, etc. The weight of solids in the strongest sewage is relatively so small that it has no appreciable effect on the specific gravity of the liquid and does not necessitate the modification of hydraulic formulas developed for application to the flow of water.

Solids in sewage may be classified as organic and inorganic. The organic solids, usually constituting 40 to 70 per cent of the total solids, cause putrefactive odors and the greatest difficulties in sewage disposal. The inorganic solids are usually innocuous and comprise the greater portion of easily settled grit.

The odor of fresh sewage is faint and not necessarily unpleasant. Sewage has a slightly pungent odor, somewhat like a damp, unventilated cellar. Occasionally the odor of gasoline, or some other predominating waste matter, may mask all other odors. Stale sewage is black and gives off nauseating odors of hydrogen sulfide and other gases. If the sewage is so stale as to become septic, bubbles of gas will be seen breaking the surface, and a black or gray scum may be present.

1-8. Types of sewer systems. Sewer systems may be laid out as a system of separate sewers and a system of storm sewers; as a system of combined sewers; or as a system containing some separate sewers, some storm sewers, and some combined sewers. Experience in many

---

[3] Equivalent to 500 parts per million (500 ppm) or mg/l.

localities has shown that regardless of care in design or operation of a separate system some storm water will find its way into the separate sewers. The fact that separate sewers are frequently abused after construction by receiving connections from roof drains and surface drainage outlets must be borne in mind, as such connections will quickly cause the surcharge of the separate sewers, resulting in an overflow of disgusting sanitary sewage.

The use of a separate system is desirable where:

a. The sanitary sewage must be concentrated at one outlet, such as at a treatment plant, and other outlets are available for the storm drainage.

b. The sanitary sewage must be pumped.

c. The topography is flat, necessitating deep excavation for combined sewers.

d. The separate sewers must be placed materially deeper than the depth necessary for the storm-water drains.

e. Drainage areas are short and steep, facilitating the rapid flow of water over street surfaces to natural drainage channels.

f. The sewers are to be laid in rock, necessitating more difficult excavation for the larger combined sewers.

g. An existing sewer system can be used to convey the sanitary sewage, but is not large enough to convey storm water.

h. The finances are such that the greater cost of the combined system cannot be met and sanitary drainage is imperative. This condition is sometimes encountered where the district to be sewered is an old residential section in which property values are insufficient to meet the necessary assessment.

i. Sewers are being built in advance of the city's settlement, to encourage growth.

j. Combined sewers will back up into house sewers, flooding basements.

A system of combined sewers may be used where:

a. Both the sanitary sewage and the storm water must be pumped.

b. The district to be sewered is densely built up and there is restricted space for two underground conduits.

c. Regulators can be provided to divert a portion of the flow during a storm, discharging it into a natural drainage channel, while an amount equal to a designed proportion of the dry-weather flow continues to another outlet.

d. A storm sewer exists or must be constructed and the additional amount of sewage is a small percentage of the maximum flow; or the additional cost of a separate sewer, including the cost of pumping and treatment, will exceed the cost of a combined sewer, and sanitary considerations will not prohibit the dischage of combined sewage at the outlet or outlets.

The construction of a combined sewer system relieves the property owner from a degree of complication and expense in his plumbing, and it relieves the city officials from the difficulties of keeping separate sewers separate. On the other hand, odors from combined sewers may become objectionable during protracted dry weather.

The trend today is towards the use of separate sewers, with generous allowance of additional capacity to care for almost inevitable abuse.

1–9. Reliability and liability. The escape of sanitary sewage into habitable portions of a community is a threat to the public health and a violation of common decency. Sanitary sewers should be so reliable that sewage cannot flow into habitable places. A storm sewer may be of such size as to permit an occasional overflow where the cost of a larger sewer cannot be justified by convenience, economy, or law.

Legal liability attaches to authorities responsible for the construction or maintenance of inadequate sewers.[4] The legal principle on which liability is based is, in general, that the authority is liable which knowingly, either carelessly or deliberately, permits a remediable condition to exist that results in damage to a complainant. If a sewer is constructed and causes damage where no damage occurred before, the constructing authority is legally liable. Where no sewer has been constructed or where the cause of flooding is unknown and could not easily have been determined, or where the flooding was due to an "act of God," the sewer authority is not legally liable. Relief from legal liability may be allowed if a competent engineer has been retained. If a remediable, potential cause of damage has been foreseen, or should have been foreseen, and reasonable precautions have not been taken promptly to avoid damage, the responsible authority is guilty of negligence and is legally liable for resulting damage.

1–10. The work of the engineer. The work of the engineer in connection with sewerage can be divided into preliminary or de-

[4] See legal decisions reported periodically in *Public Health Reports*, published by the U. S. Public Health Service.

velopmental work, design, construction, maintenance, administration, and operation. Each period calls for different qualifications. In the developmental period the engineer is dealing with economics and humanities. In the period of design he must apply knowledge of economics, physical laws, and the behavior of materials. He must avoid any tendency to overdesign in order to increase the magnitude of the works and the profits of the designers or the builders.[5] In the period of construction he must be able to handle men, to obtain materials, and to direct work economically and expeditiously, following the plans and the specifications. As an official responsible for the operation and maintenance of works the engineer must be an administrator. In his capacity as an administrator the engineer must have knowledge of the principles and practices in organization, supervision, staff and line service, administration, and management control; personnel selection, evaluation, and control; and process control.[6]

In the treatment of sewage the engineer must know the scientific principles involved in the biological, chemical, and physical methods of sewage treatment, in addition to exercising knowledge of economics, humanities, physical laws, and the forces of nature. He must have sufficient knowledge of operating procedures to design sewage-treatment works for the convenience of the operator and the success of the process, and he must be able to give advice on the proper procedure in the operation of such works.[7]

After the plant is complete the engineer may: (1) operate the plant until it is properly adjusted; (2) assist in the selection and training of the operating personnel; (3) provide manuals, catalogs, and other printed materials, records, directions, and instructions required for the operation, maintenance, and replacement of all plant equipment; (4) prepare sample forms and cards on which periodic operation and preventive maintenance reports and records are made; and (5) maintain a continuing interest in the plant by periodic visits and reports thereon. Such service after the plant has been completed cannot be continued without the cooperation of the works authority.

1-11. Publicity and public relations.[8] Good publicity, good public relations, and the distribution of adequate and proper informa-

[5] See also L. L. Sphar, *S. and I.W.*, July, 1953, p. 787.
[6] See also R. D. Bargman, *S. and I.W.*, October, 1953, p. 1145.
[7] See also K. W. Brown and D. H. Caldwell, *S. and I.W.*, November, 1955, p. 1238.
[8] Public relations in plant operation are discussed briefly in Sect. 29-3.

tion are essential to the successful development and maintenance of sewerage works. Good public relations can be maintained through adequate sewer service and sewage treatment where needed, and by utilizing the local press, service clubs, health departments, and other media for bringing the work of the sewer department to the attention of the public. Where sewers, or sewage-treatment facilities are needed but do not exist, the public must be educated to the need for them.

Chapter 2

Developmental and preliminary work

2–1. Development of a sewerage plan. Steps in the development of a sewerage plan may include: (1) a study of the sewerage needs with a preliminary report and an estimate of cost; (2) a recommendation concerning the method of financing the proposed work; (3) publicity to secure public support and a favorable vote; (4) an engineering investigation preceding the final plan, and (5) the plan, followed by the contract and completion of construction.

An example of good publicity to aid in the development of sewerage facilities would be the publication, and distribution to taxpayers, of an attractive report, describing the local situation and making comparisons with other well-sewered communities of a similar type. The publication might include such information as: (1) a description of the existing undesirable conditions in the unsewered district; (2) a description of downstream conditions with an explanation of threatening damage suits; (3) a "before-and-after" discussion of what neighboring communities have done; (4) an appeal to civic pride; and (5) a description of the plan proposed to alleviate the conditions and of the method of defraying the cost, showing each taxpayer what it will cost him. Adequate maps and good illustrations are essential for a thorough explanation of what it is proposed to do.

The sanitary engineer should be employed early in the procedure and should be active throughout the developmental period.

2–2. Preliminary duties. The engineer's duties during the preliminary or developmental period are to make a study of possible methods by which the demand for sewerage can be satisfied, to present the results of this study in the form of a report to the committee or organization responsible for the promotion of the work, and so to familiarize himself with the conditions affecting the installation of the proposed plans as to be able to answer inquiries concerning them. This work will require the general qualities of character, judgment, efficiency, and an understanding of men; the ability to address interested persons individually and collectively on features of the proposed plans; and the exercise of engineering technique in the survey and in the drawing of the plans. The engineer should assure himself that all legal requirements in the drawing of petitions, advertising, permits, etc., have been complied with. This requires some knowledge of national, state, and local laws.

2–3. Engineer's report. The engineer's preliminary report should contain a section devoted to the feasibility of one or more plans, which may be explained in more or less detail with a statement of the cost and advantages of each. The report should give particular attention to the basis of design and should set forth clearly the basis of the estimates of both construction and operation costs. A conclusion should be reached as to the most desirable plan, and a recommendation made that this plan be adopted. Other sections of the report may be devoted to a history of the growing demand, a description of the conditions necessitating sewerage, possible methods of financing, and such other subjects as may be pertinent.

An outline of the content of an engineer's final report on sewerage works, as recommended by the Upper Mississippi River Board of Public Health Engineers and the Great Lakes Board of Public Health Engineers, in 1951, covering 10 well-populated states is given below. The outline may be used as a basis for either a preliminary or a final report.

The engineer's report [1] for sewage works shall, where pertinent, present the following information:

A. General information. Describe the existing water and sewage facilities and the problems involved.

B. Extent of system. Describe the nature and extent of the area included in the present sewerage system, and the area and extent to which plans provide sewage facilities for future development. If the area to be served by existing and proposed sewers does not include the entire municipality or natural drainage area, a brief description should be given of that portion not included, together with information as to the probability of future development, and how this area can be served.

[1] An outline recommended in 1951 by the Joint Committee of the Upper Mississippi River Board of Public Health Engineers and the Great Lakes Board of Public Health Engineers, hereinafter referred to as the Joint Committee. See also Sect. 14–9.

C. Alternative plans. Where two or more solutions exist for a particular problem, each of which is feasible and practical, discuss the several solutions and reasons for selecting the one recommended. For example, if a sewerage system should require deep cuts to avoid pumping stations, the report should indicate that the comparative advantages of shallow and deep sewers have been given ample study.

D. Soil. State probable character of soil or strata through which the sewers are to be laid, and describe portions of the system that will be below normal ground-water level. Indicate any unusual soil or foundation conditions at the site of any sewage structures, also the extent of soil investigations, and outline findings as they relate to probable construction problems or as they may affect portions of the system.

E. Sewage flow. As a basis for sewage-treatment-plant design, discuss the population trend as indicated by available records, and give the estimated population for the municipality or sewer district 15 to 25 years hence, and for institutions the present and maximum anticipated capacity. Describe briefly the method used to determine future population trends. Estimate the amount of domestic sewage, ground water, industrial wastes, etc., that the collection system or various parts thereof may have to handle during a future period of not more than 50 years. Indicate basis of design of sewers.

F. Volume and strength of sewage flow. Where there is an existing sewage works the designing engineer shall confer with the reviewing agency to determine the scope of volume and strength of sewage data necessary. Where data on volume or volume and strength of sewage are required by the reviewing authority, the same shall accompany the report. These data must be obtained from actual flow measurements, preferably for both wet- and dry-weather periods when feasible, but in prolonged drought or wet-weather periods where unwarranted delay would exist from obtaining data on both extremes of flow, data for existing flows with a statement of conditions affecting the flows, and estimates of infiltration will be acceptable. The laboratory analysis must be made on composite samples taken over a continuous 24-hour period, and data must cover a sufficient period of time to be representative of actual conditions. It is recommended that the designing engineer confer with the reviewing agency for details concerning the collection and analysis of samples.

G. Water supply. Discuss the location of intake or wells, treatment plant, reservoirs, or other structures of public-health significance with relation to various portions of the sewage works. If public supply is already in use, give approximate maximum, minimum, and average daily water consumption, and analyses of water as it might affect the character of the sewage.

H. Garbage disposal. Describe present methods of garbage disposal, and discuss the possibility of the future disposal of garbage wastes with sewage.

I. Industrial wastes. List all the establishments producing industrial wastes, and state quantity, producing methods, and character of industrial wastes in so far as they may affect the sewage system or sewage-treatment works. Quantity and character of wastes should be based on flow gaging and laboratory analysis of composite samples.

J. Sewage treatment. Discuss the degree and type of treatment, reasons for adopting the proposed method, and the basis of design for each unit, both for present and future needs.

K. Site. Discuss the various sites available and the advantages of the one to be recommended. Indicate the proximity of residences or developed areas to any treatment works, and discuss the relationship of maximum high water to the plant site and various plant units.

L. Financing. Give estimated cost of integral parts of system for the contemplated installation and a detailed estimation of the annual cost of operation. Methods of financing the proposed improvements should preferably be discussed.

M. Receiving stream. Describe the stream or body of water into which the final effluent is to discharge, including its condition and uses. If a stream, give recorded or estimated minimum, maximum, and average daily flow and minimum weekly flow. State whether any unusual conditions exist which might affect the flow. If a lake, give approximate area, average depth in the vicinity of the outlet, and average inflow.

N. Recommendations. Include recommendations in detail concerning the proposed sewage works, and outline a plan for future extension of the works.

2–4. Estimates of cost. In making an estimate of cost the information should be presented in a readable and easily comprehensible manner. It is necessary that the items be clearly defined and that all items be included. The method of determining the costs of doubtful items, such as depreciation, interest charges, and labor, should be explained. The items in a cost estimate should be so grouped that the costs of the different portions of the system are separated, in order that the effect on the total cost, resulting from different combinations of items or the omission of any one or more items, can be readily computed.

The engineer's estimate may be divided somewhat as follows:

Labor.

Materials.

Overhead. This may include construction plant, office expense, supervision, bond interest, insurance, transportation, etc. The amount of this item is seldom less than 15 per cent and is usually over 20 per cent of the contract price.

Contingencies. This allowance is usually 10 to 15 per cent of the contract price.

Profit. This should be from 5 to 10 per cent of the sum of the four preceding items.

The contract price is the sum of the preceding items as estimated from the construction drawings. To this may be added:

Engineering.

Extra work. In a good design and where unexpected and unforeseeable contingencies are avoided this should not exceed 15 per cent of the contract price.

Legal expense.

Purchase of land, rights of way, etc.

The cost of the sewer, when made on the unit-price basis, may be stated as so much per linear foot for different sizes of pipe, including all appurtenances such as manholes and catch basins, or the items may be separated in detail, somewhat as follows:

Earth excavation, per cubic yard.

Rock excavation, per cubic yard.

Backfill, per cubic yard.

Brick manholes, 3 ft by 4 ft, per foot of depth.

Vitrified clay sewer pipe with cement joints, in place _____ in. in diameter, 0 to 6 ft deep; 6 to 8 ft deep; 8 to 10 ft deep.

Repaving, macadam, per square yard; asphalt, per square yard.

Flush tanks,—— gal capacity, per tank.

Service pipes to flush tanks, per linear foot.

Reliable cost data are difficult to obtain. List prices of materials and labor are published in some engineering and trade periodicals. Various books on cost estimating contain lists of the amount of material and labor used on specific types of jobs and construction. The price of labor and materials on the local market may be obtained from the local chamber of commerce, contractors and other employers of labor, and from dealers in the desired commodities. Contract prices on sewerage work published in the construction news section of engineering periodicals may be a guide to the judgment of the probable cost of proposed work, but are generally dangerous to rely upon as full details are lacking in the description of the work.

2–5. Methods of financing.[2] Sewerage work is financed in the United States by various methods, including: (1) private capital, (2)

[2] See also C. W. Klassen and W. H. Wisely, *Water Works and Sewerage,* March, 1937, p. 88. Round Table discussion, *Mun. San.,* December, 1937, p. 649. W. F. Tempest, *Water and Sewage Works,* June, 1955, p. R-20.

general taxation, (3) special assessment, (4) general-obligation bonds, (5) revenue bonds, and (6) governmental grants and loans. Knowledge of the methods for the financing of enterprises, of types of bonds and issues of stocks, of legal requirements in connection with fund raising for private and public enterprises, of the state of the money market, and of available sources of money, is essential to the engineer who is competent to act as adviser in the development of sewerage and other public work.

2–6. Private capital. Private capital is occasionally used in the financing of sewerage works. It may be used by an individual or corporation owning the system or a franchise may be granted to a private enterprise, entailing certain obligations and privileges. The return on the invested capital is received from rental or service charge paid by the community or paid directly by the users of the system. To be successful the enterprise must be popular and must fill a great need.

2–7. General taxation. In paying for public improvements by general taxation the money is taken from the general municipal funds which have been apportioned for separate purposes by the legislative branch of the municipal government. If insufficient funds are available for immediate or emergency use, money may be raised by the sale of tax-anticipation warrants. Funds for sewerage construction are seldom obtained from general taxation unless the political situation is unfavorable to the success of a bond issue or special assessment and the need for the improvement is great. It is usually difficult to appropriate sufficient funds for new construction from the general fund because the fund is ordinarily apportioned to support only the operating expenses of the municipality, and statutory provisions limit the amount of tax that can be levied.

2–8. Special assessment. A special assessment is a tax levied against that property benefited directly by the structure or service to be paid for. The amount to be paid by the individual property owner is apportioned, by law, in accordance with the benefit derived from the improvement. This form of financing sewerage works is confined mainly to the payment for lateral sewers that are a direct benefit to separate districts but are without general benefit to the municipality. Since the advent of the policy of federal grants, the special assessment method of financing sewerage works has been less frequently used.

2–9. General-obligation bonds. A municipal bond is a promise by the municipality to pay the face value of the bond to the holder at a certain specified time, with interest at a stipulated rate during the interim. The security on the bond is the taxing power of the municipality. The legal restrictions thrown around municipal bond issues and the power of the municipality to levy taxes to pay its obligations, and sometimes the federal tax-exemption feature, make municipal bond issues attractive, with a resulting low-interest rate or high premium available in the market. However, there is usually a statutory limit to the amount of bonds that may be issued by a municipality and, as there are other methods for the financing of sewerage work, administrative authorities are not always favorable to the restriction of their financial credit by the issuance of general-obligation bonds for sewerage construction.

Sometimes the amount available from municipal bonds has been increased by forming a municipality within another municipality, each with the power of issuing bonds of a value limited by the assessed value of the property within each municipality.

Bond issues must usually be presented to the voters for approval. If approved, and if other legal procedure has been followed, the bonds may be sold to a bonding house, or to individuals, and the money is immediately available for construction. The bonds are redeemed by general taxation spread over the period of the issue.

2–10. Revenue bonds. A revenue bond differs from a general-obligation bond primarily in that the security for the payment of principal and interest depends on payments to be made by users of the sewer system. The amount paid by users is sometimes called sewer rental, and is devoted to the maintenance and operation of the system and the retirement of the bonds. The revenue bond is not an obligation against the taxing power of the municipality and, therefore, it does not affect the amount of general-obligation bonds that can be issued. Revenue bonds, like general-obligation bonds, may be sold to bonding houses or to private purchasers. Such bonds have also been used as security for loans received from the federal government.

In floating revenue bonds a comprehensive financial analysis of the enterprise is desirable. A standard inquiry form has been prepared by the Investment Bankers Association of America.[3] A few of the questions to be answered are: (1) amount, rate, and due date of each coupon and each bond; (2) call provisions; (3) peak requirement for interest and principal or sinking fund; (4) amount of the securities

---

[3] See W. F. Tempest, *Water and Sewage Works,* April, 1951, p. R-111.

having claim senior to this issue; and (5) what is the covenant respecting rates to be charged for services rendered.

2–11. Governmental grants and loans. The United States government has made grants of money to states and to other divisions of government for various purposes, including sewerage. An early objective of such grants was to make work for the unemployed during financial depression years, especially subsequent to 1932. The Public Works Administration (PWA) and the Works Progress Administration (WPA) were examples of such federal activities under which sewerage work was performed. In 1956 a fund of half a billion dollars was appropriated by the Congress to aid municipalities to construct sewage treatment plants principally to aid the program of stream-pollution prevention. The amount that is awarded annually is limited to $50 million, the program to run for 10 years. Each state is to receive a share in proportion to its population. The administration of the fund and the awarding of grants are under the direction of the United States Public Health Service. Some states, such as Maryland, Maine, and Vermont, have a grant program to supplement other funds applicable to sewer construction.[4]

2–12. Sewer rentals or service charges.[5] Service charges for the use of sewers by other than industrial plants (see also Sect. 27–3) may be based on such conditions as the use of water, the number and type of plumbing fixtures, assessed value or front footage of property, and a uniform rate per sewer connection. The first is common with domestic and other small water consumers. Because of inequities of such bases under some conditions, modifications may be made as, for example, for sewer users with their own water supply, for users who do not discharge their entire water consumption into the sewer, and for other conditions. The levying of sewer service charges, sometimes called sewer rentals, is not legal in all states. Under some conditions they may be collected under a local ordinance.[6]

A satisfactory method for the collection of sewer-service charges has been to combine them with the bill for water service. This

---

[4] See also G. H. Sandenburgh, *Sewage Works Jour.*, May, 1938, p. 482. R. A. Alton, *Jour. Am. Water Works Assoc.*, August, 1938, p. 1285. *Water Works and Sewerage*, August, 1938, p. 785, and September, 1938, p. 852. *Mun. San.*, March, 1939, p. 145. Committee Report, *Proc. Am. Soc. Civil Engrs.*, November, 1942, p. 1585. J. J. Joyce, *S. and I.W.*, September, 1950, p. 1103.

[5] See also *S. and I.W.*, October, 1957, p. 1106.

[6] See also *Water Works and Sewerage*, June, 1945, p. R-171; *Water and Sewage Works*, Vol. 101, 1934, p. 430, and Vol. 102, 1955, p. 49.

necessitates cooperation between the sewer authority and the water works in the community.

2–13. Financing extensions and house connections.[7]   The financing of extensions to existing sewer systems may be based on any one, or a combination of, four conditions: (1) front footage; (2) area, with maximum area or depth of lot limitation; (3) assessed value of the property served; or (4) actual cost of extension assessed on persons benefited.   Charges for house connections may be based on actual cost, fixed sum, unit cost per foot, assessed valuation, or the full cost may be paid by the property owner.   Sewers in new subdivisions may be paid for by the developer and taken over without payment by the municipality when the area is admitted to the city.

2–14. Preliminary map.   Before any map can be drawn the district limits must be determined by a survey of the services required, economic considerations, and other factors involved, such as costs, future growth, and political and sociological considerations.[8]   When the district limits have been decided upon, a preliminary map should be drawn.

Specifications of the New York State Department of Health, given in Sect. 14–10, cover some of the salient features to be included in the preliminary map and general plan.   The map must indicate how it is proposed to provide sewerage and disposal of the sewage of areas in which it is not planned to provide sewers at the present.   It is desirable also, for an intelligent understanding of the project, that the following information be shown on the preliminary map:

> The elevation of lots and cellars; the character of built-up districts, whether inexpensive, frame residences, flat-roof buildings, manufacturing plants, etc.; property lines; width of streets between property lines and between curb lines; width and types of sidewalks and pavements; streetcar and railroad tracks; existing underground structures such as sewers, water pipes, and telephone cables; location of important structures that may have a bearing on the design of the sewers such as bridges, railroad tunnels, deep cuts, and culverts; the location of possible sewer outlets; and the sites for sewage treatment works.

2–15. Preliminary information.   Information other than that shown on the preliminary map, that may be the basis of subsequent estimates of the quantity of sewage to be cared for, may be obtained by a study of water usage and the density and growth of population,

---

[7] See also C. I. Sterling, Jr., *S. and I.W.*, June, 1956, p. 772.

[8] See also "Fringe Area Sanitation," a Symposium, *S. and I.W.*, April, 1956, p. 471.

the measurement of the discharge rate from existing sewers, and the compilation of rainfall and of runoff data. If no such data are available for the region, estimates must be made from data available concerning similar sewer districts.

2–16. Underground surveys. Underground surveys along the lines of proposed sewers are desirable, to give information concerning obstructions, difficult excavation, and other conditions that may be

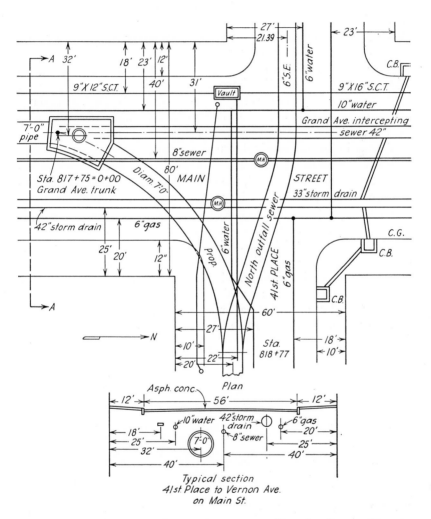

Fig. 2–1. Confusion of underground structures. Hyperion Sewage Diversion Study, Los Angeles, Calif.

met. Such data are seldom completely gathered except for costly sewer construction. For construction on small work or for extensions to an existing system the funds are usually insufficient for an extensive, preliminary underground survey. The saving in this respect may be paid unknowingly to the contractor as compensation for the risk he takes in bidding without complete information.

Pertinent information obtained may include type of material to be excavated; ground-water level; and the location and sizes of water, gas, and sewer pipes, telephone and electric conduits, streetcar tracks, steam pipes, and other structures that may interfere with subsurface construction. These structures should be located with reference to some permanent point on the surface. The elevations of the tops of pipes, except sewers, rather than the depth of cover, should be recorded, as the depth of cover is subject to change. The elevation of sewers should be given to the invert, where possible, rather than to the top of the pipe. A portion of the map of the subsurface conditions in a street in Los Angeles is shown in Fig. 2–1.

2–17. Location of sewers. Practice in the location of underground utilities is haphazard, the controlling influence being the convenience of the particular utility at the moment. A standard practice, proposed by the American Society of Civil Engineers in 1937, is shown in Fig. 2–2. It continues to represent good practice. In streets in undeveloped territory, in which only a single lateral sewer or submain is to be laid, the sewer is frequently laid in the middle of the street. Under more crowded streets and where a storm sewer is to be laid in addition to a sanitary sewer, the storm sewer may be laid on the side of the street most convenient for good drainage. Where conditions are favorable, storm and sanitary sewers may be

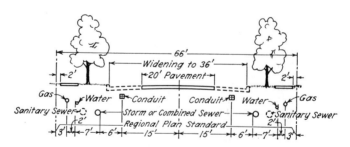

Fig. 2–2. Standard location of underground utilities. (From "Location of Underground Utilities," *Manual of Practice* 14, American Society of Civil Engineers, 1937.)

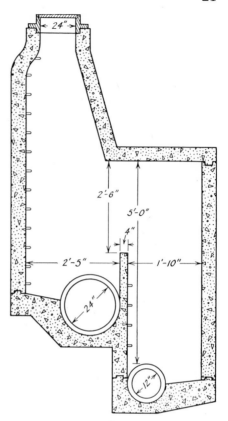

Fig. 2–3. Manhole for two sewers in the same trench.

placed economically in the same trench, using the same manholes, as shown in Fig. 2–3.

The location of sanitary sewers should be such as to give the most desirable combination of low cost, short house connections, proper depth of cellar drainage, and avoidance of paving. Some difference of opinion exists as to the advisability of placing sewers in alleys, although this meets with less opposition than placing other utility conduits there. The principal advantage of placing sewers in alleys is the avoidance of disturbance of street pavement, but if both street and alley are paved it is usually more economical to place the sewer in the street since the house connection will be shorter. Sewers should not be located on easements through back yards where there are no alleys for many reasons such as: (1) manholes get covered and lost; (2) residents object, sometimes violently, to trespassing by maintenance men; (3) dogs are dangerous; (4) shrubbery, trees, and land-scaping may be ruined, and their presence adds to the cost of mainte-nance; (5) there is greater trouble from roots in the sewers; and (6) good public relations are jeopardized.[9]

On boulevards and other wide streets, such as Meridian Avenue in Fig. 5–3, sewers are placed in the parking on each side of the street so as not to disturb the pavement and to avoid long house connec-tions to the center of the street.

2–18. Borings.   Methods for the investigation of subsurface conditions preliminary to sewer construction include the making of test holes.   This may be done by punch drilling, boring with an earth auger, jet boring, wash boring, percussion drilling, abrasive drilling, hydraulic drilling, and hand or open excavation.   The drilling of holes is done principally for deep borings in rock.

Excavations yield more reliable information than borings, but bor-ings are more commonly made because they are cheaper.   Information obtained from punching, boring, or drilling may be misleading on account of the various types and the condition of the materials brought to the surface for observation, and such methods of investigation will give no conception of the amount of underground water to be handled. The presence or absence of rock must be reported with circumspection because some underground materials that are apparently as hard as rock when beneath the surface will turn soft when exposed to air, and occasionally the chance striking of a few boulders may be interpreted as ledge rock.   When it is certain that rock has been found the bore holes should be located with reference to some fixed point on the surface so that the profile of the rock can be shown.   Some of the holes should be driven to the maximum depth to which the sewer is to be laid, to ascertain whether or not the rock is more than a thin stratum.

Quicksand may be overlooked because sand may not turn "quick" until the trench has been opened and drainage has been allowed for the confined water.

Knowledge of the geology of the region, or nearby wells, and of previous excavations may be helpful in interpreting underground bor-ings.

2–19. Boring tools.   Boring tools used for underground prospect-ing for sewer excavation include punch drills, earth augers, rock drills, well-drilling tools, and excavating equipment.

Punch drills are of two sorts.   The simplest punch drill consists of an iron rod $7/8$ in. to 1 in. in diameter, in sections about 4 ft long.

---

[9] See also C. Webster, *S. and I.W.,* September, 1954, p. 179.

One section is sharpened at one end and threaded at the other so that the next section can be threaded into it without increasing the diameter of the rod, as shown in Fig. 2–4. The drill is driven by a sledge striking upon a cap held at the top of the drill to prevent injury to the threads. The drill should be turned as it is driven, to prevent sticking. It is pulled out by a hook and lever, as shown in Fig. 2–5. It is useful in soft ground for soundings as deep as 8 to 12 ft. Another form of punch drill consists of a cylinder of steel or iron, 1 to 2 ft long, split along one side and slightly spread. The lower portion is very slightly expanded and is tempered into a cutting edge. In use it is attached to a rope or wooden poles and is lifted and dropped in the hole by means of a rope, which is given a few turns about a windlass or drum. By this process the material is forced into the bit, slightly springs it, and so is held. When the bit is filled it is raised to the surface and emptied. Deeper holes can be made with the bit than with the sharpened solid rod.

Types of earth augers about 1½ in. in diameter are shown in Fig. 2–6. They are threaded onto the end of a section of the pipe or rod, and as the hole is deepened successive lengths of pipe or rod are added. The device is operated by two men. It is pulled by straight lifting or with the assistance of a link and lever similar to that shown in Fig. 2–5. The device is suitable for soft earth

Fig. 2–4. Punch drill.

or sand free from stones and can be used for holes 15 to 25 ft in depth. For deeper holes a block and tackle should be used for lifting the auger from the hole. It is not suitable for holes deeper than about 35 ft.

In the jetting method, water is led into the hole through a ¾-in. or 1-in. pipe and is forced downward through the drill bit or nozzle

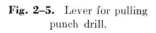

Fig. 2–5. Lever for pulling punch drill.

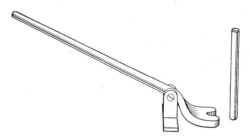

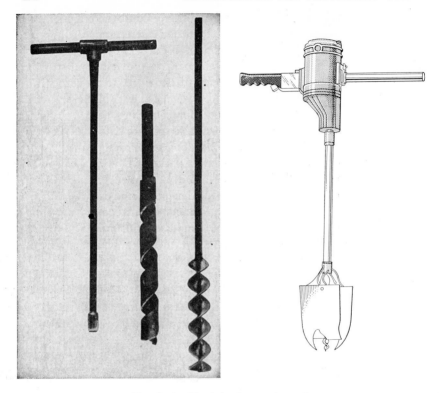

Fig. 2–6. Earth-boring equipment.

against the bottom of the hole. It is not always necessary to case the
hole, as the muddy water and the vibration of the pipe puddle the
sides so that they will stand alone. The jet pipe may be churned in
the hole by a rope passing over a block and a revolving drum. In
suitable soft materials such as clay, sand, or gravel, holes can be
bored to a depth of 100 feet, and samples can be collected of the
material removed. An objection to the method may be the difficulty
of obtaining sufficient water.

Methods of drilling in rock to depths of 20 feet are described in Sect.
9–4. For deeper holes in rock or gravel, percussion, abrasive, or
hydraulic methods as used for deep well drilling must be employed.

Chapter 3

Quantity of sewage[1]

3–1. Dry-weather flow. The volume of dry-weather flow or sanitary sewage to be expected from a community depends on the population, the character of the sewered district, the water usage, underground water conditions, materials and type of joints in the sewer pipes, and other conditions. The population to be served is an important factor and design capacities may be based on estimates of future population.

3–2. Sources of information on population. The United States decennial census furnishes valuable information on population. Unfortunately it becomes somewhat inadequate towards the end of a decade. Recent information can be obtained from local sources such as schools, lists of voters, the post office, the chamber of commerce, newspapers, and public utilities. A marked correlation has been shown to exist between population changes and changes in public services. A count and classification of the buildings in a community, combined with an assumption of the number of occupants of each building, may give valuable information.

3–3. Methods of predicting population.[2] Future population may be predicted either mathematically or by logical methods. Mathematical methods include: (1) arithmetical progression, (2) geometrical progression, (3) decreasing rate of increase, (4) differential plot, (5) graphical extension of plotted data, (6) Verhulst's theory,[3] and (7) graphical comparison with other cities. The first four methods have no basis of reason and may be expected to give results of little

---

[1] A symposium on rates of sewage flow is given in *Eng. News-Record,* Oct. 14, 1948, p. 102; Nov. 25, 1948, p. 76; Dec. 23, 1948, p. 78; and Jan. 6, 1949, p. 57.

[2] See also E. Sibley, *Am. Jour. Public Health,* February, 1944, p. 174; and M. Zitter, *Public Works,* June, 1957, p. 110.

[3] See also J. E. McLean, *Civil Eng.,* February, 1952, p. 35; and V. B. Stanbery, *Better Population Forecasts for Areas and Communities,* September, 1952, Superintendent of Documents, Washington, D. C.

more value than a blind guess. In the fifth method a graph is plotted
with population as ordinates and time as abscissas. The graph is
extended into the future by personal judgment guided by knowledge
of the past and an estimate of probable future conditions. An example of such a curve is shown in Fig. 3–1. Verhulst's theory [3] is
based on the principle that the population of any area will increase
to a terminal number that might be called the saturation limit. The
determination of this limit is based on the logistic curve of Pearl.[3]

The method of graphical comparison with other cities involves a
combination of mathematics with judgment that should give a probable result. Judgment must be exercised in the selection of the cities
with which the comparison is to be made, and it should be based on
the history of the community, probabilities of its development, and
a rational analysis of governmental and other forecasts of economic,
political, and other national and local conditions. An example of
the application of the method of graphical comparsion with other

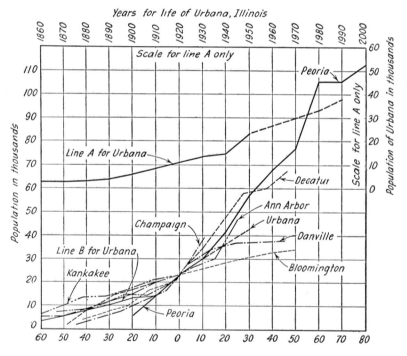

Fig. 3–1. Graphical methods for estimating future population.

cities is illustrated in Fig. 3–1. In this figure the population of Urbana, Ill., the city in question, is first plotted to any convenient scale, the year 1950 being taken as the base for the abscissas, years before and after 1950 being measured to the left and right, respectively, of the zero point. Similar curves are plotted for cities similar to and larger than Urbana, the zero of abscissas for each city being taken at the year when its population was the same as that of Urbana in 1950. Line B for Urbana is then extended as judgment dictates, guided by the experience of the similar cities and by other knowledge of the situation. Line B in Fig. 3–1 indicates that the population of Urbana in 1980 will be about 43,000. Line B is based on the data given in Table 3–1.

Logical methods are most commonly used in good practice. These include: (1) the component method, (2) the cohort-survival method, and (3) the ratio method. In the first method birth and death rates, migration trends for future years, and other conditions are developed and applied to the present population. In the cohort-survival method the computations are carried out for each age group of the population for the full period of prediction. In the ratio method the technique of the process consists of extrapolating the ratio of the population of the area for which the prediction is required to the population of a larger area and then applying extrapolated ratios to the population ratios of the population projections for the larger area to obtain projections for the smaller area.

There are several other methods that may be useful under proper conditions.

3–4. Extent of prediction. The length of time into the future for which predictions are made depends on such factors as economy, available funds, relative performance of structures, and the judgment of the persons involved in making the prediction. Practice varies, in general, between 10 and 40 years.[4] This time is fixed, to some extent, by legal limitations on bond issues in some states. Certain parts of sewerage works may be designed for longer periods into the future although they will not be built immediately.

A sewer system should be designed and financed so that each generation bears its share of the cost, as nearly as possible. It is unfair for the present generation to build and pay for an extensive system that will not be utilized for 25 years. It is likewise unfair to the

[4] A staff review in *Sewage Works Eng.*, March, 1948, p. 117.

Table 3-1

POPULATION STUDIES

	Urbana, Ill.			Population of						
Year	Population	Absolute Increase for Each Decade	Per Cent Increase for Each Decade	Decatur, Ill.	Danville, Ill.	Champaign, Ill.	Kankakee, Ill.	Peoria, Ill.	Bloomington, Ill.	Ann Arbor, Mich.
1850	210	...	...	...	736	...	...	5,095	1,594	...
1860	2,038	1,828	870.0	3,839	1,632	1,727	2,984	14,045	7,075	5,097
1870	2,277	239	11.7	7,161	4,751	4,625	5,189	22,849	14,590	7,368
1880	2,942	665	29.2	9,547	7,733	5,103	5,651	29,259	17,180	8,061
1890	3,511	569	19.3	16,841	11,491	5,839	9,025	41,024	20,484	9,431
1900	5,728	2,217	63.1	20,754	16,354	9,098	13,595	56,100	23,286	14,509
1910	8,245	2,517	43.9	31,140	27,871	12,421	13,986	66,950	25,786	14,817
1920	10,230	1,985	24.1	43,818	33,750	15,873	16,721	76,121	28,638	19,516
1930	13,058	2,828	27.6	57,511	36,646	20,332	20,620	104,788	30,915	26,872
1940	14,064	1,006	7.7	59,305	36,919	23,302	22,241	105,087	32,868	29,815
1950	22,995	8,931	63.5	67,801	37,892	39,397	25,873	111,523	34,048	47,279

next generation to construct a system sufficient to comply with present needs only and to postpone the payment for it by a long-term bond issue. An ideal solution would be to plan a system which would satisfy present and future needs and to construct only those portions which would be useful during the period of the bond issue. Unfortunately this solution is not entirely practical because first, the total expenses will be less if portions of the system, such as the outfall and the treatment plant, are constructed now to care for conditions in advance of the present needs; and, second, the life of practically all portions of a sewer system is greater than the legal or customary time limit on bond issues. A compromise may be reached between the practical and the ideal by the design of a complete system to fill all probable demands and the construction of such portions as are needed now in accordance with this plan.

The prediction of the population, therefore, should be made such that a comprehensive system can be designed with intelligence. Practice has seldom called for predictions more than 50 years into the future, with the life of bond issues usually 20 years.

3–5. Trends in population growth. Economic, political, and sociological factors over long periods of time enter into the life of a nation, to affect the smoothness of the curve of population growth. The effects of wars, rural mechanization, restriction of immigration, industrial growth, and transportation facilities can be seen in the curve of population growth of the United States. Publications by the Scripps Foundation for Research in Population Problems will be found to contain valuable information on population trends.

Economic and other conditions since the Second World War have tended to increase the rate of movement of population from the farm to the city and to encourage the increase of the total population of the nation, especially in urban areas. Probably the most important factor affecting the growth and the distribution of urban population is transportation facilities.

3–6. Distribution of population. It is frequently necessary to predict the population of a district or a small section of the city. Experience shows that in older cities districts have increased in population until a maximum has been reached and the population has thereafter decreased in the district. Population statistics for the city of Cleveland, Ohio, that bear out these experiences are shown in Table 3–2. The figures in columns 6 and 7 show that areas annexed before 1870 started to decline in population before 1930. The net

Table 3-2

POPULATION STATISTICS FOR CLEVELAND, OHIO

(H. W. Green, *Eng. News-Record*, Feb. 9, 1953, p. 187.)

District	Year of First Census after Annexation	Area, square miles	Gross Area, acres	Built-up or Net Area, acres	Population at First Census after Annexation	Year of Maximum Population	Maximum Population	Maximum Density of Population per Acre Gross *	Net †	Net Density of Population, First Census after Annexation
A	1830	0.74	474	4	1,691	1870	9,090	19	2,280	423
B	1840	1.27	814	222	13,752	1910	30,943	38	139	62
C	1850	3.39	2,630	1,150	61,226	1920	89,910	41	79	53
D	1860	2.02	1,292	775	32,497	1910	39,982	31	52	42
E	1870	2.47	1,580	1,119	50,291	1920	53,950	34	48	45
F	1870	2.12	1,358	604	33,864	1920	38,140	27	63	56
G	1880	2.58	1,650	741	38,620	1930	38,620	23	52	52
H	1880	13.41	8,600	5,380	247,599	1930	260,995	30	48	46
I	1890	0.15	96	77	3,637	1930	3,637	38	47	47
J	1900	4.68	3,000	1,930	63,704	1930	63,704	21	33	33
Col.	1	2	3	4	5	6	7	8	9	10

* Includes entire area.

† Includes only private property. The figure is estimated on data given by Green.

Table 3–3

DENSITIES OF POPULATION

Type of District	Density per Acre
The most crowded conditions with five-story and higher contiguous buildings in poor-class districts	750–1,000
Five- and six-story contiguous flat buildings	500– 750
Six-story high-class apartments.	300– 500
Three- and four-story dwellings, business blocks, and industrial establishments, closely built up	100– 300
Separate residences, 50- to 75-foot fronts, commercial districts, moderately well built up	50– 100
Sparsely settled districts and scattered frame dwellings for individual families	0– 50

increase in population of the city as a whole takes place in districts recently annexed. Rapid growth is confined to the peripheral areas, much of which may be outside of the municipal boundaries.

Sources of information on the population of a district may be the same as those for the entire city. Local zoning ordinances may greatly affect the density of population in a district. Densities of population in various types of districts are indicated in Table 3–3. Population and area were predicted in 1911 for Cincinnati, Ohio, in 1950. These predictions, together with the actual figures, are shown in Fig. 3–2. The comparison of the predictions made in 1911 and the actual figures are significant in indicating the accuracy of population forecasts.

3–7. Relation between quantity of water and of sewage. The amount of used water discharged into a sewer system is generally slightly less than the amount of water supplied to the community. The entire public water supply does not reach the sewers because of leakage from the water pipes, lawn sprinkling, manufacturing processes, etc., but these losses are largely made up by additions from private water supplies, surface and underground drainage, and other accretions. Under unusual circumstances underground water and surface water entering sewers may exceed the used water supply discharged into them. The estimated quantity of water that was used but did not reach the sewers in Cincinnati is shown in Table 3–4. The amount represents 38 per cent of the total amount of water used.

The public water supply is generally installed in advance of the sewer system. By collecting statistics on the rate of supply of water

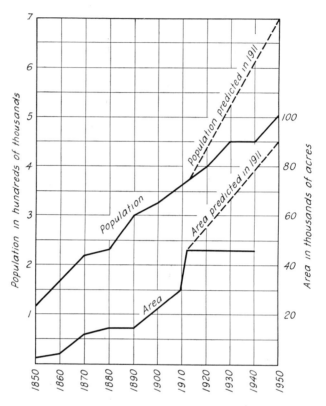

Fig. 3–2. Area and population of Cincinnati, Ohio, up to 1950, and as predicted in 1911. (For prediction see *Eng. and Contr.*, June 17, 1914, p. 697.)

Table 3–4

ESTIMATED QUANTITY OF WATER USED BUT NOT DISCHARGED
INTO THE SEWERS IN CINCINNATI

Expressed in gallons per capita per day and based on a total
consumption of 125 to 150 gallons per capita per day

Steam railroads	6– 7	Manufacturing and mechanical	6– 7
Street sprinklers	6– 7	Lawn sprinklers	3– 3½
Consumers not sewered	9–10½	Leakage	18–21

Table 3–5

RELATION OF SIZE OF CITY TO PER CAPITA USE OF WATER

(W. B. Langbein, *Jour. Am. Water Works Assoc.*, November,
1949, p. 997; also February, 1948, p. 195.)

Population in thousands	0.5	1.0	5.0	10.0	50	100
Average water used in gallons per capita per day	60	85	135	140	140	140

a fair prediction can be made on the quantity of sewage which must
be cared for. Experience has shown that the use of water increases
after the installation of sewers. The rate of water supply varies widely
among cities. It is controlled by many conditions such as meters,
cost and availability of water, water pressure and water quality,
climate, and population. In American cities a rough average of
water usage is 100 gallons daily per capita, although the national
average is higher. The ratio of sewage flow to water usage is tending to increase.[5] Low cost, good quality, and good quantity increase
the rate of water usage; and the rate increases slowly with increase
of population up to about 10,000 persons. Beyond this number, as
shown in Table 3–5, population seems to bear no relation to rate of
water usage. Statistics[6] of rates of water use and of sewage flow
are given in Tables 3–5 and 3–6.

3–8. Type of district. The various sections of a city may be
classified as residential, commercial, or industrial. Residential districts can be subdivided into sparsely settled, moderately settled,
crowded, wealthy, poor, etc. Commercial districts may comprise
retail stores, office buildings, or wholesale houses. Industrial districts
may be either large factories, foundries, refineries, etc., or they may
be made up of small industries and loft buildings.

In cities of less than about 3,000 population the refinement of such
subdivisions is generally unnecessary in the study of sewage flow, all
districts being considered alike. The data in Tables 3–7 and 3–8
indicate the rates of sewage flow from various sources.

Sewage flow is commonly expressed in gallons per capita per day

[5] See also J. M. Hepler, *S. and I.W.*, October, 1950, p. 1282.
[6] See also L. H. Kessler and J. T. Norgaard, *Sewage Works Jour.*, July, 1942,
p. 757. H. F. Seidel and others, *Jour. Am. Water Works Assoc.*, December,
1953, p. 1309. H. F. Seidel and E. R. Baumann, *Jour. Am. Water Works Assoc.*,
December, 1957.

Table 3-6

RATES OF FLOW OF SEWAGE

Place	Flow, gcd	Pop., in 1,000's	Year and Page in S and I.W.	Place	Flow, gcd	Pop., in 1,000's	Year and Page in S. and I.W.
Minneapolis-St. Paul, Minn.	143	740	1947, p. 1076	Detroit, Mich.	144	2,500	1949, p. 342
	140	900	1949, p. 338		158	2,400	1950, p. 946
	141	870	1952, p. 334		164	2,700	1955, p. 1095
Galesburg, Ill.	217	30	1949, p. 154	Aurora, Ill.	113	56	1950, p. 1492
	190	34.2	1953, p. 856		139	58.5	1953, p. 96
De Kalb, Ill.	98	13.3	1949, p. 1079	New Britain, Conn.	141	80	1950, p. 1490
	130	14	1952, p. 1314		156	80	1952, p. 1540
Green Bay, Wis.	151	60	1949, p. 1079	Cranston, R. I.	90	27.8	1952, p. 1315
	150	60	1952, p. 1317	Muskegon, Hts., Mich.	87	20	1952, p. 102
Racine, Wis.	187	78	1950, p. 256	Port Washington, N. Y.	120	11.7	1955, p. 750
	292	...	1952, p. 1538	Niles, Mich.	207	14	1953, p. 975
Worcester, Mass.	139	187	1950, p. 948	Washington, D. C.	196	819	1952, p. 1179
	116	187	1952, p. 100	Columbia, Pa.	53	13	1956, p. 819

Table 3–7

RATES OF SEWAGE FLOW FROM VARIOUS SOURCES

Character of District	Gal per Capita per Day	Gal per Acre per Day	Source of Sewage	Gal per Capita per Day
Domestic			Trailer courts	50 *
average	100		Motels	53 *
high-cost dwellings	150	7,500	State prisons:	
medium-cost dwellings	100	8,000	maximum	280 †
lowest-cost dwellings	80	16,000	average	176
			minimum	104
Commercial			Mental hospitals:	
hotels, stores, and of-			maximum	216 †
fice buildings		60,000	average	123
markets, warehouses,			minimum	38
wholesale districts		15,000	Grade school	4.4 ‡
			High school	3.9 ‡
Industrial				
light industry		14,000		

* From report of State Sanitary Engineers. See *Public Works*, March, 1957, p. 108.

† From J. C. Frederick, *Public Works*, April, 1957, p. 112.

‡ Average of 4.4 gal per day per pupil between 7.30 A.M. and 5.30 P.M. The average for the high school is spread over more hours per day. From C. H. Coberly, *Public Works*, May, 1957, p. 143.

(gcd) or in cubic feet per second (cfs). Rates of flow from commercial and industrial districts are sometimes expressed in gallons per square foot per day of floor area or per acre in the district. Rates of flow expressed in such units are shown in Tables 3–7, 3–8, and 3–9. A satisfactory method of predicting the flow from a commercial district is to study the probable activities of the district and to base the estimate on the known rates of water use in such activities. Some rates of water pumping are shown in Table 3–10.

3–9. Military allowances. Rates of flow used in the design of sewers for army installations are shown in Table 3–11.[7] Fluctuations in rates of flow of sewage at military and institutional installations

[7] See L. H. Kessler and J. T. Norgaard, *Sewage Works Jour.*, July, 1942, p. 757.

Table 3–8

RATES OF USE OF WATER FOR VARIOUS PURPOSES

(From *Water Supply Engineering*, 5th edition, by H. E. Babbitt
and J. J. Doland, 1950, McGraw-Hill Book Co., New York.)

Use	Unit	Gallons per Unit
Office buildings	Capita, per day	27–45
Hospitals	Bed, per day	125–350
Hotels	Room, per day	300–525
Laundries	Pound	3–5.7
Restaurants	Meal	0.5–4
Oil refining	Barrel	770
Gasoline	Barrel	360
Paper	Ton	39,000
Wool scouring	Pound	1.3
Meat packing, hogs	Hog	11
Rayon	Pound	0.16
Cotton bleaching	Ton	60–80
Soap	Pound	0.5–4.5
Steel, finished	Ton	65

are usually high and rapid because similar activities of the personnel occur simultaneously. There may be so many local conditions that affect sewage flows at military and institutional installations that large factors of safety must be allowed. Ellsworth [8] shows the relation of minimum to average to maximum rate of flow at Camp Edwards, expressed in gcd, to be 51:90.5:196, and from a hospital in the same camp to be 36.5:80.7:148.

3–10. Fluctuations in rate of sewage flow. [9]   The rate of flow of sewage from any district varies with the season, the day, the hour, and other conditions. The maximum and minimum rates of flow are the controlling factors in the design of sewers. The capacity must be sufficient to carry the maximum load and they must be on such a slope that deposits will not occur in them during periods of minimum flow. The maximum and minimum rates of flow are usually expressed as percentages of the average rate of flow.

The relation between the maximum and the average rates of flow

[8] S. M. Ellsworth, *Am. Jour. Public Health,* January, 1942, p. 21.
[9] See also H. W. Gifft, *Water Works and Sewerage,* May, 1945, p. 175.

Table 3–9

RATES OF WATER CONSUMPTION PREDICTED FOR DIFFERENT DISTRICTS FOR NEW YORK CITY

(From data by Kenneth Allen in *Municipal Engineer's Journal*, February, 1918.)

District	Net Bldg. Area in Sq Ft per Acre for Ultimate Consumption	Avg Number of Floors	Observed Cons., gcd per 1,000 sq ft max	Observed Cons., gcd per 1,000 sq ft avg	Predicted Mean Cons.	Predicted Mean, mgd per acre	Predicted Dry-Weather Flow, cfs per acre	Predicted Max Dry-Weather Flow, cfs per acre	Measured Avg Dry-Weather Flow, cfs per acre	Measured Max Dry-Weather Flow, cfs per acre
Hotel and midtown	24,800	15	634	526	500	0.20	0.29	0.34	0.104	0.146
Midtown and financial	24,800	15	338	219	300	0.12	0.18	0.23	0.078	0.110
East and West of midtown	24,800	10	297	230	300	0.074	0.12	0.15	0.057	0.097
Apartment, 59th to 155th Sts.	20,400	7		230	300	0.043	0.06	0.09		
Manhattan north of 155th St.	20,400	5		230	300	0.031	0.05	0.08		

Midtown district consists of department stores, large railroad terminals, industrial and loft buildings, and skyscraper office buildings.

Table 3–10

MAXIMUM AND MINIMUM RATES OF PUMPING WATER

(Design recommendations by C. B. Burdick, *Water and Sewage Works*, April, 1952, p. R-35.)

Rate of Pumping, in per cent of annual average

Period of Time	City of Less than 100,000		City of More than 100,000	
	Maximum	Minimum	Maximum	Minimum
Month	120–150	75–90	110–130	80–90
Day	150–250	50–75	125–175	60–80
Hour	300–400	25–50	200–300	50–75

Table 3–11

SEWAGE-TREATMENT DESIGN FACTORS FOR ARMY INSTALLATIONS

(From L. H. Kessler and J. T. Norgaard, *Sewage Works Jour.*, July, 1942, p. 757.)

Post Population, thousands		10	20	30	40	50
		Basic Flow, gallons per capita per day				
Camps and cantonments	24-hr avg	70.0	140	105	87.5	77	70
	16-hr avg	87.5	175	131	109	96.5	87.5
	4-hr max	122.5	245	183	153	135	122.5
	Extreme peak	210	420	315	262	231	210
	4-hr min	28	56	42	35	31	28
Airfields, permanent posts, and hospitals	24-hr avg	100	200	150	125	110	100
	16-hr avg	125	250	212.5	156	137.5	125
	4-hr max	175	350	262	219	193	175
	Extreme peak	300	600	450	375	330	300
	4-hr min	40	80	60	50	44	40

of sewage [10] for *residential areas* has been formulated empirically as

$$Q = 5q/P^{0.2} \qquad (3\text{--}1)$$

$$Q = \left[q \frac{14}{4 + P^{0.5}} \right] \qquad (3\text{--}2)$$

$$Q = 5q/P^{0.167} \qquad (3\text{--}3)$$

in which Q is the maximum rate of sewage flow, q is the average rate of flow, P is the population in thousands. Formula 3–1 is restricted to a maximum value of P equal to 1,000 and a minimum value of 1. No limitation has been set by Harmon [11] on the values in formula 3–2. Although the agreement between the formulas is fair, results from the use of any formula may be far from correct.

For rough estimates and for comparative purposes the ratio of the average to the minimum flow can be taken as the same as the ratio of the maximum to the average flow, unless gagings or other information have shown it to be otherwise.

The relation between maximum, average, and minimum rates of flow in commercial and industrial districts varies so greatly among cities and industries that it cannot be formulated with reasonable accuracy for all conditions. Predictions can be based on a study of similar districts or industries.

Hourly, daily, and seasonal fluctuations of sewage flow for a city affect the design and operation of pumping stations, treatment plants, and flow-control equipment. These fluctuations follow similar changes in the rate of water usage, exclusive of fire protection, except that fluctuations in rate of sewage flow are smaller and lag behind those of water usage. This fact is due, in part, to the equalizing effect provided by storage in sewers. Some 24-hour hydrographs of sewage flow in large cities are shown in Fig. 3–3. In smaller communities the variation in rate will be greater, as indicated by formulas 3–1, 3–2, and 3–3, but the size of the city has no relation to the hour of occurrence of peaks and valleys in the hydrograph. If the annual average rate of flow be taken at 100, then the maximum seasonal flow will be about 120, the maximum month about 140, the maximum day about 150 to 180, and the maximum hour 200 to 300. Variations of rate of flow among hours, days, and months are indicated in Tables 3–10, and 3–12. Temperature and rainfall are the principal causes

[10] See also C. F. Johnson, *Eng. News-Record*, Oct. 8, 1942, p. 90.
[11] W. G. Harmon, *Eng. News-Record*, Vol. 80, 1918, p. 1233,

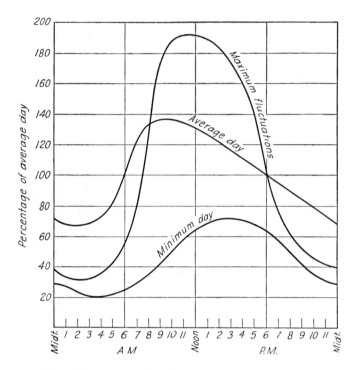

Fig. 3–3. Typical hourly variations in sewage flow.

Table 3–12

RATES OF FLOW OF SEWAGE FOR DIFFERENT MONTHS

(From L. D. Gayton, *Jour. Am. Water Works Assoc.*,
Vol. 29, 1937, p. 808, and Vol. 30, 1938, p. 892.)

Month	Flow in Terms of Average	Month	Flow in Terms of Average	Month	Flow in Terms of Average
January	0.90	May	1.00	September	1.08
February	0.92	June	1.13	October	0.96
March	0.89	July	1.24	November	0.90
April	0.87	August	1.18	December	0.92

of these changes in temperate climates. The use of water for air conditioning in commercial districts has become a serious factor in the overloading of sewers not designed to provide for the service.[12]

3–11. Infiltration and exfiltration.[13] Infiltration is the leakage of water from the surrounding ground into the sewer, and exfiltration is leakage from the sewer into the surrounding ground. Both are undesirable. The former is undesirable because it decreases the capacity of the sewer for its primary purpose and the latter is undesirable because, under most conditions, the pollution of the ground and of the ground water may lead to unhealthful conditions. Infiltration is generally considered the more undesirable, and more attention is paid to its prevention. It may be avoided by laying sewers in dry ground. Both can be prevented by the construction of tight joints in the sewer pipe.

Specifications for sewer construction may state a limit of permissible infiltration which has been used in designing the sewer. In fixing the permissible limit a balance must be struck between the cost of making tighter joints and the cost of increasing the size of sewer required by leaky joints.

Units used in expressing infiltration rates include: gallons per day per acre of sewered area; gallons per day per unit length of pipe, usually per mile; and gallons per day per inch diameter per mile of pipe. The last unit is probably the most logical, but the precision is scarcely worth the refinement and the unit often used is gallons per day (gpd) per mile of pipe. Rates of infiltration in wet ground have been found by Emerson [14] between 1,240 and 240,000 gpd per mile of pipe, and Horne [15] and Brooks [16] found up to 1,400,000. Specifications sometimes allow 1,600 up to 12,000 gpd per mile of 8-in. pipe, and up to 4,000 to 36,000 for 24-in. pipe.[17]

After the sewer has been completed a large part of the infiltration may enter through poorly made joints and also through abandoned house connections, leaky manholes and manhole covers, and illicit sewer connections. It has been found [18] that as much as 150 gpm

[12] L. D. Gayton, *Jour. Am. Water Works Assoc.*, Vol. 29, 1937, p. 808, and Vol. 30, 1938, p. 892.

[13] See also T. T. Hay, *Wastes Eng.*, March, 1954, p. 121; and S. Borland, *Public Works*, September, 1956, p. 97.

[14] C. A. Emerson, *Sewage Works Jour.*, November, 1933, p. 998.

[15] R. W. Horne, *Sewage Works Jour.*, March, 1945, p. 209.

[16] J. N. Brooks, *Trans. Am. Soc. Civil Engrs.*, Vol. 76, 1913, p. 1909.

[17] See also C. R. Velzy and J. M. Sprague, *S. and I.W.*, March, 1955, p. 245.

[18] A. M. Rawn, *Water Works and Sewerage*, December, 1937, p. 459.

may leak through a manhole cover. With manholes placed 300 to 500 ft apart this would amount to 3.5 to 2.0 million gallons per day per mile of pipe. It is evident that such a contribution is worthy of attention to prevent its occurrence.

Amounts contributed by the connection of roof drains, yard drains, cellar drains, and other drains for surface water have never been adequately reported in general terms because of the difficulty of expressing the flows accurately. That such contributions are of appreciable magnitude, even when prohibited, is undeniable, and some provision is usually made for them in the design of separate sewers.

3–12. Rate of flow of sewage. To determine the rate of flow of sewage to be carried: determine the period in the future for which sewers are to be designed; estimate the population and tributary area at the end of the period; estimate the rate of use of water; estimate the maximum and minimum rates of sewage flow; finally, estimate the maximum rate of infiltration and of surface water and add it to the maximum rate of sewage flow to give the required capacity of the proposed sewers.

Various state boards of health have adopted standards for rates of flow to be used in sewerage designs. The Illinois State Department of Public Health states: [19]

Sewage-collection systems should be designed for conditions anticipated at least 40 years in the future. Sewers serving strictly domestic areas should have a capacity, when flowing full, of at least 300 gallons and preferably 350 gallons per day for each person ultimately to be served. Proper allowance must be made for appreciable volumes of industrial wastes.

The Joint Committee report, referred to in Sect. 2–3, states: "New sewerage systems shall be designed on the basis of a per capita flow of not less than 100 g.c.d., laterals and submains . . . with a capacity of not less than 400 g.c.d., and mains, trunks and outfalls with not less than 250 g.c.d., plus industrial wastes but including infiltration."

Quantity of Storm Water

3–13. The rational method. The rate of runoff from a watershed, on which there is no storage nor retention of water, can be expressed as $Q = CAIR$, in which A is the area of the watershed, I is the relative imperviousness of the surface, R is the rate of rainfall

[19] "Items considered in the review of sewerage plans and specifications submitted to the state sanitary water board," issued by the Department of Public Health, Springfield, Ill., July 1, 1939.

or precipitation on the surface, and C is a coefficient which permits the expression of the factors in convenient units. If Q is expressed in cubic feet per second (cfs), A in acres, and R in inches per hour, the value of C will be very close to unity, and the basic expression for the so-called rational method can be written $Q = AIR$. In practice the value of A is measured by a land survey. The values of I and R are discussed in the three succeeding sections.

In view of the fact that judgment must be exercised in selecting coefficients of imperviousness and rates of rainfall to be substituted in the formula, it is to be expected that "in its application there will usually be as many results (differing widely from each other) as the number of men using it." [20] In spite of such objections the rational method is in greater favor with engineers than any other method when applied to small areas. Because of uncertainties in the selection of coefficients, rates of rainfall, etc., on areas greater than about 1,000 acres, empirical formulas are more commonly used for predicting the runoff from large areas.

3–14. Rate of rainfall. The value of R to be used in the solution of any problem of runoff depends on local rainfall records, on the frequency with which surcharging of storm sewers is to be permitted, and on the duration of the storm. As a result of studies of rainfall statistics in various parts of the world numerous rainfall formulas are available. A few formulas are given in Table 3–13. The formula most suitable to the problem in hand should be selected for its solution. Valuable discussions of rainfall formulas will be found in *Transactions of the American Society of Civil Engineers*, Vol. 54, 1905, p. 192, and in *Proceedings of the American Society of Civil Engineers*, Vol. 60, 1934, p. 157.

It is to be noted that t, the only variable in the formulas on which R is dependent, represents the duration of the storm which is equal to the time required for runoff to be contributed to the point of concentration from the entire area. This period is known as the "time of concentration."

3–15. Time of concentration. The time of concentration is defined as the longest time, without unreasonable delay, that will be required for a drop of water to flow from the upper limit of a drainage area to the point of concentration. The time of concentration to any point in a storm sewer is a combination of the "inlet time" and the time of flow in the sewer. The inlet time is the time required for

[20] C. H. Buerger, *Trans. Am. Soc. Civil Engrs.*, Vol. 78, 1915, p. 1139.

Table 3–13

RAINFALL FORMULAS

Name of Originator or Compiler	Conditions for Which Formula Was Devised	Rate of Rainfall, in. per hr *
A. N. Talbot [1]	Ordinary storms in eastern United States	$105/(t + 15)$
A. N. Talbot [1]	Maximum exceeded 2 or 3 times a century	$360/(t + 30)$
Emil Kuichling	Heavy rainfall near New York City	$120/(t + 20)$
S. D. Bleich [2]	2-yr storm near New York City	$12.38/t^{0.53}$
S. D. Bleich [2]	10-yr storm near New York City	$150/(t + 15)$
L. J. LeConte [3]	San Francisco, Calif.	$7/t^{0.5}$
C. W. Sherman	Maximum for Boston, Mass.	$25.12/t^{0.687}$
G. S. Webster	Ordinary for Philadelphia, Pa.	$12/t^{0.6}$
C. W. Hendrick [4]	Ordinary for Baltimore, Md.	$105/(t + 10)$
J. de Bruyn Kops	Ordinary for Savannah, Ga.	$163/(t + 27)$
C. D. Hill	For Chicago, Ill.	$120/(t + 15)$
A. J. Schafmeyer [5]	For Chicago, Ill.	$90/(t^{0.09} + 11)$
Metcalf and Eddy	For Denver, Colo.	$84/(t + 4)$
W. W. Horner [6]	For St. Louis, Mo.	$56/(t + 5)$
R. A. Brackenbury [7]	For Spokane, Wash.	$0.154 + 23.92/(t + 2.15)$

* t is time of concentration in minutes.

[1] *The Technograph*, published at the University of Illinois, 1891–1892, p. 103.

[2] *Proc. Am. Soc. Civil Engrs.*, Vol. 60, 1934, p. 157.

[3] *Trans. Am. Soc. Civil Engrs.*, Vol. 54, 1905, p. 198.

[4] *Eng. and Contr.*, Aug. 8, 1911, p. 158.

[5] *Jour. Western Soc. Engrs.*, December, 1944, p. 300.

[6] *Eng. News*, Sept. 29, 1910, p. 326.

[7] *Eng. Record*, Aug. 10, 1912, p. 156.

the water to flow over the surface of the ground to the sewer inlet. Because the area tributary to most sewer inlets is relatively small it is customary in practice to assume the inlet time on the basis of experience under similar conditions. The inlet time decreases as the slope and the imperviousness of the surface increase, and it increases as the distance over which the water has to travel and the storage on the watershed increase. The shortest time normally assumed in practice for an impervious area on a steep slope is 3 minutes. The longest time assumed for an ordinary city block in storm-sewer design is seldom greater than 20 minutes. Between these limits an approximation of the time of concentration may be reached by assuming that it varies with the distance of flow and the volume of storage on the watershed, and inversely as the relative imperviousness and the square root of the slope of the ground surface.

The time of flow in the sewer may be assumed to be the quotient of the velocity of flow in the sewer when full and the length of the sewer, the velocity of flow being computed from knowledge of the hydraulic elements of the sewer. The time so found is usually less than the actual time for the flood crest to reach the point of concentration from the sewer inlet because of the time required to fill the sewer, known as the time of storage. Although the time of storage may represent an appreciable increment of the time of concentration, particularly in large sewers, it is usually neglected in practice, the effect of such negligence being to give a larger assumed rate of flow.

3–16. Nature of surface. The proportion of the total rainfall that will reach the sewers depends on the relative porosity, or imperviousness, and the slope of the surface. Completely impervious surfaces, such as asphalt pavements or roofs of buildings, will give nearly 100 per cent runoff, regardless of the slope, after the surface has become thoroughly wet. When the ground is already watersoaked, or is frozen, the percentage of runoff is high, and in the event of a warm rain on snow-covered or frozen ground the runoff may exceed the rainfall. Table 3–14 shows the relative imperviousness of various types of surfaces when dry and on low slopes.[21]

3–17. Effect of storm duration on imperviousness. Gregory [22] states that the imperviousness of a watershed increases with the duration of the storm. If t is the time of duration of the storm, in minutes, then according to Gregory, $I = 0.175t^{1/3}$. I cannot be greater than the imperviousness of the area when it is saturated and t cannot be greater than 186 minutes. Such refinements as are introduced by Gregory's formulas are often disregarded in practice.

3–18. Shape of the area. The shape of the area may affect the rate of runoff from the area. Under some conditions it is hypothet-

---

[21] See also E. Kuichling, *Trans. Am. Soc. Civil Engrs.*, Vol. 65, p. 399; and W. L. Malcolm, *Water Works and Sewerage*, June, 1944, p. 227.

[22] C. E. Gregory, *Trans. Am. Soc. Civil Engrs.*, Vol. 58, 1907, p. 483.

Table 3–14

VALUES OF RELATIVE IMPERVIOUSNESS

Roof surfaces assumed to be watertight	0.70–0.95
Asphalt pavements in good order	.85– .90
Stone, brick, and wood-block pavements with tightly cemented joints	.75– .85
The same with open or uncemented joints	.50– .70
Inferior block pavements with open joints	.40– .50
Macadamized roadways	.25– .60
Gravel roadways and walks	.15– .30
Unpaved surfaces, railroad yards, and vacant lots	.10– .30
Parks, gardens, lawns, and meadows, depending on surface slope and characteristics of subsoil	.05– .25
Wooded areas or forest land, depending on surface slope and characteristics of subsoil	.01– .20
Most densely populated or built-up portion of a city	.70– .90

ically possible for the product of the area of a part of a watershed near the point of concentration and the rate of rainfall on this part to exceed the product of the entire area and the rate of rainfall on it. Area E in Fig. 3–6 is an example of such a condition. This condition is due to the fact that the area contributing runoff increases with time of concentration, whereas rate of rainfall on the area decreases, the decrease being proportionally greater. The ratio of the area which will contribute the maximum rate of runoff to the total area of the watershed is called the *coefficient of retardation.* No allowance is ordinarily made for this coefficient in storm-sewer design.

3–19. Limit of storm-sewer size. In the design of storm sewers it is necessary to decide how heavy a storm must be provided for. The very heaviest storms occur infrequently. To build a sewer capable of caring for all storms might involve a prohibitive expense, over the investment necessary to care for the ordinary heavy storms encountered annually or once in a decade. A larger investment would lie idle for a long period, entailing a considerable interest charge for which no return is easily seen. The alternative is to construct only for such heavy storms as are of ordinary occurrence and to allow the sewers to overflow on exceptional occasions. The amount of damage caused by inundation must be balanced against the extra cost of a sewer system that would avoid the damage.

The selection of the 5-year or the 10-year storm in the design of storm sewers for residential areas, and a somewhat longer period in commercial districts, is considered to be good practice. The greater the prospective losses in the event of flooding the longer the period of storm occurrence should be selected. The relation between rainfall and time of concentration may be based on a study of local rainfall records, or an appropriate formula may be selected or derived.

A municipality which does not provide adequate storm drainage is liable, under some circumstances, for damage occasioned by this neglect. It is not liable if no drainage exists, nor is it liable if the storm is of such unusual character as to be classed legally as an act of God.

3–20. Frequency of great storms. Kuichling's studies of the probabilities of the occurrence of heavy storms are published in *Transactions of the American Society of Civil Engineers*, Vol. 54, 1905, p. 192. Information on the extent of rainstorms is given by Francis in Vol. 7, 1878, p. 224, of the same publication. Kuichling expresses the intensity of storms which will occur once in 10 years as

$$R = 105/(t + 20) \qquad (3\text{--}4)$$

and once in 15 years as

$$R = 120/(t + 20) \qquad (3\text{--}5)$$

in which R is the intensity of rainfall in inches per hour, and t is the duration of the storm in minutes.

The frequency of great storms can be estimated from Fuller's empirical expression for Q_T in formula 3–10 or by the application of mathematical principles of probability. This latter method is explained by G. M. Fair and J. C. Geyer in *Water Supply and Waste-Water Disposal*.[23]

3–21. Computation of runoff by the rational method. At the start of a storm, runoff from a watershed commences at the point of concentration on that watershed; as, for example, at the street inlet and the manhole 4 in Fig. 3–4. The runoff may be expected to increase in rate as the rainfall continues until the entire watershed is contributing. This increase is due to the fact that, in the expression $Q = AIR$ during the time of concentration the rate of increase of A is greater, on most watersheds, than the rate of decrease in R. After the completion of the time of concentration, A is constant and R decreases. Hence, after the completion of the time of concentration the rate of runoff from a watershed will decrease.

[23] Published by John Wiley and Sons, 1954.

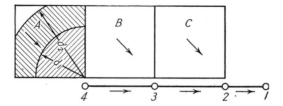

Fig. 3–4. Diagram for runoff computations. Time of flow between manholes is 5 min. Each area = 10 acres. Imperviousness = 0.80. Time of concentration on each area is 8 min.

Computations of the rate of runoff from the three adjacent city blocks indicated in Fig. 3–4, at each minute of time after the start of a rainstorm, are shown in Tables 3–15 and 3–16, and a summary of the steps in the solution is shown in Table 3–17. Results of the computations are plotted in Fig. 3–5. This figure shows that: (1) the rate of runoff may be expected to increase with the time of duration of the rainfall; (2) the greatest rate of runoff from a watershed occurs at the end of the time of concentration on that watershed; and (3) the greatest rate of runoff from all three watersheds occurs near to, but not necessarily at, the moment when the entire area of all watersheds begins to contribute runoff to the point of concentration.

A comparison of the maximum flood flow between manholes 2 and 1, as shown in Tables 3–16 and 3–17, shows a discrepancy. This is due partly to the effect in Table 3–16 of adding flood peaks without allowance for storage in the sewer and partly to the effect of applying rates of rainfall for shorter periods of time to contributing areas. A greater discrepancy would be shown by adding peak flows from each of the three areas, giving a flood flow of 110.4 cfs. The method shown in Tables 3–17, 3–18 and 3–19 is commonly followed in solutions by the rational method.

Table 3–15

TRIBUTARY AREAS IN FIG. 3–4

(Between Manholes 4 and 3)

Time in minutes after rain starts	1	2	3	4	5	6	7	8
Value of d, in feet	116.5	233	349.5	467	587.5	699	816	934
Contributing area, in acres	0.25	1.0	2.2	4.0	6.2	8.4	9.6	10

Table 3–16

COMPUTATION OF STORM FLOW BETWEEN MANHOLES IN FIG. 3–4

Time after Start of Storm, min	Rainfall, R,* in. per hr	AI = Area Contributing, I = 0.8	Manholes 4–3 Increment from Area A cfs from MH 4-3	Manholes 3–2 Increment from Area A Reaching MH 3, cfs	Increment from Area B Reaching MH 3, cfs	Flow from MH 3-2, cfs	Manholes 2–1 Increment from Area A Reaching MH 2, cfs †	Increment from Area B Reaching MH 2, cfs ‡	Increment from Area C Reaching MH 2, cfs §	Total Flow MH 2–1, cfs ‖
	A	B	C	D	E	F	G	H	I	J
1	6.56	0.2	1.3	0	1.3	1.3	0	0	1.3	1.3
2	6.17	0.8	4.9	0	4.9	4.9	0	0	4.9	4.9
3	5.83	1.8	10.5	0	10.5	10.5	0	0	10.5	10.5
4	5.52	3.2	17.7	0	17.7	17.7	0	0	17.7	17.7
5	5.25	5.0	26.3	0	26.3	26.3	0	0	26.3	26.3
6	5.00	6.7	33.5	1.3	33.5	34.8	0	1.3	33.5	34.8
7	4.77	7.7	*36.8* ¶	4.9	*36.8* ¶	41.7	0	4.9	*36.8* ¶	41.7
8	4.57	8	36.6	10.5	36.6	47.1	0	10.5	36.6	47.1
9	4.37	8	35.0	17.7	35.0	52.7	0	17.7	35.0	52.7
10	4.20	8	33.6	26.3	33.6	59.9	0	26.3	33.6	59.9
11	4.03	8	32.2	33.5	32.2	65.7	1.3	33.5	32.2	67.0
12	3.88	8	31.0	*36.8* ¶	31.0	*67.8* ¶	4.9	*36.8* ¶	31.0	72.7
13	3.75	8	30.0	36.6	30.0	66.6	10.5	36.6	30.0	77.1
14	3.62	8	29.0	35.0	29.0	64.0	17.7	35.0	29.0	81.7
15	3.50	8	28.0	33.6	28.0	61.6	26.3	33.6	28.0	87.9
16	3.38	8	27.0	32.2	27.0	59.2	33.5	32.2	27.0	92.7
17	3.28	8	26.2	31.0	26.2	57.2	*36.8* ¶	31.0	26.2	*94.0* ¶
18	3.18	8	25.4	30.0	25.4	55.4	36.6	30.0	25.4	91.0
19	3.09	8	24.7	29.0	24.7	53.7	35.0	29.0	24.7	88.7
20	3.00	8	24.0	28.0	24.0	52.0	33.6	28.0	24.0	85.6

* $R = 105/(t + 15)$.
† Line A in Fig. 3–5.
‡ Line B in Fig. 3–5.
§ Line C in Fig. 3–5.
‖ Line $A + B + C$ in Fig. 3–5.
¶ Maximum.

Procedure in the rational method. In the computation of the maximum runoff from a sewered district with branching sewers the procedure should be: (1) start computations at the upper end of the highest lateral and proceed downstream to the first junction; (2) proceed to the upper end of each branch entering the junction and, in a similar manner, compute the flow in it down to the junction. When all have been computed, proceed to the next step: (3) compute the rate of flow into each junction as the product of the sum of all of the values of AI tributary to the junction and

Table 3–17

MAXIMUM RATE OF FLOW IN THE STORM SEWERS IN FIG. 3–4

From Man-hole	To Man-hole	Additional District Drained	Area A, acres	Imperviousness I	ΔAI	ΣAI	Time of of Concentration t	Rainfall R,* in. per hr	Flow in Sewer Q, cfs
4	3	A	10	0.8	8	8	8	4.57	36.6
3	2	B	10	0.8	8	16	13	3.75	60.0
2	1	C	10	0.8	8	24	18	3.18	76.3
1	2	3	4	5	6	7	8	9	10

* $R = 105/(t + 15)$.

the rate of rainfall due to the longest time of concentration in any sewer entering the junction. It is possible that the longest time will not give the greatest rate of flow. If greater precision is desired, determine by trial the time of concentration which will give the greatest flood wave leading downstream from the junction when applied to all of the branches entering the

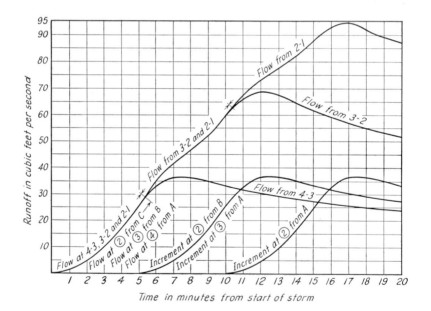

Fig. 3–5. Runoff from watersheds shown in Fig. 3–4.

Table 3-18

DATA FOR RUNOFF COMPUTATION

Block	Area, acres	Imperviousness	Inlet Time, minutes
A	10	0.8	7
B	10	0.7	8
C	1	0.4	15
D	10	0.6	8
E	5	0.5	10
F	1	0.5	10

Time in each sewer between manholes is 5 minutes.

Table 3-19

MAXIMUM RATE OF FLOW IN THE STORM SEWERS SHOWN IN FIG. 3-6

Line	From Man-hole	To Man-hole	Additional District Drained	Area A, acres	Imper-vious-ness I	ΔAI	ΣAI	Time of Concen-tration t, min	Rate of Rainfall R,* in. per hr	Total Runoff Q, cfs
1	5	4	A	10	0.8	8	8	7	4.77	38.2
2	4	3	B	10	0.7	7	15	12	3.88	58.2
3	3-1	3	E	5	0.5	2.5	2.5	10	4.2	10.5
4			C	1	0.4	0.4				
5	3	2	D	10	0.6	6.0	23.9	17	3.28	78.4
6	2	1	F	1	0.5	0.5	24.4	22	2.84	78.4 †

* $R = 105/(t + 15)$.

† The value of the product AIR in line 6 is 69.4. Since the maximum rate of flow cannot diminish downstream, the highest preceding figure is carried forward.

junction. Such refinements are not commonly made in practice unless the necessity is obvious. (4) Continue downstream in a similar manner, computing the maximum flood flow from each junction.

The following example is given as an illustration of the procedure to be followed:

Example. Let it be desired to compute the maximum rate of flow between each pair of adjacent manholes in the storm sewer illustrated in Fig. 3-6 with the data shown in Table 3-18.

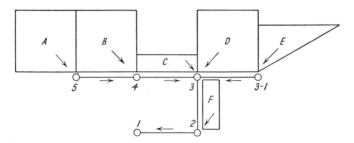

Fig. 3–6. Diagram for runoff computations.

Solution. Computations in this solution are summarized in Table 3–19. The method of tabulation is recommended in recording computations by the rational method. The use of a double line in the table at the end of the computation of the flow in a branch sewer is convenient in scanning the computations.

A more extensive problem is solved in Sect. 5–15.

3–22. Effect of storage. No allowance has been made in the suggested form of solution for the quantity of sewage required to fill the sewers between manholes, called storage. The computation of storage effects is tedious and is usually unnecessarily precise, except where large storage or holding basins are involved. The neglect of storage gives somewhat larger flows than are computed with an allowance for storage. Its effect should not be neglected in the design of large storm sewers.

3–23. Empirical formulas. The difficulty of determining the maximum rates of runoff with accuracy has led to the derivation by engineers of many empirical formulas. Some of these formulas have attracted wide attention and they have been applied extensively, sometimes under conditions to which they are not applicable. In general, these formulas are expressions of the runoff in terms of the area drained, the relative imperviousness, the slope of the land, and the rate of rainfall. Sometimes the storm flow is assumed to be a multiple, such as 4 or 5, of the dry-weather flow.[24] The Burkli-Ziegler formula,[25] devised by a Swiss engineer for Swiss conditions and introduced into the United States by Rudolph Hering, was one of the earliest of the empirical formulas to attract attention in this country. It has been used extensively in the form

[24] See also G. Chanin, *Water and Sewage Works*, July, 1955, p. 300.

[25] *Grösste Abflussmengen in städtischen Abzugskanäle*, Zurich, 1880. (Greatest Discharge of Municipal Sewers.)

$$Q = CRA \sqrt[4]{S/A} \tag{3-6}$$

in which Q = runoff, cfs.

    R = maximum rate of rainfall in inches per hour over the entire area. This is determined only by experience in the particular locality and is usually taken at from 1 to 3 in. per hour.

    S = slope of the ground surface, ft per thousand.

    A = area, acres.

    C = a coefficient representing the nature of the ground surface or relative imperviousness. In this form of the expression C is recommended as 0.7.

The McMath formula [26] was developed for St. Louis conditions. With the above notation the formula is

$$Q = CRA \sqrt[5]{S/A} \tag{3-7}$$

McMath recommended C equal to 0.75, R equal to 2.75, and S equal to 15. The formula has been extended for use, with all values of C, R, S, and A ordinarily met in sewerage practice.

Results obtained by the application of a few formulas to the same conditions are compared graphically in Fig. 3–7. It is to be noted that the divergence between the smallest and the largest results is more than 750 per cent. Since these formulas are not all applicable to the same conditions, the differences shown are due partially to an extension of some of them beyond the limits for which they were prepared.

3–24. Runoff from large areas. Empirical formulas have been devised that are applicable to drainage areas of more than 1,000 acres.[27] Kuichling's formulas, published in 1901 in the report of the New York State Barge Canal, were devised for areas greater than 100 square miles. The following modification of these formulas for ordinary storms on smaller areas was published for the first time in *American Sewerage Practice*, Vol. I, by Metcalf and Eddy:

$$Q = \frac{25,000}{A + 125} + 15 \tag{3-8}$$

It is to be noted that the only factor taken into consideration to express Q, the maximum rate of runoff, is A which represents the area of the

[26] *Trans. Am. Soc. Civil Engrs.*, Vol. 16, 1887, p. 179.

[27] See also A. F. Meyer, *Elements of Hydrology*, 1917.

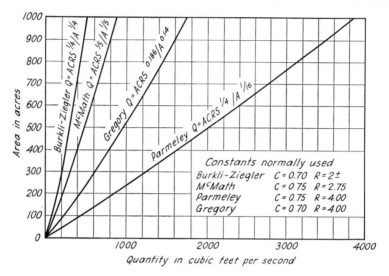

Fig. 3–7. Comparison of empirical runoff formulas.

watershed. It is obvious that there are other factors to be considered such as rate of rainfall, slope, and imperviousness. Fuller [28] devised the following formulas to care for time, area, and nature of surface:

$$Q = CM^{0.8} \tag{3-9}$$

$$Q_T = CM^{0.8}(1 + 0.8 \log T) \tag{3-10}$$

$$Q_M = CM^{0.8}(1 + 0.8 \log T)\left(1 + \frac{2}{M^{0.3}}\right) \tag{3-11}$$

where Q = average flow, cfs.
Q_T = greatest 24-hr runoff in period of T yr, cfs.
Q_M = greatest rate of runoff in maximum flood, cfs.
M = drainage area, sq mi.
T = length of period, yr.
C = coefficient determined from the area by substituting observed flows from the stream in question, or runoff records from similar streams, in the above formulas.

Some other runoff formulas devised for particular conditions are of as general applicability as those quoted. Two commonly applied formulas are: Fannings, $Q = 200M^{5/6}$; Talbot's, $Q = 500M^{1/4}$; in both, Q is rate of runoff in cfs, and M is watershed area in square miles.

[28] W. E. Fuller, *Trans. Am. Soc. Civil Engrs.*, Vol. **77**, 1914, p. **564**.

Chapter 4

Hydraulics of sewers

4–1. Flow in sewers. The hydraulic properties of sewage and of water are considered identical in sewer design. The flow of sewage may occur under closed-channel or open-channel conditions. Under conditions normally met in sewerage practice, open-channel flow occurs where the hydraulic grade line lies in or on the surface of the flowing sewage; and closed-channel flow occurs when the hydraulic grade line does not lie on the surface of the flowing sewage. In both cases when the average velocity is known, the rate of flow may then be determined by the rational relationship

$$Q = AV$$

in which Q = the average rate of flow.

A = the wetted area of the cross section of the sewer.

V = the velocity of flow.

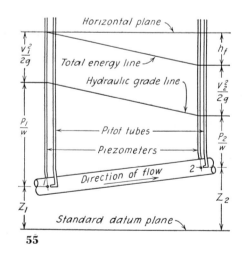

Fig. 4–1. Closed-channel flow.

4–2. Closed-channel flow. Solutions of closed-channel flow problems may be obtained by applying the Bernoulli equation to the condition. This relationship utilizes the law of conservation of energy as applied to fluid flow, stating that the energy at section 1 in a pipe is accounted for as energy at section 2 or as lost energy. See Fig. 4–1. Bernoulli's equation states:

$$\frac{p_1}{w} + \frac{V_1{}^2}{2g} + Z_1 = \frac{p_2}{w} + \frac{V_2{}^2}{2g} + Z_2 + h_f$$

where

$\dfrac{p_1}{w}$ and $\dfrac{p_2}{w}$ = the pressure heads at sections 1 and 2, respectively.

$\dfrac{V_1{}^2}{2g}$ and $\dfrac{V_2{}^2}{2g}$ = the velocity heads at sections 1 and 2, respectively.

Z_1 and Z_2 = the elevation heads at sections 1 and 2, respectively.

h_f = the head lost between sections 1 and 2.

The various heads are normally expressed in terms of the head of water, in feet.

Generally, Bernoulli's equation is not used in the solution of sewage-flow problems in closed channels due to the large number of computations which must be completed. A simplified relationship, presented by Hazen and Williams, is found to give a close approximation of the average velocity of flow in closed channels. This relationship may be written in the form:

$$V = 1.31CR^{0.63}S^{0.54} \tag{4–1}$$

in which C = a coefficient whose value depends upon the roughness of the conduit.

         R = hydraulic radius = $\dfrac{\text{wetted area}}{\text{wetted perimeter}}$.

         S = hydraulic gradient.

Values of C obtained with different materials used in conduit manufacture are given in Table 4–1.

Other formulas may be used, but information on the values of coefficients and exponents is generally less available.

4–3. Open-channel flow. The application of the Bernoulli equation to open-channel flow when uniform, steady [1] flow conditions

---

[1] Uniform, steady flow is discussed in Sect. 4–13.

Table 4–1

VALUES OF C TO BE USED IN HAZEN AND WILLIAMS' FORMULA

Material			C
Ordinary tar-dipped cast iron:		new	135
		5 yr old	120
	Average effect	10 yr old	110
	of tuberculation	15 yr old	105
	on values of C	20 yr old	95
		30 yr old	85
		40 yr old	80
New unlined cast-iron pipe			130
Cement-lined pipes			140
New bituminous enamel-lined pipes:			
Supply and transmission pipe 16 in. or larger			155
16 in. or smaller			145
Concrete, best-workmanship, large diameter			150

exist in the channel results in an expression for the average velocity of flow,

$$V = \sqrt{\frac{8g}{f}} \sqrt{RS} \qquad (4\text{--}2)$$

where g = acceleration due to gravity.

f = friction coefficient.

R = hydraulic radius.

S = hydraulic gradient.

The component $\sqrt{8g/f}$ is normally expressed in the form of a coefficient, C_c, which is determined empirically in accordance with observed velocities and discharges. The resulting relationship, $V = C_c\sqrt{RS}$ is commonly referred to as the Chezy formula. Its use is limited by the evaluation of C_c which depends upon f, which in turn depends upon Reynolds' number and the size, shape, and roughness of the channel.

The Chezy formula has been modified by Kutter [2] to evaluate the coefficient, C_c. By Kutter's formula

[2] *A General Formula for the Flow of Water in Rivers and Other Channels*, translated by J. G. Trautwine, John Wiley and Sons, New York, 1907.

$$V = \left[\frac{\dfrac{1.81}{n} + 41.67 + \dfrac{0.0028}{S}}{1 + \dfrac{n}{\sqrt{R}}\left(41.67 + \dfrac{0.0028}{S}\right)} \right] \sqrt{RS} \qquad (4\text{-}3)$$

where n is a coefficient dependent upon the roughness of the channel. Values of n are given in Table 4–2. Kutter's formula is commonly used for the solution of problems involving the flow of sewage in open-channel sewers.

Another formula which is applicable to open-channel flow conditions has been developed by Manning.[3] Manning's formula expresses:

$$V = \frac{1.486}{n} R^{\frac{2}{3}} S^{\frac{1}{2}} \qquad (4\text{-}4)$$

in which the nomenclature is the same as in the Kutter and Chezy formulas. This relationship is much less cumbersome than either of the previous formulas and can be applied to all types of channels regardless of shape, or of R, V, and S. The precision of either Kutter's or Manning's formulas in the determination of the average velocity of flow in open channels is limited by the evaluation of the roughness coefficient and by other factors. Within the limits of normal usage, both the Kutter and Manning formulas produce essentially the same results. Because of the empirical nature of the formulas, their use should be limited to values of R less than 10 ft, of V less than 10 fps, and of S greater than 0.0001. Within these limits, an accuracy better than 5 per cent can be expected.

Although many other empirical relationships have been developed which are applicable to open-channel flow problems, it is generally accepted that those mentioned above provide the most satisfactory results.

4–4. Circular pipes running full.[4] Problems involving flow conditions in circular pipes running full include five different elements or factors. These are: Q, V, D, S, and n. Q is the average rate of flow, D is the diameter of the sewer, and the other nomenclature is as previously described in this chapter. The three factors V, Q, and D are related in the form $Q = AV = \pi D^2 V / 4$. This relationship is in-

[3] R. Manning, "Flow of Water in Open Channels and Pipes," *Trans. Inst. of Civil Engrs. of Ireland*, Vol. 20, 1890.

[4] See also Thomas R. Camp, "Design of Sewers to Facilitate Flow," *Sewage Works Jour.*, January, 1946, p. 3.

Table 4–2

VALUES OF "n" TO BE USED WITH KUTTER'S AND MANNING'S FORMULAS

Character of the Materials	n
Well-planed timber	0.009
Neat cement or very smooth pipe	0.010
Unplaned timber. Best concrete	0.012
Smooth masonry or brickwork, or concrete sewers under ordinary conditions	0.013
Vitrified-clay pipe or ordinary brickwork	0.015
Rubble masonry or rough brickwork	0.017
Smooth earth	0.020
	0.035
Rough channels overgrown with grass	0.030
	0.050

dependent of S and n. All five factors are, in turn, related by the expression $Q = AC_k\sqrt{RS}$, where C_k, the Kutter coefficient, includes the roughness factor n as well as R and S. Therefore, if any three of these factors are known except V, D, and Q together, the remaining two parameters can be solved by substitution in Kutter's or other formulas. Since there remain only nine different combinations of any three of the five factors, there are only nine typical problems that can be encountered with circular pipes running full. Illustrative solutions of these nine typical problems are given in Table 4–3.

Table 4–3

ILLUSTRATIVE SOLUTIONS OF PROBLEMS BY KUTTER'S FORMULA
APPLIED TO CIRCULAR PIPES FLOWING FULL, $n = 0.015$

	Given					Found				
Case No	Q, cfs	V, fps	D, in.	S	n	Q, cfs	V, fps	D, in.	S	n
1	1.0	2.8			0.015			8	0.012	
2		4.0	30		0.015	20			0.0033	
3	100		42		0.015		10.3		0.013	
4	5			0.03	0.015		6.4	12		
5		5.4		0.01	0.015	13		21		
6			120	0.001	0.015	460	5.9			
7	0.6	3.0		0.021				6		0.015
8	600		168	0.00029			3.9			0.015
9		2.6	48	0.0007		32				0.015
	1	2	3	4	5	6	7	8	9	10

4–5. Solutions by Kutter's formula. The use of diagrams for the solution of problems is justified only where large numbers of solutions by a complicated formula are anticipated. Since Kutter's formula is complicated and numerous problems involving it are met in sewerage practice, the use of diagrams for its solution is justified by the time saved in solving the problems.

Nomographs have been prepared, as shown in Figs. 4–2, 4–3, and 4–4, to aid in solutions of Kutter's formula. The value of n can be read from the charts to about the third decimal place. This gives an accuracy of about 90 per cent which is approximately as close as n can be determined by measurements in the field.

The use of these nomographs is dictated by the data supplied. As indicated in Sect. 4–4, two types of problems may be presented:

1. Given any two of the factors Q, V, and D, determine the third factor. This is done by solving the equation $Q = AV$. Solutions of this problem may be accomplished simply. In the nomographs, the values on the diameter reference line, which are proportional to values of A, are independent of n and S. Consequently, when solving the relationship $Q = AV$, the Q, D, and V lines may be used without regard to the values of n and S.

2. Given any three of the five factors Q, V, D, S, and n, other than Q, D, and V together, let it be required to determine the values of the other two factors by a solution of Kutter's formula. Solutions of these problems are based upon the relationship $Q = AC_k \sqrt{RS}$, where Q is dependent on both n and S. In constructing the charts for use with different values of n, it was found necessary to change the scales only on the vertical reference line for the diameter, leaving the positions and the scales of the vertical reference lines for quantity and slope unchanged. In solving problems of this type, utilize only the Q, D, and S scales and neglect the V reference line.

In order to use the diagrams in solving Kutter's formula, the diameter reference line must be corrected for the proper value of n. The location of pipe diameters for values of n other than 0.015 can be found by the use of the inset diagram to the left of the diameter reference line. Entering this inset diagram at the top at the proper value of n, drop vertically down until the desired slanting diameter line is intersected. The intersection of the n line and the diameter line may then be projected *horizontally* over to its proper location on the diameter reference line.

When using the nomographs to solve flow problems, the type 1 problems should be solved first before adjusting the result in accordance with type 2.

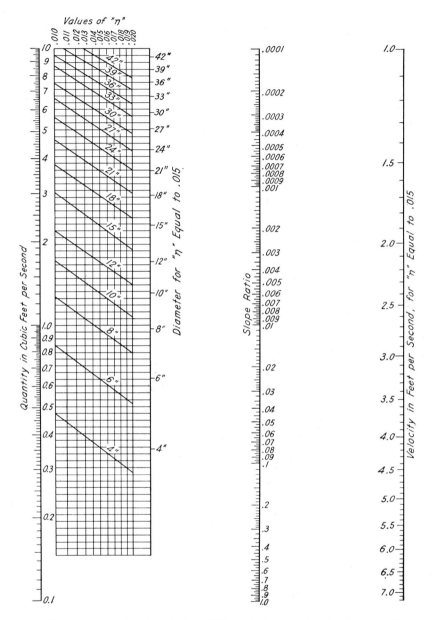

Fig. 4–2. Diagram for the solution of Kutter's formula for circular pipes flowing full; 0.1 to 10 cfs.

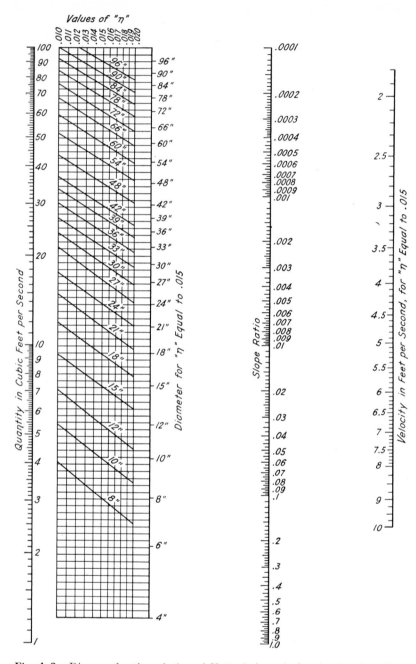

Fig. 4–3. Diagram for the solution of Kutter's formula for circular pipes flowing full; 1.0 to 100 cfs.

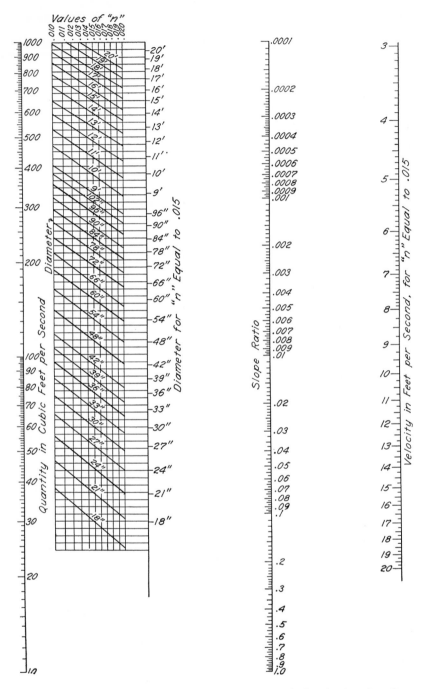

Fig. 4–4. Diagram for the solution of Kutter's formula for circular pipes flowing full; 10 to 1,000 cfs.

63

4–6. Illustrative solutions of problems using nomographs of Kutter's formula applied to circular pipes running full.

1. When $n = 0.015$.

The solution of a problem when $n = 0.015$ is made by laying a straight-edge across the diagram, touching the two given points on the appropriate vertical scales, and reading the solution at the intersection of the remaining two vertical lines on which the scales of the unknown factors are given. In each case, the nomograph to be used is the one in which the straightedge will be most nearly horizontal. In cases 7, 8, and 9 in Table 4–3, the three given factors lie in a straight line on the scales for $n = 0.015$, indicating that this is the value of n.

2. When $n \neq 0.015$.

The following cases explain the solution, using the nomographs, of the typical problems given in Table 4–4. In general, when any two of the three factors Q, V, and D are given, the third should be found on the nomograph for $n = 0.015$, regardless of the true value of n.

Case 1. First lay the straightedge on Fig. 4–4 at $Q = 100$ and $V = 8$. Read $D = 48$ in. Second, find the scale of $D = 48$ in. for $n = 0.010$, and then project the value of 48 from this scale horizontally onto the reference line for D. With the straightedge at this point and $Q = 100$, read the value of S as 0.0026.

Case 2. First, D is found as in Case 1. Project the value of 48 in. horizontally from the $n = 0.020$ scale onto the reference line for D. Second, with the straightedge at this point and at $Q = 100$, read the value of S as 0.0123.

Table 4–4

ILLUSTRATIVE SOLUTIONS OF PROBLEMS BY KUTTER'S FORMULA
APPLIED TO CIRCULAR PIPES RUNNING FULL, $n \neq 0.015$

		Given					Found			
Case No	Q, cfs	V, fps	D, in.	S	n	Q, cfs	V, fps	D, in.	S	n
1	100	8			0.010			48	0.0026	
2	100	8			0.020			48	0.0123	
3		8	48		0.020	100			0.0123	
4	100		48		0.010		8		0.0026	
5	100	8		0.0123				48		0.020
6			48	0.0123	0.020	100	8			
7	100			0.0123	0.020		8	48		
8	100		48	0.0123			8			0.020
9			48	0.0026		100				0.010
10		8		0.0026	0.010	100		48		
11	100	8	48						unsolvable	

Case 3. First, lay the straightedge on $V = 8$ and $D = 48$ in. for $n = 0.015$, and read $Q = 100$. Second, proceed as in the second step in Case 2.

Case 4. First, lay the straightedge on $Q = 100$ and $D = 48$ in. for $n = 0.015$, and read $V = 8$. Second, proceed as in the second step in Case 1.

Case 5. First lay the straightedge on $Q = 100$ and $V = 8$ for $n = 0.015$, and read $D = 48$ in. Second, with straightedge at $Q = 100$ and $S = 0.0123$, find the point of intersection of the straightedge with the vertical reference line for D and project it horizontally to intersect the sloping line for 48 in. The vertical line passing through this intersection represents the value of n. In this case $n = 0.020$.

Case 6. First, find the scale position for $D = 48$ in. when $n = 0.020$ on the vertical reference line for D. Second, with the straightedge at this intersection and at $S = 0.0123$, read $Q = 100$. Note, do *not* read V on the vertical reference line with the straightedge in this position because the scale on the V line is for $n = 0.015$, not 0.020. Third, with the straightedge at $Q = 100$ and $D = 48$ for $n = 0.015$, read the value of $V = 8$.

Case 7. First, with the straightedge at $Q = 100$ and $S = 0.0123$ proceed as in the second step in Case 5 and read D for $n = 0.020$ as 48 in. Second, with $Q = 100$ and $D = 48$ for $n = 0.015$, read $V = 8$.

Case 8. Determine V as in Case 4. Determine n as in Case 5.

Case 9. Determine Q as in Case 3. Determine n as in Case 5.

Case 10. This case must be solved by trial and error. It is convenient to assume that V varies approximately inversely as n, where S and R are constant. First, assume V for $n = 0.015$ is $(8 \times 0.010) \div 0.015 = 5.3$. Second, with the straightedge at $V = 5.3$ and $S = 0.0026$ read $D = 51$ in. Third, with $D = 51$ and $V = 8$, read $Q = 114$. Fourth, with $Q = 114$ and $D = 51$ for $n = 0.010$, read $S = 0.0024$. This value does not check the given value of 0.0026. It is necessary to repeat the procedure with different values of V until the value of S checks that given in the data. When V for $n = 0.015$ is assumed as 5.1, it is found that, for $n = 0.010$, $D = 48$ in. and $Q = 100$, with $S = 0.0026$, a check.

Case 11. In this case, there are an infinite number of combinations of S and n which will complete the problem. The problem, therefore, cannot be solved.

4–7. Flow in circular pipes flowing partly full. It is customary to base the computation of sewers on full-flow conditions, although sewers seldom flow full. Under some conditions it is possible for a covered conduit to carry water at a higher rate when flowing partly full than when flowing full. This apparent anomaly adds no factor of safety in design because the hydraulic conditions at maximum rate of flow are usually unstable, and the sewer may suddenly run full

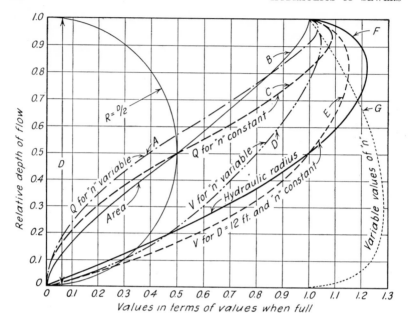

Fig. 4–5. Hydraulic elements of circular sections.

at a diminished rate of flow, or under pressure at the same maximum rate of flow.

The hydraulic elements of a conduit are the hydraulic radius, the cross-sectional area of the flowing stream, the average velocity of flow, and the rate of discharge. Values of these hydraulic elements for flow at different depths in a circular conduit are plotted in Fig. 4–5. The curves for R and A are the same for all diameters of pipe, but the curves for V and for Q depend both on the formula used in computing them and on the values of R, S, and n assumed. The effect of varying these factors on the shape of the graphs is so slight as usually to be negligible within the limits of the ordinary sewerage problem. In this diagram, n has been assumed constant, for all depths of flow, in lines C and E.

Rohwer [5] has shown that variations in discharge from the ideal relationship are accentuated above half depth. This is primarily due to the unstable hydraulic conditions which exist in the pipe in this flow range. As a result, the value of the hydraulic elements curves

[5] Carl Rowher, *Civil Eng.,* October, 1943, p. 488.

above half depth in circular and similarly shaped channels may be principally academic.

Sundin [6] has demonstrated both theoretically and empirically that the value of n will vary as much as 20 per cent or more with the depth of flow in circular and other shaped conduits. Figure 4–5 shows in line G the variation of n with depth as suggested by Sundin. The value of n tends to increase as depth of flow increases for relative depths of flow up to approximately 0.35. If proper consideration is given to the variations of n, the results with the hydraulic elements diagram will be more accurate.[7]

4–8. Examples of flow in circular pipes partly full. In the solution of problems involving partly full flow in a circular conduit, the method followed is either to solve the problem as though it were for full-flow conditions by means of Figs. 4–2, 4–3, or 4–4, and then to convert to partly full conditions by means of Fig. 4–5, or to convert from partly full conditions to full-flow conditions using Fig. 4–5 and solve as in the preceding section.

Example Problems:

I. Determine the rate of discharge in a 12-in. circular sewer with $n = 0.015$, when the slope is 0.005, and the depth of flow is 3 in.

Solution. 1. Under full-flow conditions, $Q = 2.1$ cfs (determined from Fig. 4–2).

2. Converting to partly full conditions: A depth of 3 in. = 0.25 of the total depth. From Fig. 4–5, the proportionate discharge at this depth is 0.13 of the total discharge.

3. The rate of discharge when the pipe is 3 in. full is, therefore, $2.1 \times 0.13 = 0.27$ cfs.

II. Determine the diameter, full capacity and value of n in a sewer with $S = 0.002$ if the velocity of flow is 3.0 fps when the sewer is discharging at 20 per cent of its full capacity and the depth of flow is 9 in.

Solution. 1. Since the sewer is discharging at 20 per cent capacity, the relative depth of flow as given in Fig. 4–5 is $0.30D$.

2. At 30 per cent depth, the velocity is 75 per cent of the full-flow velocity. Therefore, full-flow velocity = $3.0/0.75 = 4$ fps, and $D = 9$ in./0.3 = 30 in.

3. Knowing $D = 30$ in., $V = 4$ fps, solve for Q by the relationship $Q = AV$ (Use Fig. 4–3). *Answer:* $Q = 20$ cfs.

[6] H. S. Sundin, *The Hydraulic and Structural Design of Large Sewers*, unpublished Ph.D. thesis, University of Illinois, 1953.

[7] T. R. Camp, "Design of Sewers to Facilitate Flow," *Sewage Works Jour.*, January, 1946, p. 3.

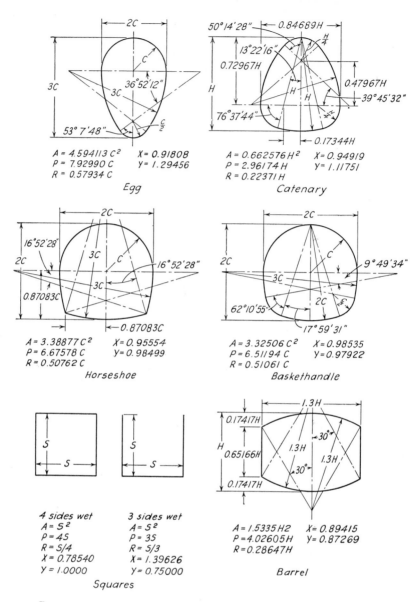

$X = \dfrac{Po}{P}$ = factor by which to multiply the capacity of the given section to find the capacity of a circular sewer with equal velocity.

Y = height of section divided by height of a circular section with equal hydraulic radius.

Fig. 4–6. Sections of non-circular sewers.

68

4. Knowing $Q = 20$ cfs and $S = 0.002$, solve for n using Fig. 4–3. *Answer*: $n = 0.012$.

4–9. Sections other than circular. Shapes of sections other than circular are frequently used in sewage conveyance, particularly for pipes large enough for a man to enter.[8] Non-circular shapes are used for structural reasons to secure greater strength to resist the loads to be met, for economic reasons to reduce the cost of construction, to simplify problems in construction, to improve the velocity of flow at low depths of flow, and for other reasons.[9] Illustrations of some non-circular sections are shown in Fig. 4–6. Originators of sections have given names to them as egg, ovoid, U-shaped, etc. The shape of a section is fixed by the radius of each curve in the cross-section, the radii being expressed in terms of the vertical height of the section. Various shapes have different advantages. For example, the catenary section is used for its structural advantage.

The egg-shaped section will give a slightly higher velocity at low flows than the equivalent circular section carrying the same rate rate of flow. The difference is so small that Sundin has concluded [10] that the governing factor in the shape of a sewer is structural economy. There is no "standard" egg-shaped section, the section shown in Fig. 4–6 being only one of many different egg shapes.

Relatively high velocities for low flows in large, flat-bottomed conduits can be secured by concentrating the flow in a small, longitudinal channel or trough, in the bottom of the larger sewer. This trough, or channel, is called a cunette.

4–10. Flow in sections other than circular. When the hydraulic elements of a channel are known, problems of flow can be solved by substitution of the appropriate hydraulic elements in any one of the desired formulas. The hydraulic elements of various sections, when full, are given in Table 4–5, and the hydraulic elements of one form of egg-shaped section and of a square section, at various depths, are shown in Figs. 4–7 and 4–8 respectively. It is possible to solve problems involving irregularly shaped sewer sections by changing the conditions of the problem to those in an equivalent circular section, and using the diagrams for circular sewers for the solution of the problem.

4–11. Equivalent sections. Two conduits, or systems of conduits, are said to be hydraulically equivalent when they will discharge at

[8] See *Eng. News-Record,* Sept. 30, 1948, p. 70.
[9] See also, Thos. Donkin, *Jour. Inst. of Civil Engrs.,* December, 1937, p. 261.
[10] Sundin, *op. cit.*

Table 4–5

Hydraulic Elements of Sewer Sections. Sewers Flowing Full

Section	Area in Terms of Vert. Dia. Squared, D^2	Hydraulic Radius in Terms of Vert. Dia., D	Vert. Dia. D in Terms of Dia. d of Equivalent Circular Section	Source
Circular	0.7854	0.250	1.000	
Egg	0.5105	0.1931	1.25	*Eng. Record*, 72:608
Ovoid	0.5650	0.2070	1.19	*Eng. Record*, 72:608
Semi-elliptical	0.8176	0.2487	1.041	*Eng. News*, 71:552
Catenary	0.6625	0.2237	1.17	*Eng. Record*, 72:608
Horseshoe	0.8472	0.2536	0.942	*Eng. Record*, 72:608
Basket handle	0.8313	0.2553	0.976	*Eng. Record*, 72:608
Rectangular	1.3125	0.2865	0.7968	*Hydraulic Diagrams and Tables*, Garrett
Square (3 sides wet)	1.0000	.333	0.856	
Square (4 sides wet)	1.0000	.250	0.913	

the same rate when both are flowing full on the same hydraulic gradient. The coefficients of roughness, n, of equivalent conduits may or may not be the same. The vertical height of a non-circular section, usually called its diameter, can be expressed in terms of the diameter of an equivalent circle, d, through use of the continuity equation by equating $A_1V_1 = A_2V_2$, in which $A_1 = $ the area of the non-circular section; $A_2 = $ the area of the equivalent circle $= \pi(d^2/4)$; $V_1 = $ the velocity of flow in the non-circular section, and $V_2 = $ the velocity of flow in the equivalent circle. If Manning's formula is applied, the expression becomes:

$$A_1 \frac{1.486}{n_1} R_1{}^{2/3}S_1{}^{1/2} = A_2 \frac{1.486}{n_2} R_2{}^{2/3}S_2{}^{1/2}$$

If the sections are hydraulically equivalent, $S_1 = S_2$ by definition. If $n_1 = n_2$, then

$$A_1 R_1{}^{2/3} = \frac{\pi d^2}{4} \times \left(\frac{d}{4}\right)^{2/3} = \frac{\pi d^{8/3}}{4^{5/3}}$$

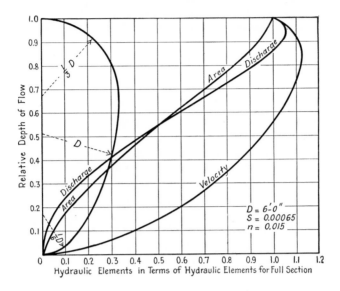

Fig. 4–7. Hydraulic elements of Phillip's egg-shaped sewer.

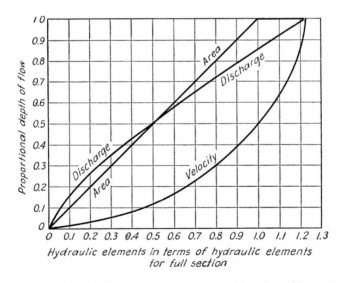

Fig. 4–8. Hydraulic elements of square section, four sides wet.

It is now necessary to find A_1 and R_1 of the non-circular section in terms of D_1, its diameter. For example, in a square section flowing full with four sides wet, $A_1 = D_1{}^2$ and $R_1 = D_1/4$; hence for a square section:

$$(D_1)^2 \left(\frac{D_1}{4}\right)^{\frac{2}{3}} = \frac{d^{\frac{8}{3}}}{4^{\frac{5}{3}}}$$

hence $D_1 = 0.913d$.   (See Table 4–5.)

It is important to note that the velocities of flow in equivalent sections are not necessarily equal because the areas of equivalent sections are not necessarily equal. Since $Q_1 = A_1V_1 = A_2V_2$ and $A_1 \neq A_2$ then $V_1 \neq V_2$. The velocity of flow in a circular section is greater than the velocity of flow in any section equivalent to the circular section if both sections are flowing full.

If the coefficients of roughness are not equal in the two sections, it may be shown that the diameter of the non-circular section is proportional to the ratio, $n_1 : n_2$. The equation above thus becomes:

$$\frac{A_1 R_1{}^{\frac{2}{3}}}{n_1} = \frac{\pi d^{\frac{8}{3}}}{n_2(4)^{\frac{5}{3}}}$$

Using the square section for illustrative purposes:

$$\frac{(D_1)^2 (D_1/4)^{\frac{2}{3}}}{n_1} = \frac{\pi d^{\frac{8}{3}}}{n_2(4)^{\frac{5}{3}}} \quad \text{or} \quad D_1 = 0.913d \times \frac{n_1}{n_2}$$

Problems involving partly full flow in sections other than circular are solved in a manner similar to those involving partial flow in circular sections. They necessitate the construction of a diagram showing the hydraulic elements at various depths in the non-circular section, as shown, for example, in Fig. 4–7 for an egg-shaped section, and in Fig. 4–8 for a square section with four sides wet when full.

If the diameter of the circular section equivalent to that of the non-circular section is known, Figs. 4–2, 4–3, and 4–4 may be used for solving flow problems in non-circular sections.

4–12. Problems involving flow in an egg-shaped section.

I. Determine the rate and velocity of flow in a 60-in. egg-shaped sewer, flowing full, on a slope of 0.0065 when n is 0.015.

Solution. 1. From Table 4–5, the diameter of the equivalent circular section is $60/1.25 = 48$ in.

2. From Fig. 4–4, the rate of flow in a 48-in. sewer on a slope of 0.0065 is 100 cfs. Therefore, from $Q = AV$, $V = 100/(0.5105)(5)^2 = 7.8$ fps. This is slightly less than the velocity in the equivalent circular section.

II. Assume that the 60-in. egg-shaped sewer is made of steel and is connected to a 48-in. circular cast-iron pipe. If both conduits are on the same slope and flow full, determine the velocity of flow in the egg-shaped sewer.

Solution. The variation in velocity in the egg-shaped sewer will differ from the previous result only by an amount attributable to the differences between the coefficients of roughness of the two materials. From Table 4–2: n_1 for concrete = 0.012; n_2 for cast iron = 0.015. Corrected $V = (0.012/0.015) \times 7.8 = 6.24$ fps.

4–13. Conditions of open-channel flow. Open-channel flow may be laminar or turbulent, uniform or non-uniform, steady or unsteady, subcritical or supercritical. The definitions of subcritical and supercritical flow are presented in Sect. 4–15. Flow is said to be *laminar* when the paths of the individual particles do not cross or intersect, or when the stream lines remain distinct from one another over their entire length except for the very minor effect of molecular mixing. *Turbulent flow* occurs when the particles of the flowing stream occupy successively transverse positions without regularity, and their paths are neither parallel nor fixed. It is basically rotational flow. *Uniform flow* exists when the velocities of flow past all sections of the channel are the same at any instant. It is *non-uniform flow* when the velocities of flow past two or more sections of the channel are not the same at any instant. If the rates of flow in the channel remain constant at all sections over a period of time, the flow in the channel is said to be *steady;* and if the rates of flow vary, the flow is *unsteady.* The illustrative problems listed in the balance of this chapter assume uniform, steady conditions to exist.

4–14. Normal flow. When the flow in an open channel is such that it will satisfy the Chezy or Manning formulas, or an equivalent formula for open-channel flow, it is said to be normal flow, and the depth of flow under such conditions is known as *normal depth.* This is the depth at which streams ordinarily flow. Normal depth can be found by substituting known data in the appropriate formula.

For example, in a channel whose shape is an isosceles triangle with apex down, and whose width is 1.5 times the depth,

$$V = C\sqrt{RS} = \frac{Q}{A} = \frac{4Q}{3d^2} = C\sqrt{3dS/10}$$

Solving, it is found that d_n, the normal depth of flow, is

$$d_n = 1.4Q^{0.4}/(C^{0.4}S^{0.2})$$

in which C is the coefficient in the Chezy formula, Q is the rate of flow, and S is the hydraulic gradient.

4–15. Critical flow. The specific energy (E_s) of a flowing stream in open-channel flow is the sum of its hydrostatic head, or depth (d), and its velocity head $(V^2/2g)$. This can be expressed as: $E_s = d + (V^2/2g)$. When the specific energy is a minimum for given conditions of channel cross-section and discharge, the flow is said to be critical. Under these conditions, the depth of flow is critical depth, the velocity of flow is critical velocity, and the hydraulic gradient is known as critical slope. It must be recognized that for any flow conditions other than critical, there are two depths of flow at which the specific energy of the stream will be equal. Depths of equivalent specific energy are termed "alternate" depths. Flows at depths greater than critical are known as *tranquil* or *subcritical flows;* flows at depths less than critical are known as *rapid* or *supercritical flows.*

Critical depth, d_c, can be found by determining the depth of flow when the specific energy is a minimum. It is a function of the channel discharge and channel cross-section and is independent of the slope or any other channel characteristic. For example, in the triangular channel in the illustrative problem in the preceding section:

$$V = \frac{Q}{A} \frac{4Q}{3d^2}$$

Therefore

$$E_s = d + \frac{V^2}{2g} = d + \frac{16Q^2}{18gd^4}$$

If now, the first differential of this expression is found with respect to d, and equated to zero and solved for d, the value of d will be such that the expression is a minimum and by definition the depth is critical. Consequently

$$\frac{\delta E_s}{\delta d} = 1 + \frac{16Q^2}{18g}\left(\frac{-4}{d^5}\right) = 0$$

from which

$$b_c = \sqrt[5]{32Q^2/9g}$$

Critical depth may also be determined graphically. Such a procedure is shown in Fig. 4–10. A convenient relation applying to channels normally encountered in sewerage is: critical depth occurs in a channel when $V^2/2g = A/2b$ in which A is the cross-sectional area of the channel, and b is the surface width.[11]   This relation may be useful in solving problems in irregularly shaped channels [12] or in channels in which R and A are not easily expressed in terms of d.   In the case of rectangular or square sewers, critical depth is given by the relationship,

$$d_c = \sqrt[3]{Q^2/(b^2g)}$$

where b is the width of the channel.

4–16. Types of open-channel flow.   Examples of all types of open-channel flow are common in sewers.   Steady, uniform flow occurs in a channel on a long, continuous slope when there are no additions to or withdrawals from the sewage.   Steady, non-uniform flow occurs when there are no additions to or withdrawals from the sewage but the slope of the invert changes.

When the slope of a channel is changed at a point or cross-section so that critical depth occurs at or above that section, the depth of flow being greater above the section and less below it, the section is known as a *control section*.

A *dropdown* curve is the curve, upstream from a control section, formed by the intersection of the surface of the stream and a plane passed vertically and longitudinally through the center of the stream when the rate of flow is uniform.   The rate of curvature of the water surface and the velocity of flow in a dropdown curve increase downstream.   A *dropdown* curve is shown in Fig. 4–9a, and a *backwater* curve in Fig. 4–9b.

A *backwater curve* is the curve above an obstruction or sudden decrease in the slope of the channel, formed by the intersection of the surface of the stream with a plane passed vertically and longitudinally through the center of the stream parallel to the direction of flow, when the velocity of flow is decreasing downstream and the slope of the invert is less than critical.   The occurrence of dropdown curves and backwater curves is common in sewers.

When the slope of the bottom of a channel changes suddenly from greater than critical slope to less than critical slope, a *hydraulic jump* will occur.   The *hydraulic jump* may be defined as the sudden transition of the stream from low stage at less than critical depth to high stage above critical depth.   A hydraulic jump may be formed also when a stream flowing at less than critical depth impinges upon water whose depth is greater than critical.   Such depth can result when a

[11] Julian Hinds, *Eng. News-Record*, Vol. 85, 1920, p. 1035.

[12] A nomograph for the determination of critical-flow conditions in circular conduits is given by F. T. Mavis, *Eng. News-Record*, March 7, 1946, p. 105.

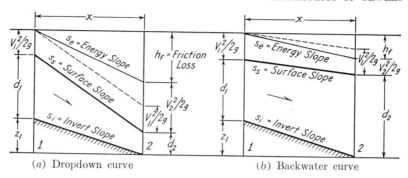

(*a*) Dropdown curve   (*b*) Backwater curve

Fig. 4–9. Diagrams of dropdown and backwater curves.

submerged obstacle of short length and sufficient height is placed across the stream to produce a change in normal depth. If the barrier does not exceed a certain height, a *standing wave* may be formed. In a standing wave, the depth may increase in the form of a single undular surface rise for a short distance above and below the barrier. The depths above and below the barrier are the same.

Where the rate of flow in an open channel changes suddenly at a point, or changes continuously along the channel in the direction of flow, unsteady flow exists. If the rate of change of flow is sufficiently rapid, a *hydraulic bore* is created which may move either upstream or downstream, depending on the condition of flow. A bore moving upstream may result from a sudden decrease in the velocity of flow, which may be caused by the sudden placing of an obstruction across the stream, partially or completely blocking the flow. The bore moving downstream may result from a sudden increase in the rate of flow such as might occur on the bursting of a dam holding back a large reservoir. The bore moving downstream is useful in sewer flushing.

4–17. Dropdown and backwater curves.[13] Longitudinal profiles of flow in open channels have been conveniently classified according to the bed slope, S_0, and the depth of flow, y, as shown in Table 4–6.[14]

---

[13] See also Lee, Babbitt, and Baumann, "Gradually Varied Flow in Uniform Channels on Mild Slopes," *Eng. Exp. Sta. Bull.*, Series 404, University of Illinois, 1952. Ven Te Chow, "Integrating the Equation of Gradually Varied Flow," *Proc. Am. Soc. Civil Engrs.*, Vol. 81, Paper 838, 1955. F. F. Escoffier, "Graphical Determination of Water-Surface Profiles," *Proc. Am. Soc. Civil Engrs.*, Vol. 82, Paper 1114, 1956.

[14] See Hunter Rouse, *Elementary Mechanics of Fluids,* John Wiley and Sons, 1946.

Table 4–6

Types of Surface Profiles in Uniform Channels

Slope *	Designation of Type of Surface Profile	Relation of Depth, y,† to Normal and Critical Depths
Adverse, $S_0 > 0$	A_2	$y_n > y > y_c$
	A_3	$y_n > y_c > y$
Horizontal, $S_0 = 0$	H_2	$y_n > y > y_c$
	H_3	$y_n > y_c > y$
Mild, $S_0 < S_c > 0$	M_1	$y > y_n > y_c$
	M_2	$y_n > y > y_c$
	M_3	$y_n > y_c > y$
Critical, $S_0 = S_c > 0$	C_1	$y > y_c = y_n$
	C_2	$y_n = y_c > y$
Steep, $S_0 > S_c > 0$	S_1	$y > y_c > y_n$
	S_2	$y_c > y > y_n$
	S_3	$y_c > y_n > y$

* S_0 = slope of the bottom of the channel.
  S_c = critical slope of the channel.
† y = depth; y_n = normal depth; y_c = critical depth.

Of the surface profiles in Table 4–6, the more common types are those on mild slopes, particularly the M_1 and M_2 profiles. The M_1 profile refers to the portion of the water surface lying above the uniform depth and is commonly known as the backwater curve. The M_2 profile refers to the portion of the water surface lying between the uniform and critical depths and is commonly referred to as the dropdown curve.

The shape of the dropdown and backwater curves can sometimes be expressed by mathematical formulas of more or less simplicity, depending on the shape of the conduit. The formula for a circular conduit is complicated. Owing to the assumptions of coefficients, etc., that must be made in the deduction of the mathematical formulas, the results obtained by their use are of no greater value than those obtained by approximate methods. A method for the determination of these curves is given in *Engineering News-Record*, Vol. 89, 1922, p. 1067, and Vol. 92, 1924, p. 719. In this method it is necessary that flow be steady and that the depth of flow be known at some point on the curve. The shape, size, coefficient of roughness, slope of invert, and rate of flow must also be known. Methods for the computation of surface curves in steady, non-uniform flow in open channels are summarized in an article by Jansen [15] with discussion, and in most books on hydraulics.[16] The method of solution presented here is known as the *step method*.

Coordinates of the points on dropdown and backwater curves can be determined within any desired degree of approximation by assuming the slope of the surface of the stream and of the energy line to be constant between any two points on either of them, and substituting in the formula given below. The shorter the distance between the points, the greater is the precision of the result. This assumption that uniform flow conditions prevail in dropdown and backwater curves is a limiting condition which is approached but never truly attained. Before uniform flow limits are reached, however, decelerations due to boundary resistance may be negligible. In order to ignore these effects, the analysis should be restricted to cases in which the non-uniformity of motion is very slight. In such cases, we may call the motion *gradually varied flow*.

Diagrams of the conditions in a dropdown curve and in a backwater curve are shown in Fig. 4–9. If the total energies at points 1 and 2, in Fig. 4–9, for either the dropdown or the backwater curve, are equated we have:

$$Z_1 + d_1 + \frac{V_1{}^2}{2g} = d_2 + \frac{V_2{}^2}{2g} + h_f$$

but

$$S_i = \frac{Z_1}{X} \quad \text{and} \quad S_e = \frac{h_f}{X}$$

Hence

$$X S_i + d_1 + \frac{V_1{}^2}{2g} = X S_e + d_2 + \frac{V_2{}^2}{2g}$$

and

$$X = \frac{[d_1 + (V_1{}^2/2g)] - [d_2 + (V_2{}^2/2g)]}{(S_i - S_e)} \tag{4-5}$$

[15] R. B. Jansen, *Proc. Am. Soc. Civil Engrs.*, October, 1951.

[16] Hunter Rouse, *Engineering Hydraulics*, John Wiley and Sons, New York, 1950.

The value of S_e can be determined from any hydraulic formula for normal flow, such as Manning's formula. From this formula we get

$$S_e = 0.453 \left(\frac{n^2 V_m{}^2}{R_m{}^{4/3}} \right) \qquad (4\text{-}6)$$

in which V_m and R_m are the velocity and the hydraulic radius, respectively, at the mean section between points 1 and 2 in Fig. 4–9.

In finding the coordinates of the surface curve the procedure should be to start at some known depth, such as d_1 or d_2, and assume the other depth, d_2 or d_1, and compute the value of x from formula 4–5, corresponding to the assumed depth. The coordinates of one point, measured from the starting point, have thus been found. The procedure should be to assume another depth and to determine its distance from the point just found. The shape of any surface profile can be computed by means of the step method using formula 4–5.

4–18. Practical applications of dropdown curve. The dropdown curve will exist at the outfall of a sewer that is discharging freely into a stream in such a manner that the depth of flow at the outfall is less than normal depth, but greater than critical depth. The minimum depth which is usually assumed to exist at the end of the channel is critical depth, unless the invert slope is greater than critical. Actually, O'Brien [17] has demonstrated that in an open channel with a free fall of water from the outlet, the point of critical depth occurs a distance 18 times the end depth or 11.6 times the critical depth upstream from the end of the channel. Since the depth of flow at the outfall is less than normal, the height of the sewer section, its diameter, can be constructed less than normal, saving in expense and possibly passing beneath overhead structures. The necessary heights of the sewer barrel at various points can be determined from the shape of the dropdown curve.

4–19. Energy and momentum. The analysis of flow in both closed and open conduits must be based on an adaptation of three important relationships of hydrodynamics: the *continuity principle,* the *energy principle,* and the *momentum principle.* Oversimplification of these principles is a dangerous policy, and the student should refer to a standard hydraulics or fluid mechanics book for a derivation and discussion of these principles.

[17] M. P. O'Brien, *Eng. News-Record,* Sept. 15, 1932.

In the following discussion, the nomenclature used is:

A cross-sectional area of the flowing stream.

b width of a rectangular channel.

d depth of flow at any section.

d_c critical depth.

d_{cg} depth to the center of gravity of the cross-section of a stream measured from the surface.

d_n normal depth.

d_n' sequent depth or the depth of flow where the pressure $+$ momentum of the stream is equivalent to that at d_n.

E_s specific energy in the stream $= d + (V^2/2g)$.

g acceleration due to gravity.

K a constant.

M momentum of the flowing stream $= QwV/g$.

P total pressure against the vertical cross-section of a stream $= WAd_{cg}$.

Q rate of flow in the stream.

S_c critical slope.

S_i slope of the invert of the channel.

S_s slope of the surface of the water in the stream.

V average velocity of flow across any cross-section.

w unit weight of water.

The equation of continuity states that in steady flow the product of average velocity and wetted cross-sectional area must be constant. In other words, $Q = AV$.

The total energy in a stream is of two types, potential energy and kinetic energy. The potential energy is that due to depth plus the elevation above datum $(d + Z)$; whereas, kinetic energy is that due to velocity head, $V^2/2g$. If the energy is measured with respect to the bottom of the channel as datum, we refer to it as specific energy. $E_s = d + (V^2/2g)$.

The pressure plus momentum in a stream may be expressed by the equation

$$P + M = \left(Ad_{cg} + \frac{QV}{g} \right) w \qquad (4\text{--}7)$$

One of the important principles involved in hydrodynamics is the fact that the pressure plus momentum in a flowing stream cannot change without the application of an external force. The specific energy can change, however.

The pressure plus momentum and the specific energy in a channel are functions only of the shape of the channel, the rate of flow, and the depth of flow. For each value of E_s at any depth there is an equal value for E_s at one other depth. These two depths with equal specific energies are known as *alternate* depths. The term *alternate depth* is commonly used to refer to the depth of flow at which the specific energy is the same as the specific energy at normal depth of flow. A similar condition exists for values of pressure plus momentum where the two depths at which $P + M$ are equal are known as *sequent* depths. Specifically, the depth at which the $P + M$ is the same as it would be at normal depth is known as the sequent depth.

The changes in specific energy and in pressure plus momentum with depth for a rectangular channel 1 ft wide when Q is 20 cfs are shown in Table 4-7 and in Fig. 4-10. It is to be noted that the minimum

Table 4-7

TABLE OF VALUES FOR E_s AND $P + M$ FOR ONE FOOT WIDE CHANNEL
THAT IS DISCHARGING 20 CFS

$$d_c = \sqrt[3]{\frac{Q^2}{b^2 g}} = \sqrt[3]{\frac{(20)^2}{1^2 \times 32.2}} = 2.31 \text{ ft}$$

Depth, ft	V, fps	$V^2/2g$, ft	$(E_s) = d + V^2/2g$, ft	$\dfrac{wbd^2}{2}$, lb	QwV/g, lb	$P + M$, lb
0.70	28.57	12.67	13.37	15.6	1,110.6	1,126.2
0.90	22.22	7.67	8.57	25.6	850.0	875.6
1.00	20.00	6.21	7.21	31.2	777.5	808.7
1.40	14.29	3.17	4.57	61.2	554.4	615.6
1.80	11.11	1.92	3.72	101.2	431.9	533.1
2.20	9.09	1.28	3.48	151.2	353.1	504.3
2.31 *	8.66	1.16	3.47	168.1	335.6	503.7
2.50	8.00	0.99	3.49	195.6	310.6	506.2
2.80	7.14	0.79	3.59	245.0	278.1	523.1
3.20	6.25	0.61	3.81	320.0	243.1	563.1
3.80	5.26	0.43	4.23	450.6	205.0	655.6
4.20	4.76	0.35	4.55	551.9	185.0	736.9
5.00	4.00	0.25	5.25	781.8	155.6	936.8
6.00	3.33	0.17	6.17			
7.00	2.86	0.13	7.13			
8.00	2.50	0.10	8.10			

* Critical depth.

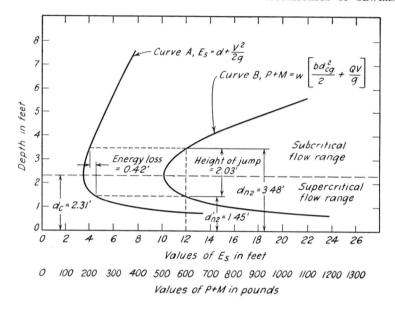

Fig. 4–10. Pressure-plus-momentum and energy curves for a rectangular channel one foot wide with a rate of flow of 20 cfs.

values of both E_s and $P + M$ occur when $d = d_c$. Also, for any value other than d_c, there are two values of d that will satisfy the expression for $P + M$ in equation 4–7. One of these values is d_n and represents the actual or normal depth of flow. The other value, d_n', is the sequent depth. For example, from curve B when $d_n = 1.0$ ft, then d_n', the sequent depth, $= 4.5$ ft. Similarly, from curve A the alternate or conjugate depth, with equal E_s corresponding to the normal depth $d_n = 1.0$, is found to be 6.9 ft.

4–20. The hydraulic jump. The hydraulic jump is a phenomenon of open-channel flow in which the depth of flow changes abruptly from the lower *sequent* depth to the corresponding *upper sequent* depth. A hydraulic jump will occur when the slope of the invert of the channel changes abruptly from greater than critical to less than critical. The jump may be "free" as shown in Fig. 4–11, or "submerged" as shown in Fig. 4–12.

Under most circumstances, the occurrence of a hydraulic jump is undesirable in a sewer, due to the amount of energy lost through the jump. Since most sewer systems are designed to operate by means

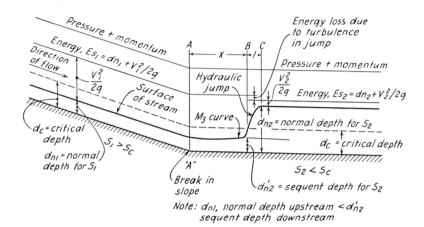

Fig. 4–11. Diagram of a free hydraulic jump.

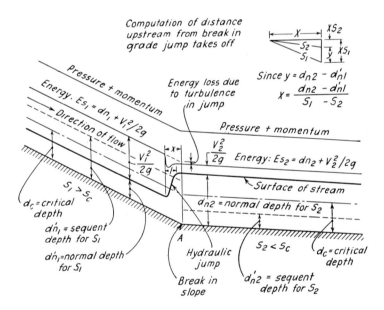

Fig. 4–12. Diagram of a submerged hydraulic jump.

of the force of gravity, the unexpected head losses caused by a hydraulic jump might seriously interfere with normal flows. Thus, the occurrence of a hydraulic jump on a steep slope may influence the conduit design. However, in other fields the jump may be used advantageously to dissipate the energy in a channel of rapid flow in order to prevent erosion and undermining when the flow impinges into a stream or pool.

A *free jump* occurs below the abrupt change in grade with the depth increasing from d_{n2}' to d_{n2} as shown in Fig. 4–11. For this type of jump to occur, the sequent depth, d_{n2}', sequent to d_{n2}, on the flatter slope must be greater than the normal depth of flow d_{n1} on the steeper slope. The *submerged jump* shown in Fig. 4–12 occurs above the abrupt change in grade on the slope which is greater than critical; the depth increasing from normal depth, d_{n1}, to the sequent depth, d_{n1}', on the steeper slope. In this type of jump, d_{n2}' on the flatter slope must be less than d_{n1} on the steeper slope. The submerged jump "takes off" where the extended line of the surface of the stream below the break in grade, d_{n2}, intersects the line representing d_{n1}' for the steeper slope.

From the principle of the conservation of momentum, it is evident that the pressure plus momentum $(P + M)$ in a flowing stream cannot change without the application of an external force. Since no external force is applied in a hydraulic jump, the height of jump will be the difference in height between corresponding sequent depths. However, there can be a change in the specific energy of a stream, E_s, due to internal friction resulting from turbulence without the application of an external force. The energy loss due to turbulence in a hydraulic jump may be computed from the specific energy in the stream before and after the jump occurs as shown by Fig. 4–10. It may be calculated by subtracting the E_s in the stream at final depth from the E_s in the stream at initial depth.

4–21. Location, length, and height of jump. The distance X in Fig. 4–11 represents the length of the M_3 backwater curve from the break in grade of the channel invert to the point of take-off of the jump from sequent depth d_{n2}'. This distance can be determined by use of formula 4–5. When a submerged jump occurs the distance may be computed graphically as shown in Fig. 4–12, or as shown in step III in Sect. 4–23.

The length of hydraulic jump l (Figs. 4–11 and 4–12) is a function of the state of flow and the height of jump. Many formulas have been suggested in the literature by means of which the length of jump may be calculated. Baumann [18] found close correlation between measured lengths of jump and those calculated by the relationship given by Ivanchenko.[19] This empirical relationship for open rectangular channels is:

$$l = 10.6 d_j \lambda^{-0.185} \tag{4-8}$$

where l = length of hydraulic jump.

d_j = height of jump.

λ = kinetic flow factor, $V_1{}^2/g d_1$.

d_1 being the depth before the jump, V_1 the average velocity at depth d_1, and g, the acceleration due to gravity.

In a trapezoidal channel, no definite conclusions may be made regarding the length of hydraulic jump. Posey and Hsing [20] found that a close approximation of this distance with side slopes, horizontal to vertical, of 1:2, 1:1, and 2:1 may be obtained by the relationship.

$$\frac{l}{d_{n2}} = 5\left[1 + 4\frac{(W_2 - W_1)^{0.5}}{W_1}\right] \tag{4-9}$$

where l = length of hydraulic jump.

d_{n2} = depth after the jump.

$\dfrac{(W_2 - W_1)}{W_1}$ = dimensionless parameter, W_1 being the surface width before the jump and W_2 the surface width after the jump.

When W_2 equals W_1, the formula gives $l = 5 d_{n2}$, which agrees fairly well with published values of the length in rectangular channels if d_{n1} is small in comparison to d_{n2}.

The height of the free jump is the difference between the sequent depths on the flatter slope. The height of a submerged jump is the difference between the sequent depths on the steeper slope.

4–22. Loss of energy. The loss of energy in a hydraulic jump is the difference between the specific energies, $d + (V^2/2g,)$ above and below the jump. The loss of energy can be determined either analytically, or graphically, as in Fig. 4–10. Analytically, using the nomenclature in Fig. 4–11, when $d_{n2}' = 1.0$ ft with $Q = 20$ cfs, $P + M = 808.7$ lb.

[18] E. R. Baumann, *An Investigation of the Hydraulic Jump in Small Open Channels;* unpublished M.S. thesis, University of Illinois, Urbana, Ill., 1947.

[19] Ivanchenko, "The Hydraulic Jump in Terms of Dynamic Similarity," *Trans. Amer. Soc. Civil Engrs.*, Vol. 62, 1936, pp. 101 and 670.

[20] C. S. Posey and P. S. Hsing, *Eng. News-Record,* Vol. 121, Dec. 22, 1938, pp. 25 and 797.

For this value of $P + M$, $d_{n2} = 4.51$ ft.   The magnitudes of specific energy, E_s, for $d_{n2}' = 1.0$ and $d_{n2} = 4.51$, are 7.21 ft and 4.80 ft respectively.   This loss of head of $(7.21 - 4.80) = 2.41$ ft represents an energy loss of 20 cfs $\times w \times 2.41$ ft $= 3,012.5$ ft lb per sec.

Losses of energy resulting from standing waves caused by obstructions, by the junction of two streams, or by other causes can be computed in a manner similar to the preceding illustrative example for the loss in a hydraulic jump.   Such losses may possibly be avoided by the absence of obstructions, by proper guiding of streams at junctions, by the construction of transition sections, and by other means.

4–23. Illustrative hydraulic jump problem.

The open rectangular channel described in Sect. 4–19 with a base width of 1 ft and a discharge of 20 cfs is placed on an invert slope of 0.0625.   At point A, the slope of the invert changes to 0.0049.   Assuming steady, uniform flow conditions and using Manning's formula with $n = 0.01486$ as needed, determine:

1. The type of hydraulic jump which will occur, whether free or submerged,
2. The height of the hydraulic jump,
3. The distance and direction from point A where the jump takes off,
4. The length of the jump,
5. The loss of specific energy due to the jump, and
6. The profile of the surface curve if a free jump exists.

Solution:

I. Type of jump.

Step 1.   Determine normal depth of flow, d_{n1}, on upstream slope from Manning's relationship:

$$Q = AV = A \times \frac{1.486}{n} R^{2/3} S^{1/2}$$

$$20 = d_{n1} \times 100 \times \left(\frac{d_{n1}}{1 + 2d_{n1}}\right)^{2/3} \times (0.0625)^{1/2}$$

$$0.8 = d_{n1} \left(\frac{d_{n1}}{1 + 2d_{n1}}\right)^{2/3}$$

By trial and error substitution, $d_{n1} = 1.53$ ft.

Step 2.   Using Fig. 4–10, determine depth d_{n1}' sequent to normal depth d_{n1}.

By definition: Pressure plus momentum at sequent depth d_{n1}' equals pressure plus momentum at normal depth, d_{n1}. From curve B, Fig. 4–10, $d_{n1}' = 3.32$ ft.

Step 3.   As in steps 1 and 2, determine the normal depth d_{n2} and sequent depth d_{n2}' on downstream slope.

$$2.86 = d_{n2} \left[\frac{d_{n2}}{1 + 2d_{n2}}\right]^{2/3}$$

$$d_{n2} = 4.85 \text{ ft.}$$

From Fig. 4–10, curve B, $d_{n2}' = 0.90$ ft. Since $d_{n1} = 1.53$ ft, the normal depth on upstream slope is greater than d_{n2}', 0.90 ft, the sequent depth on downstream slope, the jump is submerged. It is similar to the jump shown in Fig. 4–12.

II. Height of the jump. The height of a submerged jump is equal to the difference in elevation between the sequent depth, d_{n1}', and the normal depth, d_{n1}, on the upstream slope.

$$\text{Height of jump} = d_{n1}' - d_{n1} = 3.32 - 1.53 = 1.79 \text{ ft.}$$

III. Location where the jump "takes off." Since this is a submerged jump, the location of the take-off point is upstream from point A. From the relationship given in Fig. 4–12, the approximate horizontal distance x upstream from point A where the jump occurs, may be computed as follows:

$$x = \frac{d_{n2} - d_{n1}'}{S_1 - S_2} = \frac{4.85 - 3.32}{0.0625 - 0.0049} = 26.6 \text{ ft}$$

IV. Length of jump. The length of jump computed by Ivanchenko's formula:

$$l = 10.6 d_j \lambda^{-0.185} \qquad\qquad d_j = 1.79 \text{ ft}$$
$$l = 10.6 \times 1.79 \times (3.46)^{-0.185} \quad d_1 = 1.53 \text{ ft}$$
$$l = 15.1 \text{ ft}$$
$$V_1 = \frac{20}{1.53 \times 1} = 13.06 \text{ fps} \qquad \lambda = \frac{V_1^2}{g d_1} = \frac{(13.06)^2}{32.2 \times 1.53} = 3.46$$

V. Loss in E_s due to the hydraulic jump. From Fig. 4–10:
1. Determine the specific energy in the stream at normal depth, d_{n1}:

$$E_{s1} = 4.19 \text{ ft}$$

2. Determine the specific energy in the stream at depth, d_{n1}':

$$E_{s1}' = 3.88 \text{ ft}$$

3. Loss of E_s due to jump:

$$E_{s1} - E_{s1}' = 4.19 - 3.88 = 0.31 \text{ ft} \quad \text{or}$$

$$20 \times 62.5 \times 0.31 = 388 \text{ ft-lb per sec of energy loss}$$

4–24. Illustrative hydraulic jump problem, free jump.

If the invert slope on the channel in Sect. 4–23 is changed so that $S_1 = 0.1600$ and $S_2 = 0.0100$, what will be the new characteristics of the hydraulic jump formed?

I. Type of jump. Step 1. Determine the normal depth of flow, d_{n1}, on the upstream slope.

From Manning's relationship:

$$Q = AV = d_{n1} \times \frac{1.486}{n} \left[\frac{d_{n1}}{1 + 2d_{n1}} \right]^{2/3} \times (0.1600)^{1/2} = 20$$

$$0.5 = d_{n1} \left[\frac{d_{n1}}{1 + 2d_{n1}} \right]^{2/3}$$

By trial and error substitution, $d_{n1} = 1.03$ ft.

Step 2. Using Fig. 4–10, determine the depth, d_{n1}', sequent to normal depth, d_{n1}.

By definition: Pressure plus momentum at sequent depth, d_{n1}', equals pressure plus momentum at normal depth, d_{n1}, from curve B, Fig. 4–10, $d_{n1}' = 4.46$ ft.

Step 3. Determine the normal depth, d_{n2}, and the sequent depth, d_{n2}', on the downstream slope.

$$20 = 100 \left[\frac{d_{n2}}{1 + 2d_{n2}} \right]^{2/3} (0.0100)^{1/2} \times d_{n2}$$

$$2.0 = d_{n2} \left[\frac{d_{n2}}{1 + 2d_{n2}} \right]^{2/3} \quad \text{and} \quad d_{n2} = 3.48 \text{ ft}$$

From Fig. 4–10, curve B, $d_{n2}' = 1.45$ ft.

Since d_{n1}, the normal depth on upstream slope, is less than d_{n2}', the sequent depth on the downstream slope, $d_{n1} = 1.03$ ft $< d_{n2}' = 1.45$ ft, the jump is a free jump similar to that appearing in Fig. 4–11.

II. Height of jump. The height of a free jump is equal to the difference in elevation between the normal depth d_{n2} and the sequent depth d_{n2}' on the downstream slope.

$$\text{Height of jump} = d_{n2} - d_{n2}' = 3.48 - 1.45 = 2.03 \text{ ft}$$

III. Location where the jump "takes off." Since this is a free jump, the location of the take-off point is downstream from the break in grade at point A.

IV. The length of the jump computed by Ivanchenko's formula:

$$l = 10.6 d_j \lambda^{-0.185} \qquad\qquad d_1 = 1.45 \text{ ft}$$

$$l = 10.6 \times 2.03 \times (4.07)^{-0.185} \qquad d_j = 2.03 \text{ ft}$$

$$l = 16.7 \text{ ft} \qquad\qquad\qquad V_1 = \frac{20}{1.45} = 13.8 \text{ ft per sec}$$

$$\lambda = \frac{V_1^2}{g d_1} = \frac{(13.8)^2}{32.2 \times 1.45} = 4.07$$

V. Loss of E_s due to the hydraulic jump. (See Fig. 4–10.)

1. Determine the specific energy in the stream at normal depth.

$$d_{n2} : E_{s2} = 3.48 + \frac{400}{64.4(3.48)^2} = 3.99 \text{ ft}$$

2. Determine the specific energy in the stream at sequent depth.

$$d_{n2}':E_{s2}' = 1.45 + \frac{400}{64.4(1.45)^2} = 4.41 \text{ ft}$$

3. Loss of E_s due to jump:

$$E_{s2}' - E_{s2} = 4.41 - 3.99 = 0.42 \text{ ft} \quad \text{or}$$

$$20 \times 62.5 \times 0.42 = 525 \text{ ft-lb per sec}$$

VI. Computation of distance X using step method. It is known that the surface curve increases in depth from $d_{n1} = 1.03$ ft at point A to 1.45 ft, the sequent depth, d_{n2}', at some point downstream. By using these known values, and assuming various intermediate depths, the distance X may be computed by equation 4–5. The computations are shown in Table 4–8.

4–25. Transition without jump.[21] It is possible to design a channel in such a form that the flow will pass from the lower to the upper sequent depth or normal depth without the occurrence of a hydraulic jump. This is accomplished by the construction of a hump in the bottom of the channel, to furnish the shape of bottom necessary to provide the smooth transition of the flow to the normal depth. The channel below the hump is raised so that this change in channel elevation plus the normal depth plus the velocity head is equal to the specific energy in the stream before transition. Essentially, the utilization of the specific energy lost in a jump accomplishes this transition. The condition is illustrated in Fig. 4–13.

The application of the principle can be explained by the solution of an illustrative problem:

Let it be required to construct a hump in the bottom of a rectangular channel in such a manner that the flow will pass from a depth less than critical to normal depth above critical without a hydraulic jump. The flow is 100 cfs through a rectangular channel, with $n = 0.01486$; the width of channel is 4 ft, and the invert slope is 0.034, which changes at point A, whose elevation is 100.0 ft above datum, to a slope of 0.00245. The solution will include the drawing to scale of lines indicating the following: (a) the surface of the water as it would pass through the hydraulic jump if there were no hump, (b) the surface of the water as it passes from the low to the high stage with the hump, (c) the longitudinal section of the hump in the bottom of the channel which will cause the desired transition, and (d) the highest possible elevation of the channel below point A which will

[21] See H. W. King, C. O. Wisler, and J. G. Woodburn, *Hydraulics,* 5th edition, John Wiley and Sons, 1948.

Table 4-8

TABLE OF VALUES FOR CALCULATION OF M_3 BACKWATER CURVE FORMED BEFORE THE FREE JUMP

Depth, ft	V, fps	$V^2/2g$, ft	E_s, ft	A_2, ft²	p, ft	R, ft	R_m, ft	$R_m^{4/3}$	V_m, fps	V_m^2	$\dfrac{V_m^2}{R_m^{4/3}}$	S_e	X, ft	ΣX, ft
1.03	19.4	5.85	6.88	1.03	3.06	0.337								
							0.340	0.238	18.8	354	1485	0.1485	4.55	4.55
1.10	18.2	5.15	6.25	1.10	3.20	0.343								
							0.348	0.244	17.5	306	1255	0.1255	5.71	10.26
1.20	16.8	4.39	5.59	1.20	3.40	0.352								
							0.356	0.252	16.1	259	1027	0.1027	6.58	16.84
1.30	15.4	3.68	4.98	1.30	3.60	0.361								
							0.365	0.261	14.8	219	840	0.0840	5.40	22.24
1.40	14.3	3.18	4.58	1.40	3.80	0.368								
							0.370	0.266	14.0	196	737	0.0737	2.67	24.91
1.45	13.8	2.96	4.41	1.45	3.90	0.372								

Length of M_3 backwater curve = x = 24.91 ft.

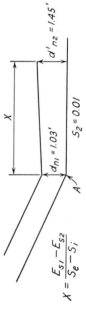

$$X = \frac{E_{s1} - E_{s2}}{S_e - S_i}$$

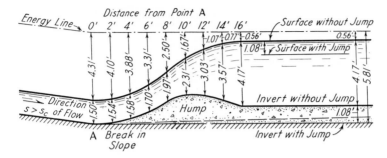

Fig. 4–13. Transition section to suppress the hydraulic jump.

permit steady uniform flow on a slope of 0.00245. Use Manning's formula as required.

Solution. 1. Compute the depth of flow above point A as d_{n1}. This is done by solving the expression

$$Q = VA = A \times 100 \times R^{2/3} S^{1/2}$$

where $A = 4d_{n1}$, $R = \dfrac{4d_{n1}}{4 + 2d_{n1}}$, and $S = 0.034$

$$1.0 = 4d_{n1} \times \left(\frac{4d_{n1}}{4 + 2d_{n1}}\right)^{2/3} \times 0.1845$$

$$4d_{n1} \times \left(\frac{4d_{n1}}{4 + 2d_{n1}}\right)^{2/3} = 5.42$$

By trial and error, find $d_{n1} = 1.50$ ft and $V_1 = 16$ fps.

2. Find the normal depth of flow below point A, d_{n2}, in a similar manner.

$$d_{n2} = 4.17 \text{ ft}$$

$$V_2 = 6.0 \text{ fps}$$

3. Determine the elevation of the total energy line at low stage, from the expression

$$\text{Energy} = d_{n1} + \frac{V_1{}^2}{2g} = 1.5 + \frac{278}{64.4} = 5.81 \text{ ft}$$

The elevation of the total energy line at low stage is, therefore, 105.81.

4. Determine the elevation of the total energy line at high stage. This is done in a similar manner, and is found to be 104.73.

5. Determine the elevation from which the jump will take off. This is done by finding the depth, d_{n2}', at which the pressure plus the momentum are equal to the pressure plus the momentum at d_{n2}. The expression, with w eliminated, is

$$\frac{bd_{n2}'^2}{2} + \frac{QV}{g} = \frac{bd_{n2}^2}{2} + \frac{QV}{g}$$

The value of d_{n2}' is found to be 1.62 ft. The height of the jump would be, therefore, $4.17 - 1.62 = 2.55$ ft.

6. Compute the length of the surface curve as the distance of the take-off below point A. Substituting in formula 4–5

$$x = \frac{\left[1.5 + \dfrac{278}{64.4}\right] - \left[1.62 + \dfrac{238}{64.4}\right]}{S_e - S_i} = \frac{5.81 - (1.62 + 3.70)}{0.0308 - 0.00245}$$

$$= \frac{0.49}{0.02835} = 17.3 \text{ ft}$$

$$S_e = \frac{V_m^2}{10{,}000 R_m^{4/3}} = \frac{100^2}{10{,}000(4 \times 1.56)^2 \left[\dfrac{4 \times 1.56}{7.12}\right]^{4/3}} = 0.0308$$

The backwater curve has been assumed to be a straight line.

7. Locate the position of the bottom of the channel below point A, so that there will be no hydraulic jump. Since the total energy line below A will coincide with the total energy line above A, and since the energy below A is $d + (V^2/2g) = 4.17 + (36/64.4) = 4.73$ and the energy above A is, similarly, 5.81, the elevation of the bottom of the channel must be raised $5.81 - 4.73 = 1.08$ ft.

8. Construct the surface curve of the water as it passes from the depth of 1.50 ft at the break in grade, point A, to the final depth of 4.17 ft after the hump in any convenient and logical curve. In this case, the distance from the break in grade to the point where a depth of 4.17 ft is first obtained will be taken as 16 ft. It should not be greater than the distance X

Table 4–9

COMPUTATIONS FOR SUPPRESSION OF HYDRAULIC JUMP IN FIG. 4–13

Ft below Point A	$\dfrac{V_x^2}{2g}$ *	V_x^2	V_x	d_x	Ft below Point A	$\dfrac{V_x^2}{2g}$ *	V_x^2	V_x	d_x
2	4.10	264	16.25	1.54	10	1.67	117	10.8	2.31
4	3.88	250	15.81	1.58	12	1.07	68	8.3	3.03
6	3.31	217	14.70	1.70	14	0.77	49	7.0	3.57
8	2.50	161	12.70	1.97	16	0.56	36	6.0	4.17

* Scaled from Fig. 4–13.

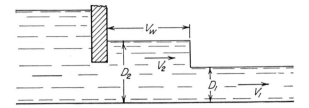

Fig. 4–14. Diagram of a hydraulic bore or traveling wave.

found in the 6th step, above. The shape of the curve is taken as a symmetrical, reverse curve, as shown in Fig. 4–13.

9. Construct the profile of the hump. At every point along the stream over the hump the distance from the water surface up to the total energy line represents $V_x^2/2g$, where V_x is the velocity of flow at that point. The depth of flow d_x at that point is the distance from the surface curve to the top of the hump. The distances from the surface curve to the energy gradient are scaled from the drawing, Fig. 4–13, and the corresponding values of d_x are computed as shown in Table 4–9.

It will be noted in the preceding solution that the friction between the flowing water and the sides of the channel has been neglected, but within the degree of precision of the solution, the magnitude of the friction is practically negligible.

Although the insertion of the hump, in the preceding problem, has made it possible to raise the invert 1.08 ft, the fact is that conditions of flow at other than 100 cfs must be considered, as jumps and standing waves may result at other rates of flow from the insertion of the hump, and at the lowest flows a quiet pool will exist above the hump. Where such conditions are not permissible the expedient of inserting a hump cannot be resorted to.

4–26. Hydraulic bore or traveling wave.[22] If the flow in a channel is suddenly increased from Q_1 to Q_2, conditions will develop somewhat as indicated in Fig. 4–14. The figure indicates the conditions 1 sec after increased flow. During the second of time, the total volume of water that enters the channel is $Q_2 = A_2 V_2$. If the wave produced travels with the velocity V_w, then

$$Q_2 - Q_1 = V_w(A_2 - A_1) \quad \text{and} \quad A_2 V_2 - A_1 V_1 = V_w(A_2 - A_1)$$

also

$$V_2 = (A_1 V_1 + A_2 V_w - A_1 V_w) \div A_2 \qquad (4\text{–}10)$$

[22] See also H. W. King and E. F. Brater, *Handbook of Hydraulics*, McGraw-Hill Book Co., N. Y., 1954, pp. 8–47.

The mass of water has had its velocity increased from V_1 to V_2 and its momentum has thereby been increased. The increase in momentum, F, is

$$F = M(V_2 - V_1) = (V_w - V_2)(wA_2)(V_2 - V_1) \div g \quad (4\text{--}11)$$

The force required to produce this change in momentum is equal to the difference in hydrostatic pressures at the cross-sections corresponding to the areas A_1 and A_2. Thus

$$F = w(A_2\bar{d}_2 - A_1\bar{d}_1) \quad\quad\quad (4\text{--}12)$$

where $\bar{d}_1$ and $\bar{d}_2$ are the depths, respectively, from the surface of the water to the centroid of the cross-section of the channel at A_1 and A_2.

Since the forces are equal

$$\frac{(V_w - V_2)A_2(V_2 - V_1)}{g} = (A_2\bar{d}_2 - A_1\bar{d}_1) \quad (4\text{--}13)$$

This is a general formula applicable to the conditions of a wave moving upstream or downstream. A positive value of V_w is the velocity of the wave traveling downstream when Q_2 is greater than Q_1. A negative value of V_w will result when the wave travels upstream when Q_2 is less than Q_1, i.e., when the rate of flow is suddenly diminished, as might occur as a result of a sudden partial or complete stoppage of flow. If the change in rate of flow is not instantaneous, a series of waves will travel, one on top of the other, in accordance with the preceding expressions. Since the waves at greater depths have greater velocities, each wave will be gradually overtaken by the wave in back of it. The tendency, therefore, is for the waves to combine and form a single larger wave. The single larger wave would become practically the same as if the rate of change of flow had taken place instantaneously. The solution of an example will more clearly explain the use of the formula in sewer design.

Problem. A rectangular sewer 2 ft wide is on a slope of 0.0004, with $n = 0.013$. If water is added suddenly to create a depth of 12 in. in the sewer which previously was empty: (a) At what velocity will the wave travel down the sewer? (b) At what rate must water be added to the sewer to create the traveling wave? (c) How much water must be added to force the wave to travel a distance of 500 ft down the sewer?

Solution.

(a) $V_1 = 0$

$$V_2 = \frac{1.486}{n} R^{\frac{2}{3}}S^{\frac{1}{2}} = \left(\frac{1.486}{0.013}\right)\left(\frac{2}{4}\right)^{\frac{2}{3}}(0.0004)^{\frac{1}{2}} = 1.44 \text{ fps}$$

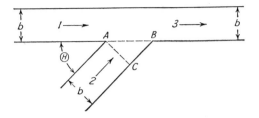

Fig. 4-15. Hydraulic conditions at channel junctions.

From formula 4-12:

$$\frac{(V_w - 1.44)(2)(1.44)}{32.2} = (2.0)(0.5) - 0$$

$$V_w = 12.64 \text{ fps}$$

(b) $Q_2 = 12.64 \times 2 = 25.28$ cfs

(c) Total Volume $= 500$ ft $\times 2 = 1,000$ ft^3

or $\dfrac{500 \times 25.28 \text{ ft}^3}{12.64} = 1,000$ ft^3

4-27. Head loss at junctions. The study of phenomena associated with combining flow of water in open channels is one in which the variables involved are so numerous that only an empirical solution is feasible. The conformity of actual behavior to theory is discussed by Taylor for rectangular channels.[23] For other channels or for natural streams, the flow characteristics at a junction are best determined by models controlled in a hydraulic laboratory.

When two streams combine in a single channel, the depth just below the junction will be fixed by the hydraulic characteristics of that channel and the magnitudes of the combined rates of flow. The problem is to predict the depth in each tributary channel just upstream from the junction. An unlimited number of different types of stream intersections are possible. The scope of the discussion will be limited to the case shown in Fig. 4-15. In the discussion, the following restrictions are made:

1. The channels are of equal width.
2. The bottom slopes are all zero.
3. The flow is from channels 1 and 2 into channel 3.
4. Channels 1 and 3 lie in a straight line.

[23] E. H. Taylor, *Trans. Am. Soc. Civil Engrs.*, Vol. **71**, 1944, p. 893.

In the theoretical development, it is assumed that the flow is parallel
to the channel walls, that ordinary wall friction forces are negligible,
and that the depths in channels 1 and 2 are equal immediately above
the junction.

From the principle that the net force acting on a fluid system is
equal to the rate at which the momentum of the system is changed,
the following formulas result:

$$P_{1\text{-}3} = \frac{wbd_1{}^2}{2} + \frac{wbd_2{}^2}{2} \cos \theta - \frac{wbd_3{}^2}{2} + U \qquad (4\text{-}14)$$

where U is an unknown reaction. The rate at which momentum is
changed in the direction 1 to 3 is

$$M_{1\text{-}3} = \frac{Q_3 w V_3}{g} - \frac{Q w V_1}{g} - \frac{Q_2 w V_2}{g} \cos \theta \qquad (4\text{-}15)$$

It is apparent in examining formula 4–14 that U must be the component
of the pressure force acting on the part of the wall marked BC in Fig.
4–15. If the depth in the triangle ABC is everywhere equal to d_2, then

U must be equal and opposite to the term $\dfrac{wbd_2{}^2}{2} \cos \theta.$

Formula 4–14 then reduces to

$$P_{1\text{-}3} = \frac{wbd_1{}^2}{2} - \frac{wbd_3{}^2}{2} \qquad (4\text{-}16)$$

Equating formulas 4–15 and 4–16:

$$\frac{Q_1 w V_1}{g} + \frac{wb_1 d_1{}^2}{2} + \frac{Q_2 w V_2}{g} \cos \theta = \frac{Q_3 w V_3}{g} + \frac{wbd_3{}^2}{2} \qquad (4\text{-}17)$$

Formula 4–17 is a general formula for rectangular junctions and
may be expressed in dimensionless terms. The agreement between
theory and experiment for the 45° junction supports the conclusion
that the assumptions are justified for this case of combining flows.
As the angle of junction increases, there is a lack of agreement due
to the distortion of the velocity distribution below the junction and
to the fact that the flow does not remain parallel to the channel walls.
Formula 4–17 should, therefore, be limited for use to angles of an
order of 45° or less. For other conditions, the use of model studies
is recommended.

4–28. Open-channel flow around bends.[24] The flow of water around a bend in an open channel is affected by many factors. As a result, the mechanism of flow around bends is extremely complicated and the resultant difficulties of experimentation and observation have kept the number of published investigations small in spite of the pressing practical need for information. The analyses of Shukry[25] and Mockmore[26] are particularly important in an understanding of this phenomenon of open-channel flow.

[24] See also, W. D. Mitchell and L. Harrold, *Eng. News-Record,* Vol. 105, 1931, pp. 739, 939, and Vol. 106, 1931, p. 161.

[25] A. Shukry, *Proc. Am. Soc. Civil Engrs.,* June, 1949, p. 713.

[26] C. A. Mockmore, *Trans. Am. Soc. Civil Engrs.,* Vol. 71, 1944, p. 593.

Chapter 5

Design of sewer systems

Design of a Separate System

5–1. Requirements of a separate system. A system of separate sewers is provided for the primary purpose of removing domestic sewage from a community or district. Good practice demands that a comprehensive plan be designed for the needs of the community for a reasonable period into the future, and that sewers be constructed in accordance with this plan as need for them arises. The first sewers in a city are seldom laid out in accordance with such a plan, immediate local needs having been the primary consideration in their design. Although such sewers are sometimes too small for their requirements, it is desirable to utilize them to the fullest possible extent in any plan for the future.[1] In many states the plans for a sewer system must be submitted to the state department of health for approval before construction is started.

5–2. Scope and contents of plans. The complete plans for a sewer system should include: (1) a general map of the municipality or sewer district showing the principal drainage districts and the location of sewers and appurtenances, (2) plans and profiles of all sewers, (3) details of appurtenances, (4) a comprehensive report on the proposed system, and (5) specifications.

A Joint Committee of the Upper Mississippi Board of Public Health Engineers, representing public health authorities in ten states, recommended [2] the contents and scope of the general plans for comprehensive sewage works, as follows:

A. *Miscellaneous.* A suitable title and the name of the municipality, sewer district, or institution, the scale in feet, a graphical scale, the north point,

---

[1] *Public Works,* July, 1937, p. 26.
[2] "Standards for Sewage Work," January, 1951.

date, and the name of the engineer and imprint of professional engineer's seal.

The scale for general plans should be not less than 100 ft nor greater than 300 ft to the inch. The plans should be 12 in. by 18 in., 24 in. by 36 in. or of such size as can be conveniently folded to those dimensions. The lettering and figures on the plans must be of appropriate size and distinct outline. Surface elevations should preferable be placed just outside street lines opposite their respective positions. Datum used should be indicated.

Figure 5–1 is an example of the lettering and symbols to be used.

B. *Boundaries.* The boundary line of the municipality or sewer district to be sewered.

C. *Existing sewers.* The location, size, length, slope, and direction of flow of all existing sanitary and combined sewers affecting the proposed improvement.

D. *Proposed sewers.* The location of all proposed sewers, with the size, grade, length, and direction of flow indicated. All manholes should be numbered on the layout and correspondingly numbered on the profile.

E. *Topography and elevations.* Existing or proposed streets and all streams or water surfaces should be clearly shown. The elevations of all sewer inverts should be clearly and distinctly written close to the manhole, parallel with sewer line, and expressed to the nearest 0.01 ft. Contour lines should be included on the general plan at suitable intervals.

F. *Stream flow.* The direction of flow in all streams and high- and low-water elevations of all water surfaces at sewer outfalls and overflows.

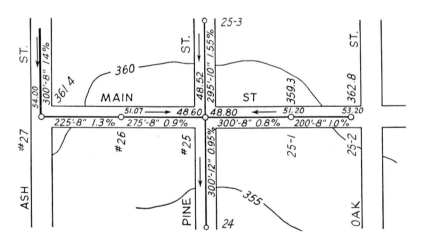

Fig. 5–1. Symbols for sewer plans based on recommendations by the Joint Committee.

G. *Public water supplies.* The location of wells, or other sources of public and semi-public water supply, water-treatment plants, reservoirs, or other structures of public-health significance.

H. *Sewage works.* The location of outlets, treatment plants, by-passes or overflows, manholes, lampholes, siphons, pumping stations, and other accessories. Suitable symbols appropriately referenced should be shown in the title for all such works.

A small section of a map on which pertinent data are entered is shown in Fig. 5–2, and a preliminary map for a larger section of a city is shown in Fig. 5–3. Maps, if not available, may be made by conventional ground-surveying methods or, under favorable conditions, by photogrammetry.[3] In this particular map it is assumed that all streets are paved with brick except Meridian Ave., which is paved with concrete, and that alleys are not paved. The entire section is built up with high-class, detached residences averaging slightly less than one to a lot, together with some apartment buildings along Meridian Ave. and a small business district near the depot. The lots are from 1 to 3 ft above the elevation of the street. The top of the map is west.

5–3. Locating the pipes. Upon the completion of the map a tentative plan of the system is laid out. The lines of the sewer pipes are drawn in pencil, usually along the center line of the street in such a manner that a sewer will be provided within about 50 ft, or less, of every lot, and in accordance with principles outlined in Sect. 2–17. Where basements are so unusually deep as to be below a reasonable depth for the sewer, it may be desirable to install pumps in the building to raise the drainage from the building into the sewer. All sewer pipes should be made to slope, if possible, in the direction of the natural slope of the ground, to secure minimum excavation and gravity drainage. Pumping should be avoided as far as possible. Cost of excavation must sometimes be balanced against the cost of pumping.

Pipes too small for a man to enter should be laid in a straight line between manholes. Turns greater than 90° in a manhole are undesirable in sewers smaller than 24 in. to 36 in. Special manholes may be constructed for greater angles of turn. Large sewers should turn on long, easy curves, or two or more manholes may be constructed on the curve with the sewer as a part of the curve between them.

5–4. Location of manholes. Good practice calls for the location of a manhole at every change of direction, grade, elevation, or size of

[3] See also K. A. Thompson, *Public Works,* June, 1957, p. 106.

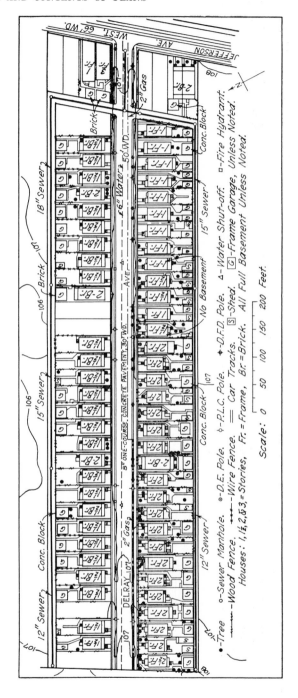

Fig. 5–2. Portion of a typical map used in sewer design.

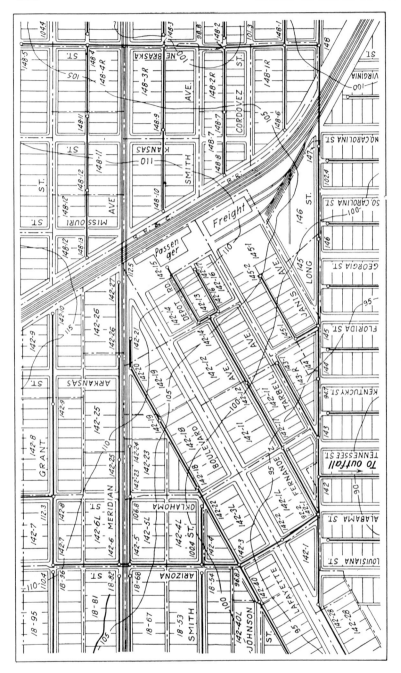

Fig. 5–3. Street plan used in design of separate-sewer system.

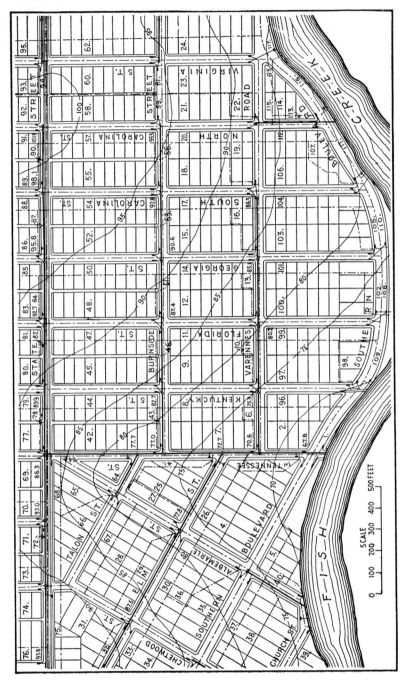

Fig. 5-4. Typical city map used in the design of a storm-sewer system.

pipe, except in sewers about 60 in. in diameter or larger. In sewers too small for a man to enter, the manholes should not be more than 300 to 500 ft apart, and preferably as close as 200 to 300 ft, although spacing is sometimes longer. The distance is fixed, partly, by the length of sewer rods that can be worked successfully between manholes. In large sewers the distances between manholes are sometimes made greater, but this is inadvisable since a means of quick escape should be provided for workmen from a sudden rise of water in the sewer, or from the effect of asphyxiating or combustible gases. It is good practice to place manholes at street intersections, with due regard to the maximum distance between manholes, whether or not there is a junction at this point, because if manholes become covered they are more easily found if their location is known.

5–5. Numbering of manholes. It is desirable to adopt a simple system of manhole numbering, for such numbers serve as a guide in subsequent computations in design, and in records during maintenance. A system that avoids confusion and is subject to unlimited extension is to number the manholes consecutively upward, beginning with number 1 nearest to the lowest point in the sewer system, and ending this series of numbers at the manhole on the system furthest from the outlet, as measured along the sewer contrary to the direction of flow. This line may be called the "main line." Submains and laterals can be similarly numbered, with the number of the manhole on the main line into which the submain drains as a prefix. This system has been followed in Fig. 5–3.

5–6. Drainage areas. The drainage area tributary to each manhole should be delimited as a basis for future computations. The drainage-area line generally follows property lines and the center lines of streets and alleys, its position being such that it includes all the area draining into one manhole and excludes all areas draining elsewhere. An entire lot is assumed to lie within the drainage area into which the buildings on the lot drain. It is not permissible to change the diameter or slope of a sewer between manholes. The rate of flow entering a manhole will determine the size of the pipe entering, or above, that manhole. Each manhole becomes a point of concentration for the increment of flow added between it and the next manhole above. The watershed lines for drainage areas on Fig. 5–3 are determined on this basis and are shown as dot-and-dash lines on the figure.

A drainage area is given the same number as the manhole into which it drains. However, a drainage area which drains into a branch line just above its junction with the main line or another branch line is given the same number as the manhole at the junction, with the letter R or L placed after the number. This condition occurs at manhole 143, at each manhole on Nebraska Street, and at manhole 142–6 in Fig. 5–3. The letter R is used if the branch line enters the main line from the right, and L if it enters from the left. The right side of a sewer is to the right hand of an observer standing on the sewer and facing downstream.

5–7. Maximum rate of flow of sewage. An estimate of the average rate of flow of sewage from a drainage area may be based on the per capita sewage flow times the population in the area; on the product of the number of buildings of different classes in the area and an estimate or census of the occupants in the buildings of each class; [4] or on the product of the area and an estimate of its population density. The last basis is used in estimates of flow in Fig. 5–3. The maximum rate of flow is computed from such formulas as 3–1, 3–2, or 3–3.

Table 5–1 shows the computations for the rates of flow in the sewers discharging from the north into manhole 142 in Fig. 5–3. The computations should begin at the upper end of a lateral, continue to a junction, and then start again at the upper end of each lateral entering this junction, proceeding in this manner until the sewer system is covered. Each line in the table should be filled in completely from left to right before the next line is started. In the illustrative solution shown in Table 5–1, computations for the rate of flow have not been made between manholes where it was apparent that there would be insufficient additional flow to necessitate a change in the size of pipe. The density of population is taken as 20 per acre, with an average flow of sewage of 100 gallons per capita per day. The ratio of the maximum to the average rate of flow is given by formula 3–1, the ratio not to exceed 5 nor to be less than 1.5. The rate of infiltration of ground water is assumed as 50,000 gallons per day per mile of pipe. This rate is somewhat larger than is customarily allowed under normal conditions.

In the first line of Table 5–1 the entries in columns 1 to 6 are self-explanatory. There are no entries in columns 7 to 10, as no additional sewage is contributed between manholes 148.5 and 148.4. In column 11, 2,250 persons are recorded as tributary to manhole 148.5 in the district to the west and south. These people contribute an average

---

[4] See also G. W. Reid, *Water and Sewage Works,* August, 1955, p. 362.

COMPUTATIONS FOR QUANTITY OF SEWAGE

Line Number	On Street	From Street	To Street	From Manhole	To Manhole	Length, ft	Mark of Added Areas
1	Nebraska St.	Map margin	Alley E. of Grant St.	148.5	148.4	338	...
2	Alley E. of Grant St.	Railroad	N. of Missouri St.	148.13	148.12	328	148.12
3	Alley E. of Grant St.	N. of Missouri St.	N. of Kansas St.	148.12	148.11	355	148.11
4	Alley E. of Grant St.	N. of Kansas St.	Nebraska St.	148.11	148.4	340	148.4R
5	Nebraska St.	Alley E. of Grant St.	Alley E. of Meridian	148.4	148.3	380	...
6	Alley E. of Meridian	Railroad	Nebraska St.	148.10	148.3	800	148.9 148.3R
7	Nebraska St.	Alley E. of Meridian	Alley E. of Smith Ave.	148.3	148.2	304	...
8	Alley E. of Smith Ave.	Railroad	Nebraska St.	148.8	148.2	609	148.7 148.2R
9	Nebraska St.	Alley E. of Smith Ave.	E. of Cordovez St.	148.2	148.1	300	...
10	E. of Cordovez St.	Railroad	Nebraska St.	148.6	148.1	410	148.1R
11	E. of Cordovez St.	Map margin	Nebraska St.	148.15	148.1	380	148.1L
12	Nebraska St.	E. of Cordovez St.	Long St.	148.1	148	172	...
13	Long St.	Map margin	Nebraska St.	149	148	380	148
14	Long St.	Nebraska St.	N. Carolina St.	148	147	492	...
15	Long St.	N. Carolina St.	Georgia St.	147	146	430	...
16	Long St.	Georgia St.	Harris St.	146	145	419	146
17	Long St.	Harris St.	Tennessee St.	145	143	725	145.1 144
	Column No. 1	2	3	4	5	6	7

* The single line indicates start of computations on a lateral; the double line marks resumption of computations on main line.

† One cfs of industrial waste treated as ground water.

of 100 gallons per person per day, or a total of 0.346 cfs. This rate is entered in column 12. The figure in column 13 is obtained from formula 3–1. Column 14 is 0.01 times the product of columns 12 and 13. Column 16 is the product of column 15 and the rate of infiltration of ground water expressed in cubic feet per second per foot of pipe. Column 17 is the sum of column 16 and all of the ground water tribu-

5-1

FOR A SEPARATE-SEWER SYSTEM

Area, acres	Population per Acre	Number of Persons	Total Persons Tributary	Cumulative Average Sanitary Flow, cfs	Per Cent Max Sanitary is of Average	Total Max Sanitary Flow, cfs	Length of Additional Pipe, ft	Increment of Ground Water, cfs	Cumulative Ground Water, cfs	Total Flow, cfs	Line Number
...	...	...	2,250	0.346	425	1.47	338	0.005	0.187	1.66	1
2.7	20	54	54	.0084	500	0.042	328	.0048	0.0048	0.047	2
3.41	20	68	122	.0190	500	0.095	355	.0052	0.010	0.105	3
2.68	20	54	176	.0274	500	0.137	340	.0050	0.015	0.152	4
...	...	...	2,426	.373	423	1.58	380	.0056	0.208	1.79	5
7.14	20	142	142	.0221	500	0.111	800	.0117	0.0117	0.123	6
...	...	...	2,568	.395	414	1.63	304	.0045	0.224	1.85	7
3.82	20	76	76	.0119	500	0.060	609	.0089	0.0089	0.069	8
...	...	...	2,644	.407	414	1.68	300	.0044	0.237	1.92	9
3.10	20	62	62	.0096	500	0.048	410	.006	0.006	0.054	10
2.69	20	54	54	.0084	500	0.042	380	.0056	0.0056	0.048	11
...	...	...	2,760	.425	409	1.74	172	.0025	0.251	1.99	12
1.53	20	31	31	.048	500	0.024	380	.0056	0.0056	0.030	13
...	...	...	2,791	.430	409	1.76	492	.0072	0.264	2.02	14
...	...	...	2,791	.430	409	1.76	430	.0064	1.27 †	3.03	15
0.81	20	16	2,807	.433	407	1.76	419	.0061	1.28	3.04	16
6.6	20	132	2,936	.454	403	1.83	1,210	.024	1.30	3.13	17
8	9	10	11	12	13	14	15	16	17	18	

tary to manhole 148.5, which is not recorded in the table. Column 18 is the sum of columns 14 and 17.

No new principle is represented in the second line.

In the third line, column 11 is the sum of lines 2 and 3 in column 10.

In the fourth line, column 11 is equal to the sum of the fourth line in column 10 and the third line in column 11.

In the fifth line, column 11 contains the figure for all the population above manhole 148.3. As there is no additional area tributary between manholes 148.4 and 148.3, the figure in column 11 is the sum of lines 1 and 4 in column 11.

With this introduction the student should be able to check the remaining figures in the table and should compute the quantity of sewage entering manhole 142 from the south, making reasonable assumptions for the tributary quantities from beyond the limits of the map.

5–8. Detailed plans. The Joint Committee (see Sect. 5–2) has recommended that:

All detailed plans shall be prepared as blue or white prints and shall be drawn to a suitable scale. Plans for modifications or extensions to existing systems or plants shall indicate clearly the connections or relation thereto, and, if not already on file, submission of plans for the existing system or plant may also be required.

The detailed plans for sewage works shall show:

A. *Miscellaneous.* The scale, in feet, to which the plans are drawn, the north point, the date, and the names of the owner and the engineer shall be indicated on each sheet. A suitable subtitle shall be shown on each sheet.

B. *Plan and profile.* A plan and profile along the line of all sewers to be constructed. [A typical plan and profile are shown in Fig. 5–5 for the line between manholes 148.5 and 147 in Fig. 5–3.] Such plan and profile shall show all special features such as inverted siphons, extra strength pipe, concrete encasements, and sewer bridges. All stream crossings and sewer outlets must be shown on the profiles with elevations of the stream bed and of the normal and extreme high- and low-water levels. Where reasonably accurate contour lines are indicated on the general layout, the profiles of future lines need not be shown. Profiles should have a horizontal scale not more than 100 ft to the inch and a vertical scale not more than 10 ft to the inch. Both scales must be clearly shown on the profiles. The profile should show the nature of the material to be excavated and the location of underground obstacles which may be met. The cut is recorded to the nearest 0.1 ft at each manhole. It should not be given elsewhere on the profile without special reason, in order to avoid subsequent disputes. Stationing should be shown to the nearest 0.1 ft. It should commence at $0 + 00$ at the outlet and increase up the sewer. The station at any point on the sewer system should show the distance from that point along the line of the sewer to the outlet; or a new system of stationing may commence at important junctions on large sewers; or at each junction. Elevations of the surface of the ground should be shown to the nearest 0.1 ft, and the elevation of the invert should be shown to the nearest 0.01 ft.

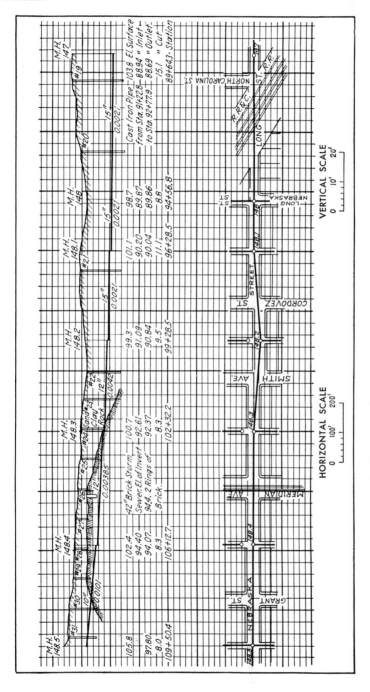

Fig. 5-5. Typical profile and plan used in design of a sewer system.

DESIGN OF SEWER SYSTEMS

Table

COMPUTATIONS FOR SLOPE AND DIAMETER OF

Line Number	On Street	From Street	To Street	From Man-hole	To Man-hole	Length, ft
1	Nebraska St.	Map margin	Alley E. of Grant St.	148.5	148.4	338
2	Alley E. of Grant St.	Railroad	N. of Missouri St.	148.13	148.12	328
3	Alley E. of Grant St.	N. of Missouri St.	N. of Kansas St.	148.12	148.11	355
4	Alley E. of Grant St.	N. of Kansas St.	Nebraska St.	148.11	148.4	340
5	Nebraska St.	Alley E. of Grant St.	Alley E. of Meridian	148.4	148.3	380
6	Alley E. of Meridian	Railroad	Kansas St.	148.10	148.9	400
7	Alley E. of Meridian	Kansas St.	Nebraska St.	148.9	148.3	400
8	Nebraska St.	Alley E. of Meridian	Alley E. of Smith Ave.	148.3	148.2	304
9	Alley E. of Smith Ave.	Railroad	N. of Kansas St.	148.8	148.7	305
10	Alley E. of Smith Ave.	N. of Kansas St.	Nebraska St.	148.7	148.2	304
11	Nebraska St.	Alley E. of Smith Ave.	Alley E. of Cordovez	148.2	148.1	300
12	Alley E. of Cordovez	Map margin	Nebraska St.	148.13	148.1	380
13	Alley E. of Cordovez	Railroad	Nebraska St.	148.6	148.1	410
14	Nebraska St.	Alley E. of Cordovez	Long St.	148.1	148	172
15	Long St.	Map margin	Nebraska St.	149	148	380
16	Long St.	Nebraska St.	N. Carolina St.	148	147	492
17	Long St.	N. Carolina St.	Georgia St.	147	146	430
18	Long St.	Georgia St.	Harris St.	146	145	419
19	Alley SW. of Janis Ave.	End of Janis Ave.	Harris St.	145.2	145.1	350
20	Harris St.	Alley SW. of Janis Ave.	Long St.	145.1	145	135
21	Long St.	Harris St.	Kentucky St.	145	144	258
22	Long St.	Kentucky St.	Tennessee St.	144	143	282
23	Tarbell Ave.	Harris St.	Long St.	143.1	143	417
24	Long St.	Tennessee St.	Alley S. of Tenn. St.	143	142	185
Column No. 1	2	3		4	5	6

[Only a portion of the main line sewer is shown in profile in Fig. 5–5. The profiles of the laterals computed in Table 5–2 have not been shown.] The approximate locations of all house inlets are shown on the profile. The exact locations are made a matter of record during construction.

C. *Sewers.* Figures showing the manhole stationing, size of sewers, surface and sewer invert elevations at manholes, and the grade of all sewers

5-2

PIPES FOR A SEPARATE-SEWER SYSTEM

Elevation of Surface		Total Flow, cfs	Slope $n = 0.015$	Diameter of Pipe, in.	Velocity when Full, fps	Capacity when Full, cfs	Elevation of Invert		Line Number
Upper Manhole	Lower Manhole						Upper Manhole	Lower Manhole	
105.8	102.4	1.66	0.0101	10	3.25	1.78	97.80	94.40	1
113.5	112.0	0.047	.0058	8	2.00	0.71	105.50	103.62	2
112.0	107.7	0.105	.0110	8	2.78	0.98	103.61	99.70	3
107.7	102.4	0.152	.0156	8	3.27	1.18	99.69	94.40	4
102.4	100.7	1.79	.0039	12	2.28	1.79	94.07	92.61	5
111.8	107.0	...	.0120	8	2.90	1.03	103.80	99.00	6
107.0	100.7	0.123	.0157	8	3.28	1.18	98.99	92.70	7
100.7	99.3	1.85	.0042	12	2.36	1.85	92.37	91.09	8
109.3	105.3	...	.0131	8	3.00	1.08	101.30	97.30	9
105.3	99.3	0.069	.0197	8	3.70	1.32	97.29	91.30	10
99.3	101.1	1.92	.0021	15	2.00	2.45	90.84	90.20	11
100.8	101.1	...	.0057	8	2.00	0.71	92.80	90.62	12
104.6	101.1	0.054	.0085	8	2.46	0.87	96.60	93.10	13
101.1	98.7	1.99	.0021	15	2.00	2.45	90.04	89.87	14
103.8	98.7	0.030	.0134	8	3.04	1.08	95.80	90.70	15
98.7	103.8	2.02	.0021	15	2.00	2.45	89.86	88.94	16
103.8	99.1	3.03	.0016	18	2.00	3.50	88.69	88.00	17
99.1	96.9	3.04	.0016	18	2.00	3.50	87.99	87.32	18
105.2	98.1	...	.0203	8	3.78	1.35	97.20	90.10	19
98.1	96.9	...	.0088	8	2.53	0.89	90.09	88.90	20
96.9	94.4	...	.0035	18	2.98	5.20	87.31	86.40	21
94.4	92.6	...	.0064	18	4.00	7.00	88.39	84.60	22
98.7	92.6	...	.0146	8	3.18	1.14	90.70	84.60	23
92.6	92.3	3.13	.0016	18	2.00	3.50	83.77	83.47	24
7	8	9	10	11	12	13	14	15	

between each two adjacent manholes must be shown on the profiles. Where there is any question of the sewer being insufficiently deep to serve any residence, the elevation and location of the basement floor shall be plotted on the profile of the sewer which is to serve the house in question. The engineer shall state that all sewers are sufficiently deep to serve adjacent basements except where otherwise noted on plans.

D. *Sewer appurtenances.* Details of all ordinary sewer appurtenances such as manholes, drop manholes, inspection chambers, inverted siphons, as well as of any special appurtenances or structures, such as regulators, tide gates, sewer bridges, pumping stations, etc. must be submitted. These detailed plans must be drawn to such a scale as will show clearly the nature of the design of each of the structures referred to and its equipment. They should have marked upon them all dimensions, elevations, capacities, and explanatory notes necessary to make them readily intelligible for examination and construction.

E. *Cross-sections.* Detailed plans and specifications of all sewer sections except standard pipe, clearly shown as such, must accompany the plans. Details of cradling and encasement must also be shown.

F. *Flooding.* Elevation of extraordinarily high water shall be included on the profile of sewers subject to flooding.

5–9. Slope and diameter of sewers. After the maximum rate of flow of sewage has been computed and the profile of the ground surface has been drawn, it is possible to determine the slope and diameter of the sewer. A table, such as Table 5–2, is made up. It may resemble Table 5–1 or it may be an extension of it, since the first six columns in the two tables may be made the same. The elevation of the surface at the upper and lower manholes of two consecutive manholes is read from the profile.

The depth of the sewer below the ground surface is first determined. Sewers should be sufficiently deep to drain cellars of ordinary depth. In residential districts, cellars are seldom more than about 5 ft below the ground surface. To this depth must be added the fall necessary for the slope of the house sewer. Six-in. pipe laid on a minimum grade of 1.67 is a common size and slope restriction for house sewers. Most states [5] restrict the minimum size of common sewers to 8 in. A few permit the use of 6-in. pipes. An additional 12 in. of depth should be allowed for vertical bends in the pipe and the depth of the pipe under the cellar floor. Where the elevation of the street is about the same as that of the lots and the street is not more than 80 ft in width between property lines, a minimum depth of 8 ft from the street surface to the invert of sewers 24 in. or less in diameter is satisfactory, assuming that the axes of the house drain and the sewer intersect. For larger pipes the depth should be increased so that, when the street sewer is flowing full, sewage will not back up into the cellars or for any distance into the tributary pipes. Sewers are laid parallel to the ground surface when the slope is sufficient or, if pos-

[5] A staff review in *Sewage Works Eng.,* March, 1948, p. 117.

sible without coming too near to the surface, they are laid on a flatter grade to avoid unnecessary excavation.

The velocity of flow in a sewer should be sufficient to prevent the sedimentation of sludge and light mineral matter.[6] Such a velocity is in the neighborhood of 1 fps, which should be available under conditions of dry-weather flow. The minimum velocity, when full, should be, therefore, about 2 fps. Under this condition the minimum permissible velocity of 1 fps occurs when the sewer is about 17 per cent full. It is desirable that the velocity at the upper end of laterals be somewhat greater, since the rate of flow seldom reaches such a percentage of the depth of flow in the sewer. The maximum permissible velocity of flow is about 10 fps in order to avoid excessive erosion of the invert of the sewer. Velocities greater than the hydraulic critical velocity are undesirable in order to avoid the hydraulic jump and other undesirable phenomena of non-uniform flow.

The method for determining the grade and diameter of sewers is best explained through the illustrative problem worked out in Table 5-2 for the profile shown in Fig. 5-5. The computed values are inserted from left to right in each line of the table, one line being completed before the next one is commenced. The headings in the first six columns are self-explanatory. The elevations of the surface at the upper and lower manholes in any line are read from the profile. The total flow is read from column 18 in Table 5-1. The slope of the ground surface is then computed and, with the rate of flow, the slope, and the coefficient of roughness, the diameter of the pipe and the velocity of flow are read from Fig. 4-2 to Fig. 4-4.

The following principles indicate good practice in design. Each has been violated under appropriate conditions.

1. Use no pipe less than 8 in. in diameter.

2. Place pipes on such a slope that the velocity of flow, when the pipes are full, is not less than 2 fps nor more than 10 fps.

3. Where the required diameter of pipe is not one of the commercial sizes shown in Tables 7-1 or 7-2 use the next larger size and record the velocity and rate of flow in this pipe when it is full. The record is to be made as in columns 12 and 13 in Table 5-2.

4. Never discharge the contents of a larger pipe into a smaller one, even though the capacity of the smaller pipe may be greater on

[6] See also *Final Report of Committee,* Boston Society of Civil Engineers, March 4, 1942.

account of its steeper slope or for any other reason. Otherwise clogging is almost certain to occur at the entrance to the smaller pipe.

It is undesirable to use a pipe larger than that called for under the preceding conditions. The inexperienced designer may be tempted to use a larger pipe on a flatter slope in order to save excavation and to be able to record a higher velocity when full in the larger pipe. A result in practice will be clogging, as actual conditions will give smaller velocities since the flow in the larger pipe will be too low.

When the slope, the diameter, and the capacity of the pipe to be used have been determined, these values are entered in the table. The elevations of the invert of the pipe at the upper and lower manholes are next computed and entered in the table. This method is followed until all the diameters, slopes, and elevations have been determined.

The slopes are computed from center to center of manholes, but an extra allowance of 0.01 ft is allowed by some designers for the loss in head in passing through the manhole. If it becomes necessary to increase the diameter of the sewer, the top of the outgoing sewer is placed at the same elevation as or below the top of the lowest incoming sewer. Some standards[7] permit placing the 0.8-depth points of sewers at the same elevation. No extra allowance is made to compensate for loss of head in the manhole. This case is illustrated in columns 14 and 15 in lines 16 and 17 of Table 5–2. All of the conditions listed above are illustrated in the table, except the condition for a velocity greater than 10 fps.

The first rule is met at the head of practically every lateral and is illustrated in the second line.

The second rule is illustrated also in the second line. The slope of the ground surface is 0.0046, which gives a velocity of only 1.8 fps in an 8-in. pipe. The slope is increased, therefore, to 0.00575, on which the full velocity is 2 fps.

The third rule is met in the first line. The diameter called for to carry 1.66 cfs on a slope of 0.0101 is slightly less than 10 in. A 10-in. pipe is used, therefore, and its full capacity and velocity are recorded.

The fourth rule is illustrated in line 14. The cut at manhole 148.1 is 11.1 ft. The slope of the ground is 0.014, much steeper than is necessary to maintain the minimum velocity in a 15-in. pipe. The pipe is placed, therefore, on the minimum permissible slope, and excavation is saved. The student should check the figures in Table

[7] See Joint Committee in Sect. 5–2.

5–2 and be sure that he understands them before he attempts to make a design independently.

5–10. The sewer profile. The profile is next completed as shown in Fig. 5–5, the pipe line being drawn as the computations are made. The cut is recorded to the nearest 0.1 ft at each manhole or change in grade. It should not be given elsewhere on the profile as it invites controversy. The cut is the difference between the elevation of the invert of the lowest pipe in the trench at the point in question, and the surface of the ground.

The stationing should be shown to the nearest 0.1 ft. It should commence at 0 + 00 at the outlet and increase up the sewer. The station at any point on the sewer may show the distance from it to the outlet, or a new system of stationing may be commenced at important junctions, or at each junction.

Elevations of the surface of the ground should be shown to the nearest 0.1 ft, and the invert elevation to the nearest 0.01 ft.

Only a portion of the main-line sewer is shown in profile in Fig. 5–5. The profiles of the laterals computed in Table 5–2 have not been shown. The approximate locations of house inlets should be shown on the plan and their exact location made a matter of record during construction. They are not shown in Fig. 5–5.

Design of Storm-Sewer System [8]

5–11. Planning the system. Storm-sewer systems are seldom as extensive as separate- or combined-sewer systems, since storm water can be discharged into the nearest suitable drainage channel, whereas dry-weather or combined sewage must be conducted to some point where its discharge will be inoffensive. The need for a comprehensive general plan of a storm-water system is as great, however, as for a separate system. The haphazard construction of sewers at the points most needed at the moment results in duplication of forgotten drains, expense in increasing the capacity of inadequate sewers, difficult construction due to thoughtlessly located underground structures, and inadequate outlets as sewers are added to the system. Where finances are low it may be desirable to construct adequate laterals and submains, saving the cost of the main outlet, which may be supplemented later by the construction of a relief sewer when the load is greater and funds are available. A comprehensive plan

[8] See also J. G. Hendrickson, Jr., and T. K. Breitfuss, *Public Works*, February, 1946, p. 91.

permits the construction of sewers where they are needed as they are needed, and enables all probable future needs to be cared for at a minimum of expense.

The same preliminary survey, map, and underground information are necessary for the design of a storm-water system as for a separate-sewer system. The principles applicable to the scope, content, and details of plans stated in Sects. 5–2 and 5–8 are applicable to the design of storm sewers. The map shown in Fig. 5–4 has been used for the design of a storm-sewer system.

The steps in the design of a storm-sewer system are: (1) Note the most advantageous points to locate inlets and lay out the system to drain these inlets. (2) Determine the required capacity of the sewers by a study of the runoff from the different drainage areas. (3) Draw the profile and compute the diameter and slope of the pipes required.

5–12. Location of street inlets. The location of storm sewers is determined mainly by the desirable location of street inlets. The inlets must, therefore, be located before the system can be planned. In general, inlets should be located so that no water will flow across a street or sidewalk in order to reach the sewer. This requires that inlets be placed on the high corners at intersections, and at sufficiently frequent intervals that the gutters are not overloaded. City blocks are seldom so long as to necessitate the location of inlets between crossings solely on account of inadequate gutter capacity. The capacity of a gutter can be computed approximately by the application of Kutter's formula. Inlet capacities are discussed in Chapter 6. When the area drained is sufficiently large to tax the capacity of the gutter or inlet, a new inlet should be installed regardless of the location of the street intersections.

The street inlets are located on the map shown in Fig. 5–4. The sewer lines are then located so as to make the length of pipe passing near to all inlets a minimum. Storm sewers are seldom placed near the center of a street because of the frequent crowded condition in this location.

5–13. Drainage areas. The outline of a drainage area is drawn so that all water falling within the area outlined will enter the same inlet, and water falling on any point beyond the outline will enter some other inlet. Therefore, the outline must follow true drainage lines rather than the artificial land divisions used in locating the drainage lines in the design of sanitary sewers. The drainage lines are determined by pavement slopes, location of downspouts, paved or unpaved yards, grading of lawns, and the many other features of the natural drainage that are altered by the building up of a city. The location of the drainage lines is fixed as a result of a study of local conditions.

The watershed or drainage lines are shown on Fig. 5–4 by means of dot-and-dash lines. A drainage line passes down the middle of each street because the crown of the street throws water to either side and directs it to different inlets. A watershed line is drawn about 50 ft south of such streets as Kentucky Street and Florida Street because the downspouts from the houses on those streets discharge or will discharge into the street on which they face. The location of any watershed line is usually a matter of judgment rather than exactness. Each area is given an identifying number which is useful mainly in design. It should correspond to the inlet number, and numbers should decrease downstream.

5–14. Computation of flow by McMath's formula. McMath's formula serves as an example of the method followed when an empirical formula is adopted for the computation of runoff. Other formulas may be more satisfactory under favorable conditions.

Computations should be tabulated somewhat as shown in Table 5–3, in which the rate of storm flow from the sewer at the foot of Tennessee Street, in Fig. 5–4, has been computed by means of the McMath formula, using the constants suggested for St. Louis conditions, $R = 2.75$, and $C = 0.75$. The column headings in the table explain the figures as recorded. The computations should begin at the upper end of a lateral, proceed to the first junction, and then return to the head of another lateral tributary to this junction. They should be continued in this manner until all tributary areas have been covered. Special computations will be necessary for the determination of the maximum rate of flow of storm water entering each inlet, to avoid the flooding of an inlet or gutter. These computations have not been shown as they are easily made by the application of McMath's formula to each area concerned.

The determination of the average slope ratio is a matter of judgment, based on the average natural slope of the surface of the ground and an estimate of the probable future conditions.

5–15. Computation of flow by rational method. The rational method for the computation of storm-water runoff is described in Chapter 3. An example of its application to storm-sewer design is given here for the district shown in Fig. 5–4. The computations are shown in Table 5–3. As in the preceding designs, the table has been

filled in from left to right and line by line. Computations have
started at upper ends of laterals tributary to each junction. The
column headed I represents the imperviousness factor in the expression
$Q = AIR$. It is based on judgment guided by the constants given

Table

COMPUTATIONS FOR THE QUANTITY OF STORM SEWAGE

Line Number	On Street	From Street	To Street	Identifying Numbers of Areas Drained	By McMath's Formula			
					Additional Acres Drained	Total Acres Drained	Slope of Surface	Runoff, cfs
1	State	N. Carolina	S. Carolina	91 and 92	2.35	2.35	0.005	5.5
2	State	S. Carolina	Georgia	88, 89 and 90	3.0	5.35	.005	10.8
3	State	Georgia	Florida	85, 86 and 87	3.0	8.35	.007	16.5
4	State	Florida	Kentucky	81, 83 and 84	3.0	11.35	.009	22.0
5	State	Kentucky	Tennessee	79, 80 and 82	3.0	14.35	.010	28.0
6	State	Texas	Louisiana	76 and others	3.8	3.8	.005	8.3
7	State	Louisiana	Alabama	73, 74 and 75	3.7	7.5	.007	15.0
8	State	Alabama	Tennessee	70, 71 and 72	3.0	10.5	.006	19.0
9	Tennessee	State	Talon	68, 69, 77 and 78	4.3	29.15	.15	52
10	Talon	Albemarle	Tennessee	65, 66 and 67	2.8	2.8	.018	8.4
11	Tennessee	Talon	Burnside	64 and 64a	0.7	29.85	.15	55
12	Burnside	N. Carolina	S. Carolina	57, 58 and 59	2.84	2.84	.008	7.2
13	Burnside	S. Carolina	Georgia	54, 55 and 56	3.88	6.72	.010	14.9
14	Burnside	Georgia	Florida	50, 52 and 53	3.88	10.60	.012	22
15	Burnside	Florida	Kentucky	47, 48 and 51	3.88	14.48	.013	29
16	Burnside	Kentucky	Tennessee	44, 45 and 46	3.88	18.36	.013	36
17	Tennessee	Burnside	Elm	42 and 43	2.84	51.05	.015	82
18	Elm	Above Chetwood	Chetwood	Included in next line below			...	...
19	Elm	Chetwood	Albemarle	31, 32 and 33	2.75	2.75	.007	7.0
20	Elm	Albemarle	Tennessee	27, 28, 29 and 30	5.75	8.50	.016	20
21	Tennessee	Elm	Varennes	25, 26 and 41	2.62	62.17	.017	100
22	Varennes	S. Carolina	Georgia	17, 18 and 19	3.17	3.17	.010	8.3
23	Varennes	Georgia	Florida	14, 15 and 16	3.17	6.34	.011	14.5
24	Varennes	Florida	Kentucky	11, 12 and 13	3.17	9.51	.013	21
25	Varennes	Kentucky	Tennessee	8, 9 and 10	3.17	12.68	.013	26
26	Tennessee	Varennes	Boulevard	6 and 7	2.32	77.17	.017	120
27	Tennessee	Boulevard	Outlet	1, 2, 3, 4 and 5	4.72	81.89	.017	122
28	...	...	...	...	...	...	...	...
29	...	...	..	...	...	...	...	...
30	...	...	...	...	...	...	...	...
	1	2	3	4	5	6	7	8

in Chapter 3 concerning imperviousness. The column headed ΔAI is the product of the two preceding columns in the same line. It reduces areas to the same terms so that they can be added for entry in the column headed ΣAI. It may be necessary to record the values

5–3

AT THE FOOT OF TENNESSEE STREET ON FIG. 5–4

					By Rational Method						
Area, acres	I	ΔAI acres	ΣAI acres	Time of Concentration, min	R	Q	S	V	Sewer Length, ft	Time in Sewer min	Line Number
2.35	0.50	1.17	1.17	7.0	4.8	5.6	0.011	4.6	300	1.1	1
3.00	.50	1.50	2.67	8.1	4.6	12.2	.010	5.5	300	0.9	2
3.00	.50	1.50	4.17	9.0	4.4	18.3	.009	5.8	300	0.9	3
3.00	.50	1.50	5.67	9.9	4.2	23.9	.009	6.0	300	0.8	4
3.00	.50	1.50	7.17	10.7	4.1	29.3	.009	6.6	300	0.8	5
3.80	.35	1.33	1.33	10.0	4.2	5.6	.005	3.2	370	1.9	6
3.70	.40	1.48	2.81	11.9	3.9	11.0	.011	5.2	300	1.0	7
3.00	.45	1.35	4.16	12.9	3.8	15.8	.002	3.2	300	1.6	8
4.30	.50	2.15	13.48	14.5	3.6	48.5	.019	9.8	450	0.8	9
2.80	.40	1.12	1.12	8.0	4.6	5.2	.004	3.0	210	1.2	10
0.70	.20	0.14	14.74	15.3	3.5	51.5	.003	5.0	120	0.4	11
2.84	.55	1.56	1.56	10.0	4.2	6.5	.010	4.5	300	1.1	12
3.88	.55	2.13	3.69	11.1	4.0	14.8	.006	4.7	300	1.1	13
3.88	.55	2.13	5.82	12.2	3.9	22.7	.008	5.8	300	0.9	14
3.88	.55	2.13	7.95	13.1	3.7	29.4	.013	7.5	300	0.7	15
3.88	.55	2.13	10.08	13.8	3.7	37.3	.019	9.2	300	0.5	16
2.84	.45	1.28	26.10	15.7	3.4	88.8	.014	10.2	280	0.5	17
...	...	...	...	...	...	...	...	...	...	...	18
2.75	.40	1.10	1.10	8.0	4.6	5.1	.018	5.3	480	1.5	19
5.75	.45	2.59	3.69	9.5	4.3	15.8	.012	6.1	410	1.1	20
2.62	.50	1.31	31.10	16.2	3.4	106	.012	10.2	180	0.3	21
3.17	.55	1.74	1.74	9.0	4.4	7.7	.013	5.2	270	0.9	22
3.17	.55	1.74	3.48	9.9	4.2	14.6	.010	5.7	300	0.9	23
3.17	.55	1.74	5.22	10.8	4.1	21.4	.017	7.7	300	0.6	24
3.17	.55	1.74	6.96	11.4	4.0	27.8	.015	7.8	300	0.6	25
2.32	.55	1.28	39.34	16.5	3.3	130	.011	10.2	230	0.4	26
0.18	.80	0.14	Area No. 1		...	...	...	...	...	...	27
1.38	.50	0.69	Area No. 2		...	...	...	...	...	...	28
2.80	.55	1.54	Areas No. 3 and 4		...	...	...	...	...	...	29
0.36	.75	0.27	41.98	16.9	3.3	138	Areas No. 1–5 inclusive				30
9	10	11	12	13	14	15	16	17	18	19	

for this column on several lines if the imperviousness of the tributary areas varies. This condition is illustrated in the last line of the table, for the length of sewer nearest the outlet. In the preceding lines the imperviousness recorded represents an average for all the tributary areas.

The time of concentration, in minutes, is assumed by judgment and in accordance with the principles outlined in Sect. 3–15. For subsequent areas on the same line and above a junction it is the sum of the time of concentration for the area or areas tributary to the inlet next above and the time of flow in the sewer from the inlet next above to the inlet in question. For example, the time of concentration in line 4, column 13, of Table 5–3 is 9.9 min. It is the sum of 9.0 min, shown as the time of concentration to the inlet in column 13 of the preceding line, and the time of flow of 0.9 min in the sewer on State Street from Georgia Street to Florida Street, shown in line 3, column 19. Where two or more sewers join, the longest time of concentration from all tributaries at a junction may be taken as the time of concentration that will give the maximum flood wave in the sewer leading away from the junction. When this time is known it is necessary to compute the magnitude of the flood wave that will reach the junction from each tributary sewer in this time. For example, in Table 5–3 it is seen, in line 28, column 20, that the longest time of concentration to this junction is 15.8 min. By assuming, as a trial, the time of concentration on Elm Street from Chetwood to Albemarle (line 31, column 12) as 13.0 min, it is found that the flood wave reaching the junction from this branch in 15.8 min is 13.0 cfs. The maximum flood wave from this junction is, therefore, $99.2 + 13.0 + 4.5$, or 117 cfs, to the nearest unit cfs.

R, the rate of rainfall in inches per hour, has been computed by Talbot's formula $R = 105/(t + 15)$ where t is the time of concentration in minutes.

Q is in cubic feet per second and is the product of columns 11 and 13. It is shown in column 14.

S is the slope on which it is assumed that the sewer will be laid. The sewer is usually assumed to lie parallel to the surface of the ground unless the velocity of flow for that slope is less than 2 fps, or the sewer is so deep that excavation can be avoided by laying the sewer on the minimum permissible slope. It may be necessary to draw the profile of the sewers simultaneous with design computations, in order to permit determination of the best slope.

V, the velocity in feet per second, is computed from diagrams for the solution of Kutter's formula with the above slope, the computed rate of flow, and $n = 0.015$. The length, in feet, is scaled from the map as the distance between inlets, and the time is the length in feet divided by the velocity in feet per minute.

The rate of flow to be carried in the sewer having been computed, the design is completed by drawing the profile and computing the diameters and slopes by the method followed in the design of separate sewers.

It is to be noted that an error has been introduced in the computation of the maximum rate of flow by taking the longest time of concentration in the tributaries at a junction and applying this longest time to the sum of all of the tributary areas in order to determine the rate of rainfall. It would be more precise to add the rates of flow arriving at the junction from each of the tributary sewers simultaneously with the arrival of the maximum flood wave from the largest contributing tributary. This has been done for the problem shown in Table 5–3, and the maximum rate of flow from the entire area was computed as 142 cfs instead of 138 as shown in the table. In view of the approximate nature of the method and the compensating effect of the neglect of storage in the sewers, the result given by the method used in computing Table 5–3 will be adequately precise in most storm-sewer designs.

5–16. Design of combined sewers. Sewer systems may be designed with separate sewers, storm sewers, or combined sewers. The flow in a combined sewer is the sum of the flows that would occur in a separate sewer and a storm sewer draining the areas served by the combined sewer. Larger capacity should be provided for the storm flow in a combined sewer than in a storm sewer, to avoid surcharge, which is objectionable in a sewer carrying human excrement.

Chapter 6

Appurtenances

6–1. General. Appurtenances are those devices, in addition to the pipes and conduits, that are essential to or assist in the operation of a sewer system. Under this head are included such structures and devices as manholes, lampholes, flush tanks, catch basins, street inlets, regulators, siphons, junctions, outlets, grease traps, foundations, and underdrains.

In the design of sewer appurtenances the problems of maintenance are important considerations; and in the location of such structures precautions must be taken, because they are often unguarded, to make them inaccessible to children, vandals, and other unauthorized persons.

6–2. Manholes. A manhole is an opening constructed in a sewer for the purpose of permitting a man to enter or to leave the sewer. Manholes are the most common appurtenances to sewer systems and are used to permit inspection, cleaning, and the removal of obstructions from the pipes. The standard manhole used at Cranston, R. I., for small sewers is shown in Fig. 6–1. A standard junction manhole is shown in Fig. 6–2, and a manhole on a large sewer is shown in Fig. 6–3. Important features of these designs are the size of the opening and working space, and the strength of the structure. Manhole openings are seldom made less than 20 in. in diameter, and openings 24 in. in diameter are preferable. A man can pass through any opening through which his hips will pass, provided he can bend his knees and twist his shoulders immediately after passing the hole. For this reason the manhole should widen out rapidly immediately below the opening, as shown in the figures.

The walls of the manhole may be built of brick, concrete blocks, corrugated metal, or concrete. Brick and concrete blocks are often used because the forms necessary for concrete increase the cost of construction unless they can be reused a number of times. The walls of the manhole should be at least 8 in. thick. Greater thicknesses

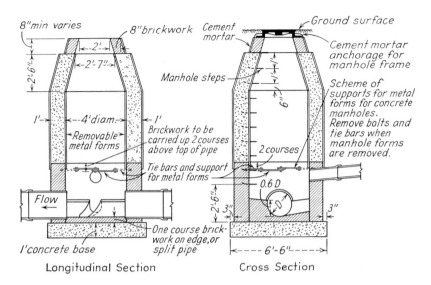

Fig. 6–1. Cranston standard manhole. (From R. B. Horne, *Jour. Boston Soc. Civil Engrs.*, April, 1943, p. 76.)

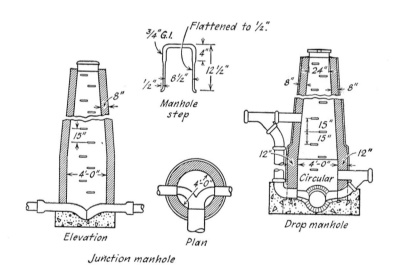

Fig. 6–2. Junction manhole and drop manhole.

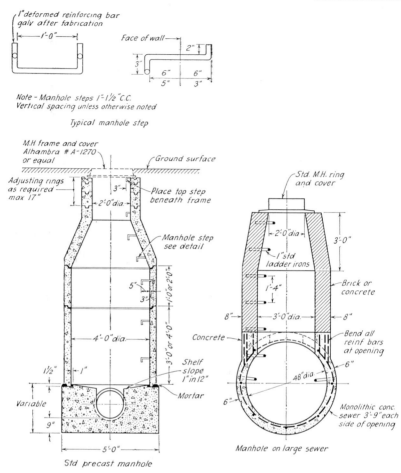

Fig. 6–3. Precast manhole and manhole on a large sewer.

are required in treacherous soil and for deep manholes, or to exclude moisture. A rough expression for the thickness of the walls of a brick manhole more than 12 ft deep in ordinary, firm material is $t = 2 + (d/2)$, where t is the thickness, in inches, and d is the depth, in feet. The thickness of brick walls may be changed every 5 to 10 ft or more. Concrete walls may be built thinner than brick walls.

The bottoms of brick manholes are frequently made of concrete, with or without a brick lining. In some jobs the pipe is laid through the ultimate location of the manhole. The manhole is later constructed over the pipe and the concrete bottom is formed against the pipe. When all is complete the upper half of the pipe is broken out, leaving a smooth, open channel through the manhole. The floor of the manhole is sloped toward the center and is constructed so that the sewage flows in a half-round or U-shaped channel of greater capacity than the tributary sewers. The sides of the channel should be high enough to prevent the overflow of sewage onto the sloping floor. This requires the sides to rise nearly to the crown of the sewer. In some sewers the depth of the flowing-through channel is made equal to the full diameter of the sewer. The floor should have a pitch towards the sewer of about 1 vertical to 10 or 12 horizontal. In manholes where two or more sewers join at approximately the same level the channels in the bottom should join with smooth, easy curves. Where the inlet and outlet pipes are not of the same diameter the tops of the pipes, or the 0.8-depth points of the pipes, should be placed at the same elevation to prevent backflow in the smaller pipes when the larger pipes are flowing full.

The manhole should be not less than 3 ft wide by 4 ft long for a height of at least 4 ft, if built in the form of an ellipse, or 4 ft in diameter if built circular. No standard method for the reduction of the diameter of the manhole near the top is observed, the rate being more or less dependent on the depth of the manhole. Sloping sides are desirable above the frost line as they are more resistant to heaving by frost action.

For sewers up to 48 in. in diameter the manhole is usually centered over the intersection of the pipes and has a special foundation. For larger sewers the manhole walls spring from the walls of the sewer, as shown in Fig. 6–3. Where it is desired to drop the elevation of the invert of a sewer for more than about 3 ft, the drop is usually made in a vertical pipe outside of the manhole, as indicated in Fig. 6–2. This is done to avoid the splashing of sewage in the manhole. An opening is made in the side of the manhole at the elevation of the higher pipe, to allow inspection. Such an opening is shown in the figure.

A well hole is a deep-drop manhole in which the sewage falls inside of the manhole, as shown in Fig. 6–4. The force of the fall may be broken by a series of baffle plates, or by a sump at the bottom of the well hole. In a deep well hole or drop manhole the energy of the falling sewage may be absorbed also by creating a vortex in the shaft. Laushey [1] suggests that this can be done by causing sewage

[1] L. M. Laushey, *Eng. News-Record,* May 5, 1953, p. 38.

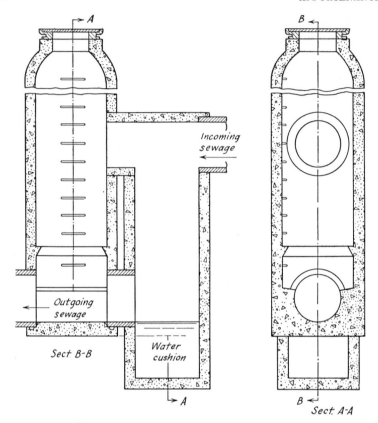

Fig. 6–4. Well hole with moderate drop.

to enter a circular tank or entrance chamber at the top of the tank tangentially. The diameter of this tank should be four to six times that of the shaft, and the width of the inlet slot should be between three-fourths and the full diameter of the shaft. Satisfactory vortexes were produced in tests when the depth in the entrance tank was more than five times the diameter of the shaft.

A flight sewer, or a flight of steps, as shown in Fig. 6–5, allows a steep grade in the sewer and serves to break the velocity of flow of the sewage. The use of a flight sewer may obviate the need for a drop manhole or a well hole.

6–3. Manhole covers, frames, and steps. Manhole covers and frames for the covers are almost invariably made of cast iron. The weights of frames and covers vary between 200 and 600 lb, the weight of the frame being about five times that of the cover. The lightest weights are used where no traffic other than an occasional pedestrian will pass over the manhole. Frames and covers weighing about 400 lb are common in residential streets, whereas 600-lb frames and covers are desirable in streets on which the traffic is heavy. Circular covers are almost universally used on sewer manholes, as they meet all needs and, if properly designed, they cannot fall into the sewer. The frame should be so designed that the pavement will rest firmly against it and wear at the same rate as the surrounding street surface. Experience has shown that sides should be vertical for the outside of the frame to approach this condition, and that the frame should not be less than 8 in. high.

The cover should be roughened in some desirable pattern, as shown in Fig. 6–6. Smooth covers become dangerously slippery. Where the ventilation of the sewers is not satisfactory manhole covers may be perforated. Such perforations are, however, ordinarily undesirable, as rising odors are obnoxious, and entering dirt and water are detrimental to the operation of the sewer. Owing to uneven wear, settling, or other causes, covers sometimes rest unevenly on the frame and are noisy under traffic. The noise may be stopped by the inser-

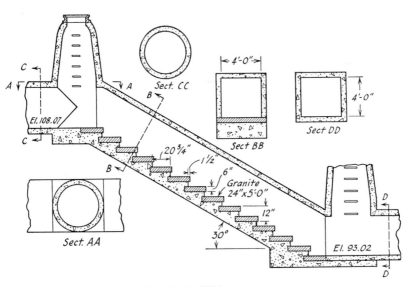

Fig. 6–5. Flight sewer.

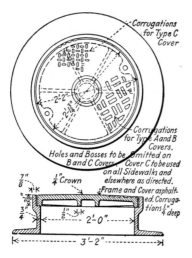

Fig. 6–6. Standard manhole frame and cover.

tion of asphalt, lead, asbestos, or old tires or tubes under the cover to act as a cushion. The theft and destruction of manhole covers and the unauthorized entering of sewers have sometimes required the locking of the covers to the frame when in place. The most common lock consists of a tumbler that falls into place when the manhole is closed and that can be opened only by a special wrench or tool. Adjustable frames are sometimes used where the street grade is settling, or the frames may be raised in order that the elevation of the top of the cover may be made to conform to that of the street surface, without reconstructing the top of the manhole. One type of adjustable cover is shown in Fig. 6–7. In some cases a precast adapter may be used to readjust the height of the cover.[2]

The danger from the blowing off of a manhole cover by an explosion may be minimized by the use of a curved bolt of the type shown in Fig. 6–8. Manhole covers should be marked so that the sanitary sewer can be distinguished from other conduits. It is desirable to adopt a uniform style and size of cover which is interchangeable on all sewer manholes in the system.

Steps are set into the walls of the manhole, as shown in Fig. 6–2, about 15 in. apart vertically, to allow entrance to and exit from the manhole. Galvanized iron and tar-dipped cast iron are preferable to unprotected metal as corrosion is particularly rapid in the moist,

[2] See also W. M. Spann, *Public Works,* February, 1955, p. 93.

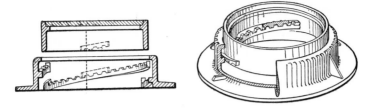

Fig. 6–7. Adjustable manhole frame and cover.

gas-laden air of the sewer. Forged aluminum is corrosion resistant, strong, and non-sparking. The step should have a firm grip in the wall, as a loose step is a source of danger.

6–4. Lampholes. A lamphole is an opening, constructed in a sewer, slightly larger than necessary to permit the insertion of a light into the sewer. Lampholes are sometimes used as a makeshift substitute for manholes to permit the inspection or the flushing of sewers, or for ventilating purposes. The Joint Committee (see Sect. 5–2) states: "Lampholes may be used only for special conditions and shall not be substituted for manholes nor installed at the end of laterals greater than 150 feet in length."

Lampholes should be constructed of 8-in. to 12-in. tile or cast-iron pipe. The lower section should be a cast-iron tee on a firm foundation, but if constructed of tile it should be reinforced with concrete

Fig. 6–8. Bolt to hold manhole cover in event of explosion. (Courtesy *Public Works Magazine.*)

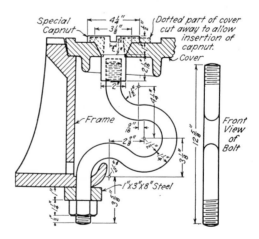

to take up the weight of the shaft. Lampholes are not commonly used on sewer systems on account of their lack of real usefulness.

6–5. Street inlets.[3] A street inlet is an opening in the street surface, usually in the gutter, designed to permit the passage of water from the street surface into the sewer. Many types of street inlets have been designed, some of which are illustrated in Figs. 6–9 and 6–10. The location of street inlets is discussed in Sects. 5–12 and 6–6. In the design of inlets, features affecting location, performance, convenience, and capacity include: (1) height of curb; (2) traffic density and traffic lane used; (3) position of inlet, whether vertical in the face of the curb, flat on the bottom of the gutter, or a combination of these two; (4) overall dimensions: height, width, and length; (5) direction of major axis of openings, whether parallel to or transverse to the direction of flow in the gutter; (6) roughness of the gutter surface, as n in Kutter's formula; (7) shape and slope of gutter at inlet, whether a continuous grade, or depressed in front of inlet, and depth and character of depression; (8) slope of gutter above, at, and immediately below the inlet; (9) use of deflectors or other devices in bottom of gutter to direct flow into the inlet;[4] (10) location, size, and shape of bars or grill; (11) cross-section of street, and crown of street surface; (12) character of street surface, particularly of pavement; and others. It is evident from all of these factors that a useful formula applicable to all street inlets cannot be devised in simple form.

Gratings with bars parallel to the direction of the flow of water in the gutter will admit water faster than transverse bars, but they will admit also more rubbish which may clog the sewer. Transverse bars, particularly in the bottom of the gutter, clog more quickly than parallel bars. A choice must sometimes be made between frequent cleaning of catch basin or sewer, and flooding of the street surface due to a clogged inlet. Openings between bars in the gutter bottom should exclude objects with the smallest dimension of about 2 in. The clear height between horizontal bars in the plane of the curb, may be 5 to 6 in. A length of 24 in. between supports for such horizontal bars is satisfactory. Shorter lengths are generally used in the bottom of the gutter. The use of gutter depressions, vanes, or other devices which break the continuity of the gutter planes may greatly increase the capacity of the gutter, but these devices may become a nuisance and danger to vehicular traffic.

[3] See also, *Public Works,* May, 1954, p. 106.
[4] See Wen-Hsuing Li, *S. and I.W.,* July, 1954, p. 836.

Inlets of low capacity which restrict the entrance of water and cause some flooding of the street surface are not always objectionable. They may permit the use of a smaller storm sewer than would otherwise be required, due partly to the smaller rate of entrance of water

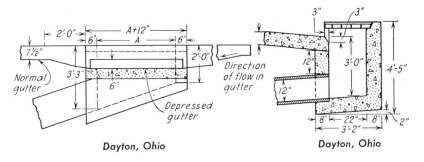

Fig. 6–9.   Street inlets at Dayton, Ohio.   (From *Public Works*, May, 1954, p. 106.)

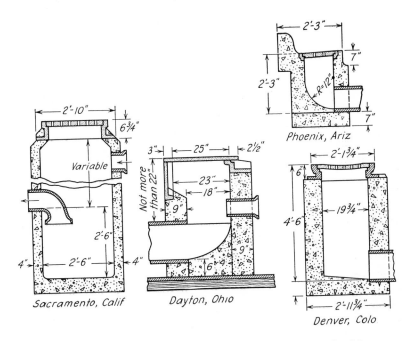

Fig. 6–10.   Street inlets and catch basins.   (From *Public Works*, May, 1954, p. 106.)

to the sewer, and partly to the increased time of concentration due to temporary storage of water on the street.

Capacities of inlets have been reported by many investigators.[5] Some capacities are shown in Table 6–1. Empirical formulas given by Li and others are

$$Q = L - \frac{\sqrt{S}}{n} + 2.8 \qquad (6\text{--}1)$$

$$Q = (0.2 \text{ to } 0.23)Ly_o\sqrt{gy_o} \qquad (6\text{--}2)$$

where Q = rate of flow into the inlet, cfs.
  L = length of inlet opening, ft.
  S = street grade.
  n = Manning's or Kutter's coefficient of roughness.
  g = acceleration due to gravity, 32.2 ft per sec².
  y_o = depth of flow in the gutter, ft.

Formula 6–1 is applicable to inlets in gutters without depression, with L between 2 and 8 ft, and Q between 3 and 6 cfs. The formula is not applicable if gutter depression or other conditions are changed. Formula 6–2 is applicable to a curb-opening inlet without depression.

The size of the pipe from the inlet to the catch basin or the sewer is usually 10 to 12 in. in diameter, or larger if required by the capacity of the inlet. Cast iron is most commonly used for the inlet structure, supported rigidly by the concrete curb and gutter. Concrete and vitrified clay make satisfactory outlet pipes.

6–6. Placing of street inlets. Inlets are usually placed near street corners to avoid unsightly breaks in pavement grade between street intersections. Where the blocks are so long that the rate of flow of storm water will overtax the capacity of the gutter, an intermediate inlet may be placed in the block.

The placing of an inlet at the intersection of the two curb lines at a corner results in a lower first cost, but on a heavily traveled street the inlet may be damaged or displaced. This position of the inlet forces pedestrians to cross the flowing stream of water in the gutter

---

[5] See W. W. Horner, *Mun. and County Eng.*, October, 1919, p. 147. L. W. Armstrong and G. S. Tapley, *Eng. News-Record*, July 9, 1931, p. 54. G. S. Tapley, *Trans. Am. Soc. Civil Engrs.*, Vol. 108, 1943, p. 409. N. W. Conner, *Eng. Exp. Sta. Bull.* 30, North Carolina State College, July, 1945. W. H. Li and others, *S. and I.W.*, January 1951, p. 34, June, 1951, p. 722, July, 1954, p. 836, August, 1954, p. 967, and July, 1956, p. 774. N. W. Nester and J. C. Guillou, *Public Works*, July, 1955, p. 96. *Public Works*, May, 1954, p. 106.

Table 6–1

CAPACITIES OF STREET INLETS

Flow in Cubic Feet per Second

(From N. W. Conner, *Eng. Exp. Sta. Bull.* 30,
North Carolina State College, July, 1945.)

Type of Inlet	Length along Gutter, ft	Slope of Gutter, per cent				
		0.5	1.0	2	4	8
A	2	0.343	0.314	0.224	0.152	0.101
A	5	1.25	1.005	0.840	0.655	0.461
A	7	. . .	. . .	1.39	1.093	0.769
A	*	0.25	0.23	0.20	0.16	0.11
B	2	0.941	0.780	0.549	0.300	0.159
E	2	. . .	1.471	1.206	0.852	0.462

Types of inlets: A. A rectangular inlet in vertical side of gutter, with bottom depressed 3 in. below bottom of gutter, and vertical height of 6 in. or more sufficient to cause no obstruction. No bars or grating across the gutter opening. B. An inlet like A, 2 ft long with a grating 2 ft by 2 ft square in bottom of gutter. Seven bars ¼ in. wide by 2½ in. thick, with openings normal to gutter. One middle bar parallel to thread of gutter. Sides of bars are vertical. E. Same as B except sides of bars normal to gutter are on 45° angle with vertical.

* The figures in this line represent the flow, in cubic feet per second, per foot length of a very long gutter. This represents maximum gutter capacity per foot length of gutter opening.

in wet weather. These objections can be overcome by having two inlets at each corner, set back far enough from the curb intersection to avoid interference with the cross walks.

6–7. Catch basins. Catch basins are used to interrupt the velocity of sewage before it enters the sewer, causing the deposition of suspended grit and sludge and the detention of floating rubbish which might enter and clog the sewer. A separate catch basin may be used for each inlet or, to save expense, the pipes from several inlets at a corner may discharge into the same catch basin.

Various types of catch basins are in successful use; some holding water in a trap, as at Sacramento, in Fig. 6–10, and others discharging directly into the sewer, as at Denver, in the same figure. Catch basins, such as that at Sacramento, are constructed like manholes with diameter from 2½ to 4 ft. Catch basins of this size will care for the inlets at the four corners of an intersection, each draining a city block. The construction of the catch basin and its cover follows the principles given for the construction of manholes. In unusual situations it may be necessary to install a larger basin, but too large a catch basin is undesirable because of the probable production of bad odors. The outlet from the catch basin may be submerged, as at Sacramento, as shown in Fig. 6–10, to prevent the odors escaping from the sewer into the street, but odors are often created in the catch basin. Some engineers arrange the trap so that it can be opened for observation down the sewer, thus combining the advantages of a manhole with the catch basin.

Catch basins are objectionable because: they furnish a breeding place for mosquitoes and other flying insects; the septic action in them produces offensive odors; on a combined sewer they permit the escape of offensive odors in dry weather when the water seal in the trap has evaporated; and the freezing of the water seal in the trap prevents the entrance of water into the sewer. The sole advantage lies in the prevention of the clogging of the sewers, but this may be sufficient to overbalance all the disadvantages. In general, catch basins should be provided where the drainage is into sewers in which the velocity of flow is less than 2 fps, or where the drainage is from an unimproved or macadamized street or from sandy country.

The trend of practice is away from the use of catch basins, except where deposition of grit is expected in the sewer without them.

6–8. Silt basins. Basins to interrupt the velocity of flow of sewage may be installed on storm sewers to provide a place for the deposition of grit, particularly on sewers where there are no catch basins. In order to promote the deposition of grit the velocity should not be greater than 2 fps, and to prevent the deposition of organic matter it should not be less than 1 fps. Silt basins are undesirable on separate or on combined sewers because of the inevitable collection of organic matter in them.

6–9. Storm-water standby tanks. The function of a storm-water standby tank is to serve as a storage basin to diminish the magnitude or the rate of storm flow; to serve as an equalizing basin to retain excess storm flow during a temporary restriction of the outlet [6] such as during high tide; to minimize pollution of receiving waters [7] by diminishing the frequency and volume of overflowing water; or to equalize the flow to a treatment plant. To accomplish these require-

[6] See also F. W. Cranem, *Eng. News-Record*, Dec. 22, 1949, p. 38.

[7] As at Seattle, Wash., to protect Lake Washington and bathing beaches.

ments it may be necessary to construct a relatively large, shallow reservoir. The tanks must be shallow because the bottom of the tank is placed high enough to permit the drainage of the contents back into the sewer by gravity when the excess flow has passed or the restriction at the outlet has been removed.

The openings between the sewer and the tank are placed above the elevation of the surface of the dry-weather flow in the sewer. In some tanks these openings are placed so that sewage will enter the tanks when the flow equals double the dry-weather flow. The capacity of a standby tank may be based on the principles of receiving wells or equalizing chambers stated in Sect. 12–8. Little is known concerning the required size of the opening between the tank and the sewer. A generous allowance of size above that required for an overflow weir, as discussed in Sect. 6–15, should be provided.

6–10. Grease and oil traps. Grease in sewers results in the formation of incrustations that are difficult to remove and cause a material loss in the capacity of the sewer. The presence of oil and gasoline has resulted in explosions. Grease, oil, and gasoline are removed by traps placed in the plumbing systems. Some cities have basins for the removal of these substances at the sewage-treatment works. One type of grease trap [8] for the drains from hotels, restaurants, or other large grease-producing establishments, is shown in Fig. 6–11.

A general feature of grease and oil traps is the provision of a channel which forces the sewage to flow downwards, beneath a free surface, in passing through the trap. Floating grease and oil rise to the surface on the inlet side of the trap, from which they may be cleaned through removable covers. It is essential that the cover be tightly sealed to avoid the escape of odors into the building, and it is preferable that the trap, if large, be placed outside of the building. The capacity of a trap should be about double that of the fixtures draining into it. Human excreta should not be discharged into the trap unless it is placed outside of and well removed from an occupied building. Grease traps are sometimes so large that they are constructed on somewhat the same principles as manholes and catch basins.

6–11. Flush tanks. Devices to hold water used in flushing sewers are called flush tanks. They are required only on combined and on separate sewers. They tend to prevent the clogging of sewers laid on flat grades, and they permit flatter grades than would be permissible

[8] See also *S. and I.W.*, September, 1955, p. 1098.

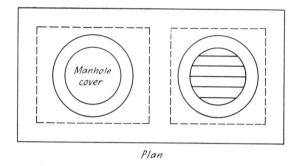

Plan

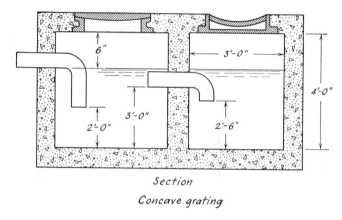

Section

Concave grating

Fig. 6–11. Combined grit chamber and oil trap for garages. Standard for South Dakota State Board of Health.

otherwise. Flush tanks should be placed at the upper ends of laterals in which the velocity of flow, when full, is less than 2 fps. The capacity of the tank or the volume of the dose is dependent on the diameter and slope of the sewer to be flushed. The method of computing the volume of water required for flushing is explained in Sect. 4–26, and information concerning the amount of water used is given in Sect. 13–10.

Flush tanks may be operated by hand or automatically, the latter being more common. Hand-operated tanks are similar to manholes so arranged that the inlet and outlet sewer openings can be plugged while the manhole or tank is filled with water, or only the outlet is closed and sewage may be allowed to accumulate in the approach sewer. When sufficient water or sewage has accumulated the outlet is opened and the sewer is flushed by the rush of water or sewage. A sluice gate, flap valve, or a specially fitted board is sufficient to fit over the mouth of the inlet and outlet during the filling of the tank. Such an arrangement has the advantage of being cheap, simple, and satisfactory, though somewhat crude. In some cases water is run into the flush tank at the same rate that it is discharged through the open outlet, a depth of 4 or 5 ft being maintained in the tank until the water passing the manhole below runs clean. Flushing-water, under a relatively high head, is sometimes obtained by means of tank wagons that are quickly emptied into the sewer from a canvas pipe dropped down a manhole. This method subjects a poorly constructed manhole to the danger of caving from the rush of water around the outlet. Precautions should be taken to minimize the risk by limiting the depth of water which may be accumulated. It can be limited by an overflow at a height of 4 or 5 ft above the bottom of the manhole, as shown in Fig. 6–12.

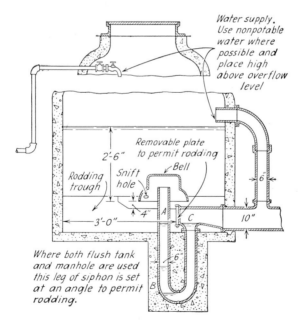

Fig. 6–12. Combination automatic flush tank and manhole. The long leg of the trap is set off of the sewer center line so that the removable plate is accessible.

Automatic flush tanks are constructed similar to manholes, but special care should be taken to make them watertight. The apparatus for providing the automatic discharge may operate either with or without moving parts, the second kind being preferable as it requires less attention and is not so likely to get out of order. In Fig. 6–12, the small pipe at the top provides the flushing-water to the tank. If this pipe is connected to a water main care should be taken to avoid a cross connection. This may be done by placing the inlet pipe well above the overflow from the flush tank. Water is allowed to flow continuously into the flush tank at such a rate as to fill it in the required interval between discharges. Flush tanks may be set to discharge about once a day.

The tank operates as follows: When the water rising in the tank reaches the bottom of the bell, air is trapped in the bell and prevented from escaping through the main trap by the water at A. As the water continues to rise in the tank the air in the bell is compressed, the water level at A is depressed, and water trickles from the siphon at C. The height of the water in the tank above the level of the water in the bell is equal at all times to the height of C above the lowering position of A. When A reaches the position of B a small amount of air is released through the short leg of the trap and a corresponding volume of water enters the bell. The head of water above the bell then becomes greater than the head of water in the short leg of the trap, resulting in the expulsion of the air from the long leg of the trap and the rapid discharge of the water in the tank through the siphon. The discharge continues until the siphonic action is broken by the admission of air when the level of water in the tank is lowered to the bottom of the bell. The size of the siphon is fixed by the diameter of the leg of the siphon.

When flush tanks are placed at the upper end of laterals, provision should be made for inspecting and cleaning the sewer by constructing a separate manhole, or by combining the features of a manhole and a flush tank in the same structure. Such a combination is shown in Fig. 6–12 from a design by Alexander Potter.

Engineers do not agree on the use of automatic flush tanks, some believing that they are a needless expense that can be avoided by hand flushing, and others feeling that a flush tank should be placed at the upper end of every lateral. These diverse opinions are a result of different experiences. It is quite certain that unnecessary and improperly maintained automatic flush tanks may be ineffective and wasteful of water.

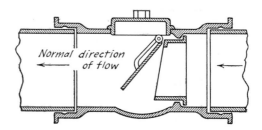

Fig. 6–13.   Backwater
valve for a small sewer.

*Normal direction
of flow*

6–12. Regulators.   Regulators are commonly used to divert a
portion of the flow of sewage in a combined or storm sewer in order
to prevent the overcharging of the sewer, or to regulate the rate of
flow to a sewage-treatment works.   Regulators in combined sewers
are sometimes designed to divert all flows greater than three to five
times the dry-weather flow, in order to avoid the discharge of too
strong a sewage into the overflow or relief sewer.   The Joint Committee (see Sect. 5–2) states: "Overflows from intercepting sewers
should not be permitted at points where they will adversely affect the
watercourse or the use of water therefrom."   Types of automatic
regulators include moving-part devices and regulators without moving
parts, such as the leaping weir and the overflow weir.

6–13. Moving-part regulators.   A moving-part regulator or
backwater valve is shown in Fig. 6–13.   In this type the flow of
sewage from a large sewer into a small tributary sewer may be prevented by the closing of the check valve.   When the valve is closed
sewage accumulates in the smaller sewer.   Although undesirable,
this action is preferable to backflow from the larger sewer.   There are
many variations in the details of float-controlled regulators.   Another
type of moving-part regulator is shown in Fig. 6–14.   Such regulators can be adjusted to fix the maximum rate of flow to a relief channel
or sewage-treatment plant, or during times of storm to cut off the
outlet to the dry-weather channel.   A type of moving-part regulator
used by the Milwaukee Sewerage Commission at the time of the construction of intercepting sewers is shown in Fig. 6–15.   A type depending on flash boards, and used at Buffalo, N. Y., is described by
F. W. Crane.[9]

Objections to all moving-part regulators are their need of attention
and their liability to clogging.   All mechanisms exposed to sewage
require frequent inspection to assure operation.

[9] *Eng. News-Record,* Dec. 22, 1949, p. 40.

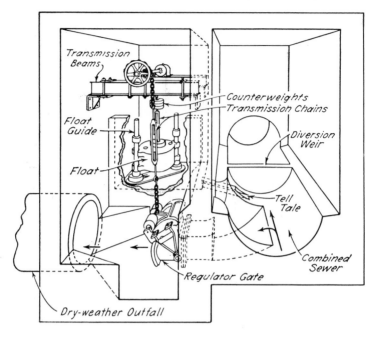

Fig. 6–14. Automatic sewer regulator. Brown and Brown, Type A.

6–14. Leaping weirs. A leaping weir is formed by a gap in the invert of a sewer through which the dry-weather flow falls and over which a portion or all of the storm flow leaps. A leaping weir in a sewer in Seattle, Wash., is illustrated in Fig. 6–16. Leaping weirs have the advantage of operating as regulators without moving parts, but they offer the disadvantage of concentrating grit in the low-flow channel. During a storm all flow may leap the gap, stopping flow in the low-flow channel with an undesirable effect on the sewage-treatment plant being fed by that channel. The falling stream may be made to pass through a sloping rack or grate to divert stones and

Fig. 6–15. Moving-part sewer regulators without float. Milwaukee type.

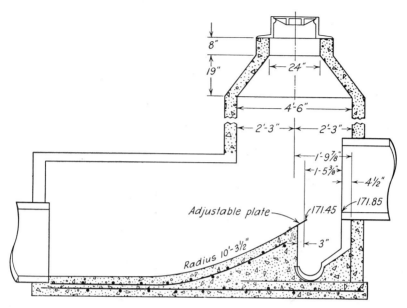

Fig. 6–16. Leaping weir. Delridge trunk sewer, Seattle, Wash.

other falling objects from the intercepter. The grating should be sloped steeply to prevent paper and leaves from sticking to it, and a channel should be provided to divert drippings from the grating back to the dry-weather intercepter.

The rate of flow at which sewage will fall through the gap can be adjusted by the relative positions of the upper and lower lips of the weir shown in Fig. 6–16. These points fall either on the inside or the outside curve of the falling stream, as indicated in Fig. 6–17. Although the center of gravity of the stream presumably falls in a parabolic path, the curves of the inside and outside surfaces of the falling stream do not. Tests made by one of the authors on a leaping weir, in which the water leaped from the smooth spigot end of a standard vitrified-clay pipe, led to the conclusion that the paths of the surfaces of the falling stream may be expressed as:

For the outside or upper surface

$$x = 0.53V^{2/3} + y^{4/7} \qquad (6\text{–}3)$$

For the inside or lower surface

$$x = 0.30V^{4/7} + y^{3/4} \qquad (6\text{–}4)$$

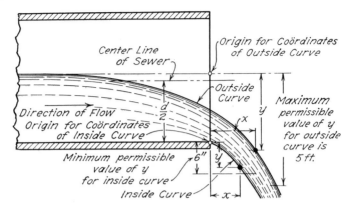

Fig. 6–17. Coordinates of curves for leaping-weir formulas.

in which V is the velocity of approach in fps, and x and y are in ft, being measured as indicated in Fig. 6–17. These expressions are limited as follows: to diameters less than 10 ft; to depths of flow in the approach sewer of less than 14 in.; to slopes of less than 0.025; to velocities of approach between 1 and 10 fps; to ordinates for the inside curve between 6 in. and 5 ft; and to ordinates for the outside curve less than 5 ft.

The following problem illustrates the use of these formulas.

Problem. If the gap in the leaping weir shown in Fig. 6–16 is made 20½ in., the vertical distance between lips is 0.6 ft, the slope of the 36-in. approach sewer is 0.0006, and n is 0.015, what is the maximum rate at which water will fall into the dry-weather intercepter?

Solution. It will be assumed that the maximum rate of interception will occur when the upper surface of the falling stream touches the "lower lip" of the weir. In this case $x = 1.71$ ft. Hence

$$0.53^{0.67} + y^{0.57} = 1.71$$

Since V and y are dependent on each other the solution is completed by trial. Let it be assumed that the depth of flow in the approach sewer is 0.6 ft. Then

$$y = 0.6 + 0.6 = 1.2 \text{ ft}$$

The velocity of flow when the approach sewer is full, from the diagrams in Chapter 4, is 2.0 fps, and the full rate of flow is 14.5 cfs.

When the depth of flow is 0.6 ft, the partly full value of V is $0.58 \times 2.0 = 1.16$.

Then $x = (0.53)(1.16)^{0.67} + (1.2)^{0.57} = 0.59 + 1.12 = 1.71$

This checks the value of x so that the assumed depth of flow is correct.

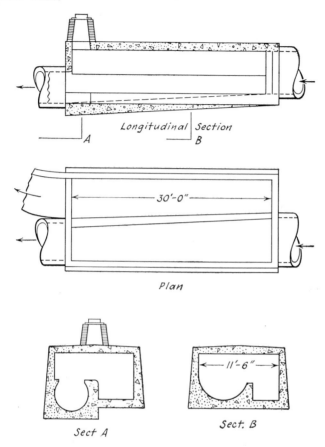

Fig. 6–18. Overflow weir in North Trunk sewer, Seattle, Wash.

Solving for rate of flow under partly full conditions, as explained in Chapter 4, the rate of flow at 0.6 ft depth is

$$(0.09 \times 14.5) = 1.3 \text{ cfs} \qquad \textit{Answer.}$$

6–15. Overflow weirs.[10] An overflow weir is formed by an opening in the side of a sewer high enough to permit the discharge of excess flow into a relief channel and to permit the dry-weather flow to continue to another outlet. It operates successfully as a regulator without moving parts, is simple to construct, and is widely used for regu-

[10] See also R. G. Tyler and others, *Jour. Boston Soc. Civil Engrs.*, March, 1929, p. 118.

lating flow in sewers. A weir of this type in Seattle, Wash., is shown in Fig. 6–18.

The capacity of an overflow weir is affected by: the shape of the approach channel; the depth of water on the upstream edge of the weir h_1; the depth of water on the downstream edge of the weir h_2; the length of the weir l; the velocity of the sewage approaching the weir, V; and the angle in a plane parallel to the water surface that the edge of the weir makes with the invert of the channel of approach. The height of the weir above the invert should be subtracted from the depth of flow above or below the weir to give the values of h_1 and h_2, respectively. Various formulas, some empirical and some hypothetical, have been devised to express the relationship of these factors. The formulas should be used with understanding of their limitations since they have not been widely checked in practice.

A formula devised by Babbitt [11] is in the form

$$l = 2.3Vd \log (h_1/h_2) \qquad (6\text{–}5)$$

in which d is the diameter of the pipe, other nomenclature is stated above, and the units are in feet and seconds. Results are limited to a weir with a sharp edge placed as an element of the inside cylindrical surface of the pipe, where the distance of the weir above the bottom of the pipe is between $d/4$ and $d/2$. The usefulness of the formula is limited because it was devised for pipes between 18 and 24 in. in diameter and the depth of flow above the weir should not exceed $3d/4$.

Ridett [12] reports the following formulas for overflow weirs:

Smith and Coleman: [13]

$$Q = 1.67Wl^{0.72}y_1^{1.645} \qquad (6\text{–}6)$$

Parmley:
$$l = \frac{WV}{1.67}\left[\frac{1}{\sqrt{h_2}} - \frac{1}{\sqrt{h_1}}\right] \qquad (6\text{–}7)$$

Lea:
$$Q = 2.22lH^{1.5} \qquad (6\text{–}8)$$

Fruhling:
$$Q = 4lH^{1.5} \qquad (6\text{–}9)$$

where additional nomenclature is H = head over sill; Q = rate of discharge over the weir; V = average velocity of flow in the main sewer; and W = width of the channel, if rectangular, at the weir, or the

[11] An unpublished Master of Science thesis at the University of Illinois, 1917.
[12] J. M. Ridett, *Surveyor*, March 1, 1946, p. 167.
[13] D. Smith and G. S. Coleman, *Inst. Civil Engrs.*, 1923.

equivalent width if the channel is curved in transverse cross-section. Units are in feet and seconds.

The lack of agreement among these formulas is emphasized by computations by Ridett. He shows that under similar conditions the lengths of weirs required by the different formulas to permit the same discharge may vary by more than 400 per cent, the Fruhling formula giving the least and the Parmley formula the greatest length of weir. Since none of the formulas, including the author's, has been widely tested in practical installations, each should be applied only with full knowledge of its limitations and uncertainties. For example:

Problem. Let it be desired to determine the length of an overflow weir in a circular sewer 24 in. in diameter, in which the height of the weir above the bottom of the channel is 8 in., the slope of the sewer both above and below the weir is 0.01, $n = 0.015$, and the rate of discharge over the weir is 5.5 cfs when the rate of flow in the sewer above the weir is 15 cfs.

Solution. The full capacity of the sewer is 19 cfs with a full velocity of 6.0 fps. The depth of flow when the quantity flowing is 15 cfs is, closely, 1.33 ft. Hence, $h_1 = 1.33 - 0.67 = 0.66$ ft. When the rate of flow below the weir is 9.5 cfs, the depth of flow is 1.0 ft and $h_2 = 0.33$ ft. The velocity of flow when the rate of flow is 15 cfs is $1.1 \times 6.0 = 6.6$ fps.

Substituting in formula 6–5

$$l = 2.3 \times 6.6 \times 2 \times \log (0.66/0.33) = 9.1 \text{ ft}$$

Various expedients may be used to secure the desired overflow in a chamber shorter than is called for by the preceding formulas. Weirs may be constructed on both sides of the sewer; they may be set at an angle with the channel; they may be set on the outer edge of a curved channel; or the effective length of the weir may be increased by crenelating or zigzagging the weir edge in plan. At Bolton, England, a weir of the last-named type was built with an effective length of 141 ft in a net length of 23 ft.[14] No general formula applicable to such conditions is available.

6–16. Measurement of rate of flow.[15] The rate of flow of sewage can be measured by standard hydraulic devices and procedures using calibrated constants. However, it is essential that no device shall offer such an obstacle to the flow of sewage that suspended or floating solids are caught or restrained, so that the flow is obstructed. Devices

---

[14] G. Holden, *Surveyor*, Dec. 24, 1937, p. 797.

[15] See also J. M. Betz, *S. and I.W.*, November, 1952, p. 1325; W. H. Brown and G. E. Symons, *S. and I.W.*, Vol. 27, 1955, pp. 148, 283, and 449; and G. E. Riepe, *Water and Sewage Works,* June 1, 1955, p. R-77.

used include gravimetric and volumetric containers, orifices, weirs, pipe bends, nozzles, parabolic flumes,[16] velocity meters, Palmer-Bowlus flumes, and Parshall flumes. Sharp-edged orifices and small orifices, nozzles that are not smooth, notched weirs, and moving-part meters will probably be unsatisfactory as measuring devices for low rates of flow of unscreened sewage. Where rates of flow are large enough to maintain self-cleansing velocities, orifices and weirs may be used, especially broad-crested or ogee spillways. Devices that will show the head loss across an orifice or the depth of flow above a weir, are used to indicate the *rate* of flow. Integrating mechanisms are required to show the *volume* of flow that has passed between two times of observation.

The rate of flow of sewage can be determined from observations of the hydraulic parameters of open-channel flow and substitution in such formulas as Manning's; or the rate of flow can be determined by means of a depth gage placed in the sewer in which the rate of flow has been calibrated against the depth. Another method applicable to a sewer whose hydraulic elements are known is to measure the velocity of flow by float observations, and the depth of flow at any point. The product of the velocity and the cross-sectional area at the point is the volumetric rate of flow at that point. It is to be noted that in many of these methods of measurement it is necessary to locate the elevation of the surface of the sewage.

The rate of flow of sewage has been determined in some cases by dilution methods.[17] These involve the introduction into the sewage of a known amount of chemical, such as sodium chloride, manganous sulphate, or other suitable substance. The amount of dilution is determined by analysis and the rate of flow is computed.

6–17. Liquid-surface indicators. The location of a liquid surface is indicated by various devices such as floats, pressure cells, pneumatic tubes, and floatless electrical devices that depend on a magnetic field generated by an electric current passing through the liquid.

An installation of a float to indicate the depth of liquid flowing over a weir is shown in Fig. 6–19. The float is in a non-turbulent location and is free from interfering floating matter. A float and cable are shown at A in Fig. 6–20. A pressure cell is shown at B in the figure. The cell is closed at the bottom by a flexible diaphragm. The instrument is sensitive and can transmit information without interference

---

[16] See F. L. Sommer, *Water and Sewage Works,* September, 1952, p. 377.

[17] W. A. Cawley, *Proc. Am. Soc. Civil Engrs.,* Paper 1084, October, 1956.

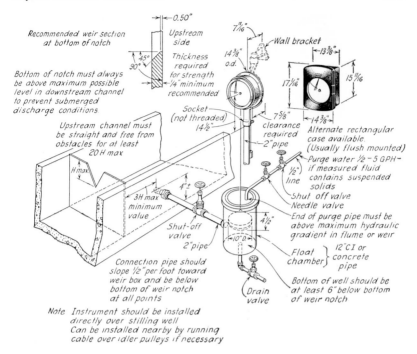

Fig. 6–19. Installation of float device to indicate liquid-surface level, showing weir installation. (Courtesy The Foxboro Co.)

by moderate turbulence or from normal floating matter in sewage. The cell may be as much as 500 ft away from the indicating gage. A set-up of a continuously purged tube is shown at C in the figure. Air or gas, such as carbon dioxide or nitrogen, flows continuously and slowly from the submerged tube, as indicated. Variations of water surface elevation are transmitted by changes in gas pressure in the bubble pipe and are indicated on the gage.

The Ohmmeter [18] measures depth of flow as the distance between an electrode resting on the bottom of the channel and a movable electrode which slides up and down on the handle of the instrument and indicates electrically the point of contact with the liquid surface. Another device [19] measures the depth of sewage in terms of the compression of carbon dioxide gas escaping from a cylinder with a sub-

---

[18] See J. D. Eye, *Water and Sewage Works*, June 15, 1956, p. R-68.

[19] *Ibid.*, July, 1954, p. 326.

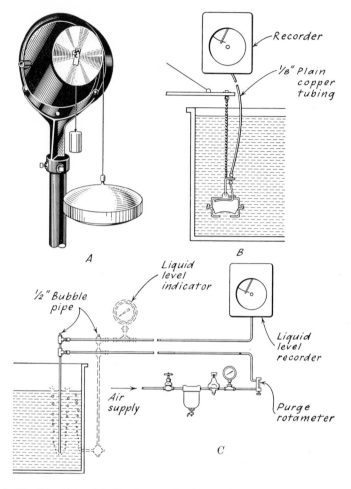

Fig. 6–20. Liquid-level indicating mechanisms. *A*. Float and cable. *B*. Pressure cell. *C*. Purged air or gas tube. (Courtesy The Foxboro Co.)

merged outlet. Floatless, liquid-level indicating devices are preferable to float-controlled devices.

Liquid surface-level, or depth, information can be transmitted mechanically, electrically, pneumatically, or hydraulically. The action of floats and of mechanical transmission is limited by friction and inertia to slow movements and to short distances; hydraulic transmission is limited to a distance of less than about 100 ft; and pneumatic devices to less than about 200 ft. Electrical devices are unlimited by distance or by speed of vertical movements of the surface. Hydraulic and pneumatic transmitting tubes must be installed to avoid gas, vapor, and liquid traps, and to avoid difficulties from freezing.

If only maximum or minimum elevations of the surface of the sewage are to be recorded, without the construction of a special float chamber, a maximum- or minimum-flow gage can be used. The gage shows the maximum by retaining in it sewage at the highest elevation reached. A minimum-flow gage consists of an open-end vertical tube submerged in the sewage with its upper end in the air. A valve at the upper end admits air but does not release it.

6–18. Weirs. Any type of weir may be used, within the limits stated in Sect. 6–16, to measure the rate of flow, provided the weir is located to avoid turbulence, disturbing velocities, and obstructions lodging on its crest. Most weirs are not reliable in the measurement of low flows unless the edge of the weir is free from obstructions when the observation is made of the head on the weir. Leaping weirs have been used to estimate the rate of flow, applying formula 6–3. Where conditions are beyond the limits of the formula, an approximation of the rate of flow has been made by assuming the outside curve of the falling stream, as shown in Fig. 6–17, is a parabola in the form

$$y = a + bx^2 \qquad\qquad (6\text{–}10)$$

where y and x are as in formula 6–3.

> $a =$ vertical distance at any point on the outside curve below the origin of coordinates.
>
> $b =$ a constant determined by the calibration of the weir.

6–19. Velocity meters. An installation of a Venturi meter is shown in Fig. 6–21. The tube is sometimes made eccentric, with its invert on a continuous, straight line, in order to prevent the accumulation of solids in the tube on the upstream side of the throat. Clogging of the pressure tubes in the indicating mechanism is avoided by discharging a small stream of clean water through them into the sewer. The clean water supply must not be connected to a potable water supply, in order to avoid the dangers of a cross connection. The effluent from a secondary, sewage-treatment plant may be satisfactory for this purpose.

A magnetic flow meter [20] is shown and partly described in Fig. 6–22. Among the advantages claimed for it are no restriction to flow, in-

[20] See also *S. and I.W.*, April, 1957, p. 154a.

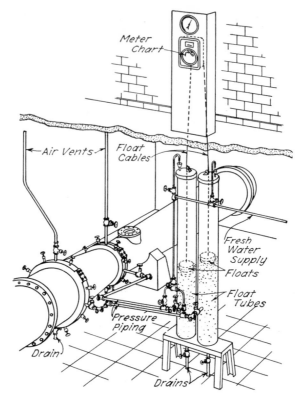

Meter
Chart

Air Vents
Float
Cables

Fresh
Water
Supply

Floats

Float
Tubes

Pressure
Piping

Drain

Drains

Fig. 6–21.   Float-controlled measuring, indicating, and recording device for a
Venturi meter.   (Courtesy Bailey Meter Co.)

stantaneous response to changes in rate of flow, sensitivity and accuracy, avoidance of maintenance, linear flow readings that can be
totalized, and installation that is simple and low in cost.

6–20. Parshall flume [21] and Palmer-Bowlus flume.[22]   The Parshall flume (see also Sect. 18–9), illustrated in Fig. 6–23B, is an open,
constricted channel so designed that the rate of flow is a function of

[21] See also R. L. Parshall, *Bull.* 336, Colorado Experiment Station, Fort Collins, Colo.; and *Trans. Am. Soc. Civil Engrs.*, Vol. 89, 1926, p. 841.   C. G. Richardson, *Jour. New Eng. Water Works Assoc.*, March, 1934.   G. D. Holmes,
Water Works and Sewerage, May, 1933.   J. Tarrant, *Water Works and Sewerage*,
June, 1945, p. R-191.   N. L. Nussbaumer, *Water Works and Sewerage*, October,
1935.

[22] H. K. Palmer and F. D. Bowlus, *Trans. Am. Soc. Civil Engrs.*, Vol. 101, 1936,
p. 1195; and J. H. and R. G. Ludwig, *S. and I.W.*, September, 1951, p. 1096.

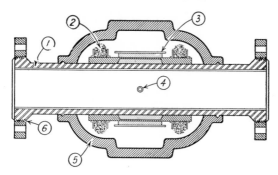

Fig. 6–22. A magnetic flow meter. 1. Non-magnetic, stainless-steel tube, lined with insulating material. 2. Copper-wire coils to produce uniform magnetic field. 3. Core, to focus magnetic field normal to flowing liquid. 4. Insulated, corrosion-resistant electrodes. 5. Cover. 6. End connections. (Courtesy The Foxboro Co.)

the depth of flow above the throat of the flume. Among the advantages of the flume as a measuring device may be included an insignificant loss of head, measurements can be made in open-channel flow, the flume is self-cleansing, and there are no moving parts. If the backing-up of the water from the lower channel causes a hydraulic jump, the flow is said to be "submerged," H_b/H_a being the ratio of submergence. Where no submergence occurs the flow is "free." The flume should be designed to prevent submergence from becoming so great as to restrict the discharge through the flume. The ratio of submergence for a flume with a 6-in.-wide throat should not exceed 50 per cent, and for wider throats up to 3 ft it should not exceed 70 per cent. For flumes with throat width between 1.0 ft and 10 ft the rate of flow is

$$Q = 4WH_a^{1.522W^{0.026}} \qquad (6\text{--}11)$$

where Q is the flow in cfs, W is the width of the throat in ft, and H_a is the depth of flow in the channel, above the throat, in ft. A problem in the design of a control flume for a special purpose is solved in Sect. 18–9.

A Palmer-Bowlus flume [23] is an adaptation of a Venturi meter for use in sewers. Its outstanding advantage is that it requires no drop along its bottom profile. The control flume consists of upstream and downstream sections, as shown in Fig. 6–23A. The downstream con-

[23] *Ibid.*

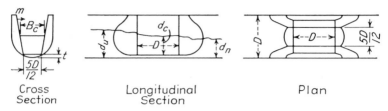

Cross
Section

Longitudinal
Section

Plan

A. Palmer-Bowlus flume. (See *Trans. Am. Soc. Civ. Engrs.,* Vol. 101, p. 1195.)

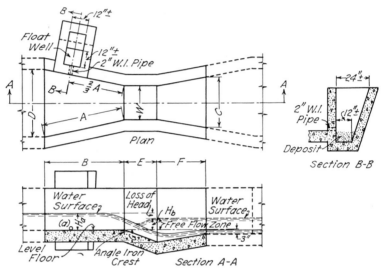

B. Parshall flume. (From *Water Works and Sewerage,* July, 1936, p. 175.)

Fig. 6–23. Two types of measuring flumes.

trol section backs up the water above the flume in such a manner that
the rate of flow can be calibrated in terms of the upstream depth.
Formulas and methods for the application of such flumes are described by Ludwig.[23]

6–21. Pipe elbows and constrictions. An elbow, or other con-
striction in a pipe, can be used successfully as a fluid-flow measuring
device.[24] Since a pipe bend offers no obstruction that might cause

---

[24] S. Jacobs and F. A. Sooy, *Jour. Elec. Power Gas,* July 22, 1911, p. 72; D. L.
Yarnell and F. A. Nagler, *Trans. Am. Soc. Civil Engrs.,* Vol. 100, 1935, p. 1018;
and W. M. Lansford, *Bull.* 289, Engineering Experiment Station, University of
Illinois, 1936.

clogging it should be satisfactory for measuring the rate of flow of
sewage. The expression for the velocity of flow around a bend is

$$V = Kh^{\frac{1}{2}} \tag{6-12}$$

where h is the difference in pressure between the inner and outer edge
of the bend, K is a constant that must be determined by calibration,
and the units are feet and seconds. Tests by Lansford [24] indicate
the K varies from about 7.0 for a 1-in., short-radius, steel elbow, to
about 5.0 for a bend in a 24-in. spiral-riveted, steel pipe with segmental elbows, with a ratio of diameter of pipe to radius of bend
equal to about 0.8.

6-22. Tracing sewage flow. The flow of sewage may be traced:
(1) to determine the velocity of flow in conduits, (2) to determine
the detention period in tanks, (3) to study the pollution of underground water, (4) to provide information in stream-pollution studies
and in the disposal of sewage by dilution, and for other purposes.
Methods used to trace the flow of sewage involve the use of aniline
dyes such as fluorescein, eosine, and uranin; soluble chemicals such
as sodium chloride, surface and submerged floats; radium, or its first
disintegration product, radon; [25] and radioactive isotopes. [26]

When fluorescein is dissolved in water it appears as a brilliant, pale
green, detectable by the naked eye in concentrations as low as 0.025
mg/l and, with the aid of a colorimeter or spectrophotometer, in concentrations as low as 0.001 mg/l. The use of dyes and soluble chemicals is not altogether satisfactory because of reaction between the
chemical solutions with the sewage, or the sinking of the solutions
because of their greater specific gravity. The use of radium to increase the concentration of radon in raw sewage, treatment-plant
effluent, or other polluted liquid to 40 to 90×10^{-15} curies per milli-
liter, has been found practicable in the study of infiltration into
sewers, and in the diffusion of sewage at outfalls. [27] Rubidium[86] is a
satisfactory radioactive isotope to use in tracing the flow of sewage
because of its relatively convenient half-life of 19.5 days. Iodine[131]
has been used also.

[25] See also T. G. Bullen and W. F. O'Connor, *S. and I.W.*, April, 1954, p. 497,
and May, 1954, p. 627.

[26] See also H. A. Thomas, Jr., and R. S. Archibald, *Trans. Am. Soc. Civil
Engrs.*, Vol. 77, Paper 84, 1951. G. A. Truesdale, *Inst. Mun. Engr.*, October,
1953, p. 232. W. Seamann, *S. and I.W.*, March, 1956, p. 296. H. Ambrose and
others, *S. and I.W.*, January, 1957, p. 24. Wm. Roman before Pacific Northwest
Sewage and Industrial Waste Association, October, 1957.

[27] See also G. A. Truesdale, *Jour. Inst. Sewage Purif.*, Vol. 97, 1953.

6–23. Siphons. True siphons and inverted siphons or depressed sewers are used in sewerage practice. A true siphon is a sewer that flows full with the flow line above the hydraulic grade line, the pressure in the sewer being less than atmospheric. An inverted siphon or depressed sewer is a sewer that runs full under gravity flow at a pressure above atmospheric in the sewer, the profile being depressed below the hydraulic grade line. Since the inverted siphon is in no sense a true siphon, an attempt has been made, but with indifferent success, to popularize the term *depressed sewer* for this device. In sewerage practice the word *siphon* has come to mean an inverted siphon, unless otherwise qualified. Siphons, both true and inverted, are used in sewers to pass over or under obstacles such as buried pipes, subways, and stream beds. They should be used only where other means of passing an obstacle in the line of the sewer are impracticable, as the siphon is an appurtenance requiring considerable attention for maintenance.

True siphons are seldom used, because to operate continuously the siphon must flow full and accumulated gas must be removed continuously from the crown of the siphon in order to maintain the necessary vacuum. Since the rate of flow of sewage fluctuates, it is difficult to control the flow so that the true siphon may function satisfactorily.

An inverted siphon usually consists of two or more pipes, the smallest of which carries the dry-weather flow, whereas the others carry additional increments of flow, all being designed to maintain a minimum velocity of about 3 fps for dry-weather flow, with somewhat higher velocities for larger rates of flow. Deposition of grit and sludge is a common cause of difficulty in an inverted siphon. The design should be such, therefore, as to maintain in it as high a velocity as feasible, and to permit the cleaning and flushing of the pipes in the siphon.

The siphon may be constructed as a U with vertical or inclined legs. If the pipes are small, vertical legs are preferred, as they can be placed in a manhole, or the shafts of the manhole may provide the channel of flow. If the pipes are placed in the shafts of the manhole, a cleanout should be provided at the bottom so that the pipe can be rodded through after the sewage has been pumped from the pipe. A siphon under a subway in New York City is shown in Fig. 6–24. This siphon consists of one 14-in., cast-iron pipe, and two 4½-ft concrete pipes. The smallest pipe passes horizontally between cleanout manholes on each side of the subway. No cleanouts are

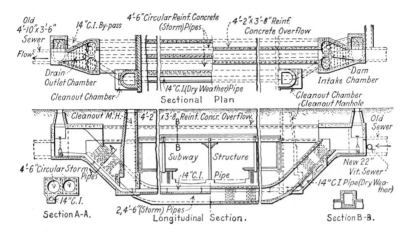

Fig. 6–24. Sewer siphon under New York subway. (*Eng. News*, Vol. 76, 1916, p. 443.)

provided on the larger pipes because they carry storm water at relatively high velocities, and the pipes are large enough to be entered
by a man if it is necessary to have them cleaned. Occasionally a grit
chamber is placed at the upper end of a siphon to prevent the deposition of grit in the siphon. The pipes of a siphon should be constructed
of cast iron or of reinforced concrete, and they should be heavy enough
so that they will not float when empty and surrounded by ground
water.

6–24. Siphon design. In the design of an inverted siphon three
conditions may be met: (1) the elevation of the inlet or the outlet is
fixed and a minimum loss of head is to be provided, commensurate
with the maintenance of a scouring velocity; (2) the elevation of the
inlet and outlet and a minimum velocity are fixed; or (3) the elevation
of the inlet or of the outlet is fixed but there is no limitation on the
head loss other than to provide a scouring or higher velocity. The
Joint Committee states: "Inverted siphons should have not less than
two barrels with a minimum pipe size not less than 6 inches."

As an illustration of design under the third condition:

Let it be desired to conduct sewage past the subway shown in Fig. 6–24.
It will be assumed that the flow is from right to left, and that the sewer is
to be cut to permit the construction of the siphon under the subway. The
old sewer is 3 ft 6 in. wide by 4 ft 10 in. high, with a full capacity of 150 cfs.
The dry-weather flow is to be 3 cfs and is to be carried in a cast-iron pipe

which has a Hazen and Williams coefficient of 100. The remaining flow is to be divided equally between two circular, concrete pipes, with $n = 0.013$. The elevation of the invert of the sewer at the upper manhole is 98.07. The horizontal distance between manholes is 175 ft, and the length of each pipe in the siphon is 187 ft.

Determine the sizes of the pipes necessary to maintain a velocity of 3 fps for the dry-weather flow, and for each of the other two pipes to carry half of the remaining flow, on the slope available. Determine also the maximum velocity in the larger two pipes.

Solution. 1. Determine the diameter of the dry-weather pipe. The nearest size of pipe to carry 3 cfs at a velocity of 3 ft per sec is 14 in.

2. Determine the head loss in the dry-weather pipe. This consists of: (1) the loss at entrance, (2) the loss due to friction in the bends, (3) the loss due to friction in "straight" pipe, and (4) the loss due to the higher velocity required in the dry-weather pipe.

They are computed as follows: If the head loss in each 45° bend is equal to the head loss in a piece of pipe 40 diameters long, then the total loss is equal to

$$0.14 + \frac{0.6V^{1.85}}{1{,}000d^{1.17}} 80d + \frac{113V^{1.85}}{1{,}000d^{1.17}} + 0.14$$

$$0.14 + 0.36 + 0.72 + 0.14 = 1.36$$

The elevation at the lower manhole will be

$$98.07 - 1.36 = 96.71$$

3. Determine the head loss in the remaining pipes, which can be expressed as: loss at entrance $= V^2/2g$; loss in bends $= (0.6V^{1.85}/1{,}000d^{1.17})80d$; loss in straight pipe, by Manning's formula $= 187V^24^{4/3}/114^2d^{4/3}$; and the loss due to turbulence $= V^2/2g$. Since $V = 4Q/\pi d^2$ and Q, in each of the two remaining pipes, $= (150 - 3)/2 = 73.5$, then $V = 4 \times 73.5/\pi d^2 = 93.4/d^2$ and the total head loss is

$$\frac{93.4^2}{2gd^4} + \frac{0.0006}{d^{1.17}} \left(\frac{93.4}{d^2}\right)^{1.85} 80d + \frac{187 \times 4^{1.33} \times 93.4^2}{115^2 d^{1.33} d^4} + \frac{93.4^2}{2gd^4} = 136$$

It is found by trial that $d = 4$ ft 6 in., closely, and hence $V = 93.4/d^2 = 4.6$ fps.

It is necessary to make an arrangement in the inlet chamber to divert the different rates of flow into the various pipes of the siphon and in the outlet chamber to prevent the low rates of flow from backing into the larger pipes, causing deposits in them. It is desirable also to provide a method of cutting off the flow from any pipe for convenience in cleaning and inspection.

6–25. Junction chambers. A junction chamber, as the name implies, is a chamber constructed to facilitate the junction of two

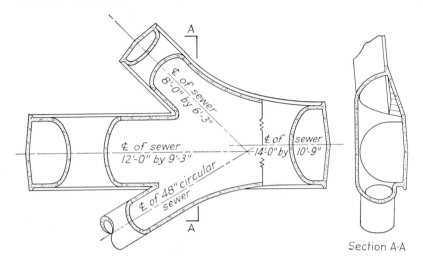

Fig. 6–25. Junction chamber for three sewers.

or more sewers. The name is applied to the junction of sewers large enough for a man to enter.

Some of the principles to be considered in the design of junction chambers include: the inverts of the joining sewers should be placed at such elevations that the normal flow lines are at the same elevation in all sewers; the sewers should approach the junction on steep grades so that when one is flowing deeper than others entering the junction, the backing-up in the other sewers will extend but a short distance up them; the velocity of flow should not be decreased and turbulence should be avoided in order to prevent sedimentation, the release of odoriferous gases, and loss of head; and the sewers should approach the junction on long-radius curves, tangent to each other at the junction chamber, in order to minimize turbulence. Sections through a junction chamber are shown in Fig. 6–25.[28]

It is difficult, if not impossible, to harmonize all of the preceding principles in one junction chamber. All that can be expected is to meet them as nearly as local conditions will permit. It is inevitable that one sewer will back up into another, and that there will be turbulence and loss of head. Where the turbulence is great, the head losses will be appreciable and should be allowed for in design. The head losses can be computed by the methods given in Sect. 4–27. The

[28] See also Paul Hansen, *Eng. News,* Oct. 14, 1909, p. 416.

construction of a junction involves appreciable expense that should be kept to a minimum. The cost may be reduced to some extent by using a flat roof, obviating the necessity for expensive concrete forms or brickwork.

6–26. Outfall sewers and outlets. Among the features to be considered in the design of a sewer outlet are: (1) the location to avoid offense to sight or smell; (2) the protection of the mouth of the sewer against swift currents, water traffic, floating debris, heavy waves, or other hazards which might damage the structure; and (3) the prevention of backing-up of water into the sewer if the outlet is on a flat grade. The ideal location for an outlet is on a swiftly running stream with currents that will always carry away floating and settleable matter that has not been removed by treatment.

If the outlet is completely submerged, provision should be made for ventilation and to relieve air pressures above and below atmospheric, which might otherwise be created in the sewer above a water-sealed outlet. The submergence of the invert to the critical depth of flow will create better flow conditions and will avoid backing-up of sewage until the depth at the outlet exceeds the critical depth.

To prevent local nuisance the mouth of the sewer may be submerged in a current that will carry away sewage without leaving dangerous deposits. If the sewage has been completely treated before discharge into a stream or body of water no special precautions need be taken to prevent deposits at the outlet. If, however, it has not been treated, no degree of submergence will avoid *sleek* (sometimes called *slick*). This is a thin, oily film that gives a characteristic appearance to the surface of the water into which the sewage or oily waste is discharged. Multiple, submerged outlets avoid too great a concentration of sewage in one spot. Such outlets may be provided by placing open T or Y branches in the outfall sewer or by constructing two or more outfall sewers. In a wide stream multiple outlets across the channel will enhance distribution and diffusion. The outlet for the Passaic Valley outfall in New York harbor spreads out like a crow's foot, with 150 nozzles at a depth of about 40 ft. The Moon Island outlet in Boston Harbor is equipped with tanks which hold the sewage until ebb tide, when it is discharged into the outgoing currents at a depth of 30 to 50 ft. It is generally considered that the deeper the submergence, the greater is the probability of satisfactory disposal. This is especially true in sea water where sewage is lighter and, rising through the sea water, is more thoroughly mixed and dispersed. The distance apart of multiple, submerged outlets has been made three to ten times the depth of submergence.

Studies of currents should be made with floats, dyes, chemicals, or radioactive tracers [29] to reveal the distance from the outlet at which floating sewage solids may be stranded, and to indicate where and to what extent sludge banks will be deposited. A study of currents at sewer outlets requires special technique and equipment.[30] Sludge banks deposited while submerged are especially obnoxious if periodically exposed to air. Some knowledge of limnology may be desirable for the intelligent location of a sewer outlet.

Among undesirable locations for sewer outlets may be included a quiescent body of water above a dam; above a falls or white-water rapids where odor may result at the point of turbulence and deposits may occur in the quieter reaches below; low land alternately submerged and exposed; streams whose currents may reverse, carrying sewage back to shore or upstream; tidal estuaries or small bays that are insufficiently flushed when the tide changes; and lakes where currents or winds will either continuously or occasionally drive sewage shoreward.

Protection of outlets from swift currents, water traffic, and so forth, requires knowledge of local conditions; and after the site of the outlet works is decided on, possibly the construction of walls, embankments, and other protective structures may be called for. Because of the hazards to which exposed outfall sewers are subject, they should be constructed of cast iron, concrete, or other strong, durable material.

To avoid the backing-up of water the sewer should approach the outlet on a steep grade. If this is not possible, a tide gate may be placed on the outlet, somewhat as shown in Fig. 6–26. Where the surface of the receiving body of water fluctuates widely a dry-weather and a storm-water outlet may be designed somewhat as shown in Fig. 6–27A. A combined sewer outlet into tide water at Seattle, Wash., is shown in Fig. 6–27B. Outfall sewers are sometimes constructed on a long trestle over low-lying, alternately submerged and exposed land in order to reach deep or swiftly running water, or the outfall pipe may be submerged. The pipe joints in submerged outfalls are not always carefully made, as some leakage may be permissible. Equal-

[29] See also F. J. Kersnar and D. H. Caldwell, *S. and I.W.*, November, 1956, p. 1336.

[30] See also Wm. Seamann, *S. and I.W.*, March, 1956, p. 296; and *Water and Sewage Works*, October, 1953, p. 418.

Fig. 6–26. Tide gate.

izing reservoirs to control the flow of sewage may be necessary to permit discharge on outgoing tidal currents only.

6–27. The house sewer. A house sewer or house connection is a pipe conveying sewage from a single building to a common sewer or to a point of disposal. It is generally considered that the house sewer extends from the wall of the building, or within a foot or two thereof, to its outlet or to a connection to a common sewer. The channel upstream from the house sewer is a part of the plumbing of the building. Strictly, in accordance with the definition of an

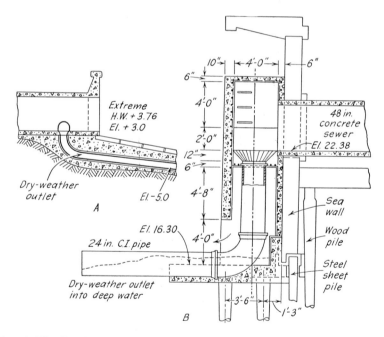

Fig. 6–27. Double sewer outlets. *A.* At Minneapolis, Minn. (From *Eng. News,* Vol. 63, p. 383.) *B.* Vine Street sewer, Seattle, Wash. Storm overflow outlets at pierhead.

appurtenance, a house sewer is not an appurtenance to the sewer system. The house sewer is usually designed and installed by the builder of the house. However, since it is connected to the common sewer its condition and its connections may be of interest to the public sewer authority.

In laying a common sewer it is customary to provide a Y or a T connection at each building lot or place where a house sewer may be connected. Unused connections should be plugged and sealed to prevent the entrance of ground water or roots. A Y is desirable in small sewers to permit a smoother junction of the flowing streams than would be secured by the use of a T. However, a T is easier to install under difficult conditions and a well-installed T is better than a poorly installed Y.[31] The T has an advantage in a sewer large enough for a man to enter as it permits inspection and cleaning of the house sewer. The openings in the T or Y branches should not be less than 6 in. in diameter. In sewers less than about 24 in. in diameter the axis of the house sewer intersects the axis of the common sewer that it joins. In larger sewers it is desirable that the house sewer enter near the top of the common sewer in order to prevent sewage from backing-up into the house sewer when the common sewer is running full.

The house sewer should not be less than 6 in. in diameter, and it should be laid on a slope of not less than $\frac{1}{4}$ in. per foot. Since house sewers are more subject to stoppage than common sewers, from accumulations of grease, large objects, roots, and from other causes, they should be constructed with tight joints, they should be carefully laid to line and grade, and provision should be made to permit rodding and flushing.

6–28. Main or house trap. At the junction between the house plumbing system and the house sewer, just inside or outside the wall of the building, it has been customary, in some cities, to require the installation of a water-sealed trap called a main trap or a house trap. Its purpose is to exclude sewer air from the pipes within the building. Experience has shown that these traps may result in more danger than protection. Unless they are properly vented by means of a fresh-air inlet connected to the trap on the side away from the house, they cut off the most effective form of ventilation of the sewer so that the building up of pressure therein, either above or below atmospheric, forces the seal of the main trap and may even force the seals of traps

[31] See also H. J. Huber, *Sewage Works Jour.*, July, 1942, p. **867**.

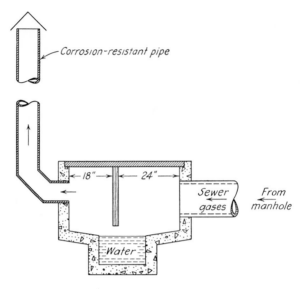

Fig. 6–28. A sewer ventilator. The device is set up alongside a manhole and the gases are drawn from it by the natural draft which passes up the ventilator. (From *Wastes Eng.*, November, 1955, p. 614.)

on fixtures within the building. Unless the main trap is properly vented by means of a vent pipe connected on the house side of the trap, high pressures will result in the plumbing pipes, endangering the security of trap seals on fixtures. The undesirability of the use of the main trap has been demonstrated by experience and research.

6–29. Ventilation.[32] The ventilation of sewers is desirable to prevent the accumulation of dangerous explosive or corrosive gases; to prevent the concentration of unpleasant odors that may escape to cause a nuisance; to prevent accumulation of hydrogen sulfide, which corrodes concrete and metal exposed to it in the sewer and in plumbing; and to prevent the creation of pressures above and below atmospheric that may break water seals in plumbing traps. Pressures are caused by wind blowing up the outlet; trapping of air due to surcharge of the sewer; and from other causes. One form of sewer ventilator is shown in Fig. 6–28.

House sewers connected to untrapped soil or vent stacks, perforated manhole covers, and unobstructed outlets ordinarily provide all the ventilation that is necessary in separate or combined sewers. Forced

[32] See also Richard Pomeroy, *Sewage Works Jour.*, March, 1945, p. 203.

draft is required occasionally. Storm sewers may be ventilated through untrapped inlet connections, unobstructed outlets, and perforated manhole covers. It is undesirable to ventilate combined sewers through untrapped street-inlet connections because of the probability of the escape of objectionable odors to the street surface. Some engineers object to the provision of perforated manhole covers for sewer ventilation because of the danger of surcharging the sewer by the entrance of surface water through the perforations, and because of the escape of odors and visible vapors from the manhole. Methods used to overcome odors escaping from sewers and ventilators have included scrubbing of the gases, activated carbon, masking, dilution, oxidation, and combinations of these. No measure has been signally successful.

If the outlet of a sewer is submerged and there are but few ventilated house connections, some special provision for ventilation is usually necessary. A ventilating shaft with a cross-sectional area at least one-half that of the sewer and sufficiently tall to extend above nearby roofs should suffice. Mechanical devices to provide forced draft, heated chimneys, and ventilating devices requiring the attention of an operator often fail through neglect. If natural draft through chimneys, the mouth of the sewer, and other openings are depended on, differences in barometric pressures resulting from wind movement or temperature variations create the draft. The Los Angeles outfall sewer is an outstanding example of forced-draft ventilation. Escritt [33] has suggested the following formula for computing air movements through unobstructed pipes:

$$Q = 39d^2\sqrt{Pd/L} \qquad (6\text{--}13)$$

where Q is air flow in cfm at the initial pressure; d is the diameter of the pipe in in.; P is the difference of pressure, in inches of water; and L is the length of the pipe in ft.

[33] L. B. Escritt, *Surveyor,* June 23, 1939, p. 815.

Chapter 7

Materials

7–1. Requirements. Sewer pipes are most commonly made of clay or of concrete. Cast iron, steel, wood, asbestos, bituminized fiber, plastic,[1] and other materials are suitable for sewer pipes, but only under special conditions. Important factors to be considered in selecting materials for sewers include resistance to corrosion, strength, durability, weight, hydraulic properties, imperviousness, and cost. Because of the corrosive qualities of sewage, resistance to corrosion is usually of prime importance. As sewers are usually buried and subjected to heavy external loads, structural strength may be an important consideration. In exposed locations alternate freezing and thawing with changing seasons may result in internal strains and changing external loads. Sewage may be erosive as well as corrosive. If it flows at a high velocity and carries grit, the constant abrasion may erode the toughest material.

After the materials have been selected and the specifications written, it is the duty of the engineer to see that the materials meet the specifications. Testing the materials delivered on the work is an important engineering duty. Ordinarily, standard specifications of the American Society for Testing Materials should be followed in specifying and in testing, but it sometimes happens that the engineer may select new materials for which he must write his own specifications.

7–2. Clay. Vitrified clay is widely used for pipes 36 to 42 in. in diameter and smaller, and for bricks and blocks that may be used for the entire sewer barrel or as liners in concrete pipe and other structures. Vitrified clay meets most of the requirements of an ideal material under all conditions except strength, weight, availability, and cost, all of which depend on local conditions. Centuries of experience have demonstrated its apparently ageless durability, resistance

[1] See also C. V. Ing, Jr., *Water and Sewage Works*, January, 1955, p. 40.

to corrosion and erosion, wide availability, and generally satisfactory performance.

The maximum size of vitrified-clay pipe is limited partly by the difficulties in forming and glazing large pipes and partly because of the weight, which makes it expensive for shipment and difficult to handle. An advantage of vitrified-clay pipe is the smooth, impervious surface that offers good hydraulic properties, sacrificed to some extent by the roughness of the ordinary bell and spigot joints that are used. A disadvantage of vitrified clay is its brittleness that may result in damage during transportation and handling on the job.

Clay pipe that has not been vitrified, sometimes called *tile* or *farm tile*, is made with plain ends and is often laid with open joints where infiltration is either desired or need not be considered. The material lacks the strength of standard vitrified-clay pipe and should not be used except for the drainage of surface water or of ground water, and when the pipe is laid at a shallow depth beneath ground on which no superimposed load will come.

7–3. Manufacture of vitrified-clay pipe and specials. Clay for the manufacture of pipe is mined or quarried. It is then taken to the grinding mill either directly or after a period of "weathering" and it is put through a screen with 10 to 16 meshes per inch. The ground clay is next "tempered" with water in a mill similar to the dry-grinding mill, the "dough" being stiff enough to pass through the press without running or cracking. After the mud cylinder in the press is filled, the clay is pressed into the annular space around the mandrel to form the hub of the pipe. The support, called the elevator, is then lowered beneath the cylinder of the press and clay is extruded through the annular space between the mandrel and the die to form the walls of the pipe.

When the required length of pipe has been extruded the press is stopped, the pipe is cut off, and three or four striations about an inch apart are indented close to the spigot end. The pipe is next turned with the bell end up and it is carried to the drying room where it may remain for a few days to 2 weeks. Burning or baking is done by raising the temperature in five or more stages to about 2,000 to 2,200° F over a period of about 10 days. The last stage involves the throwing of calcium chloride into the kiln to form the glaze on the surface through chemical combination of sodium with melted silica. A result is a smooth, hard, impenetrable surface. Improper vitrification may result in the formation of a network of fine cracks on the surface

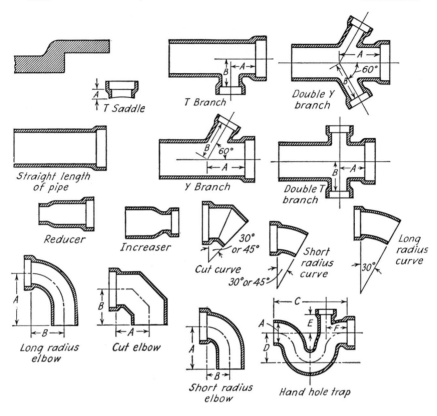

Fig. 7–1. Clay pipe specials.

called *crazing*. A ceramic glaze, sometimes called glass lining [2] is being used. Advantages advanced for it include smoothness, imperviousness, resistance to corrosion, and structural strength. It is said to be somewhat more costly than the conventional salt glazing.

Specials, such as curves, T's, and Y's, as shown in Fig. 7–1, may be made by hand or in molds. Some curves may be made by bending the pipe to the required radius as it is extruded from the press. In the making of Y's and T's, a hole, the size and shape of the outside of the branch pipe, is cut in the barrel of a recently pressed, but not baked, pipe. The end of the branch pipe is then cut in the shape of the hole in the main pipe and the two are joined; a piece of clay is then pressed by hand around the joint on the outside of the pipes.

[2] See also *Public Works,* January, 1957, p. 166.

Other such specials as traps, curves, and reducers may be cast in plaster of Paris molds in which they remain for a day or two before being placed in the kiln.

7–4. Dimensions of vitrified-clay pipe. Specifications for clay sewer pipes have been prepared by various authorities. Specifications C-13–54 of the American Society for Testing Materials are widely used. The dimensions shown in Table 7–1 are taken from these specifications. Pipes whose dimensions are not in accord with these are also available. Lengths shorter than standard have the advantage of lower weight per piece of pipe and greater ease in laying on curves. Longer pieces have fewer joints in a pipe line and, hence, less infiltration. Heavier, longer, and stronger pipes, up to lengths of about 8 ft, are made, and some manufacturers make 3-in., 5-in., 20-in.,

Table 7–1

DIMENSIONS OF STANDARD STRENGTH CLAY SEWER PIPE

(American Society for Testing Materials, C-13–54.) *

Nominal Dia., in.	Laying Length, ft †,‡	Min Difference in Length of Two Opposite Sides, in.	Outside Dia. of Barrel, in.		Inside Dia. of Socket at ½ in. above Base, in.	Depth of Socket, in.		Thickness of Barrel, in.		Thickness of Socket at ½ in. from Outer End, in.	
			Min	Max	Min	Nominal	Min	Nominal	Min	Nominal	Min
4	2	5/16	4 7/8	5 1/8	5 3/4	1 3/4	1 1/2	1/2	7/16	7/16	3/8
6	2	3/8	7 1/16	7 7/16	8 3/16	2 1/4	2	5/8	9/16	1/2	7/16
8	2	7/16	9 1/4	9 3/4	10 1/2	2 1/2	2 1/4	3/4	11/16	9/16	1/2
10	2	7/16	11 1/2	12	12 3/4	2 5/8	2 3/8	7/8	13/16	5/8	9/16
12	2	7/16	13 3/4	14 5/16	15 1/8	2 3/4	2 1/2	1	15/16	3/4	11/16
15	3	1/2	17 3/16	17 13/16	18 5/8	2 7/8	2 5/8	1 1/4	1 1/8	15/16	7/8
18	3	1/2	20 5/8	21 7/16	22 1/4	3	2 3/4	1 1/2	1 3/8	1 1/8	1 1/16
21	3	9/16	24 1/8	25	25 7/8	3 1/4	3	1 3/4	1 5/8	1 5/16	1 3/16
24	3	9/16	27 1/2	28 1/2	29 3/8	3 3/8	3 1/8	2	1 7/8	1 1/2	1 3/8
27	3	9/16	31	32 1/8	33	3 1/2	3 1/4	2 1/4	2 1/8	1 11/16	1 9/16
30	3	5/8	34 3/8	35 5/8	36 1/2	3 5/8	3 3/8	2 1/2	2 3/8	1 7/8	1 3/4
33	3	5/8	37 5/8	38 15/16	39 7/8	3 3/4	3 1/2	2 5/8	2 1/2	2	1 13/16
36	3	1 1/16	40 3/4	42 1/4	43 1/4	4	3 3/4	2 3/4	2 5/8	2 5/16	1 7/8

* See also C-200–55T for Extra Strength Clay Pipe; C-261 for Standard Strength Ceramic Glazed Sewer Pipe; C-278 for Extra Strength Glazed Clay Sewer Pipe; and C-12–54 Recommended Practice for Installing Clay Sewer Pipe.

† There shall be no maximum length. Shorter lengths may be used for closures and specials.

‡ There is no limit for plus variations in length. For minus variations in length, shall not exceed ¼ in. for diameters up to 21 in., and 3 in. for diameters up to 36 in.

Table 7–2

Safe Supporting Strength of Vitrified-Clay Pipe *

(In pounds per linear foot of pipe, the load being uniformly
distributed over 180° of the top of the pipe.)

Pipe Dia., in.	Std. Strength Pipe	Extra Strength Pipe	Pipe Dia., in.	Std. Strength Pipe	Extra Strength Pipe	Pipe Dia., in.	Std. Strength Pipe	Extra Strength Pipe
6	1,650	3,000	15	2,625	4,125	27	4,125	7,050
8	1,950	3,000	18	3,000	4,850	30	4,800	7,500
10	2,100	3,000	21	3,300	5,775	33	5,250	8,250
12	2,250	3,375	24	3,600	6,600	36	5,850	9,000

* Standard strength, ASTM C-13; Extra strength, ASTM C-200. The above figures are based
on ASTM standard methods for installing clay pipe, C-12.

and 22-in. pipes. Some of the more frequently used specials are illustrated in Fig. 7–1. Bearing strengths of vitrified-clay pipes are shown in Table 7–2.

7–5. Bricks and clay blocks. Bricks and clay blocks are now rarely used in the construction of sewers, principally because of the high cost of labor involved. Bricks are sometimes used in the construction of manholes to avoid the cost of forms required for concrete construction. Liner plates of vitrified clay, such as the plate shown in Fig. 7–2, are used to protect the inverts of concrete sewers against erosion and corrosion. They are available either flat or curved to fit concrete pipes of various sizes.

No limiting figure can be properly set as the life of brick or of clay-block sewers, as the resistance of vitrified clay to erosion and corrosion in sewage is great. An experienced engineer can expect to encounter such materials in sewers for many years to come because they were used for sewers almost exclusively through the early years of the present century, until the lower cost of concrete displaced bricks and clay blocks from use in practice.

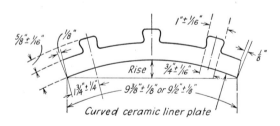

Fig. 7–2. Sewer liner.

7–6. Concrete. Concrete exposed to sewage [3] may be subjected to freezing and thawing, wetting and drying, and corrosive liquids and gases. To resist deterioration resulting from such conditions the concrete may: (1) be made with good, well-graded aggregates and good cement; (2) have a low water-cement ratio; (3) have a well-designed mix; (4) require careful placement to produce density; and (5) require adequate curing. Concrete can be made to meet these requirements.

Concrete tanks, pipes, and the joints in them can be made water-tight against appreciable hydrostatic pressure. An advantage claimed for concrete is its self-healing property as a result of which, in the presence of moisture, small cracks will heal and become stronger than before the break. Reinforced-concrete pipes are used today in the distribution of water under pressure in water-works practice. Concrete has been used in prefabricated pipes from 4 up to 152 in. in diameter, and for cast-in-place pipes and conduits of the largest size constructed. It is used also for segmental blocks shaped to the sewer to be constructed.[4] Care must be exercised in the use of prefabricated pipe to be sure that it is the product of a reliable manufacturer and that it has been made according to standard specifications.

Special attention should be paid to the protection of concrete from chemical action when it is exposed to acid or alkaline industrial wastes or to stale domestic sewage,[5] or when it is exposed to the erosive action of swiftly flowing, silt-bearing sewage.

Corrosion of concrete by sewage is due primarily to hydrogen sulfide. The mechanism of its production is explained by Parker,[6] who summarizes the precautions and procedures to avoid the effects, as follows: (1) elimination of wastes containing sulfides; (2) reduction of sulfates in sewage; (3) partial purification of sewage to diminish sulfur compounds; (4) raising of oxidation-reduction potential by dosing with nitrates or nitro compounds; (5) aeration; (6) chlorination; (7) removal of slime and silt; (8) reduction in detention in rising mains and increase in velocity in gravity sewers; (9) reduction of turbulence; (10) dosage with salts of copper, iron, or zinc, throwing sulfides out of solution; (11) dosage with alkalies, reducing concentration of available sulfides; (12) running sewer full; (13) ventila-

---

[3] See also E. C. Wenger, *Public Works,* May, 1957, p. 208.

[4] See also J. D. Watson, *Water Works and Sewerage,* December, 1937, p. 443.

[5] See also C. Hammerton, *The Institute of Sewage Purification* (British), Oct. 21, 1944, abstract in *Sewage Works Jour.,* March, 1945, p. 403.

[6] C. D. Parker, *S. and I.W.,* December, 1951, p. 1477.

tion of sewer; (14) periodic flooding of conduits or tanks; (15) ammoniation of the sewer air—a process patented by R. Pomeroy; (16) use of resistant concrete; and (17) use of protective coatings.

7–7. Linings for concrete sewers. Concrete sewers can be protected against erosion and corrosion by a protective lining. Clay liner plates have the advantage of being more resistant than ordinary concrete to erosion and corrosion, particularly when joined with a joint material containing a sulfur-cement base. Owing to the different expansion coefficients of sulfur cement and vitrified clay a carefully built-up film of asphalt must be placed between concrete and clay products in structures subjected to wide variations of temperature. This precaution is unnecessary in most sewers but might be required in certain chemical-solution storage tanks. Concrete has been successfully protected against corrosion by coal-tar base materials applied by a brush in two coats. An objection to such coatings is that ultimately the volatile oils escape and the usefulness of the coating is lost.

7–8. Manufacture of concrete pipe. Concrete pipe is made of a mixture of Portland cement, a fine aggregate passing about a ¼-in.-mesh sieve, a coarse aggregate the size of which depends on the thickness of the pipe wall, and water. The pipe is formed by ramming the well-mixed materials into molds or by a centrifugal process. Details of some molds are shown in Fig. 7–3. The method of ramming, the period of setting, the length of time of curing, and the control of moisture and temperature during this period have great influence on the quality of the resulting product.

Machine ramming is preferable to hand ramming as it produces a stronger and more uniform pipe. Various types of ramming and vibrating machines are on the market, some delivering as many as 800 blows per minute at a pressure of about 800 psi of exposed area. In another type of machine a revolving core is drawn through the pipe, packing and polishing the concrete as the core is pulled through, with special provision for packing the bell. The forms are swabbed with heavy oil before the concrete is placed in them, to facilitate removal. They are removed when the pipe has attained its first set, and then the pipe is cured under controlled conditions of temperature and moisture. In the centrifugal process the wet mixture is placed in a steel mold that is rotated rapidly about its axis, thus packing the concrete solidly and producing a highly satisfactory result.

"Roller suspension" pipe is centrifugally spun, using an inner roller and vibration to assure uniform distribution of aggregate and

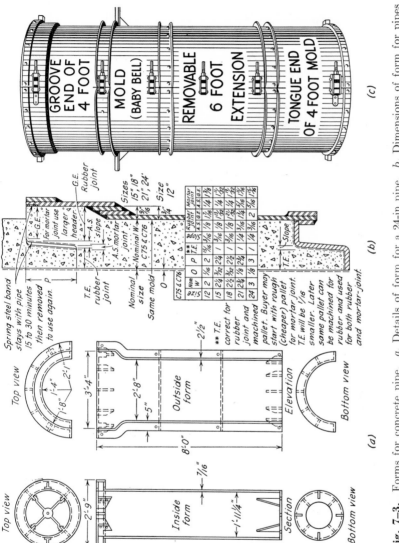

Fig. 7–3. Forms for concrete pipe. *a.* Details of form for a 24-in pipe. *b.* Dimensions of form for pipes of different sizes. *c.* External appearance of one type of form. (Figures *b* and *c* are by courtesy of Concrete Pipe Machinery Co.)

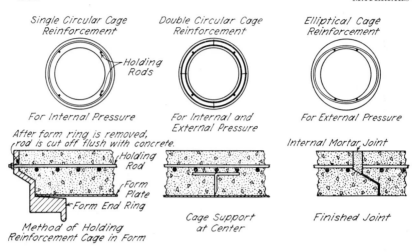

Fig. 7-4. Methods of reinforcing concrete pipe.

true wall thickness. The pipe is designed to resist an ultimate load of 4,000D lb per linear foot, where D is the internal diameter in feet.

Steel reinforcement may be placed in the hand-rammed molds or in the centrifugal molds, in the position shown in Fig. 7-4. Where elliptically placed reinforcement is used in circular pipes, the top of

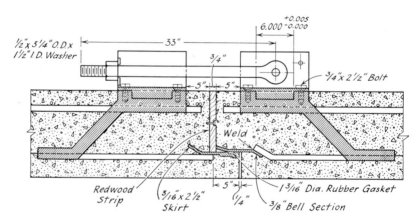

Fig. 7-5. Reinforced concrete external bolted joint, East Bay Municipal Utility District Sewer Outfall, Oakland, Calif. (Courtesy Brown and Caldwell, Engineers.)

Table 7–3

PROPERTIES OF UNREINFORCED CONCRETE PIPE

(ASTM C-14–41)

Internal Diameter, in.	Laying Length, ft	Inside Diameter at Mouth of Socket, in.*	Depth of Socket, in.†	Thickness of Barrel, in.‡	Average Crushing Strength, lb per lin ft §		Limits of Permissible Variations ‖				
							Length, in. per ft (−)	Internal Diameter, in.		Depth of Socket, in. (−)	Thickness of Barrel, in. (−)
					3-Edge Bearing	Sand Bearing		Spigot (±)	Socket (±)		
D ¶	L ¶	D_s ¶	L_s ¶	T ¶							
4	2, 2½, 3	6	1½	9/16	1,000	1,500	¼	⅛	⅛	⅛	1/16
6	2, 2½, 3	8¼	2	⅝	1,100	1,650	¼	3/16	3/16	¼	1/16
8	2, 2½, 3, 4	10¾	2¼	¾	1,300	1,950	¼	¼	¼	¼	1/16
10	2, 2½, 3, 4	13	2½	⅞	1,400	2,100	¼	¼	¼	¼	1/16
12	2, 2½, 3, 4	15¼	2½	1	1,500	2,250	¼	¼	¼	¼	1/16
15	2, 2½, 3, 4	18¾	2½	1¼	1,750	2,620	¼	¼	¼	¼	3/32
18	2, 2½, 3, 4	22¼	2¾	1½	2,000	3,000	¼	¼	¼	¼	3/32
21	2, 2½, 3, 4	26	2¾	1¾	2,200	3,300	¼	5/16	5/16	¼	⅛
24	2, 2½, 3, 4	29½	3	2⅛	2,400	3,600	⅜	5/16	5/16	¼	⅛
Col. 1	2	3	4	5	6	7	8	9	10	11	12

* When pipes are furnished having an increase in thickness over that given in column 5, the diameter of socket shall be increased by an amount equal to twice the increase of thickness of barrel.

† Minimum taper of socket for all sizes is $1 : 20 = H/L_s$.

‡ The thickness of the socket, T_s, from its outer end shall be not less than three-fourths of the thickness of the barrel of the pipe.

§ Maximum absorption 8 per cent.

‖ The minus sign alone indicates that the plus variation is not limited; the plus-or-minus sign (±) indicates variation in both excess and deficiency in dimension.

¶ The letters in these column headings refer to Fig. 7–6.

the pipe should be marked so that it can be placed in the proper position to resist external stress.

Specials in the form of T's and Y's may be made by hand similarly to vitrified-clay T's and Y's. Curves, increasers, traps, and so forth, are cast in molds or forms.

7–9. Joints in concrete pipe. Bell-and-spigot joints are used in concrete pipe where the flow is not under pressure. A plastic (neoprene) gasket has been used [7] to complete butt joints in concrete pipe. Pipes flowing under pressure are joined in special joints one type of which is shown in Fig. 7–5.

[7] News item in *S. and I.W.*, October, 1955, p. 1213.

Table 7–4

PROPERTIES OF REINFORCED CONCRETE SEWER PIPE

(ASTM C-75–41)

Internal Diameter, in.	Strength Test Requirements, lb per lin ft		Minimum Design Requirements *					
			Concrete, 3,000 psi			Concrete, 4,000 psi		
	3-Edge Bearing Method, Ultimate Load, lb	Sand Bearing Method, Ultimate Load, lb	Shell Thickness, in.	Lines of Reinforcement	Total Steel Area, sq in. per lin ft	Shell Thickness, in.	Lines of Reinforcement	Total Steel Area, sq in. per lin ft
12	2,700	4,050	2	1	0.06	...		
15	3,000	4,500	2¼	1	0.06	...		
18	3,300	4,950	2½	1	0.06	2	1	0.07
21	3,600	5,400	2¾	1	0.06	2¼	1	0.07
24	3,600	5,400	3	1	0.06	2½	1	0.09
27	3,800	5,700	3	1	0.07	2⅝	1	0.12
30	4,050	6,100	3½	1	0.09	2¾	1	0.14
33	4,300	6,400	3¾	1	0.11	2¾	1	0.17
36	4,500	6,750	4	2 †	0.14	3	2 †	0.23
42	4,800	7,200	4½	2 †	0.16	3⅜	2 †	0.27
48	5,100	7,650	5	2 †	0.21	3¾	2 †	0.32
54	5,550	8,300	5½	2 †	0.25	4¼	2 †	0.38
60	6,000	9,000	6	2 †	0.29	4½	2 †	0.44
66	6,350	9,550	6½	2 †	0.32	4¾	2 †	0.47
72	6,750	10,100	7	2 †	0.36	5	2 †	0.55
78			7½	2 †	0.40			
84			8	2 †	0.43			
90			8	2 †	0.49			
96			8½	2 †	0.57			
108			9	2 †	0.67			

* The distance from the center line of the reinforcement to the nearest surface of the concrete has been assumed in the design tables as 1 in.

† Where two lines of steel are specified, a single line placed elliptically may be used, and the area of this shall be at least 50 per cent of the total area specified in the design table.

7–10. Dimensions of concrete pipe. Standard sizes, dimensions, and permissible variations for concrete pipes up to 108 in. in diameter are shown in Tables 7–3 and 7–4, and in Fig. 7–6. Pipes 12 to 24 in. in diameter, with the dimensions shown in Table 7–3, when properly bedded and backfilled, may be used with safety in trenches 16 ft deep or less, without superimposed loads on the surface; and the pipes in Table 7–4 may be used in trenches 18 ft deep under similar restrictions. No restrictions have been placed on depth of cover for 4-in.

to 10-in. pipes of standard dimensions when properly bedded and backfilled. Pipes of dimensions other than those shown in the tables are available, but no standards of dimensions or reinforcement have been generally adopted for other sizes. There is a trend toward the use of greater lengths of pipe, even up to 16 ft, where conditions permit, in order to minimize the number of joints to be made.

7–11. Cast-iron pipe. Cast-iron pipe is used where external loads are high and watertightness is required. External loads are high under railroads and highways, under foundation walls, where movements and vibrations of the earth may occur, where there is alternate thawing and freezing, and in other situations. Cast-iron pipe may be used also: in force mains to resist internal pressure; on bridges and trestles; as a bridge spanning between piers or bents; for inverted and true siphons; in exposed outfall sewers; and as the principal material in the piping conveying sewage through pumping stations and treatment plants. Although sewer pipes are not ordinarily subjected to high internal pressure, cast-iron pipe for sewers should be as heavy as, or heavier than, water pipe to resist the corrosive action of sewage. Sizes and details of standard cast-iron pipe for both water works and sewers can be found in specifications of the American Water Works Association and the New England Water Works Association, and water-works methods used for the protection of cast-iron pipe against corrosion are applicable to sewerage practice.

7–12. Steel pipe. Steel pipe is used for sewers where lightness, imperviousness, and resistance to bursting pressure are required. A unique advantage of steel pipes, both smooth and corrugated, is that, because of their flexibility, they can resist the effects of shocks, move-

Fig. 7–6. Standards for concrete pipe. American Society for Testing Materials, C 14–41.

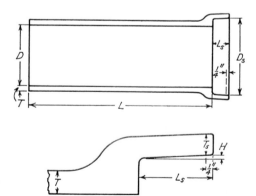

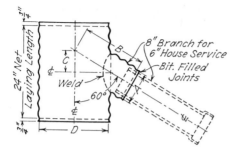

Fig. 7–7. Y-connection for corrugated steel pipe.

ments, and external pressures by deflecting, buckling, or flattening without failure and, in the process of these movements, so distributing the loads as to develop better strength to resist further distortion. Steel pipe for sewers is available in riveted, welded, and corrugated sections. Riveted pipe is somewhat objectionable both because of its cost and because of the interior roughness caused by exposed rivet heads. Riveted or corrugated pipe is sometimes used where head losses are unimportant. Where necessary, part of the head loss and erosive effect is diminished by lining the invert with bitumastic material. A friction factor of $n = 0.019$ may be used in unlined corrugated pipes.

With riveted or welded steel pipe, standard water-works practice may be followed in design. Corrugated pipe is rolled for sewers with specials and connections designed to overcome the irregularities of the corrugations. A Y branch in a corrugated pipe is shown in Fig. 7–7 and a type of transverse joint for Armco pipe is illustrated in Fig. 7–8. An outstanding advantage of corrugated-steel pipe is the relatively long sections that are available and can be handled fairly

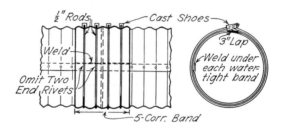

Fig. 7–8. Watertight field joint for Armco corrugated steel pipe. (From *Handbook of Culvert and Drainage Practice,* by permission of Armco Drainage and Metal Products Co.)

easily, thus reducing the number of joints required. For example, a 30-ft length of 8-in. pipe weighs only 222 lb, a weight that can be handled without special equipment. Sections are available in almost any length and diameter desired, in multiples of 2 ft of length.

The resistance of steel to corrosion is low, so that unless the pipe is well protected the life of the sewer will be short. The steel can be protected with galvanizing or bituminous coatings, or the steel itself may be of special, corrosion-resistant quality.

Steel plates for pipes should seldom be used in a thickness of less than about $\frac{1}{4}$ in. and, where long life is desired, not less than $\frac{3}{8}$ in. thick. Corrugated metal, because of the strength given by the corrugations, is used in thinner section when corrosion is not a serious item. The standard is 16-gage for 8- to 12-in. diameter, 14-gage for 24- and 30-in. pipe, 12-gage for 54-in. pipe, 10-gage for 60- to 72-in. pipe, and 8-gage for 84 to 96 in. It is considered safe to bury such pipe in trenches as deep as 20 ft, although heavier gages are available and are recommended at the greater depths.

7–13. Valves on pressure lines. Standard water-works-type valves and fittings are widely used on cast-iron pipe conveying sewage under pressure.[8] However, because of difficulties with clogging at the valve, jamming of the disk at the seat, and other difficulties with disk valves, plug valves and butterfly valves are being widely used.

7–14. Wood pipe. Creosoted, wood-stave pipe is occasionally used for sewers in the western part of the United States, and has been used in a few installations elsewhere. Ordinarily, considerations of availability, durability, and economy preclude its adoption in competition with other materials. Since wood sewer pipe is usually fabricated in the field, it can be made of any size desired. Its use is confined principally to outfall sewers since the making of connections to it is difficult.

Creosoted wood that is kept constantly submerged should last indefinitely, as it is not materially affected by the qualities of ordinary sewage. If the wood is alternately wet and dry, however, its life may be too short to justify its use. No better method than creosoting is known for the protection of wood pipes against corrosion.

7–15. Asbestos pipe.[9] Among the advantages claimed for asbestos-cement pipe for sewers are: lightness compared with concrete; long

[8] See also G. J. Manahan, *S. and I.W.*, February, 1956, p. 225.

[9] See also O. F. Gerlach, *Water Works and Sewerage*, May, 1938, p. 532; W. L. Hyland, *Jour. Boston Soc. Civil Engrs.*, January, 1941, p. 31; and C. A. McGinnis, *Sewage Works Jour.*, September, 1941, p. 1061.

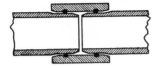

Fig. 7–9.   Diagram of Ring-Tite joint for Transite pipe.

sections to minimize the number of joints and maintain good align-ment; easily made, tight joints either poured with a bituminous com-pound or made with a rubber gasket; easy cutting and fitting, as it can be cut with a wood saw; smoothness [10] with a value of $n = 0.011$; good resistance to corrosion; and internal-pressure working strengths up to 150 psi. Durability and resistance to soil corrosion are generally reported as satisfactory.[11] Pipes are available in sizes up to 36 in. in diameter. These are not strong enough to replace cast-iron pipe.

A *Ring-Tite* joint for Transite pipe, showing the rubber gaskets used, is shown in Fig. 7–9.

7–16. Plastic pipe. Experience with buried, plastic pipe has been limited principally to service pipes in water-works practice, where it has been found to be satisfactory under favorable conditions. Ad-vantages claimed for plastic pipes in water-works practice include freedom from corrosion; freedom from damage due to freezing and thawing of water in the pipe; good resistance to shock; resistance to acids in solutions up to about 10 per cent concentration; light weight, about 11 per cent that of cast iron; easy bending and easily made joints; resistance to age, sunlight, or weather; a non-conductor of electricity; and resilience and flexibility. It is generally conceded that the installation of small-size, plastic-type sewers requires a mini-mum of labor.[12]

7–17. Bituminized-fiber pipe.[13] This material is in successful use for sewers and drains. Among the advantages claimed for it are: lightness, ease of construction of sewers with it; watertightness; re-sistance to absorption; tightness of joints; resistance to corrosion and to corrosive chemicals; resistance to shock; and flexibility or plastic flow. It has been found suitable where there is movement or vibra-tion. The pipe can be penetrated by a sharp tool, such as a pick; sustained high temperature will produce softening; and if the pipe is

[10] See also T. R. Gillen, *Water and Sewage Works,* June, 1955, p. 259.

[11] See also M. Romanoff and I. A. Denison, *Corrosion,* Vol. 10, 1954, p. 169; and abstract in *S. and I.W.,* February, 1955, p. 160.

[12] *Water and Sewage Works,* October, 1952, p. 425.

[13] See National Bureau of Standards Specifications, Commercial Standard, CS 116–44.

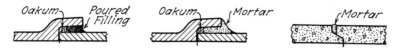

Fig. 7–10. Types of joints for bell-and-spigot pipes.

permanently laid on the ground surface exposed to direct sunlight, deterioration will occur. The pipe is available in sizes between 3 and 8 in. in diameter.

7–18. Joints and jointing material.[14] Desirable characteristics in sewer-pipe joints, or jointing materials, include: [15] (1) easily made, whether or not submerged; (2) watertight or highly resistant to infiltration and exfiltration; (3) sufficiently flexible to avoid breaking due to small movement of pipe; (4) resistant to penetration, especially by roots; (5) not easily broken or cracked; (6) make pipes available for use quickly after joint is completed; (7) resistant to corrosion, especially by hydrogen sulfide and by acids; (8) non-absorbent; and (9) available and economical.

Types of joints used in vitrified-clay and concrete pipe include bell-and-spigot, push-together, tongue-and-groove, lock-joint, rubber-ring, and open. The bell-and-spigot is the most common. This joint requires a material to fill the space between the bell and the spigot. Materials used for filling this space include cement, sand, tar, asphalt, plastics, sulfur, and polyvinyl chloride molded gaskets.

7–19. Open joints. Open joints may be used in dry ground where root penetration is not expected, and infiltration is unobjectionable. The joint may be made by butting together spigot ends of pipes or by bell-and-spigot joints without filling material. The joints are covered with tar paper, burlap, gravel, or other durable material to prevent the entrance of backfilling material into the pipe.

7–20. Bell-and-spigot joints.[16] Types of bell-and-spigot joints are sometimes designated by the materials used in making them, as open joints, mortar joints, cement joints, or poured joints. Three types of joint are shown in Fig. 7–10.

7–21. Cement joints and mortar joints. Cement is probably the most widely used joint material. It has a great advantage of wide

[14] See A. P. Collins, *S. and I.W.*, September, 1953, p. 1115; and F. C. Palmer, *Water and Sewage Works,* June 1, 1955, p. R-329.

[15] See R. B. Seymour, *Water and Sewage Works,* November, 1953, p. 1289.

[16] See also F. C. Palmer, *Water and Sewage Works,* April, 1951, p. R-120; and H. W. House and R. Pomeroy, *Sewage Works Jour.*, March, 1947, p. 191.

and satisfactory use. However, difficulties with it include: (1) skill
and care are required to make a good joint, particularly around the
inaccessible, lower half; (2) the rigidity of the joint; and (3) the
corrosion of cement by calcium and magnesium sulfates and carbonates in corrosive soils, and by acids and hydrogen sulfide within
the pipe. Cement is used in making both a mortar joint and a cement
joint, but the latter is more carefully made. The mortar joint, unless
exceptionally well made, may be but slightly more resistant than an
open joint to root penetration and to leakage. Even well-made
cement joints are not always watertight and root-resistant, as it is
difficult to secure uniformly good workmanship, particularly at the
bottom of the bell. Neither cement nor mortar joints can be made
in wet trenches, and the rigidity of the material may result in breaking of the pipe or cracking of the joint if there is subsequent movement.

A mortar joint may be made by plastering the inside of the bell
with a stiff mortar of equal parts of Portland cement and sand. After
the adjacent pipes are abutted and aligned, the remainder of the bell
is filled with similar mortar finished to a smooth bevel on the outside
and wiped clean on the inside.

The American Public Works Association has specified the quality
of mortar and the making of a cement joint as follows:

. . . a closely twisted hemp and/or oakum gasket of such diameter as required to support the spigot of the pipe at the proper grade and make
truly concentric joints, and in one piece of sufficient length to pass around
the pipe and lap at the top, shall be thoroughly saturated in cement mortar.
The gasket shall be laid in the bell for the lower third of the circumference
of the joint and covered with mortar specified for pipe joining. The spigot
of the pipe shall be thoroughly cleaned with a wet brush, inserted and carefully driven home, after which a small amount of mortar shall be inserted
in the annular space around the entire circumference of the pipe and solidly
rammed into the joint with a calking tool, the mortar previously placed
being driven ahead of the gasket. The remainder of the joint shall then be
completely filled with mortar and beveled off at an angle of 45° with the
outside of the pipe. On pipes 18 in., or larger, in diameter the joints shall
be pointed or smoothed from the inside.

If the cement is not stiff it may slump from the joint or run into
the pipe when no gasket has been used. Under such conditions the
inside of the pipe may be cleaned after the mortar has set slightly by
dragging a large, burlap-wrapped block of wood or straw, called a
go-devil, through the pipe. Care must be taken to see that the go-

devil is not left in the sewer when work is interrupted or completed. While working in cement it is usually necessary for the workman to wear rubber gloves, because cement causes sores on bare hands.

Machine-made cement joints using a machine to inject the mortar into the joint can be made successfully and watertight even when subsequently submerged.[17]

Mortise or tongue-and-groove joints, of a type similar to that shown in Fig. 7–10, are used in large pipes. In constructing this type of joint where pipe is being laid in an upstream direction, a small excavation is made beneath the pipe at the joint after the downstream section of pipe has been laid. The lower half of the bell of the downstream pipe is plastered with mortar. Then the spigot end of the next upstream section of pipe, coated with mortar on the upper half, is inserted into the bell of the downstream section of pipe until mortar is squeezed out of the bell. The joint is filled with mortar, pointed, and smoothed, and the interior of the pipe is brushed smooth.

7–22. Flexible joints. Flexible joints are used under conditions in which the shape of the trench may be changed later, as by movement of the ground, or when laying submerged pipe. Where watertight joints are desired joints such as those used in water pipe may be used for sewers. The Ceramicweld pipe and couplings involve a flexible rubber joint, developed and first used in Los Angeles.[18] The rubber is corrosion resistant, will give or bend 4 to 6 in., and can be laid under water, and the joint is not difficult to make.

7–23. Poured joints. Poured joints have many advantages over cement joints, but they are more expensive. They are made by pouring a compound, while in a fluid state, into the joint, where the material hardens. The outstanding advantage of poured joints is watertightness. The requisite qualities of a poured-jointing material include: (1) imperviousness; (2) ability to resist the entrance of roots; (3) low cost, (4) long life; (5) resistance to corrosion by sewage or ground water; (6) good adhesion to pipe surface; (7) fluidity below 400° F, as higher temperatures might crack the pipe; (8) hardness and solidity at temperatures below 250° F, so that the material of the joint may not run out if hot liquids enter the sewer; (9) flexibility to permit slight movement of the sewer; (10) quick setting; and (11) simplicity and ease in handling and working so as to avoid the need for specially skilled labor.

[17] See also C. S. Seabrook, *Civil Eng.*, June, 1947, p. 28.
[18] See R. F. Brown, *Water and Sewage Works,* December, 1949, p. 486.

Materials used for poured joints include cement grout; sulfur and sand; bituminous compounds made of vulcanized linseed oil, clay, and other substances, the resulting mixture having the appearance of vulcanized rubber or coal tar; rubber; and lead. The bituminous materials most nearly approach the ideal requirements.

7–24. Cement grout. Cement grout is made up of pure cement and water mixed into a soupy consistency. Its main advantages are its cheapness and ease in handling in wet trenches or difficult situations. The result is no better than a well-made cement joint. There is no elasticity to the joint, a movement of the pipe will break it, and on setting the cement is likely to shrink and crack.

7–25. Sulfur and sand. Sulfur and sand are inexpensive and comparatively easy to handle, and they make an absolutely watertight and rigid joint stronger than the pipe itself. The joint frequently results in the cracking of the pipe and is objected to by some engineers on that account. In making the mixture, powdered sulfur and very fine sand are mixed in equal proportions. It is essential that the sand be fine so that it will mix well with the sulfur and not precipitate out when the sulfur is melted. Ninety per cent of the sand should pass a No. 100 sieve, and 50 per cent should pass a No. 200 sieve. The mixture melts at about 260° F and does not soften at lower temperatures. For a joint in an 8-in. pipe about 1½ lb of sulfur, 1½ lb of sand, ½ lb of jute, and 0.4 lb of pitch are required. The pitch is painted on the surface of the joint while still hot in order to close up any possible cracks.

7–26. Bituminous joint compounds. Bituminous joint compounds are of two types: those that are heated and poured, and those that are run into the joint or are pushed into it when cold. Practically all the materials available are proprietary articles or patented mixtures. These compounds meet nearly all the ideal conditions except low cost and easy handling. They are somewhat expensive and if overheated or heated too long become carbonized and brittle. In cold weather they do not stick to the pipe well unless the pipe is heated before the joint is poured. On some work, joints have been poured under water with these compounds, but success is doubtful without skillful handling. Moisture will make steam in the joint, causing explosions which will blow the joint clean. An underheated compound may harden before the joint is completed.

As a result of tests at the University of Illinois [19] Crandell found

---

[19] See J. S. Crandell, "Bituminous Compounds for Sewer Pipe," 37th Annual Meeting, American Society for Testing Materials.

that asphaltic materials containing admixtures of fillers (40 to 50 per cent by weight) can be poured successfully when water is in the trench, but pure asphalt, or asphalts with a low percentage of filler, will foam so excessively as to make an imperfectly filled joint. If the amount of filler is more than about 10 per cent there is a tendency for the filler to settle and cause overheating, coking, or burning. Gasoline, petroleum, ether, and similar solvents sometimes found in sewage will destroy asphaltic compounds if exposed for two or three days, but in practice no harm is done provided that the solvents are not concentrated and are washed away fairly rapidly. Coal-tar pitches are not affected by the ingredients in sewage, but some compounds have a tendency to flow out of the joint. A satisfactory cold, plastic compound can be made from powdered asphalt, a suitable flux, and a solvent.

Cold bituminous plastic compounds can be applied much like plaster, and many such proprietary compounds are available. Most of them consist of an asphalt cement of high penetration mixed with powdered asphalt and held in suspension in a volatile solvent. A combination of rubber and of asphalt held in colloidal suspension has given promise of making satisfactory cold joints.

7–27. Polyvinyl chloride. Polyvinyl chloride, molded gaskets form a watertight and root-resistant joint for use in bell-and-spigot joints on specially prepared clay pipes. The material is relatively inert to acid, alkali, oil, and grease, and it is flexible enough to allow some movement in the joint. The trench may be backfilled immediately after the pipe has been laid. To make the joint, which requires no special skill and can be done with the pipe under water, the gaskets are lubricated with a soap solution and are pushed together by hand or with a pry bar. In some joints a threaded, vinyl plastic ring is hot-molded into place. Joints are made also with corresponding, hard-molded, phenolic, plastic rings.[20]

7–28. Other materials for joints. A soft, rubber ring, calked into the annular space of a specially designed joint, and other materials made into a ring and calked or pressed into the opening between two pipes, have made satisfactory joints. Rubber gaskets, either with or without a steel ring, make satisfactory joints.[20] Lead is rarely used for bell-and-spigot joints in clay or concrete pipe, but it has been used in the cold calking of concrete pipes already laid.

[20] See also *S. and I.W.*, October, 1955, p. 1210; Committee Report, *Proc. Am. Soc. Civil Engrs.*, Paper 1013, June, 1956; and *Public Works*, December, 1956, p. 140.

7–29. Pouring joints. In making a poured joint the pipes are first lined in position. A hemp or oakum gasket is forced into the joint to fill a space of about ¾ in. An asbestos or other noncombustible gasket, such as a rubber hose smeared with clay is forced about ½ in. into the opening between the bell and the spigot, or the gasket is wrapped tightly around the spigot and pressed or tied firmly to the bell, leaving an annular space between the gasket and the bell. The compound is poured through a hole broken in the bell or the gasket at the top of the pipe. It runs down one side of the pipe until it appears on the other side, showing that the space is filled.

Bituminous materials to be melted should be heated in an iron kettle over a gasoline furnace, or other controllable fire, until they just commence to bubble and are of the consistency of a thin sirup. Only a sufficient quantity of material for immediate use should be prepared; and it should be used within 10 to 15 min after it has been properly heated. The ladle should be large enough to pour the entire joint without being refilled.

In pouring cement-grout joints a paper gasket is used, being held to the bell and spigot by drawstrings. Greater speed in construction and economy of materials may be achieved by joining two or three lengths of pipe on the bank and lowering them into the trench as a unit. The pipes are set in a vertical position on the bank with the bell end up, one length resting in the other. The joint is calked and poured without the use of the gasket. The joint should be poured immediately after being calked so that the hemp cannot become watersoaked. Whenever a gasket is used it should be removed as soon as possible after the joint is poured in order to prevent sticking, with resulting danger of the breakage of the joint when the gasket is pulled free. One man can pour about thirty-three 8-in. joints and two men can complete about twenty-six 12-in. joints per hour on the bank.

A method of making joints that involves the use of bituminous materials in a somewhat different fashion is called the *slip-seal* method. Bituminous rings in the bell and around the spigot are tapered and fitted snugly into each other when the pipes are joined, the surfaces first being painted with a solvent which soon evaporates.

7–30. Mechanical joints. When two pieces of pipe are joined by bolts, collars, or other special devices for holding the pipes together the joint is called a mechanical joint. This joint is commonly used on cast-iron and other metallic pipes in water works and where metallic pipes are used for the conveying of sewage. The joint shown in Fig. 7–5 is one type of mechanical joint used for a reinforced-concrete pipe.

7–31. Corrosion and its prevention.[21] Most sewages are highly corrosive and quickly attack metals and other substances exposed to it. Sewerage materials are protected against corrosion by being mixed or alloyed with resistant materials or being covered with a resistant coating. Grease in sewage, together with a lack of oxygen, may serve to protect constantly submerged metallic materials. If sewage contains corrosive industrial wastes or is high in sulfur compounds, special care must be taken in the selection of corrosion-resistant material exposed to the sewage or to fumes from it.

Corrosion-resistant [22] metallic substances include Armco and Toncan iron, Monel metal, silicon bronze, manganese bronze, copper-bearing steel, stainless steel, tin, nickel, aluminum,[23] copper, brass, chromium, molybdenum, Stelite, Meonite, and Everdur metal.[24] Very few, if any, metals or alloys are completely corrosion resistant under all conditions. For example, all metals and alloys are affected in a damp atmosphere containing chlorine; copper and galvanized metals in a damp atmosphere containing hydrogen sulfide; stainless steel in exhaust-gas heat exchangers; and silicon-bronze in heavily chlorinated sewage. Corrosion resistance is needed especially in recording devices and other automatic equipment where a small amount of corrosion may affect the performance of the mechanism. The copper content of alloys in such mechanisms should be low in the presence of hydrogen sulfide and some nitrogen compounds such as ammonia and some amines. Bronze, red brass, silicon bronze, copper, copper-bearing alloys, Monel metal, and aluminum and aluminum alloys have been found to resist corrosion satisfactorily under mildly corrosive conditions.

It is not always possible to predict when certain metals will or will not corrode. For example, cast iron has resisted in some digestion tanks and not in others. Most piping used around sewage-treatment plants include cast iron, red brass, or steel coated and lined with bituminous paint, cement, enamel, or rubber.

High-silica cements, containing very little lime, have been found to be more acid-resistant than ordinary Portland cement. Vitrex

---

[21] See also R. C. French, *Water and Sewage Works,* October, 1952, p. 402.

[22] See also C. E. Keefer and K. M. Huston, *S. and I.W.,* October, 1952, p. 1209.

[23] See also *Sewage Works Jour.,* September, 1943, p. 985.

[24] See also *ibid.,* July, 1947, p. 713.

is a silicate cement that resists the corrosive action of acids, oils, and certain solvents. Formica is a non-metallic, corrosion-resistant material used satisfactorily to cover laboratory table tops and other surfaces on which corrosion-causing materials may fall.

Linings, coatings, and paints are used more extensively than alloys to resist corrosion where the structure is in contact with the sewage. Electric grounding and cathodic protection of metals have been successful in protecting metallic substances against corrosion. Metalizing [25] has been found to be successful in protecting against corrosion. The use of vitrified-clay liners, cemented with sulfur cement, as mentioned in Sect. 7–6, and certain surface treatments that react with the concrete have proved to be effective in the protection of concrete.

7–32. Paints.[26] Agents that are destructive to paints include hydrogen sulfide, grease and oil, ammonia, water, organic matter, sunlight, mill scale, and improper cleaning of surface before painting. In general, light-colored lead paints cannot be used about sewage, as the sulfur from the sewage reacts with the lead of the paint to form dark sulfides. The only light paints that can be used are aluminum and zinc-titanium oxides. Asphaltic or bituminous paints provide good protection except when exposed to softening and solvent greases when submerged. Chlorinated rubber, called Parbon,[27] is highly resistant to most corrosive agents. It can be used successfully on concrete and metallic surfaces. Rubber paints, such as Amolac, and synthetic types of cellulose varnishes seem to be successful under water. An asphaltic-clay emulsion loaded with asbestos fiber and zinc oxide has been used for submerged steelwork.

Priming paints should not be applied on steel until the mill scale has been completely removed. Aluminum paint with the proper paint vehicle is satisfactory for outside structures. In basements, tunnels, and other moist locations where hydrogen sulfide may be troublesome, the priming paints may be covered with aluminum paints or a gilsonite paint made with tung oil. Steel not exposed directly to sewage may be cleaned by wire brushing and covered with a heavy coat of asphalt-clay emulsion loaded with asbestos fiber and containing zinc oxide. After steel has been submerged in sewage it is difficult to make paint

[25] See also R. Mansell, *Water and Sewage Works,* November, 1949, p. 435.

[26] See also W. T. McClenahan, *Sewage Works Jour.,* September, 1941, p. 885; and *S. and I.W.,* January, 1952, p. 1. W. A. Sperry, *Sewage Works Jour.,* March, 1948, p. 319. *Recommended Maintenance Painting Systems for Sewage Treatment Plants,* a manual published by the Tropical Paint Co.

[27] See also F. K. Shankweiler, *Water and Sewage Works,* June, 1953, p. 230.

bond to it, even after sandblasting. It is frequently said that the cleaning and preparation of the surface is as important as the paint.

Paints may be specified by their composition or by their performance. If the former, the engineer takes the responsibility for their performance. If the latter, a quickly and easily applied accelerated test should be specified, since long-time tests are unfair to the manufacturer and are difficult to enforce.

Chapter 8

Loads on buried pipes

8–1. Loads on pipe. Loads or conditions that cause stresses in sewer pipes include external loads, handling, temperature, and internal bursting pressure. The first is the most important and may be the only stress considered in design. Strength sufficient to resist external loads will be sufficient to resist other stresses.

8–2. Internal pressure, handling, and temperature. The thickness of the wall of a pipe designed to resist internal bursting pressure can be expressed as $t = PR/f_t$, in which P is the intensity of internal pressure, R is the radius of the inside of the pipe, and f_t is the unit strength of the material in tension.

Stresses due to handling cannot be computed with accuracy. They are cared for by a thickness of material dictated by experience and included in such specifications as are quoted in Tables 7–1, 7–2, 7–3, and 7–4.

Temperature stresses can be computed from the expression $S = ETC$, in which S is the intensity of the stress due to change in temperature, E is the modulus of elasticity of the material, T is the temperature change, and C is the coefficient of expansion of the material. If the pipe is to be allowed to expand and contract with changes in temperature, provision must be made for the movement of the pipe. The amount of this movement can be computed from the expression $M = LCT$, in which M is the change in length of the pipe, L is the length of the pipe affected, C is the coefficient of expansion of the material, and T is the change in temperature. Ordinarily in sewerage practice no provision is made for temperature stresses in buried pipe. However, pipes exposed above the ground surface may be subjected to appreciable temperature stresses, which must be cared for by expansion joints or other provisions more common in water-works practice.

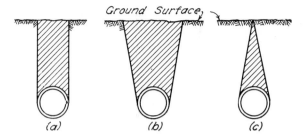

Fig. 8–1. Hypothetical load transmission to buried pipes.

8–3. Character of external loads on buried pipes. External loads ordinarily control in the design of a sewer ring. Buried pipes may be subjected to such forces as are indicated in Figs. 8–1 and 8–2. In addition to the forces and conditions affecting the loads on buried pipes as indicated in the figures, there may be included such factors as the length of the trench, the flexibility of the pipe material, and the distribution of the load.

If the external loading is uniform and concentric around the circumference of a *circular* pipe, the internal stresses in the barrel of the pipe will all be compression. If the loading is not uniform or the pipe is not circular, all possible forms of internal stress may exist. The first condition is rarely encountered in sewerage practice since the loads are seldom uniformly distributed and the sewers are not always circular.

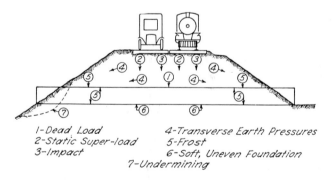

```
1-Dead Load                4-Transverse Earth Pressures
2-Static Super-load        5-Frost
3-Impact                   6-Soft, Uneven Foundation
               7-Undermining
```

Fig. 8–2. Loads and pressures on underground structures. (From *Handbook of Culvert and Drainage Practice,* by permission of Armco Drainage and Metal Products Co.)

The flexibility of the pipe affects the loads and stresses because the change of shape affects the distribution and intensity of external loads. The load on a rigid pipe may be somewhat as indicated in Fig. 8–1*b*, whereas the deflection of the top of a flexible pipe might cause arching in the surrounding ground with a load distribution somewhat as indicated in Fig. 8–1*c*. Marston [1] has defined a *rigid* conduit as a conduit in which a change of more than 0.1 per cent of its horizontal or its vertical dimensions would cause definitely injurious cracks; for semi-rigid conduits the limits are set at more than 0.1 per cent but less than 3 per cent; and for flexible conduits the limits are set at more than 3 per cent. Vitrified-clay, concrete, and cast-iron pipes are rigid pipes. Steel pipes are flexible.

The length of the trench has been found by test to affect the intensity of the load on a buried pipe, probably because of the effect on the possibilities of arch action and even distribution of loading along the pipe. Short trenches are represented by culverts under highways and railroads, the pipe probably protruding from the side of the embankment, as indicated in Fig. 8–2.

The nature of the load placed on the ground surface over the pipe, called a superimposed load, affects the intensity of load transmitted to the pipe. Such loads may be classified as concentrated, in truck wheel loads for instance, or as distributed, as in piles of construction materials on the surface.

The manner in which the pipe is supported in the trench, as indicated in Fig. 8–3, and the nature of the backfill material affect the distribution of the load and the internal stresses. Boulders, broken stone, and rough debris placed on top of a buried pipe will cause greater concentrations of load than the same weight of dry sand or wet clay.

8–4. Characteristics of transmitted loads. Loads due to or transmitted by granular fill materials have certain characteristics that must be borne in mind when using the ensuing methods in determining the loads transmitted to buried pipes. First, the loads vary with variations in the properties of the materials, such as weight, settlement, moisture, temperature, internal friction, and cohesion; second, the formulas given on page 194 represent only ultimate conditions. The ultimate, limiting load to which a conduit may be subjected may not develop for a long time, and it may never develop; and third, external loads on buried conduits usually vary with time.

[1] Anson Marston, *Bull.* 96, Iowa Engineering Experiment Station, 1930.

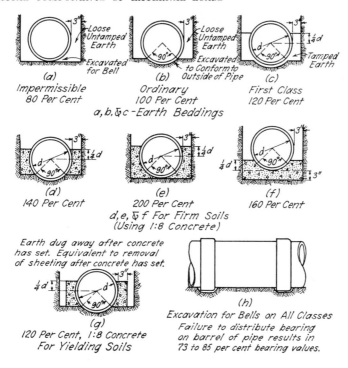

Fig. 8-3. Methods of pipe laying and relative bearing values. The percentages indicate the supporting strength that may be developed. (From *Bull*. 96, Iowa Engineering Experiment Station.)

8-5. Vertical components of external loads. The exhaustive investigation of loads on buried pipes made at Iowa State College by Anson Marston remains the basis for much that is known and practiced in the field. The results are published principally in *Bulletins* 31, 45, 57, 76, 96, 108, and 112 of the Iowa Engineering Experiment Station. A review of Marston's work, made by Spangler, was published in *Proceedings of the American Society of Civil Engineers*, June, 1947, p. 855. Other valuable publications in the field include: *Concrete Pipe Handbook*, American Concrete Pipe Association, 1951; *Handbook of Drainage and Construction Products*, Armco Drainage and Metal Products, Inc., 1955; and *Clay Pipe Engineering Manual*, Clay Products Association, 1956. Much of the following material is taken from Marston and Spangler.

Conditions under which conduits are buried may be classified as: (1) completely buried in a ditch, with undisturbed ground as the bottom and side walls of the ditch—this is called a *ditch condition;* or (2) partly buried in a shallow ditch, the remaining part of the conduit being covered with an earth embankment or backfill projecting above the surface of the surrounding ground. This is called a *projection condition* or *projection conduit.* If there is a load on top of the backfill it is called a *superimposed load.* A moving vehicle or a concentrated load which does not extend along the ditch is called a *short load.* A load extending along the ditch, such as a pile of building material, is called a *long load.*

In the discussion of the empirical formulas developed by Marston the following nomenclature is used:

B = horizontal breadth of a conduit or ditch, feet.

B_c = greatest horizontal breadth of a conduit, feet.

B_d = horizontal breadth of trench at top of conduit, feet. If trench has sloping sides B_d is measured 0.15 of the outside diameter below the top of the conduit.

C = a coefficient, abstract number.

C_c = a coefficient for projection conduits, abstract number. See Fig. 8–5.

C_d = a coefficient for ditch conduits, abstract number. See Fig. 8–4.

C_t = a coefficient for vertical loads on conduit tops due to superimposed loads, abstract number. See Fig. 8–6.

C_{us} = a coefficient for long loads on ditch conduits, abstract number. See Table 8–1.

d_c = increment of deflection of conduit, i.e., shortening of vertical height, feet.

H = vertical height from top of conduit to the upper surface of the fill, feet.

I_c = impact coefficient for calculation of impact loads on conduit tops due to moving concentrated superloads, abstract number. I_c = 1.00 for static loads; 1.50 to 2.00 for wheel loads moving 20 mph.

$k = \dfrac{\sqrt{\mu^2 + 1} - \mu}{\sqrt{\mu^2 + 1} + \mu}$ (Rankine's formula), abstract number.

L = arbitrary length of conduit used for application of short loads. Usually taken as 3 ft.

p = the projection ratio = the ratio of the vertical height of the top of the conduit above the embankment subgrade level to B_c, abstract number. The conduit projection = pB_c. In many cases the ratio p should be regarded as a semi-empiric physical factor representing the best judgment of the engineer as to the characteristic field conditions in actual use. Whenever practicable p should be determined by measurement or observation for each structure.

pr_{sd} = the product of the projection ratio and settlement deflection ratio. For cast-iron pipe with outside diameter of 27 in. p_{rsd} varies between 0.71 and 1.20; it is between 0.22 and 0.60 for vitrified-clay pipe with outside diameter of 1.31 ft; and one observation on a vitrified-clay pipe 3.43 ft in diameter was 0.81.

r_{sd} = "settlement deflection" ratio, abstract number.

$$r_{sd} = \frac{(S_m + S_g) - (d_c + S_f)}{S_m}$$

Note: r_{sd} is negative for the ditch condition; it is positive for the projection condition. r_{sd} indicates the effect of conduit deflections, the settlement of the conduit foundations, and the embankment subgrade settlements, relative to the yielding of the embankment-fill materials adjacent to the conduit.

S_f = increment of settlement of conduit foundation, feet.

S_g = increment of settlement of embankment subgrade, feet.

S_m = increment of settlement of materials adjacent to the conduit between the levels of the conduit top and the adjacent embankment subgrade, feet. Note: d_c, S_f, S_g, and S_m are the increments due to the addition at or above the height of settlement of any (the same for all) incremental, uniform layer of fill materials.

T = concentrated superimposed load, pounds. See Table 8–2.

U_s = uniformly distributed, superimposed load, pounds per square foot. See Table 8–3.

w = unit weight of fill materials, pounds per cubic foot. See Table 8–4.

W = the vertical external load on a buried conduit, pounds per foot of length.

W_c = the vertical external load on a conduit due to fill materials, pounds per foot of length.

W_c' = vertical external load on a buried conduit due to fill material for the case of flexible pipes and thoroughly compacted side fills.

W_t = the average total vertical load on a section of a conduit due to concentrated superload T, pounds per linear foot.

W_{us} = the average total vertical load on a section of a conduit due to U_s, pounds per linear foot.

μ = the coefficient of internal friction in the fill materials, abstract number. See Table 8–4.

μ' = the coefficient of sliding friction between the fill materials and the sides of the ditch, abstract number.

Marston's empirical formulas for the loads on buried pipes are:

General formula:
$$W = CwB^2 \qquad (8\text{--}1)$$

Projection conduits:
$$W = C_c w B_c{}^2 \qquad (8\text{--}2)$$

Ditch conduits:
$$W = C_d w B_d{}^2 \qquad (8\text{--}3)$$

Concentrated superloads:
$$W = (1/L)I_c C_t T \qquad (8\text{--}4)$$

Uniform superload:
$$W_{us} = C_{us} B_d U_s \qquad (8\text{--}5)$$

Flexible conduits:
$$W_c = C_d B_c B_d \qquad (8\text{--}6)$$

The values of the constants are read from the charts in Figs. 8–4 to 8–7 inclusive. Where a buried conduit is subjected to both a backfill load and a superimposed load the total load on the conduit is the sum of the two loads.

The refinements involved in the use of Marston's method may not be justified on most sewer work because of ignorance of the value of the coefficients involved. If Marston's method is used, the results should be checked against the weight of the prism of backfill and the

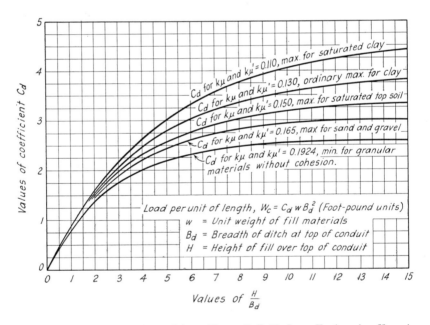

Fig. 8–4. Loads on ditch conduits. (From *Bull.* 96, Iowa Engineering Experiment Station.)

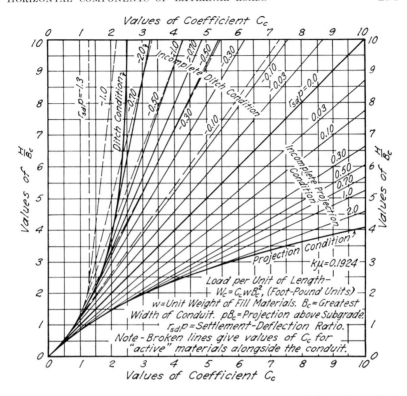

Fig. 8–5. External loads on projection conduits. (From *Bull.* 96, Iowa Engineering Experiment Station.)

superimposed load immediately above the buried pipe. The sum of the weight of the backfill and superimposed load should be used as a check against any solution by Marston's method. Where knowledge of conditions is uncertain, this sum may be used as the vertical component of load on the pipe.

8–6. Horizontal components of external loads. The horizontal components of external loads, or pressures on ditch conduits, are wholly dependent on the class of bedding and are best taken into account by using conduit supporting strength bedding ratios of field supporting strength to laboratory test strength, as given in Table 8–5. For projecting conduits: (1) for rigid conduits the active horizontal pressure is equal to k times the vertical pressure against the projecting sides; (2) for semi-rigid conduits the pressure should be assumed as somewhat greater than for rigid conduits; and (3) for flexible and

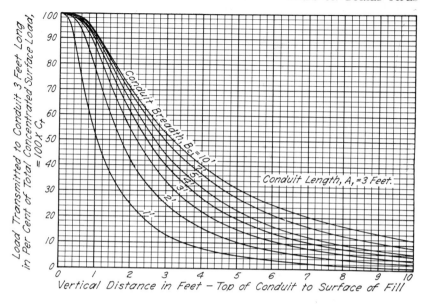

Fig. 8–6. Concentrated surface load coefficients. (From *Bull.* 96, Iowa Engineering Experiment Station.)

Table 8–1

SAFE VALUES OF C_{us}

(*Bull.* 96, Iowa Engineering Experiment Station.)

$\dfrac{H}{B_d}$	Sand and Damp Top Soil	Saturated Top Soil	Damp Yellow Clay	Saturated Yellow Clay
0.0	1.00	1.00	1.00	1.00
0.5	0.85	0.86	0.88	0.89
1.0	0.72	0.75	0.77	0.80
1.5	0.61	0.64	0.67	0.72
2.0	0.52	0.55	0.59	0.64
2.5	0.44	0.48	0.52	0.57
3.0	0.37	0.41	0.45	0.51
4.0	0.27	0.31	0.35	0.41
5.0	0.19	0.23	0.27	0.33
6.0	0.14	0.17	0.20	0.26
8.0	0.07	0.09	0.12	0.17
10.0	0.04	0.05	0.07	0.11
1	2	3	4	5

Table 8–2

WEIGHTS OF LIVE LOADS ON SEWER TRENCHES

Adapted from Specifications of the American Bridge Company for Bridges

Street railways, heavy	A load of 24 tons on 2 axles on 10-ft centers.
Street railways, light	A load of 18 tons on 2 axles on 10-ft centers.
For city streets, heavy traffic	A load of 24 tons on 2 axles 10 ft apart and 5-ft gage.
For city streets, moderate traffic	A load of 12 tons on 2 axles 10 ft apart and 5-ft gage.
For city streets, light traffic or country roads	A load of 6 tons on 2 axles 10 ft apart and 5-ft gage.
Road rollers	Total weight 30,000 lb. Weight on front wheel, 12,000 lb, and on each of two rear wheels, 9,000 lb. Width of front wheel, 4 ft, and of each of two rear wheels 20 in. Distance between front and rear axles 11 ft. Gage of rear wheels, 5 ft, center to center.

badly cracked conduits the horizontal pressures may equal the vertical pressures.

8–7. Effect of width of trench. It is to be noted that the load transmitted to the pipes is a function of the width, B_d, of the trench, and that no limit has been put on this width. The width of the trench is the distance between the walls at about 15 per cent of the pipe diameter below the top of the pipe. Some recommended widths of trenches are listed in Table 8–6. On page 6 of *Bulletin* 108 of the Iowa Engineering Experiment Station it is stated that "as the width of the trench increases, other conditions remain constant, the load on the conduit increases . . . until it equals that by the projection-

Table 8–3

WEIGHTS OF COMMON BUILDING MATERIAL WHEN PILED FOR STORAGE

Pounds per Cubic Foot

Brick	120	Lumber	35
Cement	90	Granite paving	160
Sand	90	Coal	50
Broken stone	150	Pig iron	400

198

LOADS ON BURIED PIPES

Table 8-4

COEFFICIENTS OF FRICTION AND WEIGHTS OF DITCH MATERIALS

Coefficients of Friction μ, for Earthy Materials   Approximate Weights of Ditch Filling Material

Material	Coefficient μ	Ditch Filling Material	Pounds per Cubic Foot
Earth on earth	0.25–1.0	Partly compacted top soil	
Earth on earth, damp clay	1.0	(damp)	90
Dry sand, clay, and		Saturated top soil	110
mixed earth	0.38–0.75	Partly compacted damp	
Wet clay	0.31	yellow clay	100
Shingle and gravel	0.81–1.11	Saturated yellow clay	130
		Dry sand	100
		Wet sand	120

Table 8-5

THE RELATION OF ACTUAL SUPPORTING STRENGTHS TO LABORATORY TEST STRENGTHS FOR CONDUITS COMPLETELY BURIED IN DITCHES

(From *Bull.* 96, Iowa Engineering Experiment Station, 1930.)

Condition of Bedding, Fig. 8–3	Ratios
Impermissible bedding	$S_{mb} = 0.75S_{sb} = 1.12S_{eb}$
Ordinary bedding	$S_{ob} = 1.00S_{sb} = 1.50S_{eb}$
First-class bedding	$S_{cb} = 1.25S_{sb} = 1.87S_{eb}$
	$S_{cb} = 1.50S_{sb} = 2.25S_{eb}$
Concrete-cradle bedding	$S_{cc} = 2.25S_{sb} = 3.37S_{cb}$

S_{sb} = sand bearing laboratory strength; S_{eb} = 3-edge bearing laboratory strength; S_{mb} = supporting strength, "impermissible loading"; S_{ob} = supporting strength, "ordinary bedding"; S_{cb} = supporting strength, "first-class bedding"; and S_{cc} = supporting strength for "concrete-cradle bedding"; all in pounds per foot of length.

conduit load theory, and then remains constant for all greater widths." It is convenient to express this transition width in terms of the ratio of the horizontal breadth of the ditch at the top of the conduit (B_d) to the greatest horizontal breadth of the conduit (B_c), that is B_d/B_c. The transition width of the trench is that width for

Table 8–6

MAXIMUM RECOMMENDED WIDTHS OF TRENCHES
FOR STANDARD VITRIFIED-CLAY PIPE

Diameter of pipe, in.	6	8	10	12	15	18
Width of trench, ft and in.	2–0	2–2	2–4	2–6	2–10	3–1

Diameter of pipe, in.	21	24	27	30	33	36
Width of trench, ft and in.	3–5	3–8	4–0	4–3	4–6	4–10

which the ditch-conduit load equals the load by the projecting-conduit load theory. The transition-width ratio varies with values of H/B_c. Relations of H/B_c to B_d/B_c for various values of $r_{sd}p$ are shown in Fig. 8–7.

The probable maximum load for widths of ditch equal to or greater than the transition width may be calculated by the ditch-conduit

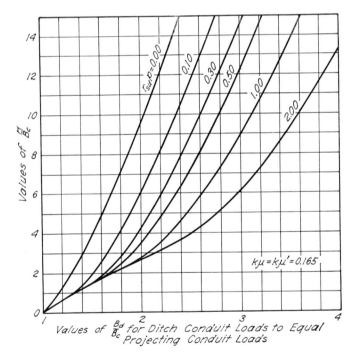

Fig. 8–7. Curves for determining the transition width ratio. (From *Bull.* 108, Iowa Engineering Experiment Station.)

load theory with the width factor equal to the transition width. The width of the ditch, if near to the transition width, should be calculated with the highest value of the settlement projection ratio, $r_{sd}p$, that seems probable under the particular circumstances, and the safe supporting strength of the pipe should be determined with the field-laboratory strength ratio for ditch conduits, given in Table 8–5.

Example. (a) Determine the load per foot length on an 18-in. diameter unreinforced concrete pipe in a trench that is 36 in. wide, with a cover of 6 ft of saturated yellow clay. The trench is in a city street with moderate traffic. (b) What would be the factor of safety against crushing if standard-strength, vitrified-clay pipe were used?

Solution. The ratio of $H/B = \%_3 = 2$. From Fig. 8–4, $C_d = 1.6$. From Table 8–4, $w = 130$. Then $W = C_d w B^2 = 1.6 \times 130 \times 3^2 = 1{,}875$ lb per ft length of pipe. For part (b): From Table 7–2 the crushing strength of 18-in. pipe is 3,000 lb per ft of length. The factor of safety is, therefore, $3{,}000/1{,}873 = 1.6$.

8–8. Stresses in flexible rings. Stresses in thin, flexible rings under different loadings are shown in Table 8–7. The bending moment in the barrel of a circular sewer can be approximated with sufficient accuracy for practical purposes from Table 8–7, provided that the ratio of thickness to diameter is normal. The stresses in the sewer barrel or in the reinforcement, at the critical sections, can be determined by the application of the information in Table 8–7 in the

Table 8–7

MAXIMUM STRESSES IN FLEXIBLE RINGS DUE TO VARIOUS LOADINGS

(From Marston.)

Symmetrical Vertical Loadings		Moment at Crown of Sewer	Moment at End of Horizontal Diameter	Compressive Thrust at Crown	Compressive Thrust at End of Horizontal Diameter	Shear at Crown	Shear at End of Horizontal Diameter
Character	Width *	$W/12$	$W/12$	$W/12$	$W/12$	$W/12$	eter
Concentrated	0°	$+0.318R$	$-0.182R$	0.000	$+0.500$	0.500	0.000
Uniform	60°	$+0.207R$	$-0.168R$	0.000	$+0.500$	0.000	0.000
Uniform	90°	$+0.169R$	$-0.154R$	0.000	$+0.500$	0.000	0.000
Uniform	180°	$+0.125R$	$-0.125R$	0.000	$+0.500$	0.000	0.000

* Degrees of arc covered by the central angle shown.

R = radius of pipe in inches; W = total weight of ditch filling and superimposed load plus $\%_3$ of the weight of the pipe itself (usually neglected), expressed in pounds per foot of length of pipe. Moments are inch-pounds per inch length of pipe. Shears and thrusts are in pounds per inch length of pipe.

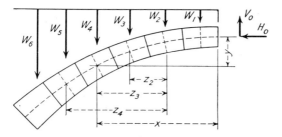

Fig. 8–8. Diagram for arch analysis.

ordinary column or beam analysis. If, however, the sewer barrel is not circular or is not uniformly loaded, the stresses must be determined by an analysis of the arch. The following example illustrates the procedure:

Example. Determine the bending moment in inch-pounds per inch length of a thin-walled, 48-in. pipe, uniformly loaded over the full diameter, with a load of 1,200 lb per ft length of pipe. The weight of the pipe is to be neglected.

Solution. $M = (W/12)(0.125R) = (1,200/12)(0.125)24 = 300$ in-lb per in. length of pipe, or 300 ft-lb per ft length of pipe.

8–9. Arch analysis. Three methods of arch analysis applicable in sewer design are the static or voussoir method, the elastic theory, and the method of indeterminate structures. The three methods are presented in *American Sewerage Practice* by Metcalf and Eddy, Vol. I, 2nd edition, 1928.[2] Stress computations by the three methods show results differing more than 25 per cent.

In the elastic arch analysis the three principal formulas are:

Horizontal thrust at crown:
$$H_0 = \left(\frac{W}{2}\right)\frac{n\Sigma zy - \Sigma y \cdot \Sigma z}{n\Sigma y^2 - (\Sigma y)^2} \qquad (8\text{–}7)$$

Moment at crown:
$$M_0 = \frac{\tfrac{1}{2}W\Sigma z - H\Sigma y}{n} \qquad (8\text{–}8)$$

Shear at crown:
$$V_0 = \frac{\tfrac{1}{2}W\Sigma zx}{\Sigma x^2} \qquad (8\text{–}9)$$

where W = load on the left semi-arch of Fig. 8–8, n = number of voussoirs in the semi-arch, and other nomenclature is shown in Fig. 8–8. For symmetrical loading such as W on the left and W on the

[2] Published by the McGraw-Hill Book Co.

right, the horizontal thrust and crown moment due to both loads are double those found by the above formulas, while the crown shear V_0 is zero. For several loads unsymmetrically placed the formulas are to be applied to each in succession and the results added algebraically, the value of V_0 being taken as negative for the left semi-arch and positive for the right semi-arch.

For any joint whose middle point is at a distance x from the crown

$$M = M_0 + Hy + V_0 x - \Sigma W z$$

$$V = V_0 - \Sigma W$$

where ΣW is the sum of all the loads between the joint and the crown, and $\Sigma W z$ is the sum of the moments of those loads with respect to the middle of the joint. The components of the resultant thrust normal and parallel to the joints are, respectively,

$$N = H \cos \theta - V \sin \theta$$

$$F = H \sin \theta + V \cos \theta$$

in which θ is the angle which the plane of the joint makes with the vertical.

The distances from the neutral axis of the arch to the resistance line are

At the crown $e_0 = M_0/H$

At the joint $e = M/N$

The resistance line may be located as in the voussoir method, and if not within the middle third a new design should be studied, unless the arch is to be reinforced.

8–10. Reinforced-concrete sewer design. In the determination of the stresses in a reinforced-concrete arch the following expression can be used:

$$f_s = (Me/I) \pm (H/A)$$

where f_s = the intensity of fiber stress.

M = the moment at the section.

e = the distance from the stressed fiber to the neutral axis.

H = the thrust at the section.

A = the cross-sectional area of the stressed section.

$I = I_c + nI_s$.

I_c = moment of inertia of concrete section about the neutral axis.

I_s = moment of inertia of steel section about the neutral axis.

n = ratio of moduli of elasticity of steel to concrete, usually taken as 15.

Sewers cast in place are ordinarily designed to avoid reinforcement, except where the depth of cover is small and the sewer may be subjected to superimposed loads. Sometimes, where a standard sewer section has been adopted, the same section will be maintained under various conditions of loading to avoid changing the concrete forms, and the portions of the sewer with additional loads will be reinforced.

Concrete sewers are sometimes reinforced longitudinally, with expansion joints from 30 to 50 ft apart. This reinforcement is to reduce the size of expansion and contraction cracks by distributing them over the length of the section. The amount of longitudinal reinforcement to be used is a matter of judgment. It varies in practice from 0.1 to 0.4 per cent of the area of the section.

Because of the uncertain and difficult conditions under which concrete sewers are frequently constructed, it is advisable to specify the best grade of concrete and not to stress it over about 450 psi in compression, with no allowable stress in tension. The concrete covering of reinforcing steel should be thicker than is ordinarily used for building design, because of the possibility of poor concrete allowing the sewage to gain access to the steel, resulting in more rapid deterioration than would be caused by exposure to the atmosphere. A minimum covering of about 2 in. is advisable, except in very thin sections not in contact with sewage. A minimum thickness of concrete of about 9 in. is frequently used in design, although crown thicknesses of $4\frac{1}{2}$ in. have been used with success. Greater thickness should be used near the ground surface, particularly in locations subjected to heavy or moving loads.

Brick or vitrified-clay linings may be provided for the invert where velocities of 10 fps or more are to be expected. Although concrete may erode no faster than brick or clay linings under similar conditions, the linings can be replaced more easily and at smaller expense.

Chapter 9

Construction of sewers

9–1. Work involved. Among the factors or conditions involved in sewer construction that are not applicable to most other construction work are the excavation of trenches, and the laying and construction of sewer pipe in trenches and tunnels. Most trench work involves open-cut excavation. It includes: (1) the removal of pavement; (2) the removal of material from the ground, and its separation, its classification where necessary, and its final disposal; (3) sheeting and bracing the sides of the trench; (4) the removal of water from the trench; (5) the protection of other structures, both underground and on the surface, whose foundations may be affected; (6) backfilling; and (7) the replacement of pavement. On all excavation work, safety precautions for the protection of life and property are essential, and measures to avoid too great inconvenience to the public are desirable. Such measures and precautions include the erection and maintenance of signs, barricades, bridges, and detours; the placing and maintenance of lights, both for illumination and as danger signals; the provision of watchmen to exclude unauthorized persons, particularly children, from trespassing on the work; and such other precautions as local conditions may dictate.

9–2. Removing pavement. The removal of pavement is often necessary as the first step in sewer excavation. It may be done manually with hammer and chisel, or with the aid of a pneumatic hammer as illustrated in Fig. 9–1. Various cutting tools are fitted into the head of the pneumatic hammer. A wide chisel blade is used for bituminous, macadam, or gravel pavements; an asphalt cutter for sheet asphalt; and a moil point for concrete pavements or foundations. Power-driven saws are used which make straight cuts of concrete without the shocks and jagged edges accompanying percussion tools. Joints in brick or block pavements can be pried loose in large pieces with a crowbar.

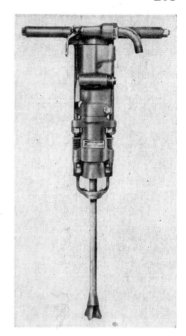

Fig. 9–1. Rockdrill. (Courtesy Worthington Corporation.)

The pavement aids in supporting the trench and, for this reason, it should be cut along the edge of the trench or no more than an inch or two back of it.

9–3. Excavation in quicksand.[1]   Sand, or other granular material in which there is sufficient upward flow of ground water to lift it, is known as quicksand.   It is a condition, not a quality, of the sand.   Sand is "quick" only when water is moving upward through it with sufficient velocity to separate and to support the grains of sand in the rising water.   A subsurface stratum of firm, saturated sand may become "quick" when a trench is excavated in it, allowing contained water to escape as additional water flows through it.   Quicksand behaves as a fluid.   It will support weight only by flotation. It must be borne in mind that the presence of quicksand cannot be readily determined by test borings.   The borings may show only the presence of wet sand which may not be "quick."   Quicksand may develop in excavations and test pits that disturb the normal groundwater table.

[1] See also J. R. Gow, *Jour. New Eng. Water Works Assoc.*, September, 1920; and *Public Works*, Vol. 50, 1921, p. 98.

Excavation in quicksand is troublesome, expensive, and frequently dangerous. The material will flow as a liquid. It cannot be pumped easily, and its excavation causes the sides of the trench to fall in or the bottom to rise. The foundations of nearby structures may be undermined, causing serious damage. These conditions may arise even after the backfilling has been placed, unless proper care has been taken. The greatest safeguard against such dangers is not only to exercise care in the backfilling to see that it is compactly tamped and placed, but also to leave all sheeting in position after the completion of the work.

The ordinary method of combating quicksand and of conducting work in wet trenches is to drive watertight sheeting 2 or 3 ft below the bottom of the trench, and to dewater the sand by well points outside of the trench, as described in Sect. 10–28. The sand can be excavated without great difficulty when it is free from water. Successful excavation in quicksand requires experience, resourcefulness, and a careful watch for unexpected developments. It should be borne in mind that a fluid, not a solid, is being handled, if excavation of sand is attempted when it is "quick."

9–4. Rock excavation. Rock is commonly defined in specifications as follows: whenever the word *rock* is used as the name of an excavated material it shall mean the ledge material removed or to be removed properly by channeling, wedging, barring or blasting; boulders having a volume of 9 cu ft (this volume may be varied) or more; and any excavated masonry. No soft disintegrated rock which can be removed with a pick, nor loose shale, nor previously blasted material, nor material which may have fallen into the trench will be measured or allowed as rock.

Channeling consists in cutting long narrow channels in the rock to free the sides of a large block of stone. The block is then loosened by driving in wedges, or it is pried loose with bars. This method is more common in quarry than in trench excavation where it is not necessary to preserve the stone intact. In blasting, a hole is drilled in the rock and loaded with an explosive which when fired shatters the rock and loosens it from its position.

In hand drilling of rock the drill is manipulated by one man, who holds it and turns it in the hole with one hand while striking it with a hammer weighing about 4 lb held in the other hand; or one man may hold and turn the drill while one or two others strike it with heavier hammers. In churn drilling a heavy drill is raised and dropped in the hole, the force of the blow developing from the weight of the falling drill. Hand drills are steel bars of a length suitable for the depth of the hole, with the cutting edge widened and sharpened to an angle as sharp as can be used without breaking. The drill bar is usually about $\frac{1}{8}$ in. smaller than the diameter of the face of the drill. Wedges used are called plugs and feathers. The feathers are wedges with one round and one flat face on which the flat faces of the plug slide.

9–5. Power drilling. In power drilling a reciprocating machine either strikes and turns the drill in the hole, or lifts and turns it as in churn drilling, or the drill may be driven by a rotary machine which is revolved by compressed air, steam, or electricity. There are many different types of machines suitable for drilling in the different classes of material encountered and for utilizing the various forms of power available.

A jackhammer drill is shown in Fig. 9-1. In its lightest form the drill weighs about 20 lb and is capable of drilling $\frac{7}{8}$-in. holes to a depth of 4 ft. Heavier machines are available for drilling larger and deeper holes. The same machine can be adapted for the use of steam or compressed air. When in action the point of the drill is placed against the rock and a pressure on the handle admits air or steam. The piston is caused to reciprocate in the cylinder, striking the head of the drill at each stroke. The drill is revolved in the hole by hand or by the mechanism of the machine. A hollow drill can be used by means of which the operator admits air or steam into the hole, thus blowing out dust and keeping the hole clean. These machines have the advantage of small size, portability, and simplicity. They can be easily and quickly set up, and the drill bits can be changed rapidly. Their undesirable features include vibration transmitted to the operator and dust raised in the trench. Dust may be removed through suction hose leading from the top of the hole that is being drilled. Types of drill heavier and larger than the hand drill shown in Fig. 9–1 are shown in Fig. 9–2. Both require some form of carriage for transport, as indicated. Another type of drill that is frequently used is supported on a tripod, or in tunnel work it can be braced against the roof or sides.

An electric drill operated on the principle of the solenoid does away with motor, valves, pipes, vapor, freezing and other difficulties attendant on the use of steam or air.

Frequent changes of drills and relocation of tripods will materially reduce the performance of a drill.

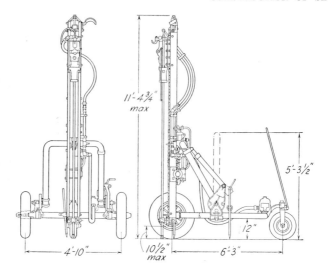

Wagon drill. (Courtesy Worthington Co.)

Fig. 9–2. Tripod drill and "Wagon" drill.

Tripod drill

9–6. Type of power. Electricity, compressed air, or steam may be used for power drilling. Electric equipment is relatively portable and is clean, quiet, and efficient. There is, however, some danger in its use because of broken wires and insulation. Electricity can be generated on the job by portable generators driven by internal-combustion engines or it may be taken from nearby power lines. Compressed-air drilling is convenient in open-cut work and is especially suitable in tunnels, aiding in their ventilation. Compressed air is less dangerous than electricity, but the length of the transmission pipes, the temperature of the outside air, and the pressure at which the compressed air is used affect the volume of free air to be compressed. Air compressors may be driven by electric motors, internal combustion engines, and, rarely, by steam engines. Steam is infrequently used in power drilling because of cost, transportation of fuel and water, heat generated, particularly in tunnels, dangers of burns and burst steam hose, and clouds of vapor given off. Leaks in steam hose are more easily discovered than in air hose, it requires less equipment than compressed air, and under favorable circumstances it may be less expensive.

9–7. Depth of drill hole. The depth of the hole is dependent on the type of work. The deepest holes can be used in open-cut work where the shattered rock is to be removed by power shovel. The face can be made 10 to 15 ft high. The depth of the hole in center-cut tunnel facings is 6 to 10 or even 12 ft. In the bench the depth is equal to the height of the bench. In narrow trenches, where the rock is to be removed by derrick or thrown into a bucket by hand, the hole should be sufficiently deep to shatter the rock to a depth of at least 6 in. below the finished sewer. Frequently shooting to this depth cannot be done at one shot owing to the built-up condition of the neighborhood or other local factors. The depth of the hole in trench work should not much exceed the distance between holes. Deep holes are usually desirable as a matter of economy in saving frequent set-ups, but the holes cannot be made much more than 20 ft in depth without increasing the friction on the drill to a prohibitive amount.

9–8. Diameter of drill hole. The diameter of the hole should be such as to take the desired size of explosive cartridge. The common sizes of dynamite cartridges are from $\frac{7}{8}$ to 2 in. in diameter. In drilling, the diameter of the hole is reduced about $\frac{1}{8}$ in. at a time as the drill begins to stick. This reduction should be allowed for, and experience is the best guide for the size of the hole at the start. In general, the softer or more faulty or seamy the rock, the more frequent are the necessary reductions in size of bit. For hard homogeneous rock the holes can be drilled 10 ft or more without changing the size of the drill bit.

9–9. Spacing of drill holes. The spacing of drill holes in open-cut excavation is commonly equal to the depth of the hole. The type of material being excavated has much to do with the spacing

Table 9-1

DRILL HOLES IN ROCK EXCAVATION

(From Gillette.)

Kind of Material	Powder Used per Hole	Depth of Hole, ft	Distance Back of Face, ft	Distance Hole to Hole, ft
Limestone	40% dynamite	12	8	8
Sandstone	200 lb black powder	20	18	14
Granite	2 lb 60% dynamite	12	4½	4½ to 5

of the holes. The spacing, diameter, and the depths of holes used on some jobs are shown in Table 9–1. Gillette [2] states:

It is obviously impossible to lay down any hard and fast rule for drill holes. In stratified rock that is friable, and in traps that are full of natural joints and seams, it is often possible to space the holes a distance apart somewhat greater than their depth, and still break the rock to comparatively small sizes upon blasting. In tough granite, gneiss, syenite, and in trap where joints are few and far between, the holes may have to be spaced 3 to 8 ft apart, regardless of their depth, because with wider spacing the blocks thrown down will be too large to handle with ordinary appliances.

The common practice in placing drill holes is to put down holes in pairs, one hole on each side of the proposed trench; and if the trench is wide or more holes are drilled between these two side holes, but in narrow trench work, such as for a 12-in. pipe, one hole in the middle of the trench will usually prove sufficient.

After the holes have been completed they should be plugged to keep out dirt and water.

[2] H. P. Gillette, *Handbook of Cost Data,* 1910.

Chapter 10

Sewer trenches

10–1. Trench shape and dimensions. Sewer trenches should be dug as narrow as possible and yet permit the laying of pipe, making and inspecting joints, and consolidating backfill. Unnecessary width increases the load that may be transmitted to the pipe. In deep trenches upper sections are sometimes cut wider than lower sections, or the sides of the trench may be sloped, to minimize the possibilities of caving and for convenience in sheeting. In sheeted trenches it may be necessary to increase the trench width to accommodate the sheeting and bracing. No excavated material should be piled within 2 ft of the edge of the trench. This safety requirement may affect the planned width of the trench or the type of excavating equipment used.

It is generally required that when the trench has been excavated within one-half of the diameter of the pipe from the bottom of the trench, if the material is sufficiently firm, the remainder of the trench should be constructed to conform to the shape of the lower half of the outside of the pipe. The importance of preparing the trench for the proper bedding of the pipe is emphasized by the information in Fig. 8–3. When rock is encountered it is removed to a level of 3 to 6 in. below the bottom of the sewer, and the trench is refilled to grade with sand or well-tamped earth, shaped to fit the pipe. In soft materials where a poor foundation is provided it may be necessary to place a concrete foundation to support the sewer adequately.

It is good practice to excavate a trench or tunnel, and to lay a sewer, up grade primarily for the reason that drainage is facilitated, but no water should be permitted to run through a sewer until the joints have set and the pipe has been firmly bedded.

It is undesirable to open trenches for more than a short distance in advance of pipe laying because most soils tend to cave in time and because traffic hazards due to the open trench are prolonged. Some

211

specifications limit the amount of trench that may be opened in advance of the work, requiring that a maximum amount of about 20 ft may be completed in advance of the pipe laying.

10–2. Trench excavation. Trenches may be excavated by hand or by machine. Blasting may be used under favorable conditions. On work of moderately large magnitude excavation by machine is cheaper than by hand. In comparing the cost of excavation by the two methods, all items such as sheeting, pipe laying, and backfilling should be included, since these items will be affected by the method of excavation. The cost of setting up and reshipping the machine must be included as this is frequently the item on which the use of the machine depends. Because of the cost of setting up and shipping, which must be distributed over the total number of yards excavated, the cost per cubic yard of excavating by machine varies with the number of cubic yards excavated. The point of economy in the use of a machine is reached when the cost by hand and by machine are equal. For all work of greater magnitude, excavation by machine will prove cheaper. Items favoring the use of machinery, which may cause its adoption for small jobs, are its speed, reliability, ease in handling, economy in sheeting, economy in labor, and small amount of space needed, making it useful in crowded streets. Continuous bucket machines, drag lines, and occasionally power shovels are not adapted to conditions where rocks, pipes, and other underground obstacles are frequently met.

An advantage of machine excavation is that the excavated material can be deposited in neat piles along the trench, loaded directly into the trucks for removal from the site, or carried back, without rehandling, to be placed in the backfill.

In opening trenches by blasting, a series of charges is placed in holes from 18 in. to 24 in. apart along the line of the trench. They are fired simultaneously by electric fuses or by propagation of the explosive wave from charge to charge. This method is suitable mainly in open country and in soft materials. Vertical-wall trenches are sometimes opened by blasting in built-up districts and elsewhere in hard materials and in subaqueous work, where proper precautions are taken.

10–3. Types of machines. Machines particularly adapted to the excavation of sewer- and water-pipe trenches are of four types: (1) continuous-bucket excavators, (2) overhead cableway or track excavators, (3) power shovels, and (4) boom-and-bucket excavators. Other types of excavating machinery can be used for sewer trenches under special conditions. Two types of machines used for backfilling include the bulldozer and the skimmer scoop.

10–4. Continuous-bucket excavators. Self-propelling, continuous-bucket excavators, with controllable, forward speeds, are of the types shown in Figs. 10–1 and 10–2. The buckets that do the digging and raising of the earth may be supported on a wheel as in Fig. 10–1, or on an endless chain, as in Fig. 10–2. The support of the wheel or endless chain can be raised or lowered at the will of the operator so as to keep the trench as close to grade as can be done by hand work. In some machines the shape of the buckets can be made such as to cut the bottom of the trench, in suitable material, to the shape of the sewer invert. In operation, the buckets are at the rear of the machine and revolve so that at the lowest point in their path they are traveling forward. The excavated material is dropped onto a continuous belt which throws it on the ground clear of the trench, into dump wagons, or onto another continuous belt running parallel with the trench to the backfiller, by means of which the excavated material is thrown directly into the backfill without rehandling. The body of the machine supporting the engine travels on wheels ahead of the excavation and is kept in line by means of the pivoted front axle. When obstacles are encountered the excavating wheel or chain is raised to pass over the obstacle and allowed to dig itself in on the other side.

Wheel excavators are adapted to the excavation of trenches between $10\frac{1}{2}$ in. and about $5\frac{1}{2}$ ft in width, and up to 6 to 8 ft in depth. The endless-chain excavators are suitable for depths of 25 ft with widths 6 to 92 in., and owing to the arrangement permitting buckets to be

Fig. 10–1. Wheel excavator. (Courtesy Gar Wood Industries.)

Fig. 10–2. Endless-chain bucket excavator. (Courtesy Parsons Co.) Note the guide line and the guide point to the right in the picture.

moved sideways they will cut trenches of different widths with the same size buckets. This is an advantage where there are to be irregularities in the width of the trench such as for manholes or changes in size of pipe. With excavating machines pipe can be laid within 3 ft of the moving buckets, and the trench can be backfilled immediately, thus making an appreciable saving in the amount of sheeting. In the construction of trenches for drain tile at Garden Prairie, Ill., the sheeting was built in the form of a box or shield, fastened to the rear of the machine, and pulled along after it.

A method of trenching in wet, unstable soil is illustrated in Fig. 10–3. The shield and wales are dragged along by the digger, thus protecting the sides of the trench until timber can be placed. As the digger moves forward the traveling wales hold the sheeting in place until timber wales can be placed. Bedding rock drops into the trench from the hopper, providing a dry, solid working base for the laying of the pipe. The traveling wales are moved vertically, as required, by means of elevating turnbuckles.

10–5. Cableway and trestle excavators. Cableway and trestle excavators are most suitable for deep trenches and for crowded conditions. They should not be used for trenches much less than 8 ft in depth. They differ from the continuous-bucket excavators in that the actual dislodgement of the material is done by pick and shovel, the excavated material being thrown by hand into the buckets of the machine. A machine of the Carson type is shown in Fig. 10–4. The machine consists of a series of demountable frames held together by cross braces and struts to form a semi-rigid structure. An I beam or channel extending the length of the machine is hung closely below

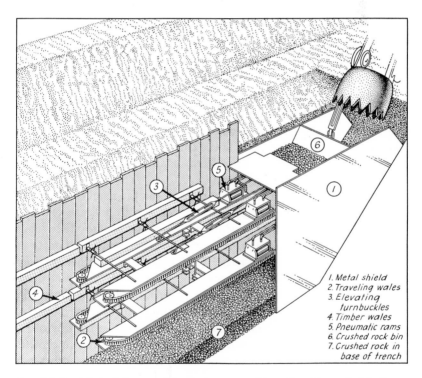

1. Metal shield
2. Traveling wales
3. Elevating turnbuckles
4. Timber wales
5. Pneumatic rams
6. Crushed rock bin
7. Crushed rock in base of trench

Fig. 10–3. Method for trenching in wet, unstable soil. (From A. M. Rawn, *Water and Sewage Works,* July, 1953.)

Fig. 10–4. Carson excavating machine. (Courtesy C. F. Henning.)

the top of the struts. The lower flange of this beam serves as a track for the carriages that carry the buckets. All the carriages are attached to each other and to an endless cable leading to a drum on the engine. This cable serves to move the buckets along the trench. The buckets are attached to another cable which is wound around another drum on the engine and serves to lower or raise all of the buckets at the same time. In operation there are always at least two buckets for each carriage, one in the trench being filled and the other on the machine being dumped. There should be a surplus of buckets to replace those needing repairs.

The machines may be 200 to 350 ft long, and the number of buckets that can be lifted at one time varies from one to a dozen or more. On trenches over 5 to 6 ft in width a double line of buckets is sometimes used. The entire machine straddles the trench and rests on rollers. It moves along the trench by its own power, either by gearing or chains attached to the wheels, or by a cable attached to a deadman ahead. In general, the capacity of such machines is limited by the amount of material that can be shoveled into them by hand.

10–6. Tower cableways. Tower cableways are essentially of the same class as the trestle-cableway machines. They differ in that the carriage supporting the buckets travels on a cable suspended between two towers instead of on a track supported on a trestle. As a rule only one bucket is handled in the machine at a time. Tower cableways are used in sewer work only in exceptional cases, as the towers must be moved each time that there is an advance in the trench greater than the distance between the towers.

10–7. Power shovels. Power shovels are driven by internal-combustion engines, electric motors, and occasionally by steam engines. Some power shovels are convertible from the stiff boom and derrick of the power-shovel type to drag line, grab bucket, trench hoe, or crane. In excavating a trench the older type shovel straddles the open trench and runs on tractors, wheels, or rollers on either side of it. The power shovel cuts the trench ahead of it, advancing with the work and on top of the open trench. One result is difficulty in setting sheeting, and another is danger of caving of the trench sides under the weight and vibration of the shovel. Power shovels are, therefore, not suitable for excavating in unstable material unless the sheeting is driven ahead of the excavation. It is only in the softest ground that ordinary wood sheeting can be driven ahead of the excavation. Steel sheet piling is more suitable for such a purpose. Shovels are equipped with extra long dipper booms to adapt them to trench excavation.

10–8. Trench hoes. A trench hoe, illustrated in Fig. 10–5, consists of a drop-bottom bucket on an arm hinged to the end of a boom. The bucket, when digging, is pulled toward the machine which travels on the line of the trench ahead of the excavation. Trench hoes are better adapted than power shovels to the excavation of small and moderate-size trenches and have an advantage in not having to straddle the trench after it has been excavated. Performance claims for one type of trench hoe include: ability to dig vertically, to undercut walls and trenches, and to change pitch of teeth during digging for the best cutting angle.[1]

10–9. Drag-line and bucket excavators. A drag-line excavator is shown in Fig. 10–6. The back of the bucket is attached to a drum on the engine by means of a cable passing over a wheel on the end of the long boom. The front of the bucket is attached to another cable leading to another drum on the engine. In operation the bucket is raised by its rear and swung out beyond the end of the boom. It is then dragged over the ground towards the machine, digging itself in at the same time. When filled the bucket is raised by tightening

[1] See J. W. Reilly, *Water and Sewage Works,* December, 1950, p. 496.

Fig. 10–5. Trench hoe, back hoe, or pull shovel. (Courtesy Gar Wood Industries.)

up on the two cables, swung to one side by means of the movable boom, and dumped.

Drag-line excavators will perform as much work as power shovels under favorable conditions. They are less expensive in first cost and operation and are equally reliable, but they are not adapted to the more difficult situations where power shovels can be used to advantage. Drag lines are suitable only for relatively wide trenches in material requiring no bracing, and in a locality where relatively long stretches of trench can be open at one time.

The bucket excavator differs from the drag line in that the bucket can be lifted vertically only, and the types of buckets used in the two machines are different. The bucket may be self-filling, of the orange-peel or clam-shell type, or a container, usually cylindrical, which must be filled by hand. A drag line can be converted easily to a boom-and-bucket excavator. These are well adapted to use in deep, closely braced trenches and shafts.

10–10. Locating excavations.   In order to locate a trench, stakes should be driven at frequent intervals along the center line of the proposed sewer before excavation is commenced.   Reference stakes or reference points to this line are located at some fixed offset distance or easily described point, or the stakes may be driven at some constant difference to one side of the trench, in order to avoid the danger of loss or disturbance of the stakes.   Elevation or cut is seldom marked on the preliminary stakes, although the approximate cut may be indicated.

Fig. 10–6. Dragline excavator opening a trench. (Courtesy Gar Wood Industries.) Note the well points on each side of the trench.

For hand excavation the foreman lays out the trench from these stakes. In machine work the operator guides the machine so as to follow the line of stakes.

Manholes and similar structures requiring wider excavation than the trench may be located by two pairs of reference stakes so placed that strings joining the reference points on each pair of stakes will intersect approximately at right angles over the center of the structure. The shape of the excavation is laid out on the ground by the foreman.

Sheeting and Bracing

10–11. Types of sheeting and bracing. Sheeting and bracing are used in trenching to prevent caving of the banks and to prevent or retard the entrance of ground water. The different methods of placing wood sheeting are called stay bracing, skeleton sheeting, poling boards, box sheeting, and vertical sheeting. Steel sheeting is usually driven to provide watertightness, and if it is braced the bracing is similar to the form used for vertical wood sheeting. Movable sheeting, either dragged through the trench by the excavating machine or self-propelled like a shield, is also used.

10–12. Stay bracing. Boards are placed vertically against the sides of the trench and held in position by cross braces which are wedged in place. The purpose of the board against the side of the trench is to hold the earth and prevent the cross brace from sinking into it. The boards should be $1\frac{1}{2}$ by 4 in. to 2 by 6 in. and 3 to 4 ft long. The cross braces should not be less than 2 by 4 in. for the narrowest trenches, and larger sizes should be used for wider trenches. The spacing between cross braces is dependent on the condition of the excavation and the judgment of the foreman. Stay bracing is a precautionary measure useful in relatively shallow trenches with sides of stiff clay or other cohesive material. It should not be used where a tendency towards caving is pronounced. Stay bracing is dangerous in trenches where sliding has commenced as it gives a false sense of security. The boards and cross braces are placed in position after the trench has been excavated.

10–13. Skeleton sheeting. Skeleton sheeting consists of rangers and braces with a piece of vertical sheeting behind each cross brace. A section is shown in Fig. 10–7 with the names of the pieces marked on them. This form of sheeting is used in uncertain soils that apparently require only slight support but may show a tendency to cave with but little warning. When the warning is given, vertical

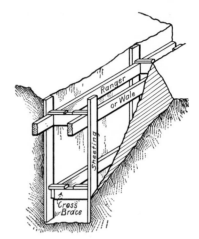

Fig. 10–7. Skeleton sheeting.

sheeting can be quickly driven behind the rangers and additional cross braces placed if necessary. The sizes of pieces, spacing, and method of placing should be the same as for complete vertical sheeting in order that this may be placed if required.

10–14. Poling boards. Poling boards are planks placed vertically against the sides of the trench and held in place by rangers and cross braces. They differ from vertical sheeting in that the poling board is about 3 to 4 ft long. This board is placed after the trench has been excavated, not driven down with the excavation like vertical sheeting. An arrangement of poling boards is shown in Fig. 10–8.

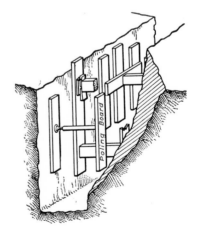

Fig. 10–8. Poling boards, showing different types of cross bracing.

This type of support is used in material that will stand unsupported for 3 to 4 ft in height. No driving is necessary, so that the trench is saved from jarring; no sheeting protrudes above the sides of the trench to interfere with excavation; and only short planks are needed.

The method of placing poling boards is as follows: The trench is excavated as far as the cohesion of the material will permit. Poling boards, 1½-in. to 2-in. planks, 6 in. or more in width, are then stood on end at the desired intervals along each side of the trench for the length of one ranger. The poling boards may be held in place by one or two rangers. Two are safer than one but may not always be necessary. If one ranger is to be used it is placed at the center of the poling board. After the poling boards are in position the rangers are laid in the trench and the cross braces are cut to fit. If wedges are to be used for tightening the cross braces, the cross braces are cut about 2 in. short. If jacks are to be used, the cross braces are cut short enough to accommodate the jacks when closed, or adjustable trench braces may be used as shown in Figs. 10–9 and 10–10. Extension braces save the labor of fitting wood braces. With everything in readiness in the trench, the cross brace is pressed against the ranger, which is thus held in place by friction. The wedge or jack is then tightened, holding the cross brace and the poling boards in position.

10–15. Box sheeting. Box sheeting is composed of horizontal planks held in position against the sides of the trench by vertical pieces supported by braces extending across the trench. The arrangement of planks and braces for box sheeting is shown in Fig. 10–9.

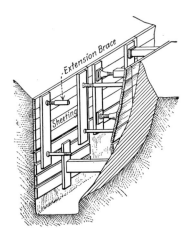

Fig. 10–9. Box sheeting, showing different types of cross bracing.

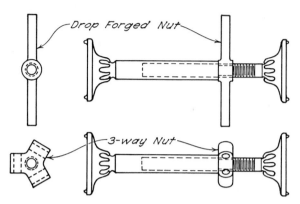

Fig. 10–10.   Extension trench braces.

This type of sheeting is used in material not sufficiently cohesive to permit poling boards and under such conditions that it is inadvisable to have vertical sheeting, which protrudes above the sides of the trench while being driven.   Box sheeting is put in position as the trench is excavated.   No more of the excavation than the width of three or four planks need be unsupported at any time.   For placing the sheeting the trench is excavated for a depth of 12 to 24 in.   Three or four planks are then placed against the sides of the trench and are caught in position by a vertical brace, which is in turn supported by a horizontal cross brace.

10–16. Plywood panels.   Plywood panels [2] held in place with vertical struts and extension braces are used for bracing trenches not more than 12 to 16 ft deep.   The method uses 4- by 8-ft plywood panels, with plywood cover plates over the ends of the panels.   Screw trench jacks bear against timber blocks on the cover plates, the jacks being spaced normally about 8 ft apart, horizontally.

Among the advantages of this type of sheeting are: a narrow trench is possible; the method of sheeting has many of the advantages of box sheeting; time is saved; a small amount of timber is used; the percentage of salvage is high; and cost is minimized.

10–17. Vertical sheeting.   Vertical sheeting is the most complete and the strongest of the methods for sheeting with wood.   Vertical sheeting consists of a system of rangers and cross braces so arranged as to support a solid wall of vertical planks against the sides of the

[2] See also staff article in *Public Works,* May, 1957, p. 113.

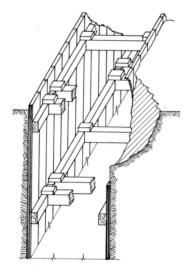

Fig. 10–11. Vertical sheeting.

trench. An arrangement of vertical sheeting is shown in Fig. 10–11. Such sheeting can be made nearly watertight by the use of matched boards, Wakefield piling, steel piling, etc. Wakefield piling is made up of three planks of the same width and the same thickness. They are nailed together so that the two outside planks protrude beyond the inside one on one side, and the inside one protrudes beyond the two outside ones on the other side. The protruding inside plank forms a tongue which fits into the groove formed by the protruding outside planks of the adjacent pile.

For vertical sheeting the trench is excavated as far as it is safe below the surface. Blocks of the same thickness as the sheeting are then placed against the side of the trench at the middle and at the ends of two rangers on opposite sides of the trench. The rangers rest against blocks and are held away from the sides of the trench by them. Rectangular timbers are usually placed with the long side vertical for convenience and stability, although this does not give the greatest strength. Round timbers are sometimes used, particularly for cross braces or struts. Puncheons or vertical props are sometimes placed between the rangers to prevent them from dropping, the lowest puncheon resting on the bottom of the trench. Where the ground is very soft it may be necessary to support the sheeting by slings hanging from cross timbers spanning the top of the trench, and where cavities have occurred unavoidably behind the sheeting it may be necessary to hold the rangers together by driving nails through the lips supporting the cross braces.

After the rangers are placed, cross braces are tightened into position opposite the blocks to hold the rangers in position. The vertical dimension of the cross brace is usually equal to that of the ranger. To avoid the sinking of the end of the cross brace into the sheeting, flat pieces are sometimes placed between the two timbers, as shown in Fig. 10–9. Extension cross braces, operating on the principle of the screw jack, as illustrated in Fig. 10–10, are sometimes used instead of struts of fixed length. After the skeleton bracing, or sheeting, is in place the planks forming the vertical sheeting are put into position with a chisel-edge cut on the lower edge of the plank with the flat side against the side of the trench, as shown in Fig. 10–12.

The framework of the sheeting should be placed with a cross brace for each end, and a cross brace for the middle, of each ranger. If the ends of two rangers rest on the same cross brace, an accident displacing one ranger may be passed on to the next and might cause a progressive collapse of a length of trench, whereas the movement of an independently supported ranger should have no effect on another ranger. The cross braces should have horizontal cleats nailed on top of them as shown in Fig. 10–11, to prevent the braces from being knocked out of place by falling objects. In driving vertical sheeting a vacant place will be left behind each cross brace, corresponding to the original block placed to hold the ranger away from the bank. This empty place is an undesirable feature of vertical sheeting. It is ordinarily remedied by slipping in planks the width of the slot and wedging or nailing them against the convenient bracing. In extremely wet trenches, after all other pieces of vertical sheeting are in place, the original cleat behind the cross brace can be knocked out, and a piece of sheeting can be slipped into this opening and driven. Care must be taken, in this event, not to drive the rangers down when driving the sheeting. If the bracing begins to drop it should be supported by vertical pieces, or puncheons, between the rangers and

Fig. 10–12. A method of cutting wood sheeting for sharpened edges.

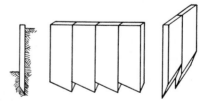

resting on a sill at the bottom of the trench, as previously mentioned. In deep trenches it may be necessary to insert back props at every third or fourth frame.

10–18. Size and quality of timbers. Timbers in trenches, shafts, and tunnels are seldom designed on the basis of an analysis of stresses. The sizes that experience has found satisfactory are used. If signs of failure occur the sizes of the timbers used subsequently are increased or spans are shortened. The growing science of soil mechanics promises to make possible more economical timbering design than is now obtained through empirical methods.

Experience and judgment should be depended on in the selection of the size and spacing of sheeting and bracing, but the following extracts from Construction Orders issued by the Industrial Accident Commission of California [3] may be helpful:

Where trench is between 4 and 7 ft in depth wood sheet piling shall not be less than 2 in. in thickness. Where trench is over 7 ft in depth wood sheet piling shall be not less than 3 in. in thickness.

All trenches over 8 ft in length and 5 ft or more in depth in hard, compact material shall be braced at intervals not exceeding 8 ft with 2 in. by 6 in. planks, or heavier material, placed vertically in the trench opposite each other against the walls.

The braces in trenches shall be supported by screw jacks or by timbers placed normal to both braces, cleated and rigidly screwed or wedged. The timbers shall not be less than the following: Width of trench 1 ft to 3 ft, 4 in. by 4 in. timbers; width 3 ft to 6 ft, 4 in. by 6 in. timbers; and 6 ft to 8 ft width, 6 in. by 6 in. timbers.

The number of horizontal strut braces, either screw jacks or timbers, required for each pair of vertical braces shall be determined by the number of zones of 4 ft each into which the depth of the trench can be divided. One horizontal brace shall be required for each of these zones . . . In no case, however, shall horizontal braces be spaced greater than 5 ft (vertically) center to center.

The timber for sheeting and bracing may be yellow pine, spruce, or oak. Hemlock and cypress splinter badly, and oak may warp. Wedges should be of hard wood, such as oak or even yellow pine.

10–19. Driving sheeting. Sheeting may be driven by hand or by machine. If it is driven by hand a maul should be used with the top of the plank protected by a malleable steel cap as shown in Fig. 10–13. If the sheeting is to start at the surface and is to be driven by hand, the first length should not exceed 4 ft unless a platform is

[3] Mimeographed sheets, not published.

erected for the driver. Succeeding lengths may be longer, the driver standing on the cross braces in the trench. Power-driven hammers and pile drivers are more commonly used to diminish labor costs. The pavement breaker, when fitted with the proper tool, makes a satisfactory hammer or driver.

In wet trenches the sheeting is driven 1 to 2 ft below the excavation as it descends, but in dry work the sheeting may lag behind the excavation, earth being removed by hand from beneath the descending planks. The advance edges of the sheeting may be beveled in two directions and placed against the wall of the trench, as indicated in Fig. 10–12. The direction of the bevel helps to hold the plank against the side of the trench and to the adjacent piece of sheeting.

Fig. 10–13. Section through a malleable-steel driving cap.

As the sheeting advances precautions must be taken to avoid cavities behind it. When they do occur they should be filled immediately. If water carrying sand with it flows through the sheeting, hay, grass, or straw should be "stemmed" behind the sheeting, more to stop the flow of sand than to check the water. If the sand is permitted to flow, the surrounding ground may become undermined or the sheeting may collapse.

10–20. Pulling wood sheeting. Wood sheeting is pulled during the backfilling of the trench or after the backfilling is completed, with the help of the device shown in Fig. 10–14. It may be possible to pull the sheeting with a lever or jack placed under the ring shown in the figure, or a block and falls operated by power may be used. In wet trenches where the removal of sheeting might permit movement of the soil, resulting in danger to the sewer and other structures, or where the arch of the sewer is supported against the sheeted sides of the trench, the sheeting should be left in place. If sufficient saving can be made, the sheeting is cut off in the trench immediately above the danger line, usually the ground-water line. The cutting is done with an axe or by a power-driven saw.

Fig. 10–14. Steel clamp for pulling wood sheeting.

10–21. Steel sheeting. Steel is coming into more general use as sheeting with the increased cost of lumber and better acquaintance with the superiority of steel over wood under many conditions. A

Fig. 10–15. Steel sheeting.

trench lined with steel sheeting is shown in Fig. 10–15. Although the first cost of steel is higher than that of wood, the fact that with proper care the steel can be reused an indefinite number of times renders it economical to use. The life of good yellow pine sheeting with the best of care may be as much as three or four seasons. With no particular care it will be destroyed on the first use. For heavy work, usually involving subaqueous excavation, standard-weight steel sheet piling must be used. Steel sheet piling can be made watertight by slipping a piece of soft wood between the steel sections when they are being driven, or by pouring in between the piles some dry material that will swell when wet. The steel sheeting is generally driven by a power hammer and is pulled by attaching a ring through a bolt hole in the pile, or by grasping the pile with a clutch that tightens its grasp as the pull increases. An inverted power hammer attached to the pile is sometimes used in pulling it. The upward impulses of the hammer together with a steady pull on the cable serve to drag out most stubborn pieces of piling.

10–22. Movable sheeting. (See also Sects. 10–4 and 10–11.) All-steel cribs, and wood-lined steel frameworks have been used as sheeting. On some work the box-like structure has been dragged along the trench by the excavating machine and in others it has been lowered into and lifted from the trench by a crane.[4]

10–23. Pumping and drainage of trenches. Ground water is to be anticipated in almost all sewer construction, and provision should be made for its care. Where geological conditions are well known, or where excavations have been made previously and it is known that no ground water exists, it may be safe to make no provision for encountering ground water. Where ground water is to be expected the amount must remain uncertain within rather wide limits until actually encountered.

In order to avoid the necessity for pumping, or working in wet trenches, it is sometimes possible to build the sewer from the low end upwards and to drain the trench into the new sewer. The wettest trenches are the most difficult to drain in this manner as the material is soft and the water so laden with sediment as to threaten to clog the sewer. It is undesirable to run water through the pipes until the cement in the joints has set. The trench must, therefore, be dammed up for a period, which may be so long as to flood the trench or delay the work. If it is not possible to drain the trench through the sewer already constructed, the amount of water to be pumped can be reduced by the use of tight sheeting.

Pumps for dewatering trenches must be proof against injury by sand, mud, and other solids in the water. For this purpose pumps with wide passages and without valves or packed joints are desirable. Two types of pumps used almost exclusively for such conditions are the diaphragm pump and centrifugal pumps, driven by either a gasoline motor or an electric motor. Other types of pumps sometimes used include jet pumps, steam vacuum pumps, and air lifts. Piston and plunger pumps are unsuitable primarily because of difficulties from clogging and wear resulting from the coarse and gritty materials commonly suspended in the water to be moved. The air lift, being devoid of valves, has been successful in pumping mud.[5] In general, all trench pumps are the simplest of their type, and not a large amount of attention is paid to the economical use of power in their operation because of the temporary nature of their service.

[4] See also *Eng. News-Record,* Vol. 82, 1919, p. 240; and *S. and I.W.,* February, 1956, p. 236.

[5] See also H. A. Fuller, *Water Works and Sewerage,* July, 1944, p. 259.

Fig. 10–16. Diaphragm pump. (Courtesy C. H. and E. Manufacturing Co.)

10–24. Diaphragm pumps. The type of pump shown in Fig. 10–16 is frequently used for removing water in small quantities from excavations. It is known as a diaphragm pump, because of the large, flexible diaphragm on which its operation depends. The pump is made of a short, cast-iron cylinder, divided by the diaphragm, to the center of which the pump handle is connected. The valve is shown at the center of the diaphragm. As the diaphragm is lifted the valve remains closed, creating a partial vacuum in the suction pipe and at the same time discharging the water which passed through the valve on the previous down stroke. When the valve is lowered the foot valve on the suction pipe closes, allowing the water to flow out on top of the disk, to be discharged on the next up stroke. The pump and motor are generally built as a unit so as to be portable and easily moved into and out of excavations without need for special foundations. The suction is equipped with a foot valve, except on some self-priming pumps, and with a coarse screen to prevent the entrance of objects more than $\frac{1}{4}$ to $\frac{1}{2}$ in. in size. The smaller sizes are the more frequently used and are equipped with 3-in. suction hose with strainer and foot valve. They are not adapted to suction lifts over 10 to 12 ft. Where greater lifts are necessary one pump may discharge into a tub in which the foot valve of a higher pump is submerged.

10–25. Centrifugal pumps. Centrifugal pumps for draining excavations should be portable, self-priming, suited to high suction lifts, and, except in unusual cases, to low discharge pressure. A centrifugal pump unit with gasoline motor is shown in Fig. 10–17. In a comparison of the diaphragm pump and the centrifugal pump, it will be found that the former will operate under more diverse conditions and will pump thicker muds. Centrifugal pumps are easy to move around and are available in either small or large capacities. They require more attention, however, and they do not wear so well as the diaphragm pump.

10–26. Jet pumps. The jet pump has no valves or moving parts and is quite free from clogging. It operates by means of a stream

Fig. 10–17. Portable centrifugal pump and gasoline motor. (Courtesy Marlow Pumps.)

of steam or water, usually the latter, entering the venturi-like throat at a high velocity. A partial vacuum is created that will lift water for 6 to 10 ft. Such pumps are not commonly used because of the need for water under pressure to operate them and the limited suction lift provided.

10-27. Steam vacuum pumps. This type of pump depends on the condensation of steam in the pump cylinder to create the necessary vacuum. Water rushes into the chamber to relieve the vacuum created when the steam condenses in the chamber. When the chamber is filled with water, steam is admitted to expel it, after which the steam condenses and one cycle for the chamber is complete. The pumps will operate continuously without attention or lubrication, so long as steam is available. The simplicity of their operation, freedom from maintenance, ruggedness, and ability to handle liquids heavily charged with solids makes their use desirable where steam is available. Unfortunately steam is not available on most sewer work. The pumps have an added advantage in that no foundation is required. They can be hung by a chain from any convenient support.

The pumps are available in sizes of 25 to 2,500 gpm at a 25-ft head, with steam consumption of about 150 lb per hp-hr. They reduce about 4 per cent in capacity for each additional foot of lift, and they will operate satisfactorily between heads of 5 to 150 ft, with a suction lift not to exceed 15 ft. Lower suction lifts are desirable, and the best operation is obtained when the pump is partly submerged. The steam pressure should be balanced against the total head. It varies from 50 to 75 psi for lifts up to 50 ft, and increases proportionally for higher lifts. The drier the steam, the lower is the necessary boiler pressure.

10-28. Ground dewatering.[6] Well points[7] have become standard in the dewatering of wet excavations for sewer trenches, tunnels, and other sewerage work. A diagram showing a method of setting up well points and pumps is shown in Fig. 10-18. It is common to use 2-in. well points connected to a 6-in. header pipe or manifold, all connected to a self-priming centrifugal pump. The spacing of the well points depends on the amount of ground water anticipated, but about 5-ft centers are not uncommon. Although the principles applicable to the design of water wells are equally applicable in the determination of the capacity of well points for drainage purposes, field tests in place will probably give more satisfactory information on which

[6] See also R. Nebolsine, *Eng. News-Record,* April 6, 1944, p. 81, and April 20, 1944, p. 94; and *Eng. News-Record,* March 11, 1943, p. 109.

[7] See also G. F. Briggs, *Public Works,* May, 1955, p. 82.

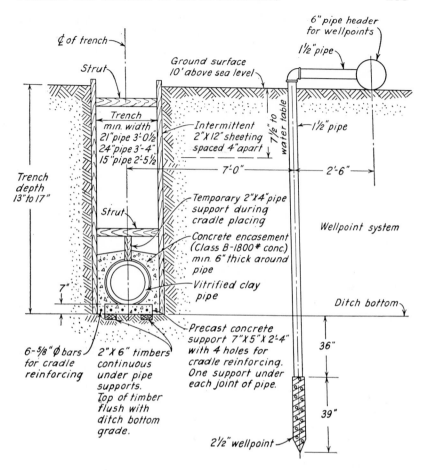

Fig. 10–18.   Diagram showing a well point system. (From *Clay Pipe Engineering Manual, 1956,* by permission of Clay Products Association.)

to estimate the number of points and the capacity of pumps to use.

Each well point should be equipped with a valve so that it may be cut off from its header. If there are two or more pumps on a header it may be desirable to separate their zones of influence by valves in the header. Vertical wells and shafts, and horizontal drainage systems may be used on large projects.

10–29. Purposes and methods of sewer tunneling.   Sewers are laid in tunnels to avoid deep, open-cut excavation, to avoid disruption of traffic, and for other reasons. An undesirable feature of laying sewers in tunnels is the inaccessibility of the sewer to adjacent house connections. In some cases connections can be made with vertical pipes from the deep sewer to the level of the house services. However, a tributary sewer at a shallow depth, discharging through a drop manhole or similar junction may be more economical and convenient.

The depth at which it may be economical to tunnel depends on the nature of the material to be excavated and on the surface conditions. In soft, dry material with unobstructed working space at the surface, open-cut may be satisfactory to 30-ft depths. Tunnels are cut in rock at depths of 15 ft or less. In some very fluid quicksand it has sometimes been found economical to tunnel at depths of 20 ft and less. Crowded conditions on the surface, expensive pavements, or extensive underground structures near the surface may make it advantageous to tunnel at shallower depths than would otherwise be economical. Winter is the best season for tunneling as the workmen are protected from the elements and labor is usually more plentiful.

10–30. Tunneling. The principles and methods of tunneling for sewers differ little, if at all, from those applicable to tunneling for other purposes. Texts on tunneling should be consulted for information on these principles and methods. The size and shape of a sewer tunnel depend on such conditions as the material penetrated, space required for construction, character of sewer and of tunnel linings, and the required capacity of the sewer. The depth of cover required for a sewer tunnel may be affected somewhat by the use to which the sewer is to be put. Depths greater than 12 to 15 ft are undesirable for sewers to which many house connections are to be made. Where such sewers are deeper it may be necessary to make connections through vertical pipes rising from the top or side of the deep sewer or tunnel and turning approximately horizontal, at a convenient depth to form the house sewer.

Tunneling has been avoided in some cases by pushing pipes horizontally underground.[8] In such work for large pipe, a man, or men, in the pipe cut material away from the advancing end of the pipe, thus guiding the direction of advancement. The pipe is pushed underground by jacks.

10–31. Pushing sewers underground.[9] Sewers up to about 18 in. in diameter have been successfully placed in suitable soil without

[8] See also *Public Works*, February, 1956, p. 158.

[9] See also *Eng. News-Record*, Vol. 101, p. 78; E. L. Tracey, *Eng. News-Record*, March 7, 1935; *Bull.* 9, American Concrete Pipe Association, 1936; W. S. Harvey, *Eng. News-Record*, July 2, 1942, p. 74.

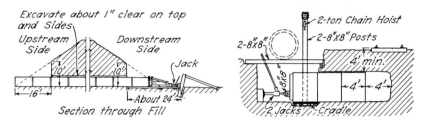

Fig. 10–19. Methods of jacking sewers underground. (M. W. Loving, *Bull.* 9, American Concrete Pipe Association.)

excavation at the surface of the ground by forcing a plug of the proper diameter horizontally through the ground along the line of the sewer by means of jacks. The plug is withdrawn after the hole has been made and the sewer is pushed into place. This method of construction is useful in passing under streets, railroad embankments, canals, or other obstructions where open-cut excavation is undesirable. It is advantageous also in that there is no settlement after construction. Difficulties may be encountered, however, in maintaining a straight alignment, particularly for distances greater than about 50 to 100 ft.

Sewers large enough for a man to enter have been pushed underground by jacks, the sewer being forced forward as the material is excavated by miners working at the advancing sewer face. A cutting edge is not always required, although it is sometimes used. Such sewers have been pushed for 100 ft or more. An advantage of hydraulic jacks is that the load can be equalized among the jacks to give an evenly distributed push. Alignment can be maintained during construction by shifting the position of the jacks, by varying the amount of excavation around the circumference of the pipe, and by varying the pressures on the jacks. When sufficient backing force cannot be obtained in the manner shown in Fig. 10–19, cables can be extended ahead of the work by pushing a 2-in. pipe through the fill, and securing the cables on the other side of the fill.

It is to be noted that the limit of jacking power is reached usually at about 100 ft. If the line begins to "freeze" owing to settlement of the soil, jacking should not stop until the job is complete. If water is encountered, it may be necessary to calk the joints to exclude both water and sand, which often accompany it.

Chapter 11

Laying and constructing sewer pipes and backfilling trenches

Laying Sewer Pipe

11–1. Position of pipe in trench. After the excavation of the trench has proceeded to within a foot or two of the final depth, the grade and line are transferred to markers supported over the center of the trench. The markers are horizontal boards spanning the trench and held in position by nails driven into stakes at the side of the trench, by nails driven into the sheeting, or by weights holding the boards on the ground. Two stakes driven into the ground at the side of the trench, as shown in Fig. 11–1, are the common method of support. If the banks are too weak to withstand the jarring of the driving of the stakes, or if pavement or other conditions prevent the use of stakes, the horizontal cross piece can be weighted down. The cross pieces are located about every 25 ft and at any convenient distance above the surface of the ground. The nearer they are to the ground the stronger the support, but the greater the interference with work in the trench. The center line of the sewer is marked on the cross pieces after they are set, and vertical struts are nailed on them with one edge of the strut straight, vertical, and on the center line,

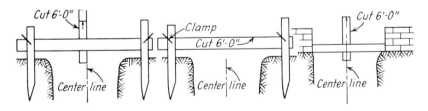

Fig. 11–1. Methods for supporting grade line for trench excavation.

236

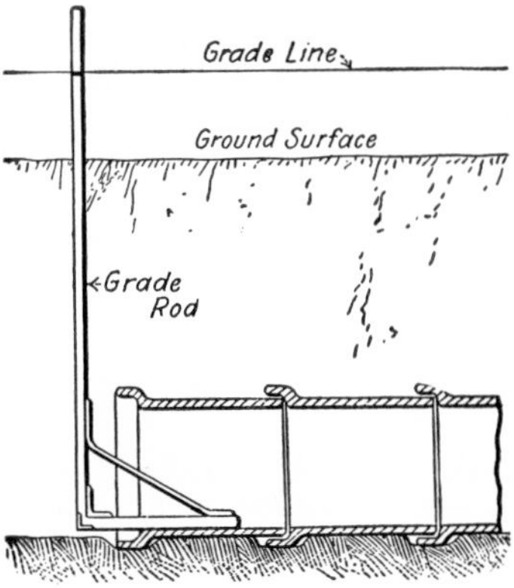

Fig. 11–2. Grade rod for fixing the elevation of a pipe in a trench.

as shown in Fig. 11–1. The corresponding edge should be used on all struts to avoid confusion. The cut to the invert is recorded to the nearest foot with a precision of 0.01 ft. A nail may be driven into the upright so that the top edge is at the desired elevation, or the upright is nailed with its top at the proper number of feet above the invert. Sometimes the upright is omitted and the top of the cross piece is placed at the correct elevation. The cut is marked in feet, tenths, and hundredths from the recorded point to the elevation of the invert.

The inspector should watch these grade markers with care by sighting back along them to see that they are in proper line and elevation. In quicksand or caving material the marks may move during the setting of the pipes and the levelman should be on the job constantly. In practically all materials except rock, whether in open cut or in tunnel, either the line, or the elevation of the excavation, or of the reference stakes may change. The engineer must be on the alert to this possibility so long as the excavation remains open.

When excavation is being done by machine the depth of the excavation is controlled by the operator, who maintains a sighting rod on the machine in line with the grade marks on the uprights or with a cord stretched beside the trench, as shown in Fig. 10–2.

11–2. Transferring line and elevation to pipe in trench. In transferring elevation and line to the sewer a light, strong cord is stretched on the uprights marking the line and elevation. A rod with a right-angle projection at the lower end, as shown in Fig. 11–2, is marked with chalk or a notch at such a distance from the end that when the mark is held on the grade cord the lower portion of the rod that projects into the pipe will rest on the invert. The pipe is placed in line by hanging a plumb bob so that its string touches the center-line cord. These marks are taken only as frequently as may be necessary to keep the sewer in line. An experienced workman can maintain the line by eye for considerable distances. Measurement should never be taken to the top of the pipe in order to determine position and grade, as the variations in the diameter of the pipe may cause appreciable errors.

The position and elevation of the forms for sewers to be fabricated in the trench are located by reference to the grade line, or they may be placed under the immediate direction of the survey party, or by reference to specially located stakes. For large sewers requiring deep and wide excavation the grade-and-line stakes may be driven in the bottom of the trench a foot above the finished excavation. This procedure requires the constant presence of an engineer during the progress of the work.

11–3. Transferring line and elevation down shafts. A method of transferring line down a shaft is indicated in Fig. 11–3. The plumb-bob lines should be about 12-gage piano wire supporting a plumb weighing from 15 to 50 lb; the greater the length the greater the required weight. The lines should be free from kinks and should

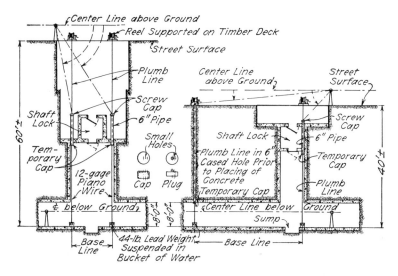

Fig. 11–3. Method of establishing base lines in tunnel. (From *Civil Eng.*)

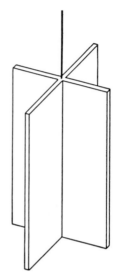

Fig. 11–4. Plumb bob for use in a deep shaft.

touch nothing between the support and the weight. The plumb bob may consist of a weight shaped somewhat as shown in Fig. 11–4 and should be immersed in water or a slightly viscous oil to prevent swinging. Plumb bobs are fixed on line by a transit on the surface as indicated in Fig. 11–3, the two reference points in the bottom of the shaft being placed as far apart as possible.

At the bottom of the shaft the line indicated by the plumb bob is transferred to the face of the tunnel or the lining of the shaft by means of a long straightedge in a small shaft, or better, if there is room, by a transit set on the line at the base of the shaft. As the distances are very short at this stage of the work the highest precision may not be necessary. After the tunnel has acquired a length of a few hundred feet another line should be dropped down a bore hole some distance from the shaft.

11–4. Line and elevation in tunnel. The line of the tunnel is carried by transit from the points fixed at the base of the shaft to

Fig. 11–5. Cross hairs in a transit for tunnel work.

Fig. 11–6. Spad. Full size.

the face. Because of the proximity of the plumb-bob line to the transit, it is usually necessary to have the cross hairs fixed as indicated in Fig. 11–5. The position of the lines in the tunnel may be marked by plumb bobs hanging from spads, of the style shown in Fig. 11–6, driven into the framing or into wooden plugs drilled into the rock roof.

Elevation is carried forward in the tunnel as it is on the surface, except that the level, like the transit, may have a short-leg tripod with special illumination for the cross hairs and for the markings on the level rod.

Pipe Sewers [1]

11–5. Laying pipe.[2] Before the pipe is lowered into the trench the sections that are to be adjacent should be fitted together on the surface, and the relative positions should be marked by chalk so that the same positions can be obtained in the trench. The "spring load"[3] cutting tool will cut clay pipe with square, clean edges. The tool operates similarly to the somewhat better-known tool for cutting steel pipe.

Pipes up to 15 to 18 in. in diameter can be handled by the pipe layer and his helper in the trench. Heavier pipes may be lowered into the trench by passing ropes around each end of the pipe. One end of the rope is fastened at the surface, and the ropes are payed out by men at the surface as the pipe is lowered. If the pipes have been fitted together and marked at the surface this method of lowering is undesirable, as the position in which the pipe arrives at the bottom cannot be easily predicted. A cradle may be used for shoving the pipe into place, as shown in Fig. 11–7.

[1] The costs of laying vitrified-clay pipe sewers up to 12-in. diameter were reported in *Public Works* for November, 1955. The costs were shown to vary so widely between various sections of the country and in any one locality as to be inapplicable to any job in a particular location. For example, based on the cost of 12-in. sewers per linear foot, including labor, material, trenching, and overhead, the highest costs were in the Middle Atlantic states and varied between $5 and $18. In the West South Central states they were the lowest and varied between $2.40 and $5.35. Likewise the costs of manholes, 8-ft or less deep, lay between $40 and $400.

[2] See American Society for Testing Materials, Specifications C-12–54.

[3] See R. F. Brown, *Water and Sewage Works*, March, 1950, p. 124.

241

Pipes too large to be handled from the side of the trench may be swung into position on a hook, such as is shown in Fig. 11–8. The hook is supported by a rope passing through a block at the peak of a stiff-leg derrick that spans the trench, or by a movable crane on one side of the trench. The pipe is lowered into position while supported from the derrick. Two methods of drawing precast concrete

Fig. 11–7. Cradle for placing sewer pipe.

Fig. 11–8. Hook for placing sewer pipe.

pipe together in a trench or tunnel are shown in Fig. 11–9, and a method of surrounding concrete pipe with a lean concrete mix in tunnel is shown in Fig. 11–10.

Pipes are usually laid with the bell end up grade, as it is easier to fit the succeeding pipe into the bell so laid and to make the joint, particularly on steep grades. Specifications used in Baltimore stated:

The ends of the pipe shall abut against each other in such a manner that there should be no shoulder or unevenness of any kind along the inside of the bottom half of the sewer or drain. Special care should be taken that the pipe are well bedded on a solid foundation. . . . The trenches where pipe laying is in progress shall be kept dry, and no pipe shall be laid in water or upon a wet bed unless specially allowed in writing by the Engineer. As the pipe are laid throughout the work they must be thoroughly cleaned and protected from dirt and water, no water being allowed to flow in them in

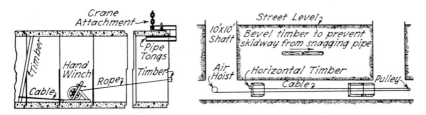

Fig. 11–9. Drawing precast concrete pipe together. (*Bulls.* 10 and 11, American Concrete Pipe Association, 1936.)

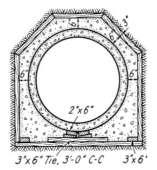

2"x6"

3"x6" Tie, 3'-0" C-C   3"x6"

Fig. 11–10. Precast concrete pipe surrounded with lean-mix concrete in tunnel.

any case during the construction except such as may be permitted in writing by the Engineer. No length of pipe shall be laid until the preceding length has been thoroughly embedded and secured in place, so as to prevent any movement or disturbance of the finished joint.

The mouth of the pipe shall be provided with a board or stopper, carefully fitted to the pipe, to prevent all earth and any other substances from washing in.

The pipe can be held in position in the trench by a little earth, placed on each side of it just back of the bell. The joints are then made, and enough earth is rammed around and on top of the pipe to hold it firmly in position without loading the joint. The go-devil should then be pulled forward to clean out such material as may have dropped into the pipe. If cement has been used in making the joints, water must be excluded from the pipe and bell holes until the cement has set.

When the sewer line reaches the site of a future manhole the lengths of pipe adjacent to the manhole should be omitted until the manhole is constructed. (See also Sect. 6–2.)

At the end of a day's work a temporary dam should be constructed across the mouth of the sewer to prevent the entrance of water and, where specials have been left for the future connection of other sewers, the inspector must assure himself that permanent, watertight plugs have been placed in the openings.

11–6. Brick and block sewers. The construction of brick and vitrified-clay block sewers in the United States is confined to periods before 1950. A few sewers have been constructed of concrete block more recently. The construction of such sewers has stopped because of the cost of labor involved, and the roughness of the interior surface. Knowledge of how brick and block sewers were constructed is desirable, however, because of the large number of brick sewerage structures constructed during and preceding the early part of the present century, and the long life of most ceramic structures.

11–7. The invert. That portion of the structure, or barrel, of a sewer below the side walls, or below the haunch of the arch if there are no side walls, is called the invert of the sewer. The term is used also for hydraulic purposes, to designate the lowest element of the inside cylindrical surface of the sewer.

In good firm ground the excavation is cut to the shape of the sewer and the bricks are laid directly on the ground, embedded in a thick layer of mortar. After the foundation has been prepared and before the bricks are laid, two wooden templates, called profiles, are prepared, similar to that shown in Fig. 11–11, to conform to the shape of the inside and the outside of the sewer. Each course of brick is represented by a row of nails in the profile, and each nail corresponds to a joint in the row. The two profiles are set true to line and grade. A cord is stretched tightly between the two lowest nails on opposite templates and a row of brick is laid.

The bricks are laid radially and on edge with their long dimension parallel to the axis of the sewer and with one edge just touching the string. All bricks should be wetted immediately before being laid. As each one of two or three rows is completed the guide line is moved up to the next nails. When the bricks are laid on the ground all but large depressions are filled in by the masons with tamped sand or mortar. Approximately the same number of rows of bricks is kept completed on either side of the center line. The succeeding courses follow within three or five rows of each other, the only bond between courses being the mortar joint. This is called row lock bond and,

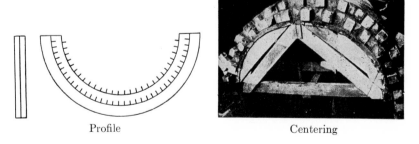

Profile   Centering

Fig. 11–11. Profile and centering for brick sewers.

with few exceptions, has been used on all brick sewers in the United States.

As the sides of the sewer become higher during construction, platforms must be built for the masons. These platforms are built of wood and rest directly on the green brickwork. They should be designed to spread the load as much as possible. The brickwork of the invert is continued in this way up to the springing line. As soon as one section is completed one profile is moved 10 to 20 ft ahead along the trench according to the standard length of sections and set in position. The line is then strung from this profile to nails driven or pushed into the cement joints of the last completed section. Between work done on separate days the bricks are racked back in courses to provide a satisfactory bond.

In ground too soft to support the brickwork directly a cradle is prepared by placing profiles in position in the sewer and nailing 2-in. planks to these profiles, first firmly tamping earth under the planks. The bricks are laid in this cradle in a manner similar to that explained for sewers with a firm foundation. In still softer ground it may be necessary to construct a concrete cradle to support the bricks.

On many brick sewer jobs the outer ring of the invert is built well in advance of the inner rings and the construction of the invert is completed well in advance of the arch to allow sufficient time for the joints to set, so that a smooth finished job may be done on the inner lining of the invert and arch.

11–8. The arch. The arch centering consists of a wooden form made up of wooden ribs as shown in Fig. 11–11. The center conforms to the shape of the inside of the arch with allowance for the thickness of the lagging. The lagging is nailed on the ribs in straight strips parallel to the axis of the sewer. The center is supported on triangular struts resting against the sides and on the bottom of the sewer and is lifted into position by wedges driven between it and the support. The centers may be placed after the completion of the invert, or a day or two may be allowed to pass to give the invert an opportunity to set. After the centers are fixed in place the arch bricks are carried up evenly on each side and are pounded firmly into place. Inside joints are as full as practicable to make a full joint and, in general, never wider than $\frac{1}{4}$ in. The extrados of the arch is plastered about $\frac{1}{2}$ in. thick with 1:2 cement mortar. The center may then be struck, and the arch brick may be cleaned and pointed up from the inside. The outside is covered with a layer of $\frac{1}{4}$ to $\frac{3}{4}$ in. of cement mortar and may be backfilled to the top of the arch in order to maintain the moisture of the mortar during setting and to press the bricks of the arch together firmly. The centers are sometimes made collapsible so that they can be carried or rolled through the finished brickwork to the advanced position. When the centers are struck the wedges are removed and the wings are folded in.

In tunneling, the invert of the sewer is constructed in the same fashion as for open-cut work. The arch centering is made in short sections, and the bricks are put in position by reaching in over the end of the centering. All the timbering of the tunnel is removed except the poling boards or lagging against which the bricks or mortar are tightly pressed, the boards being bricked in permanently.

11–9. Rate of work. It may be assumed, for rough estimates, that a mason can lay 1,000 to 1,500 bricks in an 8-hr day; that 15 to 20 man-hours of helpers and laborers will be involved, 2 barrels of cement, 0.6 cu yd of sand, and about 10 ft board measure of centering, where the work is done on sewer lining or in manholes. One thousand bricks will make about 2 cu yd of brickwork. To the costs as estimated on the basis of materials and labor must be added about 15 per cent for overhead and an additional amount for contractor's profit. A mason can lay more bricks per hour in a large sewer than in a small one as there is a smaller percentage of face work, there is more room to work, and it is easier to lay the bricks radially.

Concrete Sewers Cast in Place

11–10. Construction in open cut. In the construction of sewer pipe of cement and concrete one of two methods may be employed: (1) manufacturing the pipe in a plant at some distance from the place of final use, or (2) manufacturing the pipe in place. The methods of the manufacture of cement and concrete pipe to be transported to the excavation are treated in Chapter 7. The process of constructing the pipes in place is ordinarily used for pipes about 48 in. or more in diameter. For smaller sizes, brick, vitrified-clay, and precast cement pipes are usually more economical.

The preparation of the foundation for a concrete sewer is similar to that for a brick sewer. If the ground is suitable the trench is shaped to the outside form of the sewer and the concrete is poured directly on it. In soft material that would give poor support to a sewer with a rounded exterior, the bottom of the trench is cut horizontal and a concrete cradle of poorer quality than that in the

Fig. 11–12. Semi-elliptical, steel, invert form. (Courtesy Blaw-Knox Company.) Sloping rods, or knees, on each side aid in holding the form down. When moving ahead for next pour, form is hung by means of ratchets from trolleys running on beams supported by cross timbers.

finished sewer is poured on the soft ground, on a board platform, on piles, or on cribbing supported on piles.

If the invert of the sewer is so flat that the concrete will stand without an inside form, the shape of the invert is obtained by a screed or straightedge that is passed over the surface of the concrete and guided on two centers, or on one center and the face of the finished work.

If inside forms are to be used they are made as units in lengths of 12 to 16 ft for wooden forms, and 5 ft for steel forms. The inside form is supported by precast concrete blocks placed under it and concreted into the sewer. It is held in position by cleats nailed to the outside form or to the sheeting, or wedged against the outside of the trench. In some sewers, particularly where steel forms are used, the inside form is hung by chains from braces across the trench as shown in Fig. 11–12. The form is easily brought to proper grade by adjustment of the turnbuckles and is then wedged into position to prevent movement either sideways or upwards during the pouring of the concrete. It may be necessary to weight the forms down to prevent flotation. Cross-bracing in the trench that interferes with the placing of the form is removed and the braces are placed against the form until the concrete is poured. They are removed immediately in advance of the rising concrete.

The sewer section may be built as a monolith, in two parts, or in three parts. If it is cast as a monolith, the complete, full-round, inside form is completed as far as possible without interfering too much with the placing and tamping of the concrete. The concrete is poured from the top, being kept at the same height on each side of the form, and is tamped while being poured. The remaining panels of the outside form are placed in position as the concrete rises to them. An opening of such width that the concrete will stand without support is left at the top of the outside arch form. The casting of a sewer as a monolith is difficult and is usually undesirable because of the uncertainty of the quality of the work. It has the advantage, however, of eliminating longitudinal working joints in the sewer, which may allow the entrance of water or act as a line of weakness.

If the sewer is to be cast in two sections the invert is poured to the springing line or higher. A triangular or rectangular timber which has been well greased on the surface in contact with the concrete is set in the top of the wet concrete, as shown in Fig. 11–13. When the concrete has set the timber is removed and the groove thus left forms a working joint with the arch. After the concrete in the invert has set, the arch centering is placed and the arch is completed.

Large sewers with relatively flat bottoms are poured in two or three sections. First the invert is poured without forms and is shaped with a screed. About 6 in. of vertical wall is poured at the same time. This acts as a support for the side-wall forms. The side walls reach to the springing line of the arch and are poured after the invert has set. At the third pouring the arch is completed. A transverse working joint similar to one of the types in Fig. 11–13 is set after each day's work.

The length of the form used and the capacity of the plant should be adjusted so that one complete unit of invert, side wall, or arch can

Fig. 11–13. Construction joints for concrete sewers.

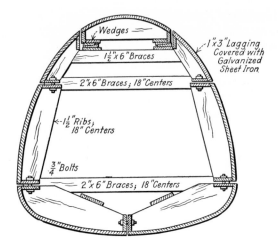

Fig. 11–14. Collapsible wood form.

be poured in one operation. The forms are left in place until the concrete has set. Invert and side-wall forms are generally left in position for at least two days, and in cold weather longer. The arch forms are left in place for double this time. For example, if 20 ft of invert and arch can be poured in a day, 60 ft of invert form and 100 ft of arch form will be required. As the forms are released they must be moved forward through those in place. For this reason collapsible or demountable forms are necessary and steel forms are advantageous. Wooden arch forms are sometimes dismantled and carried forward in sections but are preferably designed to collapse as shown in Fig. 11–14, so that they can be pulled through on rollers or a carriage.

11–11. Construction in tunnel. In tunnels the invert and side walls are constructed in the same manner as for open-cut work. The tunnel lining that acts as the outside form is concreted permanently in place. The concreting of a tunnel by hand [4] is shown in Fig. 11–15. If the work is to be done by hand the concrete is thrown in between the ribs of the arch centering and behind the plates or lagging, which are set in advance of the rising concrete. The length of the lagging plates is such as to make it possible to throw the concrete in place in the arch, and to tamp it from the end. Tamping may be by me-

[4] See also *Eng. News-Record*, Oct. 21, 1943, p. 94.

Fig. 11–15. Construction of Ogier's Run intercepting storm-water drain in tunnel, Baltimore, Md. The view shows the placing of concrete in the arch. The steel lagging of the forms is carried up in sections as the concrete is deposited. The section is horseshoe shaped, and is 12 ft 3 in. high and 12 ft 3 in. wide.

chanical vibrator [5] or by hand. A bulkhead and a well-greased joint timber are placed in position as the concrete rises.

Pneumatic transmission of concrete is also a method of filling the arch forms, the side walls, and the invert forms.[4] In this method the mixer may be placed at the surface or at the bottom of the shaft or in other convenient permanent location, which may be some distance from the form. The mixture is discharged into a pipe line through which it is blown by air to the forms. The starting pressure of about 80 lb per sq in. can be reduced after flow has commenced. The end of the concrete-conveying pipe is provided with a flexible joint, the simplest form of which can be made by slipping a section of pipe of larger diameter over the end of the transmission line. The concrete is deposited directly on the invert or into the side-wall forms and can be blown into the arch forms. The lagging rises as the forms are filled, as indicated in Fig. 11–15.

Some disadvantages of the construction of concrete sewers in tunnel include: (1) earth and rocks may fall into the concrete; (2) the concrete may become honeycombed from loss of cement through loose lining of the tunnel or because it has been made too stiff in the attempt to avoid loss of mortar; (3) it is difficult to assure the

[5] See also O. S. Bray, *Eng. News-Record,* April 20, 1944, p. 82.

complete filling of the arch with concrete tight against the roof; (4) watertight joints between parts of the sewer constructed on different days require careful workmanship and rigid inspection; and (5) careful work must be performed to assure that there will be no leakage of solids from the material surrounding the tunnel as foundations of nearby structures may be undermined, and disastrous cave-ins may occur even many years after the completion of the work.

11–12. Materials for forms. The materials used in forms for concrete sewers are wood, wood with steel lining, and steel alone. The first cost of wood forms is ordinarily lower than for steel but the life of wood forms is relatively short. If reuse is important steel is preferable. Steel, with proper care and repairs, will outlast other materials. Wood forms are not commonly used because of the high cost of lumber, and improvements in steel forms. A common type of specification under which forms are used is:

The material of the forms shall be of sufficient thickness and the frames holding the forms shall be of sufficient strength so that the forms shall be unyielding during the process of filling. The face of the form next to the concrete shall be smooth. If wooden forms are used the planking forming the lining shall invariably be fastened to the studding in horizontal lines, the ends of these planks shall be neatly butted against each other, and the inner surface of the form shall be as nearly as possible perfectly smooth, without crevices or offsets between the ends of adjacent planks. Where forms are used a second time, they shall be freshly jointed so as to make a perfectly smooth finish to the concrete. All forms shall be watertight and shall be wetted before using.

Any material in contact with wet concrete should be oiled or greased before the concrete is poured to avoid adherence of the concrete and the form.

11–13. Design of forms. The design of forms for concrete requires some knowledge of the strength of materials and the structural stresses involved. Forms can be constructed without design but that they will be both economical and adequate is improbable. The horizontal pressure of concrete against a form can be taken, with safety, as equal to that of a liquid weighing 150 lb per cu ft. However, tests and experience have shown that under normal conditions of construction such pressures are not encountered. The various factors involved have been expressed in empirical formulas, some of which have been combined as follows:

$$P = \sqrt[6]{\frac{[H^{0.2}R^{0.3} + 12C - 0.3S]10(R + 3)}{T^{0.6}}} \qquad (11\text{--}1)$$

where P = lateral pressure, psi.

R = rate of filling forms, ft per hr.

H = head of fill. Taken, usually, as $\frac{1}{2}R$, but in cold weather or when continuously agitated it may be as high as $\frac{3}{4}R$.

C = ratio, by volume, of cement to aggregate.

S = consistency in inches of slump.

T = temperature, degrees F.

The design of forms, with precision, involves knowledge of structural design involving indeterminate structures, since forces acting on the ribs are usually of this category. It is common, in practice, to follow other successful designs since conditions during construction are often difficult to predict. The sizes of lumber used in the ribs varies from $1\frac{1}{2} \times 6$ in. to 2×10 in. depending on the size of the sewer, or other structure involved.

11-14. Wood forms. Norway and southern pine, spruce and fir are satisfactory for form construction. White pine is satisfactory but is generally too expensive. The hard woods are too difficult to work. The lumber should be only partly dried as kiln-dried lumber swells too much when it is moistened, warping the forms out of shape or crushing the lagging at the joints. Green lumber must be kept moist constantly to prevent warping before use, and when it is used it does not swell enough to close the cracks. The lumber should be dressed on the face next to the concrete and at the ends. Either beveled or matched lumber may be used for lagging. The joint made by beveled lumber shown in Fig. 11-16a is cheaper but less satisfactory than a tongued and grooved joint. Plywood for the face of the form against which the concrete rests has been found to be satisfactory, economical, and time-saving.

Types of wooden forms for sewers to be built as monoliths or in two portions are shown in Fig. 11-16b and c. Figure 11-17 shows the details of a built-up wooden form used in tunnel work for a $44\frac{1}{2}$-in. egg-shaped sewer.

11-15. Steel-lined wood forms. Sheet-metal linings are sometimes used on wood forms. They permit the use of cheaper, undressed

---

[6] The application of this expression is limited to temperatures between 40 and 80° F, and to pressures less than would be caused by a fluid with a density of concrete and under the head H in the formula.

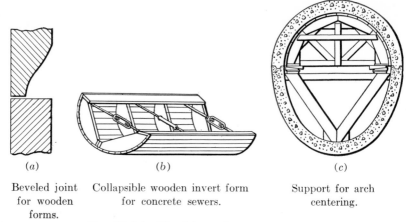

(a)   (b)   (c)

Beveled joint   Collapsible wooden invert form   Support for arch
for wooden   for concrete sewers.   centering.
forms.

Fig. 11–16.   Wood forms for concrete sewers.

lumber, demand less care in the joining of the lagging, and when in
good condition give a smooth surface to the finished concrete. They
have frequently been found unsatisfactory and more expensive than
well-constructed wood forms because of the difficulty of preventing
warping and crinkling of the metal lining and of keeping the ends
fastened down so that they will not curl. Sheet steel or iron of No.
18 or 20 gage (0.05 to 0.0375 in.), weighing 2 to $1\frac{1}{2}$ lb per sq ft, is
ordinarily used for lining.

11–16. Steel forms.   Steel forms are simple, relatively light,
durable, and easy to handle. The engineer is seldom called upon to

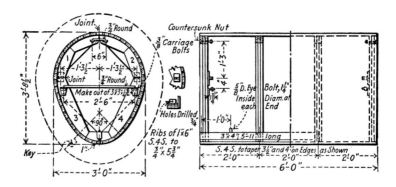

Fig. 11–17.   Wood forms used in tunnel. North Shore sewer, Sanitary District of Chicago. (*Jour. Western Soc. Engrs.,* Vol. 22, p. 385.)

design these forms, as the types most frequently used are manufactured by the patentees and are furnished to the contractor at a fixed
rental per foot of form, exclusive of freight and hauling from the
point of manufacture. The forms can be made in any shape desired,
the ordinary stock shapes such as the circular forms being the least
expensive. The smaller circular forms are adjustable within about
3 in. to different diameters so that the same form can be used for
two sizes of sewers. The same form can be used for arch and invert
in circular sewers. Figure 11–18 shows the collapsible circular forms
and the manner in which they are pulled through those still in position. Figure 11–12 shows a half-round steel form swung in position
by chains and turnbuckles from the trench bracing, and Fig. 11–19
shows the free, unobstructed working space in the interior of some
large steel forms.

11–17. Reinforcement. It is essential that the reinforcement be
held firmly in place during the pouring of the concrete. A section of
reinforcement misplaced during construction may serve no useful
purpose and may result in the collapse of the sewer. In sewer construction a few longitudinal bars may be laid, in order that the
transverse bars may be wired to them, and held in position by notches
in the centering and in fastenings to bars protruding from the finished
work. The network of reinforcement is held up from the bottom
of the trench by notched boards, which are removed as the concrete
reaches them, or better by stones or concrete blocks, which are con-

Fig. 11–18. Full-round, telescopic, steel sewer forms, showing knocked-down
sections on a truck in the sewer. (Courtesy Blaw-Knox Co.)

Fig. 11–19. Large steel form with unobstructed interior. (Courtesy Blaw-Knox Co.)

creted in. Sometimes the reinforcement is laid on top of the freshly poured portion of the concrete, the surface of which is at the proper distance from the finished face of the work. This method has the advantage of not requiring any special support for the reinforcement, but it is undesirable because of the resulting irregularity in the reinforcement spacing and position.

In the side walls the position of the reinforcement is fixed by wires or metal strips, which are fastened to the outside forms or to stakes driven into the ground. Wires are then fastened to the reinforcement bars and are drawn through holes in the forms and twisted tight. When the forms are removed the wires or strips are cut, leaving a short portion protruding from the face of the wall. The reinforcing steel from the invert should protrude into the arch or the side walls for a distance of about 40 diameters in order to provide good bond between the sections.   The protruding ends are used as fastenings for the new reinforcement.   The arch steel may be supported above the forms by specially designed metal supports, by small stones or concrete blocks concreted into the finished work, or by notched strips of wood, which are removed as the concrete approaches them.   Strips of wood are not satisfactory because they are sometimes carelessly left in place in the concrete, causing a line of weakness in the structure.   Metal chairs are the most secure supports.   They are fastened

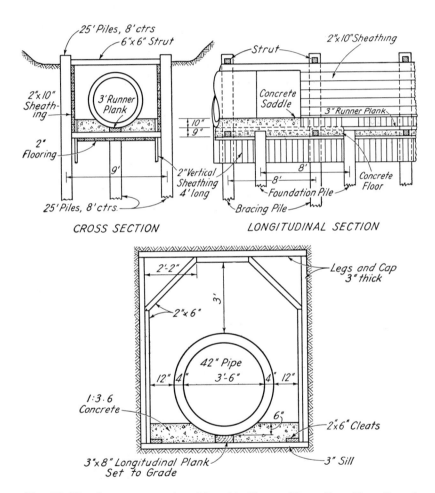

CROSS SECTION   LONGITUDINAL SECTION

Fig. 11–20.   Sewer construction, Memphis, Tenn.   (From *Eng. News-Record,* May 4, 1944, p. 97.)

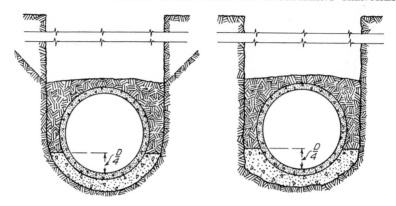

Fig. 11–21. Concrete foundations for concrete pipe. (M. W. Loving, *Bull.* 10, American Concrete Pipe Association.)

to the forms, and the bars are wired to the chairs. In some instances the entire reinforcement has been formed of one or two bars which are fastened into position as a complete ring. This ring results in a better bond in the reinforcement and requires less fastening and trouble in handling, but is in the way during the pouring of the concrete and interferes with the handling of the forms.

11–18. Foundations. Sewers constructed in firm, dry soil require no special foundation to distribute the weight over the supporting medium. In rock the pressures on sewer pipes are evenly distributed by a cushion of sand. In wet ground, such as quicksand, mud, and swamp land, a foundation must be constructed if the water cannot be drained off. Practice at Memphis, Tenn.,[7] under such conditions is illustrated in Fig. 11–20.

Whether the sewer is placed in firm material or soft muck it is essential that the foundation be spread and that the bottom of the trench, or some other support, be brought up for 90° around the bottom of the invert, as shown in Fig. 8–3. Concrete foundations, like those shown in Fig. 11–21, are desirable in porous materials on steep slopes that might be conducive to the flow of ground water at a velocity high enough to disturb the sand in the sewer foundation. A concrete proportion of about 1:3:6 will be satisfactory for protection against such a contingency.

Specifications of the *American Public Works Association,* July, 1938, provide as follows:

[7] See *Eng. News-Record,* May 4, 1944, p. 97.

If the foundation is rock, hard clay, or any unyielding surface, an equalizing bed of Class C concrete, sand, or gravel, as shown on the plans, shall be placed upon the rock or unyielding surface and well compacted. The thickness of these beds shall be not less than 4½ inches. Pipes shall be laid in these beds so that at least the lower one-third of each pipe is supported its entire length.

Equalizing beds of sand or gravel should be called for on the plans only when it is definitely known that the trenches will be free from flowing water and that the conditions will be such that the sand and gravel will never be disturbed.

If the foundation is good firm earth, the earth shall be pared or molded to give a full support to the lower one-third of each pipe. Particular care shall be taken to recess the bottom of the trench in such a manner as to relieve the bells of all load.

If there is no good natural foundation the pipes shall be laid in concrete cradles . . . the entire structure shall be supported on a foundation material specified on the plans, carried to a soil of satisfactory bearing power. . . .

On soft foundations such as swamps, or for outfalls on the muck bottom of rivers, the sewer may be carried on a platform as shown in Figs. 11–22 and 11–23. For small sewers 2-in. planks, 2 to 4 ft longer than the diameter of the pipe, are laid across the trench, and the sewer rests directly upon them. For large sewers imposing a heavy concentrated load, a pile foundation should be constructed. The foundation may consist of piles alone, pile bents, or a wooden platform supported on pile bents. The load that can be carried by a pile is determined with accuracy only by driving a test pile and placing a load on it. Where piles do not penetrate to a firm stratum the load they will support can be determined by any one of the various formulas, either theoretical or empirical, that have been devised.

A somewhat unusual job described by Amiss [8] involved the laying of a 24-in. cast-iron sewer pipe on material so fluid that it rose in the trench during construction. Conditions were stabilized by *suspending* the pipe from the cross bracing and filling under it with crushed rock.

Piles are driven at about 2 to 4 ft centers, to a depth of 8 to 20 ft, unless hard bottom is struck at a lesser depth. The butt diameter of the piles used for the smallest sewers is about 6 to 8 in. If bents are used, two or three piles are driven in a row across the line of the sewer and are capped with a timber. For brick, block, pipe and some

[8] T. L. Amiss, *Water and Sewage Works,* May, 1949, p. 190.

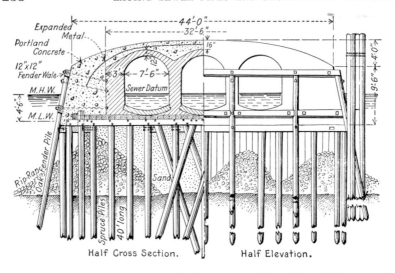

Fig. 11–22. Sewer outlet on a pile foundation. (*Eng. News,* Vol. 49, p. 9.)

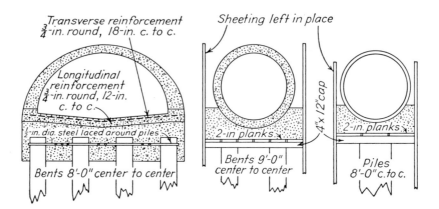

Fig. 11–23. Sewers on pile foundations.

concrete sewers, a wooden platform must be constructed between the pile bents for the support of the sewer.

11–19. Underdrains. The laying of underdrains facilitates the construction of the sewer and reduces the amount of ground water entering the sewer until the drain becomes clogged. The drains are laid under the sewer and are led to sumps or other outlets outside of the sewer trench. The underdrains may consist of 6- or 8-in. vitrified-clay tile laid with open joints wrapped with one thickness of muslin, or equivalent. The drains are laid from 1 to 2 ft below the bottom of the sewer. The underdrain pipes should be bedded in broken stone or gravel surrounding the pipe, for a thickness of at least 3 in. The underdrains are usually neglected after construction and, as a result, clog and cease to function.

11–20. Infiltration and exfiltration tests. Leakage tests of sewers may be made either by measuring the flow through the sewer by means of weirs or other methods described in Sect. 6–16 or by filling the sewer with water and observing the drop in head. The last method is comparatively simple, but there should be assurance that the test is made with the ground-water table at its maximum height where infiltration is to be observed. Results of tests under other conditions will give no indication of maximum infiltration.

The testing of sewers under light internal pressure, up to about 4 ft of head of water, makes it possible to conduct an exfiltration test at any time that the ground-water table is low. The section of the sewer to be tested is plugged at both ends, water being admitted to the lower end and air being allowed to escape at the upper end. When the sewer is filled with water the rate of flow required to keep it full is the leakage or exfiltration. Exfiltration and infiltration rates are not equal, the former usually being larger.

Backfilling Trenches

11–21. Backfilling.[9] Careful backfilling is necessary to prevent the displacement of newly laid pipe and to avoid subsequent settling of the surface resulting in uneven streets and dangers to nearby foundations and structures. The backfilling should commence as soon as the cement, or other construction or joint material has set. Clay, sand, rock dust, or other fine compactible material is then packed by hand under and around the pipe and rammed with a shovel or light tamper. This method of filling is continued up to the top of the pipe. The backfill should rise evenly on both sides of the pipe, and tamping should be continuous during the placing of the backfill. The backfill should be placed by hand, with a shovel, for 2 ft above the top of the pipe so as not to disturb the pipe, and it should be tamped while being placed, but no tamping should be

[9] See also H. E. Davis and F. N. Finn, *Jour. Am. Water Works Assoc.*, May, 1950, p. 512.

done within 6 in. of the top of the sewer. The remainder of the back-fill should not be placed until 7 days have elapsed for clay pipe sewers, and 14 days for concrete sewers, unless local conditions or materials are suitable for the earlier placing of a load on the materials. The tamping should become progressively heavier as the depth of the backfill increases.

Above a point 2 ft above the top of the sewer the method pursued and the care observed in backfilling will depend on the kind of the backfilling material and the location of the sewer. If the sewer is in a paved street the backfill is spread in layers 6 in. thick and tamped with rammers weighing about 40 lb with a surface of about 30 sq in. One man tamping for each man shoveling is frequently specified. If no pavement is to be laid but it is required that the finished surface shall be smooth, slightly less care need be taken and only one man tamping is specified for each two men shoveling. On paved streets a reinforced-concrete slab with a bearing of at least 12 in. on the undisturbed sides of the trench may be designed to support the pave-ment and its loads. On unpaved streets the backfill is crowned over the trench to a depth of about 6 in. and then rolled smooth by a road roller. In open fields, in side ditches, or in locations where obstruc-tion to traffic or unsightliness need not be considered, after the first 2 ft of backfill have been placed with proper care, the remainder is scraped or thrown into the trench by hand or machine, care being taken not to drop the material so far as to disturb the sewer.

If the top of the sewer, manhole, or other structure comes close to or above the surface of the ground, an earth embankment should be built, at least 3 ft thick, over and around the structure. The em-bankment should have side slopes of at least $1\frac{1}{2}$ on 1 and should be tamped to a smooth and even finish.

If sheeting is to be withdrawn from the trench it should be with-drawn immediately before the backfilling, and in trenches subject to caving it may be pulled as the backfilling rises.

Puddling is a process in which water is used in the trench during backfilling. The procedure is not widely approved. Under any cir-cumstances only gravel or sand may be puddled, and only the mini-mum amount of water required should be used. Clay and similar materials shrink on drying. It is claimed that puddling avoids the necessity for tamping. Under no conditions should puddling be re-sorted to before the first 2 ft of backfill has been carefully placed. More compact work can be obtained by tamping than with puddling. In general, puddling will greatly increase pipe loadings and will often crack pipes. To repeat, and for emphasis, puddling in settling backfill is not considered good practice.

Frozen earth, rubbish, old lumber, and similar materials should not be used where a permanent finished surface is desired, as they will decompose or soften and result in settlement. Rocks may be thrown in the backfill, if they are not dropped too far and the earth is carefully tamped around and over them. In rock trenches fine materials such as loam, clay, and sand must be provided for the backfilling of the first portion of the trench for 2 ft over the top of the pipe. More clay can generally be packed in an excavation than was taken out of it, but sand and gravel occupy more space than originally even when carefully tamped.

Backfilling in tunnels is usually difficult because of the small space available in which to work. Ordinarily the timbering is left in place and concrete is thrown in from the end of the pipe between the outside of the pipe and the tunnel walls and roof. If vitrified pipe is used in the tunnel, the backfilling is done with selected clayey material which is packed into place around the pipe by workmen with long tamping tools. The backfilling should be done with care under the supervision of a vigilant inspector in order that subsequent settlement of the surface may be prevented.

11–22. Backfilling and tamping machines. There are two general types of backfilling machines: the first, of the general bull-dozer pattern that pushes the dirt into the trench; and the second, sometimes called a "skimmer scoop," that moves a blade back and pulls it toward a stationary source of power. The moving blade is usually supported on a long, horizontal boom that reaches across the trench.

Tamping machines have not come into general use. One type of machine consists of a gasoline engine that raises and drops a weighted rod. The rod can be swung back and forth across the trench while the apparatus is being pushed along. It is claimed that two men operating the machine can do the work of six to ten men tamping by hand. The machine delivers 50 to 60 blows per min, with a 2-ft drop of the 80- to 90-lb tamping head. Power tamping is also performed by tamping tools set in a pavement breaker head, or a similar device. Such a machine should be able to deliver 550 or more blows a minute with a force of not less than 65 ft-lb to each blow, exerting a pressure of 90 psi or more.

Chapter **12**

Pumping

12–1. Need, reliability, and requirements.[1] In the design of a
sewer system it is occasionally necessary to concentrate the sewage
of a low-lying district at some convenient point from which it must
be lifted by pumps. In the construction of sewers in flat topography
the grade required to cause proper velocities necessitates deep excavation. It is sometimes less expensive to raise sewage by pumping
than to continue the construction of sewers in deep excavation.

In the operation of a sewage-treatment plant a certain amount of
head is necessary. If the sewage is delivered to the plant at a depth
too great to make possible the utilization of gravity for the required
head, pumps must be installed to lift the sewage. In the construction
of large office buildings and business blocks, the sub-basements are
frequently constructed below sewer level. The sewage and other
drainage from the low portion of the building must, therefore, be
removed by pumping. Because pumps are often an essential part of
sewer works their details should be understood by the engineer, who
must write the specifications under which they are obtained.

Maintenance[2] problems are an important consideration in fixing
the reliability of a pump. A highly efficient pump involving difficult
maintenance problems may be less desirable than a rugged, simple,
but less efficient pump. Automatically controlled, non-clogging pumps
should be used and, wherever possible, sewage should be given at
least primary treatment before it is pumped.

Reliability of power and equipment[3] is difficult to measure. It is
sometimes expressed in electrical-utility practice in terms of annual

[1] See also N. L. Nussbaumer, *Sewage Works Jour.*, March, 1941, p. 318; R. R.
Kennedy, *S. and I.W.*, April, 1951, p. 541; G. E. Hands, *S. and I.W.*, August,
1951, p. 959; and R. G. Martin, *S. and I.W.*, February, 1956, p. 150.
[2] See also G. M. Olewiler, *Sewage Works Jour.*, March, 1942, p. 275.
[3] See also N. L. Hadley and E. O. Potthoff, *S. and I.W.*, April, 1953, p. 393.

outages of limited duration. For example, the outages experienced by commercial consumers using less than 1,000 kw may be limited by contract to 6 per year with a maximum duration of 2 hours. Adequacy is associated with reliability. No installation can be more adequate than its weakest part. For example, the adequacy of an electric-powered pumping station is limited not only by ratings of individual units, but by current ratings, short-circuit ratings, and electrical impedances.

The protection of life, health, and property requires the greatest reliability in design, selection, and operation of the pumping equipment in a sewage-pumping station. Some general requirements of the New York State Department of Health, issued in 1934 in an attempt to aid in securing unquestioned reliability, are:

Main pumps should, in general, be provided with at least three pumping units having capacities such that if the largest unit is out of service for repairs the remaining units can pump the maximum flow of sewage. The sizes of pumps should be proportioned to the various rates of sewage flow to be cared for. Motive power should be available from at least two sources. Smaller lift stations should have duplicate equipment. The entire pumping plant should be properly housed and, in case of electrically driven pumps, the motors should, in general, be placed above the ground floor. Suction and discharge pipes should be not less than 4 inches in diameter. For purposes of cleaning and repairs, pumps should, in general, be placed in dry wells or otherwise arranged so that they can be entirely withdrawn from the suction wells. All pumps for raw sewage should be preceded by bar or basket screens unless a special type of pump be provided with sloping floor draining to a suitable sump or sumps for the pump suction lines.

An emergency overflow or bypass should be installed wherever possible for the adequate protection of a sewage-pumping station. It must be installed so that it cannot be used unobtrusively under unauthorized conditions. However, without such protection the loss of the pumping station may offer a greater hazard than the occasional emergency discharge of sewage into a body of water in which a nuisance may be created.

12–2. Pumping stations [4] and other buildings. Sewage-pumping stations are exemplified by such installations as the attractive building in a residential area shown in Fig. 12–1, the subsurface installations shown in Figs. 12–2, 12–3, and 12–7, and by large, indus-

[4] See also J. R. Patterson, *Public Works,* January, 1957, p. 117.

Fig. 12–1. Sewage-pumping station at Evanston, Ill.

trial-type buildings shown in section in Fig. 12–9. Attractively designed buildings, intended to resemble dwellings, and in fact sometimes housing the operators, can be constructed in residential areas
to avoid neighborhood complaints. Subsurface structures are undesirable but are often unavoidable. Their low first cost, convenience
of location, unobtrusiveness, and lack of land surface occupancy
force their use, especially on small sewers. However, they present
hazards to personnel, difficulties in operation and maintenance, and
corrosion of equipment. The Joint Committee (see Sect. 5–2), and
other authorities, do not approve them.

The aboveground portion of a sewerage structure should be of
pleasing design and should be surrounded by attractive grounds.
Such structures tend to remove the popular prejudice against sewerage
works and to arouse interest in sewerage problems. It has been said
that people smell with their eyes and their ideas, as well as with
their noses. Service to the public can be rendered more readily if
public interest and cooperation are aroused by the erection of attractive structures.

12–3. Mechanical equipment of buildings. The plumbing,
heating, lighting, and air-conditioning equipment constitute important
items of the mechanical equipment of a pumping station and of other
buildings. Principles and practice in the mechanical equipment of
buildings will be considered here only as they may be applicable to

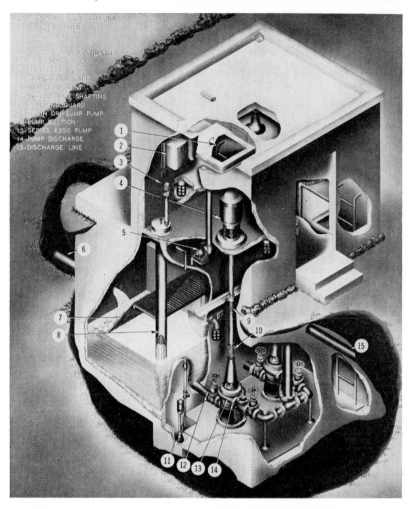

Fig. 12–2. Automatic sewage pumping station, mainly under ground. (Courtesy Yeomans Bros. Co.)

1. Wet-well access opening
2. Control panel
3. Float rig
4. Motor
5. Forced-feed ventilator
6. Inlet line
7. Bar screen
8. Float guide tube

9. Universal joint, intermediate shafting
10. Coupling guard
11. Sump pump
12. Pump suction
13. Series 6250 Pump
14. Pump discharge
15. Discharge line

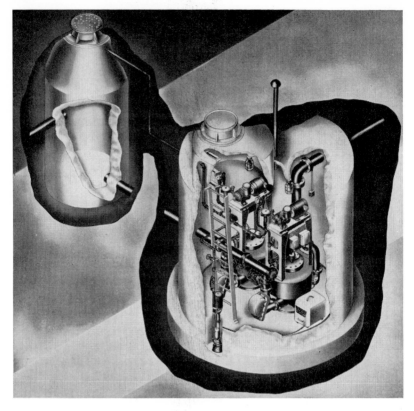

Fig. 12–3. Pumping station in a manhole, using air ejectors. (Courtesy Yeomans Bros. Co.)

the handling of sewage. In plumbing [5] design, installation, and maintenance, special care is necessary to avoid cross connections, both because of the multiplicity of pipes and because of the great hazards involved due to the presence of sewage.

Facilities for washing the hands should be generously provided in sewerage installations, including the provision of hot water where feasible. Major buildings should include toilet facilities, shower baths, and well-ventilated and lighted locker rooms where clothing may be changed and work clothes stored.

Heating equipment is installed for the comfort and efficiency of the operators, and for the safety of equipment. Allowance must be

[5] See also *Plumbing,* H. E. Babbitt, 2nd edition, McGraw-Hill Book Co., 1950.

made beyond normal for most buildings, because of the cold sewage and the possibility of cold water flowing through pipes and channels in the building.

The provision of generous ventilation is essential in the design of sewage-pumping stations to carry away odors, moisture, and gases that may escape into the building. Ventilating equipment should have a minimum capacity of six changes of air per hour. It is desirable also to control humidity in order to minimize corrosion.

Natural and artificial illumination of the interior of a building should be generous and walls should be light-colored and washable. Painted walls are less desirable than tile, brick, or concrete because of the possibility of the deterioration of the paint by vapors in the building. A bright interior is conducive to better safety and morale, and to better maintenance of equipment than a dark, noisome, and dangerous enclosure. Shadows and glare are to be avoided. Dust-proof, vapor-proof, and explosion-proof fixtures and luminaries should be used where they are exposed to hazardous conditions. Illuminating practice for industrial buildings is discussed by Hays and by the American Standards Association.[6] Some levels of illumination for sewage-pumping stations, recommended by Hays, are:

Laboratories, power houses	20 ft-candles
Chlorine room	500-watt luminaries on 10-ft centers
Pump rooms	300- to 500-watt luminaries on 12- to 16-ft centers at low height, giving 6 to 12 ft-candles; or 1,500-watt luminaries on 14-ft centers at 43-ft height
Pipe galleries	150-watt luminaries on 15-ft centers along wall
Filter and drier rooms	500-watt luminaries on 11-ft centers to give 16 ft-candles; or 1,000-watt luminaries on 11-ft centers at 40-ft height to give minimum of 5 to 10 ft-candles
Digesters	300-watt luminaries on 12-ft centers
Screen chamber and similar head works	500-watt luminaries on 14-ft centers at 30-ft height, or 18-ft centers at 17-ft height
Deck lighting and other exterior lighting as on settling tanks	250-watt mecury-vapor luminaries, on 30-ft centers at 14-ft height

[6] "American Standard Practice for Industrial Lighting," American Standards Association; see also H. M. Hays, *Public Works,* October, 1955, p. 83.

Drainage of pumping station floors should be provided sufficient to care for any break in the pumps or piping. Floors below gravity drainage should drain to a sump equipped with a float-controlled pump. Where danger of flooding exists, the suction of the main pumps may be connected to this sump, but the connection should not be used in routine operation.

Principles of safety in industrial-plant design are equally applicable to sewage-works design. Passageways should be wide enough for the purpose; adequately lighted and ventilated; free from abrupt changes in level and other obstructions; and stairways are preferable to ladders. Vertical ladders more than 10 ft long should be equipped with a hoop cage. Spiral stairways are to be used only under exceptional circumstances.

Screens, grit chambers, wet wells and other devices through which sewage passes before entering a pumping station, or in which sewage is exposed to the atmosphere, should be enclosed in a separate building or a separate portion of the pumping station. Such construction is essential to prevent odors, gases, and moisture from entering the pumping station or control building.

Some recommendations of the Joint Committee regarding pumping stations are (see Sect. 5–2):

Structures. 1. *Entrances.* Where dry-well type installations are used, wet and dry wells should be completely separated, with a separate entrance to each.

2. *Pump removal.* Provision should be made to facilitate removal of pumps and motors.

3. *Stairways.* Suitable stairways should be provided for convenient access to dry wells of pump stations and shall be provided to wet wells containing either bar screens or mechanical equipment requiring inspection or maintenance.

Some additional suggestions concerning pumping-station design [7] are: (1) Electric outlets or convenience outlets should be provided at desirable locations; (2) there should be a small drainpipe from pump packing gland to sump; (3) hose bibs to water lines must be located at convenient points for washing floors and for other purposes.

12–4. Location of pumping stations. Topographical conditions are important in selecting the location for a sewage-pumping station, as the station must be placed where it will perform its functions in the best manner and at the lowest cost. The station may be located

[7] See also M. S. Campbell, *S. and I.W.,* September, 1956, p. 1176.

in a high-class residential district, in a blighted area, or on low-lying, undeveloped land beyond the city limits.

Wherever the building is located it will probably be on low land threatened by flooding. Two methods of protecting the building against inundation are: (1) the provision of adequate pumping capacity with reserve power sufficient to lift all of the sewage that can be delivered to the station; (2) the protection of the site by dykes and backwater valves to exclude threatened flood levels.

12–5. Pumping equipment.[8] Electric power is used almost exclusively in small and medium-sized sewage-pumping stations, and in most large pumping stations. Internal-combustion engines, as standby power, are sometimes connected to the pump shaft or to an electric generator, or a separate pumping unit with an internal-combustion-engine drive may be installed. The electric wiring of the pumping station may permit the connection to it of emergency, mobile electric-power generating equipment.

A review of sewage-pumping stations reveals a wide variety of equipment in addition to the main sewage pumps. Among such items are:

Steam-generating equipment: boilers, coal- and ash-handling plants, blowers, condensers, feedwater heaters, economizers, and other items connected with the generation of power through steam.

Steam turbines.

Vacuum and priming pumps.

Sump and drainage pumps with outlet at sufficient height to minimize possibility of flooding the station.

Lubricating-oil circulating pumps, filters, and reclaimers.

Electric generators and motors.

Electric storage batteries.

Electric motor-generator sets, transformers, and rectifiers.

Air compressors and air blowers, air receivers, and air filters.

Meters for sewage, gas, and electricity.

An indicating and recording meter on the discharge line from the pumping station.

Internal-combustion engines, oil storage tanks, etc.

Liquid-level recorders and indicators.

Temperature recorders and indicators for the atmosphere, digestion tanks, hot water, etc.

[8] See also J. M. MacRea. *Water and Sewage Works,* Part II, May, 1954, p. R-204.

Water-heating and water-circulating devices for the building and for digestion tanks.

Sewage-gas receivers, storage tanks, waste-gas burners, flame traps, etc.

Gas masks, periodically checked, and safe against such gases as may be anticipated. These should include chlorine, explosive, and asphyxiating gases. The masks should be stored where they are accessible and free from a gaseous atmosphere.

Clocks for the control of various items of equipment, such as lights, motors, screens, and blowers.

Automatic control devices.

Check valves, gate valves, sluice gates, weirs, siphons, and similar devices to control the flow of sewage.

An overhead crane in large stations or a chain hoist in small ones.

A control board on which electrical control, indicating, and recording mechanisms are placed should be located in the control room, or in any other prominent and accessible place, but not in a lane of common travel. High-voltage equipment should be screened off or placed in a separate room.

Fire extinguishers containing sodium carbonate or carbon dioxide for electric fires.

Equipment essential to the successful operation of the pumping station may include also a grit chamber, a screen, and a receiving well. The grit chamber and screen are necessary to protect the pumps from wear and clogging. Grit chambers are not always used in sewage devoid of gritty matter, such as average domestic sewage. Receiving wells are used in small pumping stations with constant-speed pumps. The pumps are then operated intermittently, standing idle during some of the time that the receiving well is filling.

12–6. Automation [9] and remote control. Operations in pumping stations,[10] sewerage, and sewage treatment that may be aided by automation or semi-automatic controls include: (1) concentration of controls in laboratory or other central point where information will be instantaneously available through dials, gages, or other signals, or by closed-circuit television, and is continuously recorded by charts, tapes, and other means; (2) dispatching of command to inform or to

[9] A coined word meaning automatic operation. See also B. L. Socia and R. W. Lindsey, *Water and Sewage Works,* June 30, 1957, p. R-54; and H. W. Phillips, *Public Works,* March, 1957, p. 144.

[10] See also *Eng. News-Record,* Aug. 2, 1956, p. 19.

advise; (3) sampling; (4) physical or chemical analyses; (5) starting and speed of pumps; (6) opening and closing of valves; (7) rates of flow; (8) handling and dosing of chemicals; (9) rotation of the use of equipment to distribute wear and maintain readiness to serve; (10) warning of impending or actual trouble, such as clogging or overflow; warning of changing conditions; or predicting impending change of conditions such as approaching flood wave or change of sewage strength; (11) operating sewage-treatment devices of almost all kinds: for example, clean a screen, feed a sludge digester, or change rate of air flow in the activated-sludge process; (12) sensing of error in a procedure and application of corrections; and (13) long-, moderate-, or short-distance transmission of signals or commands by mechanical, liquid, gas- or air-operated, or electrical devices. The commands transmitted may include the starting and stopping of equipment.

Such devices reduce the work of the operator but not his responsibilities. All automatic devices require routine observation, inspection, test, and preventive maintenance. Electric power is suitable for automatic and remote control. Devices depending mainly on electricity are available for the performance of such tasks as are listed in the preceding paragraph.

Automatic devices are of two types: on-and-off and proportional, either with or without automatic reset. The first is rugged and insensitive and is suitable primarily where change is infrequent. It may be used, for example, to start a motor at a fixed time, or at a certain liquid level, or at other predetermined condition. In the second type the control is proportional to the deviation from a set normal of the conditions of operation as, for example, the electric current to a motor increases when its speed diminishes. The automatic device will adjust the conditions to safety. Unless, however, automatic reset is included this device may fall into the first class.

12–7. Piping. Steel is suitable for small pipes that are open to inspection and are protected from weather and other corrosive conditions. Wrought iron will last longer than steel and should be used for gas lines. Brass is not suited for the conveying of gas. Cast iron is preferable for larger size pipes and for burial underground, or where exposed to the weather.

Flanged joints should be used for pipes and specials that may have to be opened occasionally. Threaded or leaded joints are used for more permanent installations. Under almost all conditions joints should be located accessibly.

Color schemes for painting pipes have been proposed as an aid in plant operation and safety,[11] as for example:

Indication	Color	Example
Danger	Red	Fire protection
		Explosive gas
Caution	Yellow	Ammonia
Alert	Orange	Steam
Safety	Green or white	Potable water
		Ventilation duct
Unpleasant	Black or brown	Crude sewage
Putrid		Sludge

Pipe lines should be straight, as short as possible, and free from vertical bends that may entrap sediment, liquids, or gas, depending on the fluid being carried.

Cross connections must be avoided.

Cranes or hoists must be easily accessible to piping and other heavy equipment, to facilitate repairs and replacement. The accessibility of equipment beneath floors, in pits, and in similar places may require the installation of gratings, manholes, catwalks, bulkhead doors, and trap doors.

12–8. Receiving or wet well. One of the principal purposes of a receiving well at a sewage-pumping station is to act as an equalizing basin to minimize the fluctuations of load on the pumps. The receiving well serves as a suction pit from which the pumps draw sewage. The well should be located as high as the local conditions will permit, and the bottom should be sloped towards each pump suction to prevent the collection of deposits on the floor of the well. A gas-proof partition should separate the wet well from all other parts of the pumping station. Vertical walls, all parts of which are accessible, are desirable to facilitate cleaning and to prevent deposits. The wet well should be divided into two or more portions that can be used either together or separately to facilitate cleaning or repairs. Where possible each portion should be able to drain through any pump lifting sewage from the well. Facilities for access, inspection, cleaning, lighting, and ventilation should be provided. The opening into a wet well should be 3 ft or more above the center line of the highest pump inlet in the wet well.

The size and shape of the well should be such as to permit the pumps to run as long as possible without permitting the accumulation

---

[11] See also *S. and I.W.*, June, 1956, p. 813.

of deposits that may become septic. Dead spaces and flat bottoms are to be avoided. A satisfactory manner to avoid deposits is to slope the bottom steeply (1:1 or steeper) towards a sump or low point where the inlet to the suction pipe is located. In general, no pump should operate less than 15 minutes. Intermittent and irregular pumping are undesirable because of their effect on the operation of sewage-treatment plants.

The procedure in a study of an existing pumping-station performance, or in the design of a new pumping station is indicated in the following illustrative example.

A sewage-pumping station is equipped with a 2,500-gal capacity wet well, and with 4 pumps of the following capacities, in gpm: 200, 300, 500, and 500. The mass diagram of flow on a day when the total sewage flow was 720,000 gal is shown in Fig. 12–4. Rate lines of pumping for each pump, and their combinations, are shown to the left in the same figure. Periods of pump operation and times when the wet well is either full or empty are found by drawing the appropriate lines parallel to the corresponding rates of pumping, as indicated in the figure. When the pumping line is 2,500 gal below the sewage line the wet well is full; when the pumping line intersects the sewage line the wet well is empty; and the pumping line cannot extend above the sewage line. In this example the size of the wet well and the rates of pumping are known. Where only the rate of sewage flow is known the size of the wet well and the capacities of the pumps can be selected, by trial, by drawing the mass diagram of sewage flow for the critical day and adjusting combinations of wet-well capacities and pumping rates to the sewage-flow line to give a small-capacity wet well with infrequent stopping and starting of pumps.

The starting and stopping of pumps is often controlled by switches actuated by floats in the wet well as shown in Figs. 12–2 and 12–7. The control should be set to shut off the pump when the well is almost empty, to prevent the loss of prime. The float may be connected to the switch by a cable passing through a tube or tubes in the floor or wall. Tubes and cables should be accessible and replaceable, since they are subject to corrosion. An indicator to show the depth of sewage in the wet well should be located conveniently for observation by the operator. Electrical equipment should not be placed in a wet well. Where this is unavoidable, however, only explosion-proof equipment should be used because of explosive gases to be anticipated in wet wells. A supply of water, not necessarily potable, should be available under pressure, for flushing and cleaning.

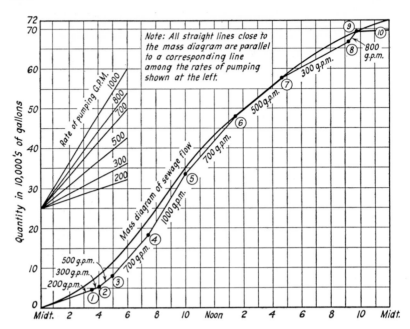

Fig. 12–4. Mass diagram to show operation of pumps in a wet well. (0) Midnight. The wet well is empty and the 200-gpm pump starts. (1) 3.30 A.M. The wet well is full. The 200-gpm pump shuts down and the 300-gpm unit takes over. (2) 4.00 A.M. The wet well is full. The 300-gpm pump shuts down and the 500-gpm unit takes over. (3) 5.00 A.M. The wet well is full. The 500-gpm continues to operate and the 200-gpm unit goes into service, making 700 gpm being pumped. (4) 7.30 A.M. The wet well is full. All three pumps go into operation giving a discharge rate of 1,000 gpm. (5) 10 A.M. The wet well is about one-half full with the level of water going down. The operator shuts down the 300-gpm pump. Rate of discharge is now 700 gpm. (6) 1.40 P.M. The wet well is empty. Operator shuts down the smallest pump. Rate of discharge is now 500 gpm. (7) 4.40 P.M. The wet well is empty. The 500-gpm pump stops and the 300-gpm unit is started. (8) 9.20 P.M. The operator wants to empty the wet well rapidly, so he starts the 500-gpm pump and pumps at the rate of 800 gpm until: (9) 9.50 P.M. The wet well is empty and all pumps are shut down until: (10) Midnight, the wet well is full.

12–9. Capacity of pumps. It may be desirable to install a minimum of four pumps in a pumping station, the capacities being divided so that one has a capacity equal to or slightly greater than the minimum rate of flow into the station, one is equal to or slightly greater than the average rate of flow, and one is equal to or slightly greater than the maximum rate of flow, the capacities of the two smaller pumps combined being equal to the capacity of the largest pump. A standby pump with standby power should be provided, with a capacity equal to the largest pumping unit. The capacity of the standby equipment depends, to a great extent, on local conditions. For example, where it is both possible and permissible to provide a bypass, standby equipment may be a minimum. Where full standby capacity is needed, the pumping equipment may be sufficient to care for the peak load with the largest pumping unit shut down. Power failures may be anticipated by providing an auxiliary form of power. For example, an electrically operated station may be equipped with easily started internal-combustion engines, or a steam-pumping station may have auxiliary electric power.

The capacities of pumps in relatively large pumping stations should be selected to permit the starting and stopping of constant-speed pumps as the load changes. The changes in load between the starting or stopping of successive constant-speed units may be cared for by a variable-speed unit whose capacity is varied as the increment of load varies between the constant-speed units. By the proper operation of such equipment there is no need for a receiving well and there are no abrupt changes in the rate of flow of sewage from the pumping station to cause undesirable surges in discharge lines or at the sewage-treatment plant.

The load on a pumping station depends on the quantity of sewage and the height it must be lifted. The head against which the pumps must operate fluctuates with the level in the tributary sewer or pump well and in the discharge conduit. If the sewage is discharged into a large body of water the lift may be lessened for the largest rates of flow because the sewage in the suction well may rise more rapidly than in the body of water receiving the discharge. If the discharge is into a large body of water, or other conditions where the discharge head is approximately constant, the fluctuations in total head should not exceed the diameter of the tributary sewer. Such fluctuations may be of great importance in the efficiency of operation of centrifugal pumps.

12–10. Pumps. Centrifugal pumps are used almost exclusively in the pumping of sewage. They are well adapted to service in either large or small units and to automatic and remote control, and to non-clog design. Compressed-air ejectors are used for pumping small loads. Centrifugal pumps, reciprocating pumps, and air lifts are in use for the pumping of sludge.

Some recommendations of the Joint Committee (see Sect. 5–2) concerning the care and installation of pumps are:

Pumps. 1. *Duplicate units.* At least two pumps or ejectors should be provided. Where the pumping installation will serve not more than 50 homes, a single unit will be permitted, provided (i) that the station is of ample size and designed to permit the installation of a future duplicate pump with no structural changes, and (ii) that an overflow is permissible and the occasional discharge of sewage will not be unduly objectionable. If only two units are provided, they should have the same capacity. Each should be capable of handling flows in excess of the expected maximum flow. Where three or more pumps are provided, they should be designed to fit actual flow conditions and of such capacity that with any one pump out of service the remaining pumps will have capacity to handle maximum sewage flows.

2. *Protection against clogging.* Pumps handling raw sewage should be preceded by readily accessible bar racks with clear openings not exceeding 2 in. unless ejectors are used or the pumping equipment is of a special type with integral screens. Where the size of the installation warrants, a mechanically cleaned bar screen with grinder or comminutor is recommended. Where screens are located below ground, convenient facilities must be provided for handling screenings. For the larger or deeper stations, duplicate units of proper capacity are preferred.

3. *Pump openings.* Pump suction and discharge openings should be at least 4 in. in diameter. Suction and discharge piping shall be at least 4 in. in diameter.

4. *Priming.* Unless self-priming pumps are used, the pump should be so placed that under normal operating conditions it will operate under a positive suction head.

5. *Electrical fixtures.* Electrical fixtures in enclosed places where gas may accumulate shall comply with the National Board of Fire Underwriters specifications for hazardous conditions.

6. *Intake.* Each pump should have an individual intake. Wet-well design should be such as to avoid turbulence near the intakes.

7. *Dry-well dewatering.* A separate sump pump shall be provided in dry wells to remove leakage or drainage with the discharge above the overflow level of the wet well. A connection to the pump suction is also recommended as an auxiliary feature. Water ejectors connected to a potable water supply will not be approved.

8. *Pumping rates.* The pumps and controls of main pumping stations, and especially pumping stations operated as part of treatment works, should be selected to operate at varying delivery rates to permit discharging sewage from the station to the treatment works at approximately its rate of delivery to the pump station.

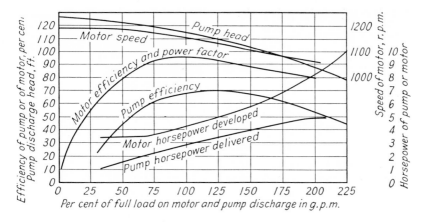

Fig. 12–5. Characteristic curves of a centrifugal pump and a 5-hp, 3-phase, 220-volt, 60-cycle, induction motor.

12–11. Selection of centrifugal pumps.[12] The characteristic curves of a centrifugal pump are important guides in its selection. A set of such curves for a pump and motor is shown in Fig. 12–5. This combination has its highest efficiency when lifting 100 gpm against a head of 114 ft. As the head increases the efficiency drops off rapidly, but the rate of reduction of discharge is less marked owing to the relatively steep characteristic (head vs. discharge curve). The importance of high efficiency and the flat efficiency curve in the selection of a pump and motor is to be emphasized. The higher first cost of a unit with a few per cent higher efficiency as compared with a unit of lower first cost and lower efficiency may be amply repaid in reduced power costs in operation.

Another desirable feature of a centrifugal pump may be a steep characteristic curve. With such a characteristic, slight changes in discharge pressure will not greatly affect the rate of discharge. This may be a feature of importance in the selection of a pump to operate under variable conditions of lift.

12–12. Settings of centrifugal pumps. Centrifugal-pump installations may be classified as: (1) pumps submerged beneath the sewage in the wet well, (2) pumps in a dry well below the level of the liquid level in a wet well, and (3) pumps set higher than the

[12] See also R. Carter and I. J. Karassik, *Water and Sewage Works,* May, 1951, p. 212, and August, 1954, p. 347, beginning a series of eight articles.

Fig. 12–6. Vertical-shaft setting of a centrifugal pump. (Courtesy Worthington Corp.) The two pumps shown are each 12.5 mgd capacity, Mixflo pumps, at Richmond, N. Y.

sewage in the wet well. The first type of pump is set with a vertical shaft reaching a motor placed above the level of the sewage, preferably in a permanently dry setting. The second and third types of setting may include either vertical- or horizontal-shaft pumps. An illustration of the second type of setting with a vertical shaft is shown in Figs. 12–6 and 12–7. Horizontal-shaft settings are shown in Figs. 12–8 and 12–9.

1. Inlet sewer
2. Stop plate groove
3. Gravel trap
4. Drain
5. Worthington comminutor
6. Downstream submergence
   control
7. Discharge to wet well
8. Suction bell
9. Worthington Freflo pump
10. Check valve
11. Discharge pipe
12. Shaft cover pipe
13. Comminutor shaft
14. Access to comminutor
15. Gear head motor & stand
16. Pump shaft
17. Guide bearing
18. 1st pump motor & stand
19. 2nd pump motor & right
    angle gear
20. Emergency gasoline
    engine drive
21. Float and guide
22. Float sheaves &
    extension shaft
23. Start-stop pump
    alternator
24. Overflow pipe
25. Wet well ventilation
26. Access to wet well sump
27. Dry well ventilation
28. Access to dry well
29. Sump pump
30. Sump pump discharge
    to wet well
31. By-pass stop plate
32. By-pass screen

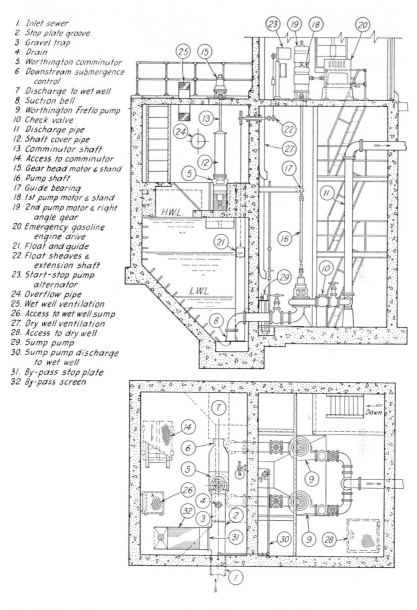

Fig. 12–7. Plan and sections of typical sewage lift station with nominal capacity of 1 mgd, showing comminutor and Freflo pumps by Worthington. (Courtesy Worthington Pump Co.)

Fig. 12–8. Horizontal-shaft setting of centrifugal pumps. (Courtesy Fairbanks Morse.) The pumps are located in Minot, N. D.

The principal advantages of vertical-shaft installations are the protection of the motor against dampness, and the saving of space below ground. The arrangement is not ideal, however, because there is difficulty in maintaining alignment of the long shaft, parts are exposed to corrosion, and the pump is not easily accessible for maintenance and repairs. It is undesirable to place a pump in a wet well, and the submergence of a pump in sewage is particularly disadvantageous because of the neglect to which the parts may be subjected and the difficulty of making repairs when they are required.

Vertical-shaft pumps in a dry well below the level of the sewage in an adjacent wet well, as shown in Figs. 12–2, 12–6, and 12–7, are common in small and moderate-size pumping stations. The Flush-Kleen pumps, shown in Fig. 12–10, operate to avoid the passage of large objects through the pumps. When the pump on the right is discharging, as shown in the figure, sewage is entering the wet well from the sewer, passing through the screen on the discharge pipe of the pump on the left, which is idle. When the wet well is empty the

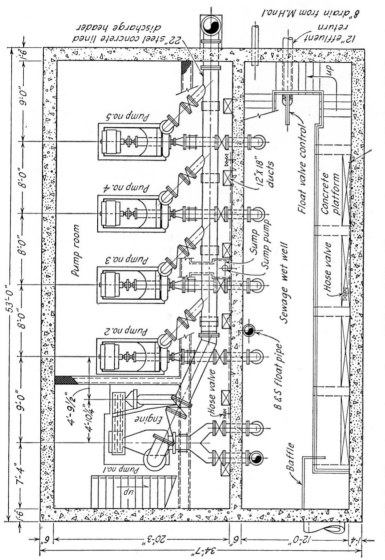

Fig. 12–9. Plan of pumping station at Vallejo, Calif. (Courtesy Brown and Caldwell, Engineers.)

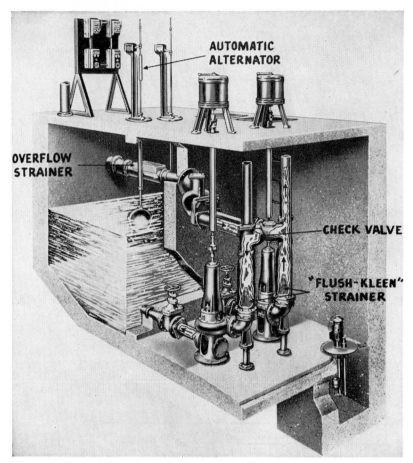

Fig. 12–10. Flush-Kleen pumps. (Courtesy Chicago Pump Co.) When pump on right is discharging, sewage flows from sewer, through discharge of pump on left, into wet well. When wet well is empty both pumps stop until well is refilled. Then pump on left starts to discharge and sewage enters wet well through pump on right. Alternating of pumps continues indefinitely.

pump on the right stops and the wet well refills through the pump on the left. When the wet well is full again the pump on the left discharges and sewage enters through the pump on the right. This alternation of pumps continues indefinitely. Discharge from each removes materials that may have accumulated on its screen.

In the installation of vertical-shaft pumps some of the difficulties from misalignment can be overcome by the use of universal joints between bearings.[13] Unless oversize shafts are used, guide bearings on at least 7-ft centers should be placed between the end bearings. Although ball bearings are commonly used, their failure is sudden and repairs are difficult and expensive, whereas babbitted, split-sleeve bearings may be operated for months at an abnormal temperature and repaired with comparative ease.

Some of the difficulties with vertical-shaft pumps may be overcome by so-called "protective shaft installations," outstanding features of which include: (1) intermediate bearings supported on flanges enclosed in a hanger pipe allow perfect alignment of shafting in the factory and eliminate need for special types of supports; (2) a flexible mounting of the motor on the floor plate permits self-adjustment of motor and shaft to compensate for any misalignment; (3) the flexible coupling at the pump is in an accessible, flexible housing; and (4) grease and oil cannot be thrown by the enclosed bearings.

Horizontal-shaft pumps in a dry well may require higher building costs but the pump-installation costs will be lowered and operation and maintenance will be less expensive. Danger from flooding of the dry well must be avoided, and ventilation to remove moisture and gases must be generously provided. Plans and sections of pumping stations are shown in Figs. 12-7 and 12-9. It is essential that a sump pump shall be installed in the dry well, and it is desirable that its motor be protected from flooding.

Horizontal-shaft, self-priming pumps with pump and motor located on the pumping-station floor above the level of the wet well have advantages over all other types of installations. Their principal disadvantage is the cost and maintenance of priming equipment. Although suction lifts of 15 to 20 ft have been operated successfully, the lowest feasible lift should be employed and a maximum of about 10 ft is recommended. Priming may be provided by a wet vacuum pump mounted on the same shaft as the main pump or operated by a different motor. The advantage of the independently driven pump is that it is used only as needed. Close-coupled, horizontal-shaft pumps, in which the pump and motor are built into the same frame, result in saving of space and avoiding alignment difficulties.

In the installation of wet vacuum pumps and water-sealed stuffing boxes a supply of clear water is required. This supply should be obtained from a water tank with a float-feed valve. The water should

[13] See also R. F. Hunger, *Sewage Works Jour.*, November, 1935, p. 1109.

enter the tank by a supply that discharges it through the air over the tank edge, in order that any danger from a cross connection may be avoided.

Pumps are sometimes installed in a row with all pumps discharging into the same pipe. Between the pipe and each pump are a gate valve and a check valve protected against slam. Such an installation is shown in Fig. 12–9. Horizontal check valves clog less easily than vertical check valves, which are frequently a source of trouble, but the interior of any check valve should be accessible for cleaning. With pumps larger than about 10 in., power-operated cone or pivot check valves are less wasteful of power and are free from slam. Centrifugal pumps discharging into the same pipe should have approximately the same shut-off head, and a rising characteristic from rated capacity to shut-off. Otherwise the pump which discharges at the highest pressure will do the work even to the extent of shutting down other pumps.

To assure proper operation and control each centrifugal pump should be equipped with:

1. An air-release valve located at the high point in the casing to release air or gas, which may accumulate in the pump regardless of its location.

2. An independent, short, straight suction pipe, free from "high" points.

3. Gages on both the suction and the discharge pipes.

4. A meter on the discharge pipe.

5. A characteristic curve that will enable the operator to detect quickly any failure of the pump's intended performance.

6. A check valve between the pump and gate valve on the discharge pipe.

12–13. Non-clog pumps. Centrifugal pumps for sewage are designed to avoid clogging. Clogging is avoided partly by the arrangement, large size, and smoothness of channels and impeller to permit the passage of solids through the pump. Sections of non-clog impellers and pumps are shown in Figs. 12–11 to 12–14. In some pumps the free passages are as large as the discharge pipe, but in most the area of the passages may be only 75 to 90 per cent of the area of the discharge pipe. To prevent clogging it is essential that the pump passages be as large as or larger than the suction pipe, and that the

Fig. 12–11. Vertical, dry-pit, bladeless trash and sewage pump. (Courtesy Fairbanks Morse and Co.)

discharge pipe be no smaller than the pump passages. Only the volute pump can provide the required non-clogging characteristics. In general, impellers and passages made to pass objects smaller than about 3 in. in diameter will be found to be unsatisfactory in service. Long stringy objects, such as rope and rubber goods, and grease are most conducive to clogging, and yet the potential clogging propensities of sewage pumps are customarily rated by the diameter of the largest ball that can pass through the pump. It is sometimes specified that non-clog pumps for domestic sewage shall pass a 2-in. diameter ball, and for combined domestic sewage and industrial sewage a 2½-in. ball.

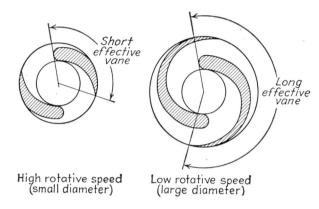

High rotative speed   Low rotative speed
(small diameter)   (large diameter)

Fig. 12–12. Non-clog pump impellers. (C. W. Lindeman, *Sewage and Ind. Wastes Eng.*, August, 1950, p. 406.)

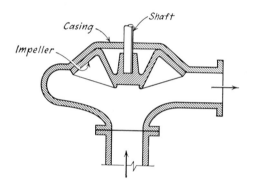

Fig. 12–13. Non-clog vortex pump. Recessed impeller is mounted outside of the flow path of sewage between the pump inlet and discharge. Solids equivalent to the pipe diameter can be passed.

Lindeman [14] states: ". . . non-clogging type impellers are generally of the two-valve (two port) construction for pumps approximately up to 14 inches in diameter discharge size. Larger pumps are generally of the 3-vane or 4-vane construction . . . Single-vane impellers have very satisfactory non-clogging characteristics." Glazebrook [15] describes a bladeless pump with an impeller of the type shown in Fig. 12–12 that has outstanding non-clogging characteristics.

The design of the impeller is probably the most important feature in a non-clogging centrifugal pump. Both closed impellers and open impellers are used with success, but most pumps are equipped with

[14] C. W. Lindeman, *S. and I.W.*, August, 1950, p. 406.
[15] R. C. Glazebrook, *Water and Sewage Works*, January, 1950, p. 41.

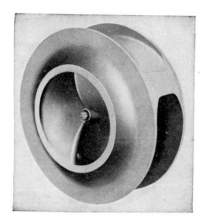

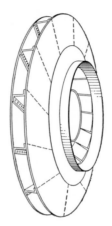

Fig. 12–14(a). Enclosed impeller. (Courtesy Chicago Pump Co.)

Fig. 12–14(b). Enclosed impeller. (Courtesy DeLaval Steam Turbine Co.)

wide, two-bladed, enclosed impellers such as are shown in Fig. 12–14a. The blades are comparatively thin, with smooth, easy curves. The blades in the impeller shown in Fig. 12–14a protrude through the back of the impeller to prevent the accumulation of material around the shaft and between the impeller and casing. On open impellers the blades are chamfered to minimize the surface adjacent to the casing. Wearing rings are sometimes recommended, to equalize the wear by gritty material and to make possible the restoration of the original tightness by the installation of new rings. However, uneven wear of the ring has been found conducive to clogging and to loss of efficiency.

Some pumps, such as the pump illustrated in Fig. 12–15, are equipped with devices, such as a screw-feed mechanism, which macerate solids before they enter the pump chamber. One type of small pump is arranged so that sewage enters the wet well through the *discharge* pipe of the pump when the pump is not running. A screen in the discharge pipe prevents large objects from entering the pump. When the wet well is full the pump goes into action, closing a check valve to prevent the sewage from returning to its source, and opening another check valve to discharge the sewage into the discharge pipe and sewer. Such pumps may be installed in pairs so that there is no interruption of the flow of sewage into the wet well through the idle pump while the other pump is in operation, as shown in Fig. 12–10.

Devices to prevent clogging reduce the efficiency and the possible discharge pressures of non-clogging pumps when compared with pumps for handling clear water. Efficiencies as low as 40 per cent for the smaller sizes, up to 85 per cent and higher for larger sizes, are to be found in non-clogging pumps, with discharge pressures per stage limited to about 100 to 120 ft.

Although there is usually little corrosive action by ordinary sewage on the parts of a pump exposed to it, and cast-iron parts have been found to be satisfactory, the use of bronze for impellers and stuffing boxes is common. In some instances cast iron with a high nickel content has been used for impellers, and some impellers and pump casings have been lined with porcelain. Occasionally pump shafts are made of stainless steel.

A stuffing box of liberal, but reasonable proportions with a clear-water seal should be provided. A vent pipe, $\frac{1}{2}$-in. in diameter or larger, should be led from a high point in the pump casing to the wet well or to some other good vent point, to release air and to avoid air binding of the pump.

Self-priming of centrifugal pumps is sometimes desirable. The feature is obtained by various expedients, some of which are proprietary. Among unrestricted methods is the use of a watertight foot valve which will keep the pump full of sewage when it is not running, or an internal reservoir may supply sewage to the pump when it is started to supplement that which is held in the suction pipe

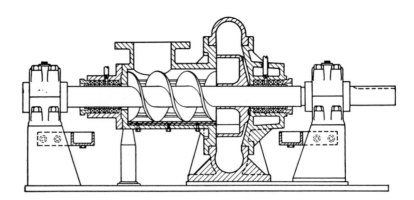

Fig. 12–15. Screw-feed centrifugal pump. (Courtesy Chicago Pump Co.)

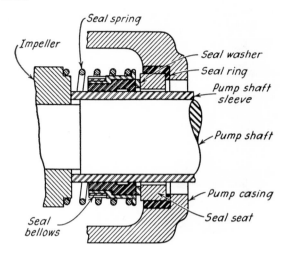

Fig. 12–16. Sealed bearing for self-priming centrifugal pump.

by the foot valve.   In either event, leakage of air along the impeller shaft must be prevented.   This is done by such a seal as is shown in Fig. 12–16.

12–14. Mixed-flow pumps. A mixed-flow pump, as shown in Fig. 12–15, is one into which water flows axially and from which it is discharged somewhat axially and somewhat radially.   The mean outlet diameter of the impeller is somewhat small in relation to the eye.   As a result the pump has a relatively high specific speed.   The high speed renders mixed-flow pumps unsuitable for high suction lifts, and the pumps are somewhat more susceptible to clogging.   However, the mixed-flow pump is less costly than standard types of non-clog pumps and, under proper conditions, is highly satisfactory in service.

12–15. Sludge pumps.[16] Types of pumps for moving sludge are confined almost exclusively to centrifugal and reciprocating. Each type is used extensively, but the centrifugal, with non-clogging impellers, being more easily clogged in the smaller sizes, is confined to the larger sizes.   The Scru-peller pump is a modification of the screw-feed impeller pump, applicable particularly to the pumping of sludge with a centrifugal pump.   It is less subject to clogging than the ordinary centrifugal pump and avoids some of the objections inherent in reciprocating pumps.

[16] See also S. E. Kappe, *Water Works and Sewerage,* November, 1941, p. 525.

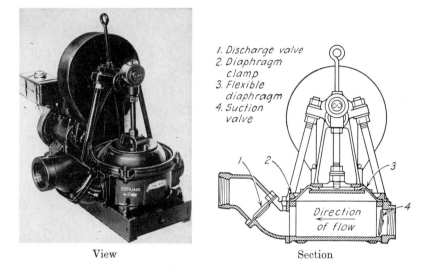

1. Discharge valve
2. Diaphragm clamp
3. Flexible diaphragm
4. Suction valve

Direction of flow

View   Section

Fig. 12–17. Diaphragm pump for sludge. (Courtesy Gen-a-Matic Corp.)

Reciprocating pumps are more easily primed and are more free from suction difficulties. The rate of discharge is unaffected by changes in the discharge pressure, which are common in sludge pumping due to variations in sludge quality. Control of the rate of discharge may be highly desirable in the operation of a sludge tank from which it is desired to withdraw sludge without disturbing the upper layer of fresh, undigested sludge. Undesirable features of reciprocating sludge pumps include: (1) noise, (2) difficulty in maintaining tight packing with resulting messy leaks if it is too loose or broken shear pins if too tight, and (3) hard wear on valves. If both reciprocating and centrifugal pumps were available an operator would probably choose the centrifugal because of its relative simplicity, cleanliness, and low maintenance. For high suction lift or high discharge pressure the reciprocating or the displacement pump is better suited.

Reciprocating sludge pumps under ordinary conditions are commonly either diaphragm or plunger pumps with large cylinders, 10 to 12 in., and a short stroke, 2 to 6 in., driven at a slow speed, 30 to 35 rpm, through reduction gears by an electric motor or internal-combustion engine. A diaphragm pump is illustrated in Fig. 12–17. The rate of pumping can be varied by adjusting the length of stroke of the arm, by controlling the motor speed, or by shifting gears as in an automobile. Higher heads may require the use of triplex power pumps with ball valves, which are somewhat less subject to clogging than flap valves, but wear so reduces the sizes of the balls that, unless promptly renewed, the balls will be pushed through the seat and the plungers will become badly scored. Sludge pumps, particularly centrifugal sludge pumps, should be set to avoid suction lift, as reduced pressure releases gas from the sludge and breaks the suction.

Greene [17] summarizes some of the features of sludge pumps as follows:

(1) When applying a motor drive have some slip in the drive. . . . (2) Avoid a solid hook-up even if shear pins are depended on to prevent breakage. (3) Use ample air chambers on both suction and discharge. (4) Install a by-pass . . . from discharge to suction. This allows easy starting and makes speed changes less abrupt. (5) Ball valves, although noisy, have less slip, less plugging, and are more easily renewable than any of the substitutes. . . . (7) Use pistons instead of diaphragms, especially if the pipe lines are long and there is a suction lift. (8) A pump with a 4-in. stroke and one or two 10-in.-diameter pistons can run smoothly at 40 rpm but gets to be a battering ram when the stroke or speed is increased. . . . (10) The disadvantages of diaphragm pumps are so obvious . . . that some other means of pumping sludge is being continually tried out.

A special type of pump has been devised for the circulation of sludge and scum in a digestion tank. It consists of a cast-iron shell inside which there is a non-clogging screw impeller actuated by an electric motor. Sludge is forced through a riser pipe in the tank in which the pump is submerged, the circulation being from bottom to top of tank or reversible by reversing the direction of rotation of the screw.

12–16. Sludge-pump lifts. A minimum positive static head of 24 in. should be provided at the suction side of all sludge pumps, particularly those of the centrifugal type. Suction lifts should be avoided to prevent difficulties in operation. Because of the uncertainties of operating conditions the operating pressure of a sludge pump can be estimated best by experience and judgment.[18] The rule should be to allow 50 to 100 per cent excess of pressure in design, unless better information is available, and to expect wide and sudden variations of pressure in operation.

[17] See *Sewage Works Jour.*, September, 1933, p. 858.
[18] See also C. R. Velzy, *Water Works and Sewerage*, January, 1945, p. 31.

12–17. Sludge suction and discharge pipes.[19]   The Joint Committee states: "Sludge withdrawal piping should have a minimum diameter of 8 inches for gravity withdrawal and 6 inches for suction. Sludge pump discharge piping should be at least 4 inches in diameter where withdrawal is by gravity, the available head on the discharge pipe should be at least 4 feet, and preferably more. . . . Slope on gravity discharge piping should not be less than 3 per cent. Provision should be made for draining and flushing discharge lines." In general, the velocity of flow in the sludge pipes should be above critical (see Sect. 24–12) to avoid clogging and the deposition of grease. Where the velocity of flow is greater than upper critical, the head loss due to the flow of sludge in a long pipe line can be determined by application of the Hazen and Williams formula, using a value of C 20 to 40 per cent less than that used for the flow of water. Velocities much above critical will involve an unnecessary amount of head loss due to friction. Velocities of flow between 5 and 8 fps will, in general, be found satisfactory.

12–18. Speed, and speed control, of centrifugal pumps.   Speed control is essential to the economical operation of centrifugal pumps in many sewerage installations. It can be obtained through variable-speed motors or variable-speed transmissions, the second being considered the more satisfactory as it permits the operation of the motor at its most efficient speed and the operation of the pump under the most economical conditions. Variable-speed transmissions include those in which the gear ratio is changed, adjustable belts, and gear motors. Speed can be adjusted also through the use of a hydraulic or fluid-filled coupling on the shaft between the motor and the pump. The most economical speed for the operation of the pump is determined by a study of the pump characteristics in conjunction with diagrams of head and discharge plotted against time.

Most non-clogging centrifugal pumps are classed as slow-speed pumps because of the relatively low lifts for which they are used. Experience shows a speed of pumps at sewage-treatment plants seldom greater than about 1,150 rpm. The slow speed is advantageous in minimizing wear in the parts but makes the selection of motor and intermediate reduction gear more difficult. The best speed or speeds of operation may be fixed after a study of the combined characteristic curves of motor and pump. Typical characteristic curves for a centrifugal pump and electric motor to drive it at approximately 1,150

[19] See also Sects. 18–14 and 24–11; and J. J. Wirts, *Water and Sewage Works,* October, 1948, p. 345.

rpm are shown in Fig. 12–5. For most installations a flat character-istic (head-capacity curve) for the pump is best, as the motor may be run at a practically constant speed and the rate of discharge can be varied without large changes in the discharge pressure.

12–19. Pump controls. Automatic pump controls include the devices in the sump or receiving well that are affected by the changing sewage levels so as to cause electric devices to actuate the starting, the speed, and the stopping of the pumps. It may be desirable to control the sharing of the load among multiple pumps discharging into the same pipe, especially if the discharge pipe is long, so that each smaller pump is shut off as the next larger one comes into service. Where two or more pumps are operated in parallel and are electrically driven, the use of an automatic alternator may be desirable to assure an even distribution of use and wear on pumps and motors. In the design of automatic pumping stations, care must be taken not to increase costs over those of manual control by the introduction of expensive safety and precautionary devices. In most small installa-tions floats placed in small chambers or vertical tubes protected from currents and turbulence in the wet well will be found satisfactory. Such an installation is shown in Fig. 12–2. Metallic floats may cor-rode, leak, and sink. The trend is toward heavy ceramic floats with positive action both upwards and downwards. Pressure cells and other devices, most of which are patented, are used on larger installa-tions.

12–20. Air ejectors and air lifts. Air ejectors are used primarily for lifting sewage from the basements of large buildings into the public sewer. They are better than centrifugal pumps for this pur-pose because the relatively small flow would call for a pump too small to prevent clogging. The air ejectors are not suitable for large in-stallations because their efficiency seldom attains 15 per cent.

A typical, compressed-air sewage ejector is illustrated in Fig. 12–18, and an installation is shown in Fig. 12–3. In operation sewage enters the ejector, shown in Fig. 12–18, from the inlet pipe B at the left, air escaping from the chamber through an open valve. When the float D has been lifted to the necessary elevation, the compressed-air valve shown at the top of the figure is opened by float D, and compressed air is discharged into the reservoir, closing the inlet check valve and the air-escape valve, and expelling sewage through the discharge pipe F, at the right. The dropping float C cuts off the air and releases the air under compression in the chamber. This causes the effluent check valve F to close, and opens the inlet valve B.

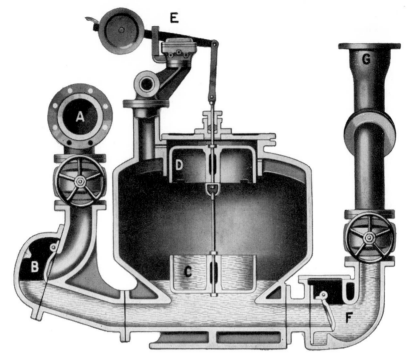

Fig. 12–18. Compressed-air sewage ejector. (Courtesy Yeomans Bros. Co.)

Air lifts are used in sewerage works primarily in moving sludge, which duty they perform satisfactorily if not efficiently. An air-lift installation for this purpose is shown in Fig. 12–19. An air lift has the advantage of freedom from clogging. In the design of an air lift for raising sludge the same principles control as for lifting water, except possibly that a slightly greater submergence ratio may be provided.

12–21. Distribution of electric current.[20] Electric current reaching a pumping station from an outside source is usually stepped down in voltage, is carried to a switchboard, and from there it is distributed to the plant. The simplest and most common system, known as the simple, radial system, involves a single power channel to each load. The type of current normally available for power applications in the United States, is 3-phase, 60-cycle alternating cur-

[20] See M. C. Boggis and N. L. Hadley, *S. and I.W.*, April, 1953, p. 391; and M. C. Smith, *Water and Sewage Works*, June 1, 1955.

rent at a high voltage which is stepped down at transformers to 120, 240, 440, 2,400, and 4,160 volts. The lowest voltage is used almost exclusively in fractional horsepower equipment. Where motors are widely scattered it may be desirable to make a part or all of the voltage transformation near the motor. This practice may be economical and will assure better voltage distribution and will minimize voltage fluctuations. Fluctuations greater than about 25 per cent

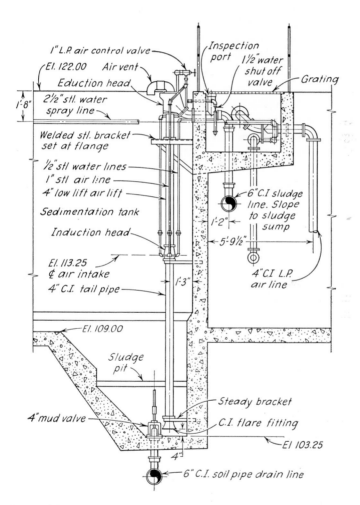

Fig. 12–19. Air lift for sludge and grit removal. Central Contra Costa, Calif. (Courtesy Brown and Caldwell, Engineers.)

may stall equipment, and greater than about 2 per cent may cause lighting flicker. Reduced-voltage starters may be used on motors that are otherwise difficult to start.

Adequate grounding is essential for safety and reliability. Such grounding may consist of metallic connection between equipment and well-grounded water pipes or structural members of the building. Voltages at or above 2,400 usually have transformer or generator neutrals grounded through a grounding resistor. Lightning arresters should function with induced currents up to 500,000 volts.

Power factor should be kept as near to unity as feasible because it bears the same relation to cost of power as does the mechanical efficiency of the equipment being driven by the electric power. A power factor of 95 means that 5 per cent of electric power is being lost. Hence, the control of power factor is desirable to avoid higher power-rate charges.

12–22. Electric motors. Specifications of electric motors for a sewage-pumping station should include the following: (1) type or class, (2) horsepower, (3) speed, (4) voltage, (5) frequency, (6) phases, (7) type of bearings, (8) type of insulation, (9) type of drive, (10) mechanical construction, and (11) mounting or setting.

Squirrel-cage induction motors are the commonest type because of their simplicity, ruggedness, and relatively low cost. They are suitable for driving sewage pumps where operation is continuous and the load is steady. This type of motor without special windings or other auxiliary control is undesirable where stopping and starting are frequent, variation in speed is required, or the character of the load fluctuates. Special windings and control equipment are available to provide greater starting torque, lower starting current demand, and any desired speed of operation. Operating characteristics of some alternating-current motors are listed in Table 12–1. Special windings and auxiliary equipment add to the first cost of the motor but may be essential to operation and may result in increased efficiency.

Synchronous motors are suitable mainly where starting and stopping are infrequent. They are suitable mainly in large installations, and are helpful in a plant with many small induction motors because of their improvement of the power factor.

High-speed motors are less costly than slow-speed machines because more power is delivered per unit weight of machine, but since sewage pumps usually operate at slow speeds some form of speed reduction is required between the pump and a high-speed motor. A gear motor is a high-speed motor combined with a simple, compact reduc-

Table 12-1

OPERATING CHARACTERISTICS OF SOME ALTERNATING-CURRENT MOTORS

(From Babbitt and Doland, *Water Supply Engineering*, 5th edition, 1955.)

Type of Motor	Characteristics, Advantages, and Applications
Induction, alternating-current, polyphase, squirrel-cage	*Starting current,* 5 to 10 times full-load current. For sizes above 5 hp special starting devices required. When frequent starting is necessary, sizes below 5 hp may require special starting windings, condensers, or other starting aids. *Starting torque:* low in terms of full load. *Maximum torque:* 2 to 2.5 times running torque. *Speed regulation:* good, may diminish 5 per cent between start and full load. *Speed control:* none, runs only at designed speed. *Sizes* available 0.1 to 400 hp. *Suitable for* constant load and continuous operation, excellent for fans and centrifugal pumps.
Repulsion-induction, single-phase, alternating-current	*Starting current:* 1.75 to 2.5 times full load. *Starting torque:* 3 to 5 times full load. *Speed regulation and control:* at no load it is above synchronism; at full load it is similar to that of an induction motor. *Sizes* available ⅛ to 15 hp. *Suitable for* heavy starting loads or frequent starting and stopping.
Synchronous, alternating-current	*Starting current:* 4 to 8 times full load. Hard to start. Field must be excited with direct current. *Starting torque:* very low. *Maximum torque:* 1.5 to 1.75 times running torque. *Speed regulation:* perfect, no variation in speed under varying load. *Speed control:* none. *Sizes* available: 20 to 5,000 hp. *Suitable for* steady load and constant operation. Excellent for pumps. Improves power factor.

Note: Starting currents are stated as 75 to 100 per cent of the blocked-rotor values. The free-rotor value may be taken as 75 per cent of the blocked-rotor value.

tion gear to give practically any desired speed reduction. Such motors are commonly used in sewage-treatment plants for the operation of screens, valves, gates, conveyors, mixers, and other slow-speed devices.

The least costly method for varying the speed of an induction motor is through the number of poles in the winding, the number of fixed speeds being an even multiple of the number of poles. It is not possible to operate such motors at any speeds other than those fixed by the number of poles.

Starters for motors, especially above about 5 hp rating, are usually necessary to avoid dangerous voltage drops or current overloads on the line. Overloads of 10 times rated current may be cared for by relays that are a part of the motor starter. High-voltage starters are protected by current-limiting fuses on the line side of the contactor. The simple, magnetic starter, with overload and underload protection, is widely used for the full-voltage starting of small induction motors.

In the selection of a pump and motor it should be required that the motor have sufficient power to operate the pump under any conditions of head and discharge. Unless this is done it may be possible to obtain a motor which will operate the pump satisfactorily under a high head but will be overloaded when the head drops with accompanying increase in the rate of discharge.[21]

12–23. Location of motors and their controls. The location of electric motors and equipment in damp or hot surroundings, in the possible presence of explosive or corrosive gases, or in other unsuitable or hazardous situations is undesirable but it may sometimes be unavoidable. Under such circumstances the choice between open, semi-enclosed, and enclosed motors must be measured against the hazard to be met. Wherever possible heat-dissipating, open-type motors should be used. High temperatures are also not uncommon in sewerage work, and load and power must be adjusted to maintain the temperature rise within the standard limitations of the National Electrical Manufacturers Association.

Fully equipped control panels can be purchased, ready for installation. Information about the dimensions and performance of such equipment should be obtained from the manufacturer before the final design details are determined.

Choosing between the location of the motor-control equipment near each motor and concentrating control devices at a central switchboard is a matter of judgment and economy. Central location offers advantages in the protection of control devices from corrosive gases and other hazards; and in operation supervision and economy of use are improved. However, installation costs are increased in proportion to the distance between the motor and the point of control. Wherever

[21] See also H. Ryon, *Sewage Works Jour.*, July, 1935, p. 673.

motor controls are placed they should be protected from corrosive gases emanating from sewage as these gases seem to be particularly active in corroding copper. This type of corrosion may be so bad as to destroy contacts and to break circuits.

Since much of the electrical equipment about sewage-treatment plants and pumping stations is automatically operated, motor-control equipment is of importance. Such equipment is available for automatically starting and stopping motors, for controlling the speed, for indicating and recording power consumed, and for protecting them against operating hazards.

12–24. Other electric equipment. Transformers of the dry type or askarel-filled are available for indoor use without expensive fireproof building construction. Oil-filled transformers are suitable only for out-of-doors locations removed from the building. Dry-type transformers are relatively light in weight and look well but they withstand only about one-half as much surge voltage as a liquid-filled unit.

Switchboards are usually totally enclosed and include, beside the switch gear, indicating, recording, and integrating mechanisms required in plant operation. Enclosed-type boards offer the greatest safety. The amount of detail in the wiring of a control board is indicated in Fig. 12–20.

Relays and circuit breakers are used mainly in starter mechanisms and for the protection of equipment. Fuses operate rapidly by the fusing of an overloaded wire placed in the line. They are limited in capacity up to about 600 amperes. Circuit breakers, actuated magnetically or by relays, are available for protection against almost all line hazards except lightning.

Electric installations and equipment should meet the standards of the National Electrical Code.[22]

12–25. Operation hazards. Dangers to which induction motors are subjected in operation may be classified as those due to variations in power delivery, to improper operation, and to improper care. A danger to which the operator of a motor may be subjected is the charging of the frame of the motor by stray currents. This hazard may be overcome by grounding the frame when the motor is installed and maintaining this ground at all times.

In the operation of the motor the power delivered may vary in phase, frequency, or voltage. If one or more phases are interrupted

[22] See A. L. Abbott, *National Electrical Code Handbook,* 7th edition, McGraw-Hill Book Co., 1952.

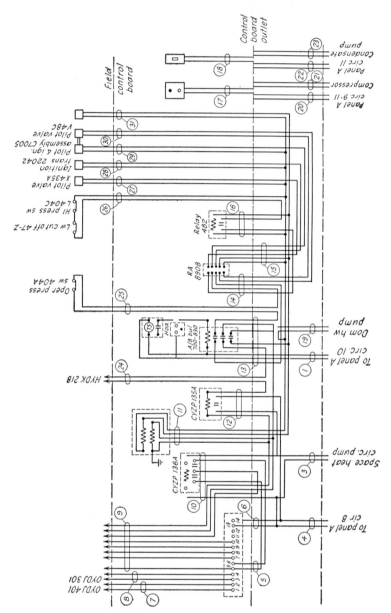

Fig. 12–20. Electric control board. Vallejo, Calif. (Courtesy Brown and Caldwell, Engineers.)

while the motor is idle, the motor will not start; but if it is running at the time of the interruption or if it is started by the application of outside power, as by pulling on the belt, the motor will run at normal speed as a single-phase motor and will deliver about 60 per cent of normal-load torque, with a pull-out torque about two-thirds to one-half normal. The effect of operating a polyphase motor under full load and single-phase conditions will be to overload the motor and to lead to its destruction. The interruption of one or more phases of an alternating-current motor is not unusual and must be guarded against in motor operation by the installation of safety devices.

The operating torque of an induction motor varies as the square of its voltage. If the voltage drops during full-load operation, the reduction of torque may cause the motor to pull out. A voltage drop of about 20 to 25 per cent with a slight increase in load would cause pull-out, with resulting destruction of the motor. If a motor is operated above normal voltage, the core losses are increased approximately as the square of the voltage, and the copper losses are decreased. An excessive increase in voltage endangers the insulation of the windings as a result of the rise in temperature of the core. The slip of induction motors varies approximately inversely as the voltage.

The speed and torque of induction motors vary approximately as the frequency of the current. At normal operating load and with increased frequency the core losses are increased, the result being to increase heating. Since the horsepower required by a centrifugal pump varies approximately as the cube of the speed, a decrease in frequency might quickly result in overloading the motor.

In general, induction motors will not be seriously affected by variations of 10 per cent, more or less, in either voltage or frequency. Interruption of phase, however, is a serious hazard. The sudden interruption of power will have no serious effect on an induction motor unless it is connected to a reversible load, such as a centrifugal pump. Under such circumstances both the motor and the pump must be protected against reversal, for instance by the installation of check valves on the pump discharge line. Unless a motor is equipped for automatic self-starting under load, it must be protected against the resumption of power in the event of interruption.

12–26. Protection of motors.[23] Electric motors are protected against the hazards of current fluctuation, overloading, and so forth, during operation, by devices that break the electric circuit when

[23] See also *Sewage Works Jour.*, May, 1941, p. 579.

danger threatens. It is not uncommon to use a station incoming-line breaker that will open all short circuits in the system, and to install smaller breakers on contactors, equipped with thermal-overload protection only, on the individual motor circuits.

Fuses are the simplest devices to prevent the application of an excessive current to the motor, but they will not prevent its destruction by surges of power, such as might be induced by lightning, which can pass a fuse; or the blowing of one fuse on a polyphase circuit might cause an improperly protected motor to "single-phase." The thermal cutout is an inexpensive form of thermostatically controlled circuit breaker that functions when the temperature on any of the power wires exceeds a predetermined limit. It will permit the passage of momentary overloads that are harmless to the motor, but for this reason it is of no value in protecting against short circuits, which must be cared for by an instantaneous cutout, such as a fuse. If the thermal cutout is placed directly in the circuit, it is limited to currents of about 20 amperes. Oil circuit breakers may be used for larger loads. Large motors may be protected by placing the cutout in current-transformer secondaries. Since fuses are not available for currents above about 600 amperes, other forms of circuit breakers are used for larger loads.

In the selection of protective devices the electrical code of the National Board of Fire Underwriters, as well as state and municipal codes, should be consulted.[24]

12–27. Internal-combustion engines. Among the types of internal-combustion engines used in sewage pumping may be included: (1) the spark ignition, low-compression, gas engine; (2) the diesel engine; and (3) the dual-fuel engine. Among the advantages of the low-compression gas engine are relatively low first cost, availability in small sizes, operation with gaseous fuel, and ease in starting. The outstanding advantage of the diesel engine is its high thermal efficiency. It is relatively high in first cost and is best suited to continuous operation.

A dual-fuel engine is an internal-combustion engine "which uses oil fuel on the diesel cycle, or predominantly gaseous fuel with oil fuel ignition, and is fully convertible from one fuel to another."[25] An outstanding advantage of the dual-fuel engine is its ability to use illuminating gas, natural gas, or other gaseous fuels, without

[24] See A. L. Abbott, *op. cit.*

[25] Definition by Diesel Engine Manufacturers Association, quoted by W. R. Crooks, *Sewage Works Jour.,* Vol. 21, 1949, p. 957.

stopping the engine.[26]   Since dual-fuel engines operate on the diesel cycle they are economical of fuel delivering 1 brake hp-hr per 11 cu ft of 650 Btu gas, compared with 15 to 15.5 cu ft of similar gas required by the four-cycle Otto engine, with less than 5 per cent of total Btu input in pilot oil.[27]   Supercharging will increase the power output of a dual-fuel engine about 50 per cent, but its heat efficiency will not be increased.   Power has been generated by such an engine for less than one mil per kwh.[28]   The heat efficiency of a dual-fuel engine is between about 24 and 35 per cent.   The amount of recoverable heat is about 47 per cent of the total fuel input.   It is about 52.5 per cent from the low-compression, Otto-cycle engine.

[26] See also *Wastes Eng.*, June, 1954, p. 270.
[27] See also N. Polakov, *S. and I.W.*, January, 1950, p. 24.
[28] See N. I. Kass and F. H. Lino, *Water and Sewage Works,* June, 1956, p. 231.

Chapter 13

Maintenance of sewers

13-1. Work involved.[1] The principal effort in the maintenance of sewers is to keep them clean and unobstructed. A sewer system, although buried, cannot be forgotten, as it will not care for itself. It will corrode, erode, clog, or otherwise deteriorate. The capital investment in a sewer system financially justifies preventive maintenance. Work to be done in the maintenance of sewerage works, particularly the sewer system, includes inspection, measurements of rates of flow, cleaning, flushing, repairs, supervision of connections, protection of existing sewers, prevention of explosions, valuation, and other duties.

The construction of sewers that are to be connected to the municipal sewer system should be supervised and inspected by the municipal authorities to avoid difficulties that may arise later through improper design and construction. Connections made to sewers by irresponsible or ignorant persons working without official supervision may cause trouble in sewers because of the weakening of the sewer structure, stoppage, foundation collapse, the admission of ground water, or other causes. Connections should be made only through openings provided therefor. New buildings should not be connected to the sewer until construction is complete unless the danger from the careless disposal of waste building materials into the sewer is guarded against. Since many troubles in sewers arise from improperly built house sewers connected to them, the house sewer should be constructed with care equal to that given to the public sewer.

Costs of maintenance are reported [2] in terms of dollars per year per mile of sewer, as follows: average municipal, $75; costs at 20 army posts, $148.

---

[1] See also *Sewage Works Jour.*, March, 1942, p. 410; and W. H. Wisely, *Water and Sewage Works,* April, 1951, p. R-124, and May, 1953, p. R-133.

[2] L. H. Kessler and J. T. Norgaard, *Sewage Works Jour.*, July, 1942, p. **757.**

13–2. Causes of troubles. The complaints most frequently received about sewers are caused by clogging, breakage of pipes, and odors. Clogging is confined principally to sewers too small for a man to enter. Sewers become clogged by the deposition of sand and other detritus that form pools in which organic matter accumulates, aggravating the situation and causing odors. Grease is a frequent cause of trouble. It is discharged into the sewer in hot wastes and, becoming cooled, deposits in layers that may eventually clog the sewer. It can be prevented from entering the sewer by the installation of grease traps. Its accumulation in sewers has been partly controlled by the use of proprietary, emulsifiable chlorobenz, such as Orthosol. The periodic cleaning of grease traps is as important as their installation.

Tree roots are troublesome, particularly in small sewers in residential districts. Roots will enter the sewer through minute holes, and they may fill the barrel of the sewer. Copper sulfate [3] placed around the outside of the pipes and the placing of a copper ring in pipe joints may successfully stop root penetration. It is occasionally reported that the flushing of copper sulfate periodically through household plumbing fixtures has aided in stopping roots in house sewers. Fungus growths occasionally cause trouble in sewers by forming a network of tendrils that catches floating objects and builds a barricade across the sewer. Difficulties from fungus growths are not common, but constant attention must be given to the removal of grit, grease, and roots. Tarry deposits from gas plants are occasionally a cause of trouble as they cement the detritus, already deposited, into a tough and gummy mass that clings tenaciously to the sewer barrel.

Sewers are sometimes misused as receptacles for rubbish, waste building materials, ashes, and other solid wastes deposited in them through manholes or unauthorized openings. Manhole covers are sometimes stolen. Such difficulties may be avoided by locking the covers or fastening them down so that they can be removed only by special tools.

Broken sewers are caused by poor foundations, excessive superimposed loads, vibration, undermining, progressive deterioration, and other causes. The changing characteristics of a district may result in the change of street grade, an increase in the weight of traffic, or in the construction of other structures causing loads on the sewer for

[3] See *Water Works and Sewerage*, March, 1933, p. 102, and March, 1942, p. 121.

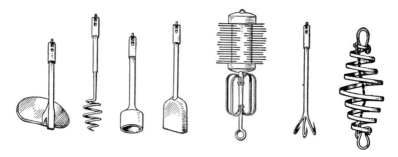

Fig. 13–1.   Tools for cleaning sewers.

which it was not designed.   The presence of corrosive acids or gases
may cause the deterioration of the material of the sewer.

13–3. Maintenance organization, personnel, and equipment.
Preventive maintenance experience shows that it is more economical
and advantageous to foresee clogging, through forecasts based on
records, than to depend on corrective maintenance involving difficult
and relatively more expensive work in clogged and overflowing sewers.

A typical sewerage organization for a large city may include [4] divisions for administration, design, construction, accounting, and maintenance.   In any city the minimum-size maintenance crew should include three men.   For routine work this crew should be provided with
a truck equipped with the following equipment and materials: a
diaphragm pump of the "mud hog" type, preferably power driven
from the truck; 500 to 600 ft of sewer rods; root cutters and other
tools such as those shown in Fig. 13–1; fire hose and flushing nozzles;
hydrant tools; shovels; picks; hammers; axes; cement working tools;
buckets; rubber boots; rope; flashlights or electric lights; first-aid
kits; safety appliances; and such other equipment as experience and
local conditions have shown to be required.   For large sewers a
maintenance crew may include: a junior engineer in charge; about
three laborers; one oiler; one truck driver; and a junior engineer for
office work.   The crew may make routine inspections; clean, oil, and
grease control mechanisms; and perform such other duties as conditions may demand.[5]

[4] See L. D. Knapp, *Water and Sewage Works,* June 1, 1955, p. R-237.
[5] See also E. T. Cranch, *Sewage Works Jour.,* March, 1945, p. 199.

Trucks of 1½-ton capacity, or larger, may be equipped with the following: [6]

Power winch.
Portable, manually operated winch.
1,000 ft flexible wire cable.
1,000 ft of fire hose.
600–800 ft flexible rods. Power drive desirable.
500 ft interlocking wood rods.
Root cutters, assorted sizes.
Sewer brushes, assorted sizes.
Sand buckets, scoops, and drags, assorted sizes.
Turbine flushing heads.
Flashlights.
Safety equipment:
  Gas detectors; H_2S, CH_4, CO. A combination is available on the market.
  Gas masks.
  Safety harness.

Steel sewer tapes and heavy wire for small sewers.
Sewer flushing bags.
100 ft ½-in. rope, with block and falls, waterproof.
Raincoats and other waterproof clothing.
Miscellaneous tools — hammers, shovels, crowbars, clawbars, wrenches, buckets, rope ladder, hydrant wrenches.
Flood lights, power driven.
Manhole guard rails.
Traffic signs and flags.
Oil lamps and flares.
Safety equipment:
  First-aid kit.
  Skull guards with electric lamps and dry cells.

An important item of sewer-maintenance equipment is a complete and detailed map of the system.

13–4. Occupational hazards.[6,7] Hazards in the maintenance of sewage works include physical injuries, infections, gas poisoning and asphyxiation.[8] As measured by comparative industrial insurance rates in four eastern states,[9] sewerage work is from 7.5 to 62.5 per cent more hazardous than work in a machine shop. A summary of gases commonly encountered in sewers is listed in Table 13–1. These gases may be met in sewers, manholes, wet wells, digestion tanks and other poorly ventilated enclosures exposed to the sources indicated in the table. The depletion of the oxygen as a result of organic processes in closed or poorly ventilated chambers may leave insufficient oxygen for the support of human life. The absence of oxygen

[6] *Sewage Works Jour.*, March, 1942, p. 413.

[7] See also *Manual of Practice* 1, Federation of Sewage Works Associations, 1944.

[8] See also L. W. Van Kleeck, *Water and Sewage Works,* July, 1953, p. 284, August, 1953, p. 330, September, 1953, p. 369, October, 1953, p. 395, November, 1953, p. 461, and December, 1953, p. 465.

[9] See p. 6 of reference **7**.

Table 13–1

Properties of Some Gases Encountered in Sewerage

Name of Gas	Specific Gravity to Air	Explosive Range, per cent volume in air		Properties	Physio-logical Effects	Maximum Safe Con-centration, per cent volume in air
		Min	Max			
Ammonia	0.6	16	...	Ou	(1)	0.03
Carbon dioxide	1.53	0	0	NT, C, O, T	(2)	2 to 3
Carbon monoxide	0.97	12.5	74.2	C, O, T, NI, To	(2)(3)(7)	0.01
Chlorine	...	...	...	Ou	(1)(9)	0.0004
Ethane	1.05	3.1	15.0	C, O, T, NT		
Gasoline *	3 to 4	1.3	7.0 *	Ou	(4)(6)	1.0
Hydrogen	0.07	4.0	74.2	C, O, T, NT	(2)	
Hydrogen sulfide	1.19	4.3	46.0	Od, C, To	(5)(8)	0.002 to 0.02
Illuminating gas	0.7 ±	5.0	...	To	(2)	0.01 ±
Methane	0.55	5.0	15.0	C, O, T, NT	(2)	
Nitrogen	0.97	0	0	C, O, T, NT	(2)	
Phosphine		†		†		
Sulfur dioxide				Ou	(1)(2)	0.005

* See also Sect. 13–14.

† Self-igniting when exposed to air. Dangerous. (1) Respiratory, eye, and mucous irritant. (2) Asphyxiating. (3) Dangerous, subtle. (4) Anaesthetic at 2.4 per cent; headache, nausea. (5) Irritant, systemic poisoning. Paralyzes respiratory center. (6) 1.1 per cent dangerous even in short exposure. (7) 0.2 per cent causes unconsciousness in 30 min. (8) Death in few minutes at 0.2 per cent. (9) A highly toxic "war" gas. C, colorless. O, odorless. Od, unique odor in small concentration. None in high concentration. Ou, unique odor. NI, non-irritant. NT, non-toxic. T, tasteless. To, toxic.

is as dangerous a hazard as is the presence of toxic and asphyxiating gases.

Precautions to be taken to avoid exposure to the presence of dangerous gases or to the absence of oxygen include the ventilation of enclosed spaces by inducing a draft, filling and emptying the space with sewage or water, or displacing the gas, by some means, with breathable air; avoiding sparks from electrical equipment, tools, shoes, matches, and other flames; providing gas masks and other safety equipment; and analyzing the atmosphere before entering.

Portable gas-testing devices are available that register the presence of any or all the more common hazardous gases, or oxygen deficiency. Combustible-gas alarms are available that automatically give the alarm both audibly and visually when a dangerous mixture exists.

Health hazards due to infectious germs demand prompt care of cuts and bruises, personal cleanliness, and continual vigilance. Wearing rubber gloves, using disinfectants, frequent washing, and immunization against typhoid and tetanus are desirable health precautions.

Employees in sewer-maintenance work and in the operation of sewage-treatment plants are more than ordinarily exposed to personal injuries. Slippery ladders, walks, and steps; heavy lifting; fast-flowing water and deep tanks to fall into; exposed machinery; electric currents; and explosive and asphyxiating gases are ever present and lead to the necessity for the exercise of every reasonable precaution. Guard rails, natural and artificial illumination, ventilation, and safety-first measures should be generously provided. First-aid kits and gas masks should be available, and all personnel should be instructed in their use, and in methods of resuscitation from drowning, electric shock, and asphyxiation.

Warnings of hazards, instructions in how to avoid them, and the provision of safety and of rescue equipment are insufficient. Enforcement of safety rules with the infliction of penalties for their violation is necessary to counteract the natural human indifference to continually present dangers. Valuable information on hazards in sewage work is contained in *Manual of Practice* 1.[10]

13–5. Precautions before entering sewers. Certain precautions should be taken before entering sewers, manholes, or other enclosed spaces about sewerage works. If a distinct odor of gasoline is evident the sewer should be ventilated. The strength of gasoline odor above which it is dangerous to enter a sewer is a matter of experience possessed by few. A slight odor of gasoline is evident in many sewers and indicates no special danger. The amount of gasoline necessary to create explosive conditions is discussed in Sect. 13–14. In making observations for odor it should be noted whether air is entering or leaving the manhole. The presence of gasoline cannot be detected at a manhole into which air is entering.

As soon as observations of odor or chemical analyses of gases [11] show that an explosive mixture is not present, a lighted lantern, safety light, or other open flame may be lowered into a manhole to test for the presence of oxygen. If the flame burns brilliantly the sewer is probably safe to enter. If conditions are unknown or uncertain, the man entering should wear a life belt attached to a rope tended by two strong men at the surface. Dangerous gases are sometimes encountered without warning owing to their lack of odor or to the presence of stronger odors in the sewer. Breathing masks and electric lights are precautions against these dangers. A Chemox oxygen-

---

[10] Published by Federation of Sewage Works Associations, 1944.

[11] A device known as an "Explosimeter" can be used to indicate the presence and content of explosive gas in the atmosphere.

breathing apparatus supplies oxygen and disposes of exhaled carbon dioxide for about 45 minutes. Whenever a man is in a sewer there should be a man on the surface to call for help in case of accident. No one should enter an untested sewer alone. The man on the surface should *not* descend into the sewer until he is assured that adequate help is coming.

A sewer may be ventilated before entering by taking the covers off of a number of adjacent manholes. This precaution may be uncertain, however, as some gases are heavier than air and will not move without a draft. A small, portable, gasoline-driven blower, with canvas discharge tube to be inserted in a manhole, is available for ventilating manholes.

It must not be felt that the entering of every sewer is fraught with danger, as it is perfectly safe to enter the average, well-maintained sewer. The air is not unpleasant and no discomfort is felt. However, unexpected conditions may arise for which the man in the sewer should be prepared. It is wise, therefore, to be cautious. Such precautions may indicate, to the uninitiated, a greater danger than really exists.

13–6. Inspection.[12] Inspection of sewers is made to reveal clogging; to observe the condition of control mechanisms, and to service them; to examine the condition of the structure; to measure the rate of flow in the sewer; and for other purposes. Attention should be given regularly to those sewers that are known to give trouble, whereas less troublesome sewers may be given less attention. Inspections and flow measurements may be necessary during storms to determine the relation between maximum flow and sewer capacity.

The routine inspection of sewers too small to enter is made by observations from manholes. It is not always necessary to enter the manhole to make required observations. For example, grit, sludge, grease, fungus, septic sewage, excessive or sluggish flow, the condition of the ladder or of the manhole cover, or the presence of rats or other pests may be observed without entering. If the sewage is flowing as freely at one manhole as it is at an adjacent manhole it may be assumed that the sewer between manholes is not clogged. No further inspection may be necessary unless there is reason to suspect some other difficulty in the sewer between manholes. If the sewage is backed up in a manhole it indicates that there is an obstruction in the sewer. If the sewage in a manhole is flowing sluggishly and scum is present, it is an indication of clogging, slow velocity, or septic action in the sewer. Sludge accumulations on the sloping bottom of

[12] See also L. W. Van Kleeck, *Wastes Eng.*, June, 1955, p. 286.

the manhole or signs of sewage having been high up on the walls indicate an occasional flooding of the sewer due to inadequate capacity or to clogging. If clogging is suspected and an explosion-proof light or reflected sunlight cast into the sewer is not visible in a mirror lowered into an adjacent manhole towards which the light is directed through the sewer, the sewer is probably clogged. The next step in the inspection may be to look into the sewer with the light behind the observer.

Sewers large enough to enter should be inspected by wading or floating through them in a boat. The inspection may include the cleaning of spots on the sewer surface and examining the wall for loose bricks, deteriorated concrete or cement, open joints, broken bond, cracks, eroded invert, and such other conditions as may be causing or may lead to trouble. An inspection in storm sewers is sometimes of value in detecting the presence of forbidden house connections.

Flush tanks. A common difficulty found in flush tanks is "drooling," that is, water trickling out of the siphon as fast as it enters the tank so that there is a continuous, small discharge from the tank and no intermittent flush. If, when the tank is first inspected, the water is at about the level of the top of the bell, it is possible that the siphon is drooling. A mark should be made at the elevation of the water surface, and the tank should be inspected again in the course of an hour or more. If the water level is unchanged the siphon has either stopped or is drooling. This trouble may be caused by the clogging of the snift hole, by a rag or other obstacle hanging over the edge of the siphon pipe under the bell, by displacement of the bell over the siphon, or by other difficulties that may be recognized when the principle on which the siphon operates is understood. It may be discovered that the flow of water into the siphon for flushing purposes has been shut off.

Control devices. In the inspection of either manual or automatic control devices clogging or sticking of their movable parts should be looked for. Floats should be examined for loss of buoyancy or for leaks that render them useless. Grit chambers and screen chambers should be examined for sludge deposits.

Catch basins, storm sewers, and siphons. These items should be inspected periodically, and they often require cleaning. A catch basin that does not require cleaning is either unnecessary or is not performing its function. The need for cleaning occurs most fre-

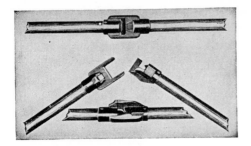

Fig. 13–2. Sewer rods.

quently after a storm. A regular schedule of cleaning should be maintained.

A record should be kept of all inspections made. It should include an account of the inspection, its date, the conditions found, the name of the inspector, and the remedies taken to effect repairs. If measurements of flow have been made, a brief description of the method used and the flows observed should be included. Methods for the measurement of rates of flow are described in Sect. 6–16.

13–7. Cleaning sewers. Sewers too small to enter are cleaned by thrusting rods into them or by dragging some form of instrument through them. The common sewer rod, shown in Fig. 13–2, may be a hickory stick or light metal rod, 3 to 4 ft long, on the end of which is a coupling which cannot come undone in the sewer but is easily disjointed in the manhole. Sections of the rod are pushed down the sewer until the obstruction is reached and dislodged. Occasionally pieces of pipe screwed together are used with success but with less speed. The front or advancing end of the sewer rod may be fitted with a cutting edge to cut and dislodge obstructions. In extreme situations such rods may be pushed 400 to 500 ft, but they are more effective at shorter distances.

Flexible rods, or steel tapes, are widely used for rodding sewers too small to enter. The steel "tape" consists of a flexible rod, about $\frac{1}{8}$-in. thick and 1 to 2 in. wide. The rod, to the advancing end of which a cleaning tool may be attached, is pushed into the sewer. It may be vigorously twisted at the same time, by a gasoline or electric motor, revolving at a speed of 750 rpm or more. This device is advantageous in a crooked sewer. It may avoid the necessity of descending into the manhole, as indicated in Fig. 13–3. Such a procedure may make possible the opening of a manhole that is filled with sewage.

Obstructions may be dislodged by shoving a fire hose down the sewer, the hose discharging water at high pressure through a 1-in. or smaller nozzle. The water pressure stiffens the hose and, together with the support from the sides of the sewer, makes it possible to push the hose 100 ft or more into the sewer. A self-propelling nozzle attached to the hose is also used. The swiveled nozzle is bulbous in shape and has, in addition to a forward jet, several backward jets that aid in driving the nozzle forward at the same time that the head is revolved. A cutter blade may be attached to the head as a root cutter.

Sewers are seldom so clogged that no channel whatever remains. As the clogging in a sewer progresses the passage becomes smaller, thereby increasing the velocity of flow around the obstruction and maintaining a passageway by erosion. This phenomenon has been taken advantage of in the cleaning of sewers by the use of "pills." These consist of a series of light spheres of different diameters. One of the smaller balls is dropped into the sewer through a manhole above the obstruction. When the ball strikes the obstruction it is jammed against the top of the sewer. Sewage is backed up and seeks an outlet around the ball, thus clearing a channel and washing the ball along with it. The ball is caught at the next manhole below. A net should be placed to catch the ball and a small dam should be built to prevent the dislodged detritus from proceeding down the sewer.

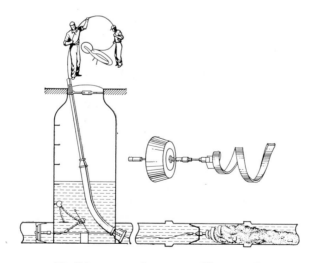

Fig. 13–3. Flexible sewer rod or tape. (Courtesy Flexible, Inc.)

The feeding of balls into the sewer is continued, with larger and larger sizes, until the sewer is clean. The method is particularly useful for the removal of sludge deposits but it is not effective against roots and grease. The balls should be light enough to float. Hollow metal balls are better than heavy wood ones.[13] A rubber beach ball, wrapped in canvas, has been used successfully.

Plows and other scraping instruments are dragged through sewers to loosen sludge banks and detritus and to cut roots and dislodge obstructions. One form of plow consists of a scoop which is pushed or dragged against the direction of flow. As the scoop is filled it is drawn back and emptied. The method of dragging the scoop is indicated in Fig. 13–4. A set of sewer-cleaning tools is illustrated in Fig. 13–1. A turbine sewer cleaner, illustrated in Fig. 13–5, consists of a set of cutting blades revolved by a hydraulic motor at an operating pressure of about 60 psi.[14] The turbine is attached to a standard fire hose and is pushed through the sewer by the stiffness of the hose or by rods connected to a pushing jack as shown in the figure. It is more commonly pulled through the sewer by means of a cable attached to the ring shown at the left in the figure. The performance of this machine is usually excellent. The revolving blades cut roots and grease and, together with the escaping water, serve also to loosen and stir up deposits. The helical motion imparted to the water is useful in pushing material ahead of the machine and scrubbing the walls of the sewer.

Movable dams or scrapers are useful in cleaning moderate-size sewers, but are of little value in small sewers. The scraper fits loosely against the sides of the sewer and is pushed forward by the pressure of the sewage accumulating behind it. The iron-shod edges of the moving dam serve to scrape grease and growths attached to the sewer and to stir up deposits on the bottom. The high velocity of sewage escaping around the sides of the dam aids in cleaning and scrubbing the sewer.

A simple and satisfactory form of root cutter consists of a steel cylinder, of slightly smaller diameter than the sewer to be cleaned, that is dragged through the pipe by a rope, as indicated in Fig. 13–4. The forward edge of the cylinder is composed of sharp, cutting teeth. The device can be made from a piece of steel pipe cut into a length about three times the diameter of the pipe to be cleand.

[13] See also G. Kemp, *The Surveyor*, April 16, 1955; and S. Preen, *Water and Sewage Works*, November, 1954, p. 490.

[14] See also *Water Works and Sewerage*, June, 1943, Appendix, p. 183.

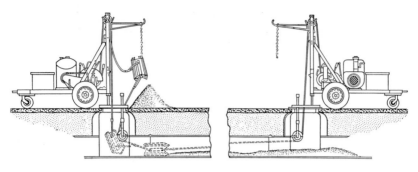

Fig. 13–4. Cable and windlass method of sewer cleaning. (Courtesy Flexible, Inc.)

Sewers large enough to enter may be cleaned by hand. Materials removed are shoveled into buckets which are carried or floated to the most convenient manhole, raised to the surface and dumped. In very large sewers temporary tracks have been laid, and small cars have been pushed to the manhole for the removal of material. Hydraulic sand ejectors, which operate on the principle of a jet pump, may be used for the removal of grit and sludge.

Barricades of logs, tree branches, and other obstructions that may form against some inward projection in the sewer must be removed by hand, either by cutting or pulling, or both. Projections from the sides of sewers are objectionable because of their tendency to catch obstacles and to form barricades.

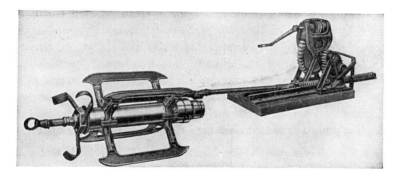

Fig. 13–5. Turbine sewer machine connected to forcing jack. (Courtesy The Turbine Sewer Machine Co.)

Fungus growths sometimes found in sewers are a result of favorable environment and suitable food supply. Successful removal may be accomplished by changing conditions in the sewer through depleting the oxygen present, changing the chemical reaction of the sewage (acidity or alkalinity), or adding a fungicide such as copper sulfate.[15] The oxygen content of the sewage may be changed by blocking the sewer to induce septic conditions, and lime may be added to increase alkalinity.

13–8. Locating lost sewers, manholes, and connections. A method for the location of lost sewers [16] consists in pushing a flexible steel tape into one end of the sewer and locating the tape by an M-scope, an electrical device.[17] Another method that has been suggested involves the creation of a sound in one end of the pipe and the location of the sound on the surface by means of sensitive, sound-amplifying equipment; or by listening, at an opening in the sewer, to pounding on the surface.[18] When the sound is loudest the pounding is over the lost sewer or manhole. Metallic manhole covers can be located with equipment similar to that used for the detection of buried mines. In the location of lost connections an instrument known as the Wyeget can be dragged through the sewer.[19] As it passes a connection an arm springs into the opening, actuating an electrical signal that is conveyed to the operator.

13–9. Cleaning catch basins. Catch basins have no reason for existence if they are not cleaned. Their purpose is to intercept settleable solids and to prevent them from entering the sewers, on the theory that it is cheaper to clean a catch basin than a sewer. If the cleaning of storm sewers below some inlet to which no catch basin is attached becomes burdensome, the engineer in charge of maintenance should install a catch basin and keep it clean. Catch basins are cleaned by hand, by suction pumps, by eductors, and by grab buckets. In cleaning by hand the accumulated water and sludge are removed by a bucket or dipper and dumped into a wagon, from which the surplus water is allowed to run back into the sewer. The grit at the bottom of the catch basin is removed by shoveling it into buckets, which are then hoisted to the surface and emptied.

Suction pumps in use for cleaning catch basins are of the hydraulic-

[15] See *Water Works and Sewerage,* March, 1933, p. 102, and March, 1942, p. 121.

[16] See also *Sewage Works Jour.,* March, 1945, p. 199.

[17] See R. P. Schulz, *Wastes Eng.,* July, 1955, p. 348.

[18] See *S. and I.W.,* August, 1954, p. 1051.

[19] G. M. Olewiler, *Sewage Works Jour.,* September, 1937, p. 808.

eductor type which works on the principle of the jet pump. The material removed may be discharged either into settling basins constructed in the street, or directly into trucks from which the water is drained back into the sewer.[20] Orange-peel buckets, about 20 in. in diameter, operated by hand or by truck motor, are used for cleaning catch basins in some cities.

Catch basins in unpaved streets and on steep, sandy slopes should be cleaned after every storm of consequence. Basins that serve to catch only the grit from pavement washings require cleaning about two or three times annually, and 1 to 3 cu yd of material may be removed at one cleaning.

In some climates catch basins serve as breeding places for mosquitoes, and other flying insects. This nuisance can be prevented by routine oiling of the basins within the first week of every dry spell during the breeding season. Oiling any sooner after a rain is not necessary as the preceding crop of larvae has been washed down the sewer and the latest crop will not have had time to mature.

13–10. Flushing sewers. Sewers can sometimes be cleaned or kept clean by flushing. The desired results are obtained most effectively by a sudden rush of deep water down the sewer at a high velocity. Depth and velocity together are necessary; either alone will be ineffective. A slow, steady flow will have little beneficial effect.

The most effective flush is obtained by a volume of water traveling at a high velocity and producing a hydraulic bore. The rate at which water must be supplied to produce a bore can be determined by the principles stated in Sect. 4–26. Data on the quantity of water needed are given in Table 13–2. As a result of a series of experiments conducted by Ogden [21] on the flushing of sewers, the conclusion was reached that the effect of a flush of about 300 gal in an 8-in. sewer on a grade of less than 1 per cent would be effective for 800 to 1,000 ft, but on steeper grades much smaller quantities of water would produce good results.

Flushing may be automatic and frequent, or hand flushing may be resorted to at intervals. Automatic flush tanks, flushing manholes, a fire hose, a connection to a water main, a temporary fixed dam, a moving dam, and other methods are used in flushing sewers. The design, operation, and results obtained from automatic flush tanks

---

[20] See also *Eng. Record*, Jan. 29, 1916, and March 24, 1917; and *Eng. News-Rec.*, Nov. 29, 1917, p. 1019.

[21] H. N. Ogden, *Trans. Am. Soc. Civil Engrs.*, Vol. 40, 1898, p. 1.

Table 13–2

CUBIC FEET OF WATER NEEDED FOR FLUSHING SEWERS

Diameter of Sewer, in.

Slope	8	10	12
0.005	80	90	100
.0075	55	65	80
.01	45	55	70
.02	20	30	35
.03	15	20	24

and flushing manholes are discussed in Chapter 6. The effectiveness of flushing may be increased if the sewer is inspected and large clogging objects are removed before flushing is attempted.

In the temporary-dam method the sewage is allowed to back up behind the dam until the sewer is about two-thirds full, when the dam is suddenly removed and the accumulated sewage is allowed to rush down the sewer. The dam may be made of sandbags, boards fitted to the sewer, or a combination of boards and bags. Air-tight bags inflated by air pumps in the sewer or filled with water under low pressure can be used for closing sewers up to about 48 in. in diameter. An inner tube for an automobile tire may sometimes serve as a successful makeshift either alone or wrapped around an obstruction, and well braced to support the pressure of the sewage. Below the dam the results of this method may compare favorably with those of other methods, but above the dam the stoppage of flow may cause deposits of greater quantities of material than have been flushed out below. A time should be chosen for the application of this method when the sewage is comparatively weak and free from settleable solids. The most convenient place for the construction of a dam is at a manhole in order that the operator may be clear of the rush of sewage when the dam is removed.

A natural watercourse may be diverted into a sewer if topographical conditions permit, or where sewers discharge into the sea below high tide a gate may be closed during flood tide and held closed until the ebb. The rush of sewage on the opening of the gate may serve to flush the sewers and stir up sludge deposits. Other methods of flushing sewers may be used, dependent on the local conditions and the ingenuity of the maintenance personnel.

13–11. Repairs. Common repairs to sewer systems consist in replacing street inlets or catch-basin covers broken by traffic; raising or lowering catch-basin or manhole heads to compensate for sinking of the foundations or change of pavement grade; tightening loose manhole covers that are rattling under traffic; replacing broken pipes or loosened bricks or mortar; relining eroded or corroded concrete sewers with bricks, precast blocks, gunite,[22] or other material; and other repairs as the need may arise. Connections between the house sewer and the street sewer are a common source of trouble. They should be made only by the sewer department or under its supervision.

13–12. Protection of sewers. Sewers are probably the least cared-for of all public utilities.[23] They are abused, misused, and neglected. They can be protected against abuse by vigilant watchfulness, aided, where necessary, by municipal ordinances. Watchfulness is necessary, for example, where road repairs or other construction on sewered streets is contemplated. Sewer manholes may be protected by the construction of a false bottom, above the flowing sewage, to intercept materials that may fall into the manhole through accident or design when the manhole cover is removed. Another too common abuse of sewers is the discharge of sanitary sewage into storm sewers or storm water into sanitary sewers. A common abuse to be guarded against is the connection of basement floor drains to storm sewers. Such incorrect connections may be traced by placing fluorescein dye, lightweight balls, or some other indicator in the suspected inlet. The recovery of the indicator will reveal the sewer to which the illicit connection is made. Smoke, or mist from a fog-making machine, blown into a sewer between temporarily plugged manholes, may escape through illicit connections that are not adequately trapped. The procedure must be used circumspectly, however, to avoid objections at legitimate connections.

Vermin and other living pests in manholes or sewers may be controlled by the application of a $2\frac{1}{2}$ to 5 per cent solution of Chlordane. Space so treated should not be entered for up to 24 hours without adequate ventilation.

Municipal ordinances drawn for the protection of sewers should be strictly enforced. Such ordinances should prohibit the discharge

[22] See also A. J. Muir, *Public Works*, January, 1955, p. 81.

[23] From "A Model Sewer Ordinance," *Manual of Practice* 3, Federation of Sewage Works Associations, 1949.

into a sewer of a substance that is corrosive, inflammable, or explosive; liquids or gases at high temperature, such as the blow-off from a steam boiler; oil [24] or other petroleum product; solids that may clog the sewer, such as sand, ashes, rubbish, and grease; or dead animals, offal, or unground garbage. The ordinance should provide also that the sewer may be used for no purpose other than that for which it was designed, prohibiting, for example, its use as a conduit for water pipes or electric wires. Finally, the ordinance should provide rules for the making of connections to the sewer, with power to enforce the regulations placed in the hands of the sewer authority.

13–13. Control of flow. Successful efforts on the part of the sewer authority to minimize the flow into a sewer system may be rewarded by prolonging the useful life of a part or all of the system and by reducing the cost of operation of pumping stations and treatment plants. Efforts to minimize the flow of sewage may be directed towards: (1) a diminution of the water consumption, (2) preventing or diminishing unauthorized contributions of ground water and surface water, (3) controlling the dumping of snow into sewers, and (4) cooperating with industrial plants with the aim of diminishing the volume of liquid wastes contributed to the sewers.

The use of water may be diminished by the repair of leaks in plumbing and by the control of waste. Contributions of ground and surface water may be diminished by the sealing of leaky joints in sewers; by plugging the tops of manholes subject to inundation; by closing unplugged openings left for house connections; by searching for and disconnecting unauthorized connections such as roof, yard, and floor drains; and by other activities dictated by local conditions. A chemical grout which forms a gelatinous stoppage in a leaking joint has been injected from the ground surface into the ground around the joint.[25]

Where cooperation with industry and other authorities to minimize sewage flow is unsuccessful it may be necessary to adopt an ordinance, with penalties, and to enforce it in order to relieve the load on the sewer. Unexpectedly large volumes of water pouring into sewers from commercial and private air-conditioning equipment are a source of overload in some communities.[26]

[24] See also C. E. Keefer, *Water and Sewage Works*, May, 1953, p. R-177.

[25] See news item, *Public Works*, March, 1957, p. 154.

[26] See also H. J. Kellog, *Jour. Conn. Soc. Civil Engrs.*, 1914; and G. A. Burrell and H. T. Boyd, *Tech. Paper* 117, U. S. Bureau of Mines, 1916.

13–14. Explosions in sewers.[27] The principal cause of explosions in sewers is the presence of gasoline, naphtha, cleaning fluids and grease solvents, illuminating gas, and methane or natural gas.[28] The proportions of some gases with air to make an explosive mixture are listed in Table 13–1.

Gasoline finds its way into sewers from garages and cleaning establishments. A mixture of 1.5 per cent of gasoline vapor and 98.5 per cent of air, by volume, at about 65° F is explosive. It needs only the spark of a stray electric current, a lighted match, or a smouldering cigar thrown into the sewer to set off the explosion. Burrell and Boyd [29] have concluded that:

One gallon of gasoline if entirely vaporized produces about 32 cu. ft. of vapor at ordinary temperature and pressure. . . . Many different factors, however, govern explosibility, such as size of sewer, velocity of sewage, temperature of the sewer, volatility and rate of inflow of the gasoline. Only under identical conditions of tests would duplicate results be obtained. A large amount of gasoline poured in at one time is less dangerous than the same amount allowed to run in slowly. With a velocity of flow of about 6½ feet per second it was evident that 55 gallons of gasoline poured all at once into a manhole rendered the air explosive only a few minutes (less than 10) at any particular point. With the same amount of gasoline run in at the rate of 5 gallons per minute, an explosive flame would have swept along the sewer if ignited 15 minutes after the gasoline had been dumped. With a slow velocity of flow and a submerged outlet the gasoline vapor being heavier than air accumulated at one point and extremely explosive conditions could result from a small amount of gasoline. Comparatively rich explosive mixtures were found 5 hours after the gasoline had been discharged. High-test gasoline is much more dangerous than the naphtha used in cleaning establishments, yet on account of the large quantity of waste naphtha the sewage from cleaning establishments may be very dangerous.

Illuminating gas is not so dangerous as gasoline vapor because it is lighter than air and is more likely to escape from the sewer than to accumulate in it. It may, however, follow along the outside of an underground pipe or other channel leading to a sewer or manhole. About 1 part of illuminating gas to 7 parts of air produces an explosive mixture.

Methane, generated by the decomposition of organic matter, is occasionally found in sewers as a result of septic conditions. It is gen-

[27] See *Wastes Eng.*, July, 1955, p. 349.
[28] See also *Sewage Works Jour.*, May, 1940, pp. 202 and 527.
[29] G. A. Burrell and H. T. Boyd, *Tech. Paper* 117, U. S. Bureau of Mines, 1916.

erated more frequently at sewage-treatment plants where its explosion has caused extensive damage. The subject of explosions at sewage-treatment plants is discussed in Sect. 25–21.

Calcium carbide discharged into sewers is dangerous because it is self-igniting, the heat of the generation of the gas being sufficient to ignite an explosive mixture. Fortunately, large amounts of this material usually do not reach the sewers today.

Sewer explosions may be prevented by the construction of traps to intercept gasoline and other liquids and gases lighter than water, and by ventilation to dilute the explosive gases that may enter the sewer. Vigilant inspection to detect the presence of explosive gases and to cut off their source is the best assurance that explosions will not occur. It is possible under favorable conditions to detect the presence of explosive gases by means of an apparatus that can be taken into the sewer or lowered into a manhole for the collection of a sample of gas. Automatic apparatus is available that will sound or give an alarm in the presence of explosive mixtures. The source of the gas may be traced and explosions avoided. After a violent explosion has occurred the detection of the cause may be difficult because of the destruction of the evidence. Additional information concerning the detection and avoidance of gas hazards is given in Chapter 25.

Chapter 14

Sewage treatment

14–1. Objectives in sewage treatment. Sewage is treated to protect public health, to avoid nuisance, to prevent the pollution of natural waters and of bathing beaches, and to avoid damage suits. Sewage is a menace to health because it contains pathogenic bacteria and other disease-producing organisms. It contains also substances that may contaminate sources of food and of water. Treatment alone cannot be depended upon to prevent the discharge of infectious agents into water.[1] Since some streams must serve both as drainage channels and as sources of public water supplies the treatment of sewage may be necessary to minimize the load on water-treatment plants.[2] As a nuisance sewage may be offensive to the eye and to the nose. It is probably the greatest potential creator of sensory nuisance, its power in this respect being out of proportion to its menace to health. There is no legally satisfactory proof that its offense to the senses, especially its odor, is a menace to health.[3]

The avoidance of damage suits is an effective incentive for sewage treatment. It may be more effective than laws and bureaucratic coercion. For example, it may be found to cost less to pay a fine for polluting a stream than to treat the sewage to prevent stream pollution; but it will be found more costly to lose a damage suit because of stream pollution.

The protection of natural recreational facilities, the conservation of natural resources, the prevention of stream pollution, the maintenance and restoration of natural conditions, the winning of public approval, and the exercise of common decency provide tangible and intangible reasons for the treatment of sewage.

[1] See also S. M. Kelly and others, *Am. Jour. Public Health,* November, 1955, p. 1438.

[2] See also L. L. Hedgepeth, *Water and Sewage Works,* September, 1953, p. 354.

[3] See also *Trans. Am. Soc. Civil Engrs.,* March, 1945, p. 799.

14–2. Values in sewage. Sewage is a liability to the community producing it. It is true that there are recoverable constituents in sewage but, like the extraction of gold from sea water, the process of recovery is more costly than the value of the recovered substances.[4] No process of domestic sewage treatment that delivers a sanitary effluent has been devised that has returned a profit. However, since sewage must be treated some of the cost of treatment may be defrayed by the recovery of valuable products.

Raw sewage or treatment-works effluents have been used: for irrigation; for cooling of evaporators in power plants; for various purposes in industrial plants as, for example, quenching coke in steel mills; for the replenishment of ground water; for washing and cleaning; and for other purposes. Other values recovered from sewage include: sludge for its fertilizing value and heat content; grease; grit as a road, walk, and filling material; and combustible gas from sludge digestion. Vitamin B_{12} has been recovered from sewage sludge but the process has not yet been shown to be economical. Dried activated sludge is being used satisfactorily as a food for cattle and poultry.[5] The biological stabilization of organic wastes may open new horizons in the disposal of organic wastes and the recovery of foods therefrom. Photosynthesis is a factor in activating biological changes.[6]

14–3. Governmental control.[7] Governmental control of stream pollution can be classified in accordance with the rank of the legal power involved as: international treaties, federal laws and regulations, interstate compacts, state laws, district or municipal codes or rules, and informal agreements among authorities. Under the Constitution of the United States an international treaty is the supreme law of the land. It is the duty of the Congress to protect it with adequate legislation. The existing treaty between the United States and Canada covering the pollution of boundary waters is an example of such a law.

The Congress has powers, under the Constitution, to control all navigable waters that are coastal, interstate, and intrastate. Under these powers it has adopted legislation prohibiting the deposit of "any refuse matter of any kind or description whatever other than

[4] See also *Eng. News-Record*, Dec. 30, 1937, p. 1055, with subsequent discussion.

[5] See E. Hurwitz, *Wastes Eng.*, August, 1957, p. 388.

[6] See also W. J. Oswald and H. B. Gotaas, *Proc. Am. Soc. Civil Engrs.*, Vol. 81, Paper No. 686, May, 1955.

[7] See also G. Feller and J. Newman, *Industry and Power*, June, 1951.

that flowing from streets and sewers and passing therefrom in a liquid state, into any navigable water of the United States or into any tributary of any water from which the same shall float or be washed into such navigable water." Studies and reports on the sanitary conditions of navigable waters are made by the United States Public Health Service. The Congress has repeatedly made it clear, however, that water-pollution control is primarily the responsibility of the states.[8]

The purpose of Public Law 845, which became effective in June, 1948, is "to provide for water pollution control activities in the Public Health Service of the Federal Security Agency, and in the Federal Works Agency." The law recognizes the primary responsibility of the states, and it provides for: (1) the development of comprehensive programs for control of pollution, (2) research, (3) construction of sewage and industrial-waste treatment plants, (4) financial and technical aid to industry, and (5) abatement of stream pollution in interstate waters. Interstate pacts and agreements involving some thirty-nine states as well as the District of Columbia were in effect in 1951, and international agreements have been made with Canada concerning pollution of the boundary watersheds of the St. Lawrence and British Columbia watersheds. The situation is indicative of the growing public interest in stream pollution and its prevention.

Legal power to control stream pollution is based, to a large extent, on the doctrine of riparian rights. Owen [9] states this doctrine as: "Each riparian proprietor is entitled to have the watercourse flow by or through his land in its natural course, quantity, and quality subject only to reasonable use of other proprietors. He, in turn, is entitled to make use of the water in the stream while on his land in any way he sees fit provided that he does not by such use affect the rights of an upper or lower proprietor."

The enforcement of state laws with respect to stream pollution and the disposal of sewage and treatment-plant effluent is often in the hands of the state department of health or of some associated administrative unit of the state, which may be given discretionary powers to recommend, and sometimes to enforce, measures for the abatement of an actual or a potential nuisance. State control over the pollution of its streams supersedes municipal control, or lack of control, where regulations disagree.[10] No project for the disposal of

[8] See also M. D. Hollis and G. E. McCallum, *S. and I.W.*, March, 1956, p. 322.
[9] G. E. Owen, *S. and I.W.*, April, 1955, p. 487.
[10] See also W. H. Resh, *S. and I.W.*, February, 1956, p. 211.

sewage should be consummated until the local, state, national, and international laws have been complied with. The action of the courts in different cases has not been uniform.

Adjacent and contiguous cities and large cities with many suburbs that have grown into metropolitan areas have sometimes found it advantageous to combine under one authority for the administration of the joint sewerage services. Various names have been given to such combinations such as a sanitary district or a drainage commission. Most populous states have laws providing for the formation of such districts.

14–4. Methods of sewage treatment. Langdon Pearse [11] stated:

> The basic principles in sewage treatment rest on a foundation in physics, chemistry, bacteriology, and biochemistry. From the time excreta leaves the human body organisms are at work breaking down organic matter and transforming its constituents. When the sewage reaches the treatment works the principles of physics are applied in the apparatus, and the aid of bacteria may also be sought, as well as of chemicals.

A classification and summary of methods of sewage treatment are given in Table 14–1. Sewage-treatment processes may be classified also as primary or secondary, as complete treatment, and in other ways. In a primary sewage-treatment process floating, suspended, and settleable solids in untreated sewage are reduced by plain sedimentation, fine screening, or in septic tanks. A secondary process receives the effluent from a primary process and involves more thorough mechanical, chemical, or biological treatment to reduce suspended and dissolved solids and biochemical oxygen demand. The line between primary and secondary treatment cannot always be drawn sharply. For example, the passing of sewage through screens or through a grit chamber may be preliminary treatment but, if the character of the sewage is noticeably altered, it is primary treatment. In general, the influent to secondary treatment has received primary treatment; the influent to a primary process may or may not have received preliminary treatment. Complete treatment involves secondary treatment to produce a high quality of effluent possibly supplemented by additional processes such as disinfection (chlorination) or intermittent sand filtration with or without disinfection.

In studying the subject of sewage treatment it must be borne in

[11] See Langdon Pearse in *Modern Sewage Disposal,* Federation of Sewage Works Associations, 1938, p. 16.

Table 14-1

METHODS OF SEWAGE TREATMENT AND OF DISPOSAL

Methods of Treatment

Screening	Filtration
Coarse	Contact beds
Fine	Trickling filters, standard
Comminution of solids	Trickling filters, high rate
Skimming	Intermittent sand filters
Preaeration	Activated-sludge process
Sedimentation	Standard procedure
Grit removal	Many modifications
Detritus removal	Sludge treatment
Plain sedimentation by	Digestion, with or without sludge thickening
gravity alone	or drying
Sedimentation with chem-	Sand beds
ical precipitation	Elutriation
Proprietary chemical	Chemical thickening
processes	Flotation
Septicization or digestion	Presses
Septic tanks	Centrifuges
Imhoff tanks	Heat dryers
Aeration and photosynthesis	Incineration
Oxidation ponds	

Methods of disposal

Into water	Onto land
Dilution	Surface or subsurface irrigation

mind that it is impossible to destroy any of the chemical elements present. They can be removed from the mixture only by evaporation, gasification, mechanical straining, or sedimentation. Their chemical combinations may be so changed, however, as to result in different substances from those introduced to the treatment plant. It is with these changes that the student of sewage treatment is interested.

14–5. Economics in sewage treatment. Under certain conditions considerations of economy may control in fixing the type and extent of sewage treatment to be adopted in a community. For example, in an industrial community it might be possible to abolish stream pollution caused by industrial wastes by prohibiting the discharge of such wastes into the stream but, at the same time, crippling the industry—a step too drastic to be considered. Where sewage treatment is being considered for the protection of the fishing industry only, the cost of sewage treatment should be balanced against the fish products protected. In considering complete sewage treatment as a relief to the load on a water-treatment plant, the relative values of the two plants as barriers against disease must be properly weighed with the knowledge that the water-treatment plant is far more effective for the purpose.

The value of sewage treatment to a community cannot be measured in financial returns, unless the value of damage suits to be avoided may be some form of measure. Indirect returns may be received, however, through the enhancement of the value of waterfront property, the attraction of industries, and improved health conditions.

14–6. Considerations in design. Among the first considerations in the design of a sewage-treatment plant are the capacity of the plant and the method of treatment. The latter is based on local considerations of character, strength, and quantity of sewage in relation to the nature and volume of diluting water available for the disposal of the plant effluent, and the facilities for the disposal of sludge. As explained in succeeding chapters the performance of sewage-treatment processes is measured in terms of certain chemical and physical changes made in the nature of the sewage during the treatment process. The load on a sewage-treatment plant is measured in terms of the quantity and strength of sewage to be treated. Since both of these fluctuate between wide limits, the capacity of the plant must be designed to care for high peak loads as well as for the normal expectancy of increased flow in the near future. Because the fluctuations of flow and strength are greater in small than in large communities, the plant for the small community should be designed to have greater flexibility in operating facilities.

Other items to be considered in treatment-plant design include: (1) accessibility of equipment; (2) flexibility in control and operation; (3) convenience of the operator in the selection of the type and in the location of equipment; (4) flexibility of piping and of valves to control flow through the plant; (5) provision against plant shutdown; (6) provision of a bypass around the plant, and around each major unit in the plant; (7) facilities for good housekeeping in buildings and on grounds; (8) adequate illumination, ventilation, and drainage for all parts of the plant; (9) facilities for operation when plant outlet is submerged under high water; (10) location for accessibility and ease in operation and maintenance of gages, controls, valves, sampling points, and other operating devices; (11) the use

Fig. 14–1. Sewage treatment plant at McMinnville, Oregon. Cornell, Howland, Hays and Merryfield, Engineers. (Courtesy Dorr-Oliver Co.)

of proper types of valves, frequently using plug-type valves instead of gate valves; and (12) the health and safety of the personnel.

An exterior view of the sewage treatment plant at McMinniville, Oregon, is shown in Fig. 14–1.

14–7. Variations in quality of sewage. The quality of sewage entering a plant varies constantly. Some of the causes of the variations are changes in the amount of diluting water due to the inflow of storm water or to the flushing of streets or sewers; variations in domestic activities such as the suspension of contributions of organic wastes during the night, Monday's wash, and so forth; and characteristics of industries that discharge different kinds of wastes according to the manufacturing process or the stage of the process. In general, night sewage is weaker than day sewage in both domestic and industrial wastes, and the strength of sewage, expressed as a percentage of the mean strength, especially in small treatment plants, will vary approximately as the rate of flow.

Information on variations of load on four sewage-treatment plants, collected by Killam,[12] shows that: (1) a substantial portion of the daily load arrives at the plant in a comparatively short period; (2) the hourly variations and the percentage of the total daily load arriving at the plant in any given period are not markedly different

[12] E. T. Killam, *Water Works and Sewerage,* July, 1934, p. 7, and June, 1943, p. 235.

regardless of whether the load is expressed in terms of flow and BOD content or in terms of flow and suspended solids content; and (3) the hourly load variations among the four plants studied are surprisingly similar regardless of their size or of other conditions that might be expected to create differences.

14–8. Engineer's report on design. The engineer's report on the design of a sewage-treatment plant, according to the ten-state standards, should cover the following subjects, among others pertinent to a particular location:

Foreword

Engineering
 Engineer's report
 General layout
 Detailed plans
 Specifications
 Summary of design data
 Revisions to approved plans

Sewers
 General
 Type of system
 Size, depth, and velocity of flow
 Capacities
 Manholes
 Inverted siphons

Primary Treatment
 Screening devices
 Grit chambers
 Preaeration and flocculation
 Sedimentation basins
 Combined units

Sludge Digestion and Disposal
 Imhoff tanks
 Separate digestion tanks
 Sludge pumps and piping

Sludge drying beds
Other dewatering facilities

Secondary Treatment
 Trickling filters
 Activated sludge

Sewage Pumping Stations
 General
 Design
 Power supply

Sewage-Treatment Works
 Plant location
 Quality of effluent
 Design
 Plant details
 Essential facilities
 Safety
 Intermittent sand filtration
 Other secondary processes

Disinfection, Odor Control, etc.
 Chlorination

Treatment or Disposal of Industrial Wastes
 Lagoons
 Flow equalizing tanks
 Raw waste sampling stations

14–9. Location of treatment plant. Conditions to be considered in the selection of the site of a sewage-treatment plant include topography, soil and underground conditions, flooding, cost, and public attitude. Health-protection requirements place no restriction on plant location unless raw sewage is to be exposed to the air. Sewage-treatment plants can be located in built-up communities and can be successfully operated without giving cause for complaint, and without justifiable detriment to real-estate values in the vicinity.

However, all other things being equal, an isolated site should be chosen as it offers a factor of safety against trouble that might arise from improper operation or insufficient administrative support. Where a plant is to be located in a built-up community it is possible that greater cost will be involved for equipment and for operation.

Iowa state requirements with respect to plant site restrict the plant location as follows:

The site should be isolated from all occupied buildings, particularly residences. Ordinarily a distance of 1,200 ft should be maintained between the plant and inhabited buildings, with a minimum of 800 ft when special precautionary measures are included for odor and insect control. Only under extreme circumstances should the distance be less than 800 ft without odor or insect control precautions. These distances should be increased in the case of large plants. Considerations should be given to the wind direction, particularly during warm months. If windward locations must be used, consideration should be given to increasing these distances.

14–10. Standards for design. Standards for the preparation of plans for sewage-treatment plants have been prepared from time to time by various regulatory bodies including most state boards of health or other stream-pollution prevention authorities. Notable among such standards are those prepared in 1951 by a Joint Board representing public health engineers of the ten states of Illinois, Indiana, Iowa, Michigan, Minnesota, Missouri, New York, Ohio, Pennsylvania, and Wisconsin. Abstracts from these standards and from other authoritative sources are quoted here as a guide to acceptable practice.

It is required in most states that plans for sewage-treatment plants shall be submitted to some authority for approval before the plant can be constructed. Many of the states have issued suggestions concerning the preparation of such plans. Requirements among the states are not uniform. Some specify size and kind of drawings. Some require more and different information than others. Standards of treatment, and approved and condemned methods and equipment are not uniform. Each designer should have a copy of the rules for the state in which the design is to be constructed.

Suggestions made by various states and by the Joint Committee are given in Sects. 12–3 and 14–8. Additional suggestions include:

Emergency power facilities. A standby power source shall be provided where the temporary discharge of raw or partially treated sewage may be reasonably expected to endanger the public health or cause serious damage.

Industrial wastes. Where appreciable amounts of industrial wastes are involved, considerations shall be given to the character of wastes in preparing the engineer's report.

Sewage flow measurement. Equipment for measuring and preferably recording the volume of sewage shall be provided at the treatment works.

By-passes. Except where duplicate units are available, properly located and arranged by-pass structures shall be provided so that each unit of the plant can be removed from service independently. Under certain circumstances, by-passes may be required even though duplicate units are provided.

Drains. Means shall be provided to dewater each unit. Due consideration should be given to the possible need for hydrostatic pressure-relief devices.

Laboratory equipment. All treatment works should include a laboratory for making the necessary analytical determinations and operating control tests.

Standards for various plant features are incorporated in the following recommendations:

1. *Permit request.* Documents submitted with applications for a permit should include: (*a*) general layout; (*b*) detailed plans; (*c*) specifications; and (*d*) summary of design data.

2. *General plans.* These should include: suitable title and name of responsible authority for plant; scale in feet; north point; date; and name of engineer and imprint of his professional engineer's seal. Scale for general plans should be 12 in. × 18 in., 24 × 36 in. or of such sizes as can be conveniently folded to these dimensions. Lettering and figures on the plans must be of appropriate size and of distinct outline.

3. *Detailed plans.* All detailed plans shall be prepared as blue or white prints and shall be drawn to a suitable scale. Detailed plans for sewage-treatment works shall show:

a. A plat of the property to be used for treatment works on which shall be indicated the topography and the arrangement of present and future treatment units. Contour interval shall not be greater than 2 ft. Hydraulic profiles shall show sewage, supernatant-liquor and sludge flow through the plant.

b. Industrial wastes. List establishments providing industrial wastes and give quantity, producing period, and character of industrial wastes insofar as they may affect sewage-treatment works.

c. Schematic piping diagrams shall show all lines and appurtenances properly labeled, with direction of flow indicated.

d. Schematic electrical circuit drawings and conduit layouts shall be included.

e. Complete details of treatment units, including elevations, shall be given, together with high and low water levels of the stream or other body of water into which the effluent will be discharged.

f. A summary of design data, and bases of design, shall accompany the documents.

g. Structural details. These are usually not checked by the health department, and are not required on the drawings.

h. Organic loading. Information should include the period of time of major organic loads and a discussion of ability of receiving stream to take these loads. A statement should be made concerning shock effect of high contributions of load for short periods of time, especially where the activated-sludge process is used.

i. Volume and strength of sewage flow. These shall be determined where a sewage works exists. The designing engineer shall confer with the reviewing authority to establish volume and strength of sewage flow data, and this information shall accompany the report. Data must be obtained from actual flow measurements, preferably for both wet and dry periods, where feasible. Where measurements are not feasible estimates on infiltration will be acceptable. The Joint Committee recommends that the designing engineer confer with reviewing authority for details concerning collection and analysis of samples.

j. Water supply. Location of intake or wells, treatment plant, reservoirs, or other structures of public health significance with relation to sewage works are to be discussed. If public water supplies are already in use give approximate maximum, minimum, and average daily water use and analyses of water as it may affect character of sewage.

k. Receiving stream. Describe the stream or body of water into which the final effluent is to be discharged, including its conditions and use. If a stream, give recorded or estimated minimum and average daily flow and minimum weekly flow. State whether unusual conditions exist which might affect flow. If a lake, give approximate surface area, average depth in vicinity of outlet, and average inflow.

l. Sewage treatment. Discuss degree and type of treatment and reasons for adopting proposed method, and basis of design for each unit. Provide quantitative flow diagram and preliminary layout.

m. Filter loading. This should be stated in pounds BOD per 1,000 cu ft.

n. Type of treatment. Topography, industrial wastes, power costs, plant location, and probable character of operation are some of important factors to be considered in choosing type of treatment.

o. Give estimated cost of integral parts of system; proposed methods of financing; and detailed estimated cost of operation.

p. Quality of effluents. "Complete" treatment plants employing biological processes should be capable of producing an effluent having a 5-day B.O.D.

not greater than 15 p.p.m. and containing not more than 30 p.p.m. of suspended solids. Such an effluent should have also a methylene blue stability of 10 days or more and should show evidence of nitrification.

q. Cross connections. No piping or other connections should exist in any part of the treatment works which under any condition might cause the contamination of drinking water.

r. Safe electrical work. Where necessary, electrical work in enclosures possibly involving explosive gases shall comply with National Board of Fire Underwriters specifications for hazardous locations (Class 1, Group D, for highly inflammable gases and volatile liquids).

s. Emergency power facilities. A standby power source shall be provided where the temporary discharge of raw or partially treated sewage may be reasonably expected to endanger the public health or cause serious damage.

Other subjects dealt with by the various standards include: new processes and equipment, guarantees, tests, fences, walks, stairways, materials of construction, paints, flow channels, piping, laboratory equipment, landscaping and site grading, and water supply for the sewage plant.

14–11. Specifications. Sewage-treatment equipment requires care in its specification because of the special nature of its application and the somewhat restricted field of manufacturers of the specialized products. If the specifications are drawn too close, competition will be eliminated or restricted and, if too broad, required quality and performance may not be provided. Cost comparisons may be based on first cost, operating cost, on cost as measured by performance, or on a combination of these bases. The method of computing costs among the bids should be clearly stated in the advertisement for bidders or in the specifications.

Specifications may be detailed in their description of equipment or they may refer by name to three or more competitive manufacturers of the desired equipment, whose product will be used as a standard for comparison of bids. The submission of bids on alternate equipment, with guarantees of performance, should be allowed. This method provides the city the saving resulting from the purchase of equipment not specified and the engineer has the opportunity to select the most economical equipment which will give the required performance. Bids on alternative designs of equipment are sometimes essential, to secure competition, because of the patent situation.

14–12. The patent situation. Difficulties with the patent situation have harassed engineers since the Cameron septic tank patents early in the twentieth century resulted in an organization of municipalities to combat them. The activated-sludge patents, now expired, have resulted in legal findings most amazing to sewer authorities involved. It was estimated [13] that by 1947 the entire sum collected from known infringers of the activated-sludge patents in the United States totaled $2.5 million.

Hansen [14] divided patents into seven classes, as follows: (1) valid and useful with reasonable royalty; (2) valid and useful, but with unreasonable royalty; (3) unexpectedly obtained and affirmed by the courts; (4) doubtful validity but useful, with small royalty; (5) doubtful validity but useful, with large royalty; (6) royalties covered in the price of equipment; and (7) royalties not covered in the price of equipment. In addition there should be included those patents that have been donated to the public by their holders to avoid financial exploitation of the ideas by other than the originators. Examples of all these classes of patents are encountered in sewerage practice. The Imhoff patents, now expired, were an example of the first class. The second class may sometimes be avoided by choosing alternative devices or methods. The third class, the most troublesome, is illustrated by the septic and activated-sludge patents. The fourth class has but a nuisance value. Hansen's remaining classes should be treated with more consideration than they sometimes receive. An excellent rule to follow is: When in doubt consult a patent attorney.

14–13. Mechanical equipment.[15] The trend of sewage-treatment processes is towards increased mechanization. The trend has been beneficial to all concerned in that reduced cost, better operation, and improved treatment have resulted. The sanitary engineer has electrical and mechanical problems to consider in the selection of such equipment as moving and self-cleaning racks and screens; screenings grinders; equipment for the cleaning of grit chambers and sedimentation chambers, including chain, sprocket, and flight mechanisms; scum scrapers; gas engines for sludge-gas utilization; electric generators for power production; electric motors for many applications; blowers and compressors for activated-sludge and air-lift equipment; devices for tapered aeration; automatic control equipment, both mechanical and electrical; relays, solenoids, and "electric eyes"; trickling filters with revolving distributors; mechanical detritors and clarifiers; sludge-drying equipment; and a host of other devices which make the modern sewage-treatment plant resemble an industrial plant, far re-

[13] *Proc. Am. Soc. Civil Engrs.,* October, 1948, p. 1354.
[14] Paul Hansen, *Public Works,* November, 1935, p. 13.
[15] See also F. L. Flood, *Water and Sewage Works,* May, 1954, p. R-219.

Table 14–2 *

SIZE AND COST OF TYPICAL SEWAGE PLANT LABORATORIES

(From Wellington Donaldson, *Sewage Works Jour.*, May, 1935, p. 494.)

Works	Population, 1,000's	Floor Space, sq ft	Floor Space, sq ft per 1,000 population	No. of Laboratory Workers	Bench Space, sq ft	Bench Space, sq ft per worker	Value of Laboratory, dollars Furniture	Apparatus	Chemicals	Total	Percentage of Plant Investment	Cost, dollars per 1,000 population
1	58	400	6.9	1	91	91	1,134	1,922	...	3,056	0.17	52
2	44	280	6.4	1	120	120	400	1,200	75	1,675	0.33	38
3	8	250	31.0	1	30	30	450	275	57	783	0.15	98
4	30	800	26.7	1	75	75	1,200	3,500	700	5,200*	1.00	170
5	200	675	3.4	2	145	73	5,200	4,000	1,000	10,200†	0.28	51
6	75	760	10.1	2	175	88	1,000	1,300	250	2,550	0.50	34
7	835	1,200	14.4	6	115	19	4,500	7,000	300	11,800	0.20	10

1 = Decatur, Ill.　　　3 = Newark, N. Y.　　　5 = Akron, Ohio　　　7 = Baltimore, Md.
2 = Urbana, Ill.　　　4 = Durham, N. C.　　　6 = Rockford, Ill.

* Includes recording gas calorimeter valued at $2,000.
† Exclusive of land.

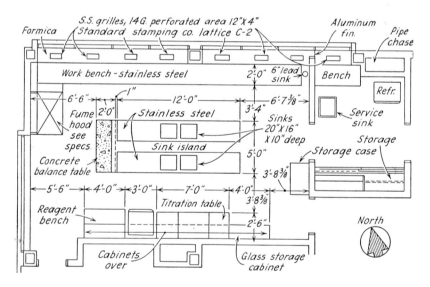

Fig. 14–2. Laboratory at Sunnyvale, Calif. (Courtesy Brown and Caldwell, Engineers.)

moved from the early "septic tank" of a past generation. Such an assembly of equipment requires a staff of engineers to design and to select, manufacturers to supply and install, and operators to maintain and operate. Such teams are making sewage treatment successful.

14–14. Laboratories.[16] Every sewage-treatment plant should be equipped with a laboratory for the performance of routine tests essential to the successful operation of the plant. In general, the space occupied by the laboratory increases in proportion to the load on the plant. The space occupied by the laboratories in a few plants is listed in Table 14–2. Floor plans for a laboratory in a moderate-size plant are shown in Fig. 14–2.

[16] See also *Water and Sewage Works,* July, 1947, p. R-255.

Chapter 15

Characteristics of sewage

15–1. Analyses. Sewage is analyzed to determine those constituents that may cause difficulties in treatment or disposal, or to aid in selecting the correct type of treatment. Analyses of samples of the liquid passing through a treatment plant are made to aid in the control and the operation of the plant. Plant effluents and polluted waters are analyzed to show the progress of pollution and of self-purification. The term "strength" of sewage is frequently referred to as an index of its nuisance-producing potentialities. The strength of a sewage is measured by the nuisance-producing potential of its odor, solids content, and its biochemical oxygen demand.

A complete analysis can be divided into a sanitary survey, physical analysis, chemical analysis, and biological analysis.

15–2. Sanitary survey. A sanitary survey to determine the characteristics of sewage should supply information concerning: (1) its source, whether domestic, commercial, or industrial, and, if industrial, the type or types of industries from which the sewage is coming; (2) variations in the rate of flow and the strength of the sewage; (3) the relative freshness of the sewage as affected by the length of time it has been in the sewer; (4) the amount of dilution from infiltration, surface, and storm water; and (4) such other environmental factors as may be pertinent.

15–3. Sampling. The quality of sewage coming from a sewer is not constant. Changes in quality take place both with time and with position, for the quality of sewage at the surface of a sewer is different from that at the bottom, and the quality in the morning is different from that in the afternoon. To collect a representative sample is, therefore, difficult. At no point in a sewer can a representative sample be taken. At the surface there is an excess of floating material; near the bottom there is too large a proportion of settling solids and gritty material; and at any intermediate point there is too small

338

a proportion of either scum or bottom drag. Below a fall, which thoroughly mixes the sewage, air will be entrained to affect oxygen determinations. No *place* is ideal for taking a sample. A fair compromise is a point slightly beneath the surface where turbulence is mixing the sewage without entraining air or comminuting solids.

There is no ideal *time* to sample sewage, as its quality is continuously varying. A "grab" sample may be taken at any moment, but it must be interpreted only on the basis of the conditions at that particular moment. Another sample taken earlier or later probably would show different characteristics. To avoid misinterpretations based on grab samples, a "composite" sample may be taken. This is composed of a mixture of grab samples taken at different times. The volumes of all grab samples may be the same to make up the composite, or the volume of each grab sample may be proportioned to the rate of flow sewage at the time the sample is taken. Grab samples to be composited are taken at regular intervals, usually hourly, over a period of 24 hours, the collections being made either manually or automatically. *Standard Methods* [1] restricts each portion to a minimum of 120 cc.

Because the quality of the sewage may change during the hours that the composite sample is being made up, it is necessary to keep the samples cool, or some form of preservative may be placed in the collecting bottle to inhibit the biologic action that otherwise would occur. Suitable preservatives include chloroform, formaldehyde, and sulfuric acid. A preservative that will not affect the results of the analyses to be made must be selected. For example, no preservative can be used in a sample on which determinations of biochemical oxygen demand (BOD) are to be made. Determinations of this important characteristic cannot be made successfully on 24-hour composite samples of a strong sewage.

The mean of the observations taken is, generally, the best estimate of a representative sample. Statistical methods [2] have not been widely applied in the interpretation of analyses of sewage samples, principally because of the relatively small number of samples taken for any one purpose.

In the design of a sewage-treatment plant sampling points should be provided wherever necessary, as for raw sewage; influent and efflu-

---

[1] American Public Health Association, *Standard Methods of Water and Sewage Analysis,* 10th edition, 1955.

[2] See also *Water Works and Sewerage,* May, 1943, p. 182.

ent of each treatment device; all types of sludge; supernatant liquors; sludge-bed underdrains; etc.

15–4. Physical analyses. The determinations made in a physical analysis may include temperature, color, odor, and turbidity.

Temperature. An observation of temperature is useful in indicating the antecedents of the sewage, its effect on biological activities, the solubility of gases in it, and the effect of viscosity on sedimentation. The normal temperature of sewage is slightly above that of the water supply because of heat added during the utilization of the water. The temperature of sewage varies slightly with the seasons. Temperatures above normal are indicative of hot, industrial wastes; temperatures below normal indicate the presence of ground or surface water. Biological activity is greater at higher temperatures up to about 60° C. As temperature rises viscosity decreases with resulting increase in efficiency of sedimentation, provided that undesirable convection currents are not produced.

Color. Normal fresh sewage is gray. Black, or a dark color, may indicate a stale or septic sewage, particularly if accompanied by septic odors. Other colors are usually indicative of typical industrial wastes.

Odor. Normal, fresh, domestic sewage is almost odorless. Rotten or putrid odors, such as those of hydrogen sulfide, and of indol, skatol, and other products of decomposition, indicate a stale, septic sewage. Certain industrial wastes will impart typical odors.

Turbidity. Sewage is normally turbid; the stronger the sewage the higher is the turbidity. It is a physical characteristic which is seldom reported.

15–5. Chemical analyses. A sanitary chemical analysis furnishes useful and specific information with respect to the state of decomposition and strength of a sewage, for the control of operation of a treatment plant, and for other purposes in sewage treatment and disposal and for stream-pollution control. The uniformity of procedure prescribed by *Standard Methods* [3] makes possible the comparison of results obtained at different treatment plants. Typical sanitary chemical analyses of sewages of various strengths are shown in Table 15–1. It is to be noted that *Standard Methods* requires that the unit milligrams per liter shall be used to replace the term parts per million.

[3] American Public Health Association, *Standard Methods of Water and Sewage Analysis,* 10th edition, 1955.

Table 15-1

TYPICAL SANITARY CHEMICAL ANALYSES OF SEWAGE,
MILLIGRAMS PER LITER *

Constituent	Strong	Medium	Weak
Solids, total	1,000	500	200
volatile	700	350	120
fixed	300	150	80
suspended, total	500	300	100
volatile	400	250	70
fixed	100	50	30
dissolved, total	500	200	100
volatile	300	100	50
fixed	200	100	50
settleable (ml/l)	12	8	4
Biochemical oxygen demand			
5-day, 20° C	300	200	100
Oxygen consumed	150	75	30
Dissolved oxygen	0	0	0
Nitrogen, total	85	50	25
organic	35	20	10
free ammonia	50	30	15
nitrites (RNO_2)	0.10	0.05	0
nitrates (RNO_3)	0.40	0.20	0.10
Chlorides	175	100	15
Alkalinity (as $CaCO_3$)	200	100	50
Fats	40	20	0

* Except as noted.

In making a sanitary chemical analysis of sewage only those chemical compounds, radicals, elements, and indicators are determined that are indicative of significant sanitary characteristics. A complete, quantitative chemical analysis showing the weight of each compound is not made. A report of a standard sanitary chemical analysis will show the characteristics listed in the first column of Table 15-1. The quantities of each of these constituents found in a typical strong, medium, and weak sewage are listed in the other three columns. These figures are suggestive only, as there is no sharp line of division between strengths of sewages. A summary of typical sewage characteristics is given in Table 15-2.

Some determinations made in routine analyses for the control of

Table 15–2

RÉSUMÉ OF SEWAGE CHARACTERISTICS, BASED ON A SEWAGE FLOW
OF 100 GALLONS PER CAPITA PER DAY

(From Report of Committee.   *Proc. Am. Soc. Civ. Engrs.*, January, 1937, p. 43.)

Item	No. of Works Reporting	Population, thousands	Parts per Million			Pounds per Capita per Day		
			Max	Min	Avg	Max	Min	Avg
Suspended solids (total)	27	3,711	612	81	254	0.51	0.07	0.21
Suspended solids (volatile)	22	2,978	445	51	171	0.37	0.04	0.14
Settleable solids (ml/l)	19	2,144	9.3	1.7	5.4	...	...	...
Settleable solids (ppm)	6	1,595	476	54	20	0.40	0.04	0.17
5-day BOD at 20°	22	3,337	473	121	262	0.39	0.10	0.22
pH value	23	3,437	8.0 *	6.8 *	7.3 *	...	...	...
Immediate chlorine demand	6	1,213	39.8	6.5	...	...	...	...
Nitrogen as free ammonia	18	1,937	34.1	6.1	14.3	0.020	0.005	0.012
Organic nitrogen	16	2,606	48.8	5.2	22.1	0.041	0.004	0.018
1	2	3	4	5	6	7	8	9

* Not ppm.

plant operation are not listed in Table 15–1. These include gas analyses such as methane, carbon dioxide, hydrogen sulfide, and some sludge analyses such as drainability, and volatile acids.

15–6. Solids. Total solids, or residue on evaporation, are important as an index to the strength of sewage, the amount of treatment required, or as a measure of the efficiency of a treatment device. However, since solids are a constituent of the water supply of which the sewage is composed, total solids cannot be depended on for a comparison of the relative strengths of sewages from different localities, without adjustment for the concentration of solids in the water supplies.

Total solids may be broken down into volatile matter and fixed matter. It is generally assumed that the volatile portion represents organic matter. This portion of the total solids is much more significant of strength, as this is the portion of the sewage that may putrefy. Fixed solids have little significance.

Solids are further divided into suspended (removed by filtration) and dissolved, each of which is broken down into volatile and fixed portions. The removal of suspended solids is frequently an indication of the adequacy of a sewage-treatment device, since dissolved solids are not so greatly affected by treatment of the sewage. It may be assumed, in general, that dissolved volatile solids will be most putrefactive and the most difficult to remove, but in special cases this may not be true. Colloidal matter is included in dissolved solids as no attempt is made to determine this characteristic separately under standard methods. There is no standard method for the determination of colloidal matter, but a method suggested by Lumb [4] may be applicable for the determination of colloidal matter in the control of precipitation and other treatment processes. A non-standard method for the determination of suspended solids in sewage by means of a photoelectric cell has been reported by Holmes [5] that promises to be faster and as precise as the present standard method. Volatile matter is usually a highly troublesome constituent of sewage. Colloidal matter is produced by the abrasion of fine suspended matter during flow through a turbulent sewer. High dissolved solids may, therefore, indicate a stale sewage or the presence of a particular industrial waste.

Settleable or settling solids, as the name indicates, are a direct indication of the solids removable by plain sedimentation, and they are an index of the sludge-forming characteristics of sewage.

15–7. Oxygen. Oxygen is reported in sewage analyses in such forms as dissolved oxygen, oxygen consumed, and oxygen demand. Oxygen demand can be of such types as immediate oxygen demand, defined by *Standard Methods* as "the depletion of dissolved oxygen in a standard water dilution of the sample in 15 min. . . ." There are demands [6] for oxygen such as: (1) that caused by inorganic matter and usually satisfied to 97.5 per cent during 24 hours at a temperature of 20° C; (2) the biochemical oxygen demand of soluble and suspended organic matter, generally reported as the oxygen utilized by biological action when incubated at 20° C for 5 days, and commonly abbreviated as BOD; and (3) the biochemical oxygen demand of sludge deposits.

15–8. Dissolved oxygen. The solubility of oxygen in water is affected by turbulence at the surface, temperature, atmospheric pressure, percentage of oxygen in the atmosphere, oxygen deficiency in the water, area of surface exposed to the atmosphere, and with other conditions. Oxygen is less soluble in saline water than in fresh water, and its solubility in sewage is about 95 per cent of that in fresh water. [7]

[4] C. Lumb, *Surveyor,* April 3, 1936, p. 495.

[5] G. W. Holmes, *Sewage Works Jour.,* July, 1935, p. 642.

[6] See also *Sewage Works Jour.,* May, 1941, p. 551.

[7] W. A. Moore, *Sewage Works Jour.,* March, 1938, p. 241.

Hatfield [8] expressed the solubility of oxygen in quiet fresh or saline waters as

$$D.O. = \frac{0.678(P - V_p)(1 - S \times 10^{-5})}{T + 35} \qquad (15\text{–}1)$$

where D.O., is the dissolved oxygen concentration in mg/l.
P is the barometric pressure, mm of mercury.
V_p is the vapor pressure in mm of mercury.
S is the chloride content in mg/l.
T is temperature in °C.

Truesdale's [9] expression is in the form

$$D.O. = 14.161 - 0.3943T + 0.007714T^2 - 0.0000646T^3$$

$$- S \times 10^{-5}(8.41 - 0.256T + 0.00374T^2) \quad (15\text{–}2)$$

using the same nomenclature as in the Hatfield expression.

The concentration of dissolved oxygen in a sample may be expressed in milligrams per liter (mg/l); in parts per million (ppm); or as the percentage of saturation. The last is 100 times the concentration of dissolved oxygen in the sample, divided by the figure given in Table 15–3. Whatever the method of expression it is desirable to state the temperature because of its great effect on the solubility. For solubilities at pressures other than those shown in the table multiply the figure in the table by $P/760$, where P is the atmospheric pressure in millimeters of mercury.

Organic matter, if present in water, may reduce the oxygen content in it ultimately to zero. Sewage ordinarily is devoid of dissolved oxygen for this reason. Normal pure ground water may be deficient in dissolved oxygen because of its chemical reactions in contact with subterranean minerals. An unpolluted surface water should be saturated with dissolved oxygen. Supersaturation may result from the presence of living organisms, such as algae, which consume carbon dioxide and release oxygen by their metabolism.

The dissolved oxygen test for slightly polluted water is one of the most significant sanitary chemical tests, especially when combined with the BOD and the relative stability tests, because so long as oxygen remains in solution in the water putrefaction cannot take place. It is possible, however, for different strata in a body of water to have different concentrations of oxygen, and putrefaction may proceed in one stratum before the oxygen is exhausted from other strata.

[8] W. D. Hatfield, *Sewage Works Jour.*, May, 1941, p. 557.
[9] G. A. Truesdale and others, *Jour. Applied Chem.*, February, 1955, p. 53.

Table 15–3

SOLUBILITY * OF OXYGEN IN FRESH WATER UNDER AN ATMOSPHERIC
PRESSURE OF 760 MM OF MERCURY, THE DRY ATMOSPHERE
CONTAINING 20.9 PER CENT OF OXYGEN.
SOLUBILITY EXPRESSED IN MG/L

Temp, deg C	Note (1)	From Trues- dale †	Temp, deg C	Note (1)	From Trues- dale	Temp, deg C	Note (1)	From Trues- dale
0	14.62	14.16	10	11.33	10.92	20	9.17	8.84
1	14.23	13.77	11	11.08	10.67	21	8.99	8.68
2	13.84	13.40	12	10.83	10.43	22	8.83	8.53
3	13.48	13.05	13	10.60	10.20	23	8.68	8.38
4	13.13	12.70	14	10.37	9.98	24	8.53	8.25
5	12.80	12.37	15	10.15	9.76	25	8.38	8.11
6	12.48	12.06	16	9.95	9.56	26	8.22	7.99
7	12.17	11.76	17	9.74	9.37	27	8.07	7.86
8	11.87	11.47	18	9.54	9.18	28	7.92	7.75
9	11.59	11.19	19	9.35	9.01	29 ‡	7.77	7.64

* Solubility varies directly with atmospheric pressure.

† From G. A. Truesdale and others, *Jour. Applied Chem.*, February, 1955, p. 53.

‡ At 30° solubility is 7.63, and by Truesdale it is 7.53.

(1) Concentrations used in practice previous to introduction of the Truesdale formula, and on which recent literature is based.

15–9. Biochemical oxygen demand. The biochemical oxygen demand (BOD) of sewage or of polluted water is the amount of oxygen required for the biological decomposition of dissolved organic solids to occur under aerobic conditions and at a standardized time and temperature. Heavily polluted bodies of water do not contain sufficient oxygen in solution to maintain aerobic conditions during decomposition and self-purification. The reduction of BOD in a natural body of water differs somewhat from its reduction in sewage treatment because, in the natural body of water, the reduction is due to biological decomposition of all putrescible organic matter. In sewage treatment the organic matter that can exert BOD is decomposed, the remainder being discharged in the effluent.

The quantity of oxygen required for the complete stabilization of polluted water may be taken as a measure of its content of organic matter. The quantity required in various periods of time and the

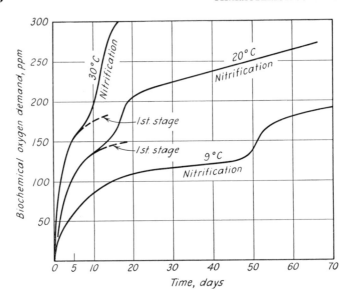

Fig. 15–1. Progress of Biochemical Oxygen Demand. (From Theirault, *Bull.* 173, U. S. Public Health Service, 1927.)

effect of temperature are indicated in Fig. 15–1. It can be observed in the figure that for each temperature the curves are smooth for the first days followed by a distinct break in the graph. During the first days, known as first stage, carbonaceous matter is being oxidized. During the second stage nitrification is taking place. Since polluted water will continue to absorb oxygen after months of incubation it is impracticable to attempt to determine the ultimate oxygen demand of a sample.

The BOD test is among the most important made in sanitary analyses to determine the polluting power, or strength, of sewage, industrial wastes, or polluted water. It serves as a measure of the amount of clean diluting water required for the successful disposal of sewage by dilution.

15–10. Mathematical formulation of BOD. During the first stage the rate of deoxidation at any instant may be assumed, for convenience, to be directly proportional to the amount of oxidizable organic matter present. Although the assumption is not correct, due to the heterogeneous nature of the organic matter and of the biologic life, the results based on the assumption are approximately correct and have practical applicability. Field tests show that the rate of

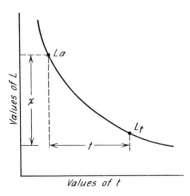

Fig. 15–2. Graphical representation of derivation of monomolecular equation for BOD.

deoxidation is not constant.[10] If, however, the rate is assumed to be constant, if L represents the oxidizable organic matter present, and t represents time, then as indicated graphically in Fig. 15–2:

$$dL/dt = -K'L \quad \text{or} \quad dL/L = -K'dt$$

Integrating

$$\log_e L = -K'T + C$$

when $L = L_t$ and $t = t_1$.

Hence

$$\log_e L_t = -K't_1 + C \quad \text{and} \quad C = \log_e L_t + K't_1$$

Therefore

$$\log_e L = -K't + \log_e L_t + K't_1$$

and

$$\log_e L_t/L = K'(t - t_1)$$

or

$$L_t = L10^{K(t-t_1)}$$

If L_a = first-stage BOD, that is, the amount of oxygen required to maintain stability during first-stage deoxygenation, then, when $t = 0$, $L = L_a$ and

$$L_t = L_a10^{-Kt}$$

But x, the oxygen absorbed in t days, $= L_a - L_t$. Hence

$$x = L_a(1 - 10^{-Kt})$$

$$(15\text{–}3)$$

[10] R. L. Woodward, *S. and I.W.,* April, 1953, p. 419, May, 1953, p. 566, and August, 1953, p. 918.

The formula is restricted to heavily polluted waters, such as recently diluted sewage, polluted river waters, sewage, and industrial wastes. In the study of stream pollution it is seldom necessary to consider periods of flow exceeding 5 to 10 days below a point of pollution. The fact that the equation is limited to this period does not detract from its applicability.

A graphical method for the determination of K and L_a has been devised by Thomas,[11] from observations of t and x. The procedure is as follows:

1. Observe values of x and t experimentally and calculate $\sqrt[3]{t/x}$ for each day.

2. Plot $\sqrt[3]{t/x}$ as ordinates against t as abscissas to natural scale and sketch in the line of best fit. Measure the intercept A on the y axis, and the slope of the line B. Then $K = 2.61B/A$ and $x = 1/(2.3KA^3)$.

For example, let it be required to determine the value of K from the following observations of t and x:

$t =$	1	2	3	4	5	6	7	8	9	10
$x =$	30	60	75	90	100	105	118	122	127	132

Plotting the values of $\sqrt[3]{t/x}$ as ordinates and t as abscissas to natural scale the value of A was found to be 0.308 and of B to be 0.0118. Hence $K = (2.61 \times 0.0118)/0.308 = 0.10$.

It has been found that the value of K varies with the temperature of incubation so that

$$K_T = K_{20}(1.047^{T-20}) \tag{15-4}$$

where K_T is the deoxygenation constant at $T°$ C.

K_{20} is the deoxygenation constant at 20° C, usually taken as 0.100.

Streeter [12] states:

In highly polluted shallow streams containing attached oxidizing growths, the value of K has been observed as high as 0.2 and 0.3. In bottom sludge deposits originating in sewage K may range downward from 0.03 to 0.05 to less than 0.01, according to the relative age of the deposit. In deposits of humoid character, much lower values, ranging below 0.001, have been observed.

[11] H. A. Thomas, Jr., *Water and Sewage Works,* March, 1950, p. 123.

[12] H. W. Streeter, *Modern Sewage Disposal,* p. 191, Federation of Sewage Works Associations, 1938.

The value of L_a varies also with the temperature so that

$$(L_a)_T = (L_a)_{20}(0.02T + 0.6) \qquad (15\text{--}5$$

where $(L_a)_T$ is the value of L_a at $T°$ C
$(L_a)_{20}$ is the value of L_a at 20° C

It is possible by means of formulas 15–3, 15–4, and 15–5 to compute the BOD of a sample at any temperature and at any time, when the BOD is known at some other time and temperature.

Example. If the 3-day, 15° BOD of a sample is 200 mg/l, what will be its 7-day, 25° BOD?

Solution. The value of K_T at 15°, from formula 15–4, is

$$(0.1)(1.047^{-5}) = 0.08$$

The value of K_T at 25°, from formula 15–4, is

$$(0.1)(1.047^{5}) = 0.126$$

The value of La_{15}, from formula 15–3, is

$$200 \div \left(1 - \frac{1}{10^{0.24}}\right) = 470$$

The value of La_{20}, from formula 15–5, is

$$470 \div (0.3 + 0.6) = 522$$

The value of La_{25}, from formula 15–5, is

$$522 \times (0.5 + 0.6) = 574$$

The 7-day, 25° BOD, from formula 15–3, is

$$(574)(1 - 10^{(-0.126)(7)}) = 500 \qquad\qquad \textit{Answer}$$

It has been found [13] that the monomolecular equation (15–3) gives only an approximate mathematical fit to small portions of the BOD curve because the parameters k and L are highly variable. A logarithmic equation has been developed by Orford and Ingram [13] which is said to fit the observations of BOD against time more closely. If the BOD of sewage, river water, activated-sludge oxidation, benthal oxidation of sewage sludge, or biological oxidation of industrial wastes [14] is plotted as ordinates to a natural scale, and time t as abscissas to a logarithmic scale, the observations for any oxidation

---

[13] See H. E. Orford and W. T. Ingram, *S. and I.W.*, April, 1953, pp. 419, 424, and 566.

[14] *Ibid.*, p. 574.

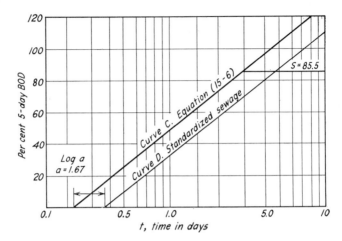

Fig. 15–3. Comparisons of monomolecular and logarithmic formulas for BOD. (From H. E. Orford and W. T. Ingram, *S. and I.W.*, April, 1953, p. 425.)

stage will fall on a straight line as shown in Fig. 15–3 with an equation in the form:

BOD (for time t and temperature T)

$$= S[0.85 \log (at\ 1.072^{T-20}) + 0.41] \qquad (15\text{–}6)$$

where t = days of incubation at $T°$ C, with t between 0.5 and 20; and T between 10 and 30.

   a = t-axis intercept of normal domestic sewage divided by the t-axis intercept of the observed BOD curve. The t-axis intercept for normal domestic sewage is 0.333.

   S = BOD when $t = 5/a$. It is independent of T.

   In applications of formula 15–6 it is necessary to know three values of the parameters, usually BOD, t, and T.

   Example. If the 5-day, 20° C BOD of a sample is 1,000 mg/l, and its 3-day, 20° C BOD is 730, what is the 5-day BOD at 37° C?

   Solution. $1,000 = S[0.85 \log (5a) + 0.41]$

                           $730 = S[0.85 \log (3a) + 0.41]$

The solution gives $a = 0.44$ and $S = 1,430$.
Then 5-day BOD at 37° C

$$= 1,430[0.85 \log (0.44 \times 5 \times 1.072^{17}) + 0.41]$$

$$= 1,620 \qquad\qquad\qquad\qquad\qquad\qquad\qquad \textit{Answer}$$

Although equations 15–3 and 15–6 can both be expressed logarith- mically and solved simultaneously, such a solution might be mis- leading as the two expressions are not mathematically identical. A correlation has been found, however, which can be shown as follows:

Values of t, days	3	5	7	10	14
k/a	0.218	0.197	0.180	0.150	0.130
L/S	1.04	1.10	1.16	1.25	1.34

This knowledge may be applied in the solution of the problem on page 349.

We have given $K = 0.1$; hence $a = 0.1/0.218 = 0.46$.

Then BOD (3-day, 15°)

$$= 200 = S[0.85 \log (0.46 \times 3 \times 1.072^{-5}) + 0.41] \quad \text{and} \quad S = 500$$

Then BOD (7-day 25°)

$$= 500[0.85 \log (0.46 \times 7 \times 1.072^5) + 0.41] = 485$$

A normal BOD curve may be expected to have a value of $a = 0.2$ when $S =$ zero, and $a = 5$ when $S = 100$ per cent of the 5-day BOD. This information can be applied in the solution of such a problem as:

Example. Let it be required to determine the 3-day, BOD value of a stream whose 5-day, BOD is 50 where the 5-day, BOD of sewage is 200.

Solution. $50 = 200[0.85 \log (5a) + 0.41]$

then $y_3 = 200[0.85 \log (3 \times 0.13) + 0.41] = 13$

It is to be noted that the graphs in Fig. 15–1 are a series of straight lines for any one temperature. This makes it possible to identify the various stages of oxidation, such as nitrification, initial lag, and final oxidation, by observing the time at which the break occurs in the straight lines of best fit for each stage. A comparison of the results of equations 15–3 and 15–6 is shown graphically in Fig. 15–3.

The 5-day, 20° BOD for raw sewage is generally greater than 100 mg/l; tannery and abattoir wastes have BOD values ranging up to 10,000 mg/l; and some unusual industrial wastes may attain values up to 50,000 mg/l. The 5-day BOD of good tap water may be as low as 0.5 mg/l. Values of BOD for various sewages are given in Tables 15–1 and 15–2.

A serious difficulty with the standard method for the determination of BOD is the 5-day period of incubation required. A 2-day BOD test has been described [15] that is claimed to give more consistent results than the standard test.

The Odeeometer, a patented, proprietary device, makes possible the determination of the immediate oxygen demand without chemical reagents. The action of the Odeeometer depends on the vacuum created when oxygen is absorbed from the air enclosed over the sample being tested. The instrument has been found useful in determining the "Nordell number" of sludges. This number is defined as the rate of utilization of oxygen in parts per million per hour by sewage or sewage-sludge mixtures.[16]

15–11. Chemical oxygen demand, COD. Chemical oxygen demand tests have been devised in an attempt to overcome objections to the BOD test such as the time required, uncertainties concerning the reaction velocity constant K, and the total, first-stage oxygen demand, L_a. The tests involve the chemical digestion of the sample with an oxidizing agent, such as potassium dichromate.[17] No COD test has been standardized nor widely adopted. Such tests have been found useful in the control of a sewage-treatment plant, but an attempt to correlate results of COD and BOD tests is not promising since the two tests do not determine the same thing. Moore and Ruchoft [18] have concluded that: "where a given industrial waste is fairly constant in composition and contains no toxic materials, a satisfactory C.O.D. to B.O.D. ratio may be determined." The relation may be found by drawing a straight line through plotted points of BOD and corresponding COD values and determining the equation of the line.

15–12. Oxygen consumed. The oxygen-consumed test is a standard method. It involves chemical digestion with potassium permanganate and may be considered as a special form of COD test. It is primarily an index of carbonaceous matter readily oxidizable by potassium permanganate. It is of little general value for comparisons of sewage characteristics among different localities because of uncertainties concerning the presence of undetermined reducing agents other than carbonaceous organic matter. The results may differ widely among sewages having different putrefactive characteristics. The test has been found of limited value for quick information as an

[15] See R. Zehnpfennig and M. S. Nichols, *S. and I.W.*, January, 1953; and W. L. Tidwell and J. H. Sorrels, *S. and I.W.*, April, 1956, p. 488.

[16] See also *Sewage Works Jour.*, September, 1935, p. 810.

[17] See *Water and Sewage Works*, August, 1949, p. 317.

[18] W. A. Moore and C. C. Ruchoft, *S. and I.W.*, June, 1951, p. 705.

aid in the control of treatment-plant operation, where tests are made under similar conditions.[19]

15–13. Relative stability. The relative stability of a polluted water is an expression of the approximate amount of oxygen available in the water in terms of the total amount required for complete stability. It can be successfully determined only for slightly polluted water. The relative stability is usually expressed as the percentage of the total oxygen requirements and is computed from the expression

$$S = 100(1 - 0.794^{t_{20}}) \quad \text{or} \quad S = 100(1 - 0.605^{t_{37}}) \quad (15\text{--}7)$$

where S = relative stability.

t_{20} and t_{37} = time, in days, for a standard sample of the polluted water to decolorize a standard volume of methylene blue solution when incubated at 20° or 37° C, respectively.

Equation 15–7 is based on equation 15–3, using L_a as 100. Although associated with the BOD test, the two tests do not show the same thing. Conditions affecting the relative-stability test include: temperature; concentration of dye; quantity of dissolved oxygen present; BOD; concentration of nitrites and nitrates; concentration of enzymes; and the number of bacteria. The blue color of the dye will disappear before the nitrites and nitrates are reduced [20] but these substances are of significance in the BOD test.

The relative-stability test is of little use in the study of raw sewage because of the effect of certain dissolved and colloidal substances in precipitating the color. The results of the test are useful principally in making a quick estimate of the pollution of a stream or the condition of a plant effluent, but they do not supplant the value of the results of the BOD test. In general, a polluted water with a relative stability greater than 90 may be discharged into a stream without danger of reducing the oxygen content to a dangerous degree, because such polluted waters will reabsorb sufficient oxygen from the atmosphere to maintain stability.

15–14. Nitrogen. There are five nitrogen determinations that may be made in a sanitary sewage analysis: free ammonia, albuminoid ammonia, organic nitrogen, nitrites, and nitrates. Organic nitrogen, free ammonia, nitrites, and nitrates constitute total nitrogen.

Organic nitrogen and free ammonia, taken together, are an index of the organic nitrogenous matter present in the sewage, and albumi-

[19] See also *Sewage Works Jour.*, March, 1937, p. 224.
[20] See also W. L. Tidwell and others, *S. and I.W.*, March, 1956, p. 136.

noid ammonia may be taken as a measure of the decomposable organic nitrogen present. Free ammonia or ammonia nitrogen is a result of bacterial decomposition of organic matter. A fresh, cold sewage should be relatively high in organic nitrogen and low in free ammonia. A stale, warm sewage should be relatively high in free ammonia and low in organic nitrogen. The sum of the two should be unchanged in the same sewage, unless ammonia is given off in septic action. The total concentration of the two is a valuable index of the strength of the sewage and is important in considerations of the type of treatment to be adopted.

Nitrites (RNO_2) and nitrates (RNO_3) (R represents any chemical element as K, Na, etc.) are found in fresh sewages only in concentrations of less than one part per million. In well-oxidized effluents from treatment plants the concentration will probably be higher. Nitrites are not stable and are reduced to ammonia or are oxidized to nitrates. Their presence indicates that change is in progress. Their presence in raw sewage usually indicates a fresh sewage or the addition of diluting water so recently as to allow insufficient time for the reduction of the nitrates and nitrites.

Nitrates represent the most stable form of nitrogenous matter in sewage, and their presence may, therefore, be an indication of stability. The presence of nitrates in effluents from sewage-treatment processes, however,[21] may be undesirable because of the promotion of algal and macroscopic plant growth. In the activated-sludge process nitrates appear when the amount of sludge in the aeration tank is too large or the flowing-through time is too long.

15–15. Chlorides and chlorine. Chlorides in sewage should not be confused with free, residual chlorine resulting from the addition of chlorine to the sewage. Chlorides are inorganic substances commonly found in the urine of man and animals. The amount of chlorides above the normal chloride content of unpolluted, natural waters in a district is used as an index of the strength of a sewage in that district. The chloride content may be affected by certain industrial wastes, as from ice-cream plants or meat-salting works. Since chlorides are inorganic substances in solution they are not affected by biological processes nor by sedimentation. Their diminution in a treatment process or in a flowing stream is indicative of dilution, and the reduction of chloride will be in proportion to the amount of chloride-free diluting water added.

[21] See also Karl Imhoff, *Public Health Eng. Abstracts,* October, 1942, p. 49.

Free chlorine is found only after its application during sewage treatment. Its presence indicates that the chlorine demand [22] of the sewage has been satisfied and that most life has been killed except possibly some spores and organisms encysted in solids. The chlorine demand or, in other words, the amount of chlorine that will produce a residual, is a measure of the amount of organic matter present. In normal sewage this may be expected to be between 5 and 50 mg/l. The indications of chlorine demand may be considered somewhat similar to BOD, oxygen consumed, and relative stability, and the method has the advantage of being relatively quickly determined. It is not, however, a "standard" method.[23]

15–16. Fats or greases. Fats or greases have recoverable market value when present in sufficient quantity to be skimmed off the surface of the sewage. Ordinarily they are undesirable constituents of sewage as they precipitate in and clog the interstices in filtering material and form objectionable scum in tanks and in streams. Although fats are carbonaceous matter they are not indicated by the oxygen-consumed test because they are not easily oxidized.

15–17. Volatile acids. The determination of volatile acids is valuable primarily as an index of the progress of anaerobic biological digestion of organic matter. *Standard Methods* states: "The fatty acids containing 10 or less carbon atoms are classified as water-soluble acids and those containing more than 10 are classified as water insoluble fatty acids. The volatile fatty acids are the first six lower molecular-weight acids classified as soluble fatty acids and are the only ones that can be distilled at atmospheric pressure." The determination of volatile acids is included in *Standard Methods* as a "nonstandard" method. The index may also be determined by the method originated by Buswell.[24] In the production of gas during decomposition of organic solids there is first a combination with water to form the simpler organic acids, such as acetic and propionic, and these acids then decompose to give carbon dioxide and methane. Buswell states,[25] "The limit of acidity for smooth, continuous fermentation

[22] Chlorine demand is defined in the 10th edition of *Standard Methods* as the amount of chlorine in milligrams per liter which must be added to sewage to produce a chlorine residual of such strength that after a definite contact time the effluent will show a desired coliform density or will meet the requirements of some other objective.

[23] See also *Sewage Works Jour.*, 1937, p. 569.

[24] A. M. Buswell, *Bull.* 30, Illinois State Water Survey, 1930.

[25] *Sewage Works Jour.*, Vol. 4, 1932, p. 973.

has been found for most materials to be about 2,000 p.p.m., calculated as acetic."

15–18. Gases. The three gases of special interest in sewage problems are hydrogen sulfide, methane, and carbon dioxide. Traces of hydrogen sulfide are detectable by the sense of smell. The presence of this odor indicates a stale sewage and, usually, active septicization under anaerobic conditions. High concentrations are toxic. Hydrogen sulfide in the presence of moisture will attack cement and certain metals. Methane and carbon dioxide are determined in routine control of sludge-digestion tanks, high methane concentration being desirable. Methane is an explosive gas the presence of which is undesirable in sewers.

15–19. Alkalinity and acidity. Ordinary sewages are normally slightly alkaline, although the presence of an industrial waste may cause acidity. An alkaline condition is desirable in a biological treatment process as bacterial life flourishes better under slightly alkaline conditions. Within normal limits, the exact amount of alkalinity found in sewages has little significance. An abnormal alkalinity or acidity may indicate the presence of industrial wastes calling for a special method of treatment.

15–20. Oxidation-reduction potentials. Oxidation-reduction potential is defined by Hood and Rohlich [26] as ". . . the electronic pressure existing in a liquid as a result of the respective concentrations of oxidant and reductant present." It is reported as E_h or emf in millivolts of positive or negative sign. Oxidation-reduction potential is quickly observable, and is a valuable index in the control of sewage-treatment processes.[27] For example, it is said that [26] "In a biological oxidation system such as the activated-sludge, a positive E_h must be maintained. A value of 200 to 600 millivolts usually reflects a favorable oxidizing intensity. . . . In anaerobic systems, such as sewage sludge decomposition, unless the E_h is maintained at a negative value in the magnitude of -100 to -200 millivolts, the process will be retarded."

15–21. Hydrogen-ion concentration or pH. The determination of pH is valuable mainly to control the operation of a sewage-treatment plant. It has no sanitary significance and has little bearing on the strength of the sewage or the method of treatment to be adopted. In some unusual situations the determination of the pH of an indus-

---

[26] See also *Water and Sewage Works,* September, 1949, p. 352; and *Sewage Works Jour.,* July, 1948, p. 640.

[27] F. E. Nussberger, *S. and I.W.,* September, 1953, p. 1003.

Table 15–4

RELATIVE VALUES OF ANALYTICAL DETERMINATIONS

Sewage Concentration	Partial Treatment	Complete Treatment
1. Biochemical oxygen demand (dissolved oxygen)	1. Biochemical oxygen demand (dissolved oxygen)	1. Relative stability (nitrite nitrogen) (nitrate nitrogen) (dissolved oxygen)
2. Suspended solids (total, volatile, fixed)	2. Suspended solids (total, volatile, fixed)	2. Biochemical oxygen demand
3. Total organic nitrogen (ammonia nitrogen)	3. Total organic nitrogen (ammonia nitrogen)	3. Suspended solids (total, volatile, fixed)
4. Chlorides	4. Oxygen consumed	4. Total organic nitrogen (ammonia nitrogen)
5. Oxygen consumed	5. Settleable solids	5. Oxygen consumed
6. Settleable solids	6. Albuminoid ammonia	6. Settleable solids
7. Total solids (total, volatile, fixed)	7. Alkalinity	7. Albuminoid ammonia
8. Albuminoid ammonia		8. Alkalinity
9. Alkalinity		

trial waste might supply needed information concerning its nature. Knowledge of pH is of value in the control of chemical processes of sewage treatment and in the control of the anaerobic digestion of organic matter. For example, in the latter process, if the pH approaches 5.0, the acid stage of digestion is becoming predominant and digestion will be unsatisfactory. Remedies must be taken to raise the pH.

15–22. Relative values of chemical analyses. The relative values of analytical determinations are summarized in Table 15–4.

15–23. Population equivalent. The population equivalent of a sewage is the number of persons from whom a "normal domestic" or "standard sewage" would produce the same measured characteristic as is produced by the sewage in question. For example, the oxygen demand by a normal sewage from 1,000 persons is about 180 lb per day. Hence, the population equivalent of any sewage whose oxygen demand is 180 lb per day is 1,000 persons. A *standard sewage* is a normal domestic sewage, that is, "sewage from which industrial wastes of all kinds are largely absent and which has been collected from separate sewerage systems or from combined sewerage systems during periods of dry-weather flow." [28] The characteristics that are most common for the measurement or expression of population equiva-

[28] See *Public Health Bull.* 173, 1927, p. 48.

lent are biochemical oxygen demand, suspended solids, and chlorine demand.

The term population equivalent was first applied to BOD and unless otherwise qualified it refers to the 5-day, 20° BOD of the per capita flow of sewage in terms of the 5-day, 20° BOD of some standard sewage.

The per capita oxygen demand of a standard sewage will probably be in the neighborhood of 0.17 to 0.18 lb per day. Hence, if a given volume of sewage consumes 36,000 lb of oxygen per day its population equivalent is 36,000/0.18 = 200,000.

In a study of chlorine demand Symons and others [29] have concluded that the chlorine demand of a domestic sewage is about 0.00466 lb per capita per day, or between 5 and 15 mg/l, usually determined on the basis of a 15-minute contact.

15–24. Organic life in sewage. Organisms of various size live in sewage. The smallest are the viruses and phages, too small to be seen with a microscope. Next in size are bacteria. These may be identified with the aid of the microscope supplemented by observations of their reactions to their environment. Others, slightly larger, are known as microscopic organisms because the species can be identified by the aid of a microscope alone. The part taken in the biolysis of sewage by macroscopic organisms belonging to the animal kingdom, such as birds, fish, insects, and rodents, which feed on the substances in the sewage, is so inconsequential as to be of no importance.

Organisms in sewage may be harmful, harmless, or helpful. The organisms that are harmful to mankind are the pathogenic organisms. Their condition of life in sewage is usually abnormal and, in general, their existence therein is of short duration. It may be of sufficient length, however, to permit the transmission of disease. Diseases transmitted by sewage are principally those contracted through the discharges from the alimentary canal, such as typhoid fever and dysentery. Sewage-borne diseases are not commonly contracted by contact of sewage with the skin or by breathing the air of sewers. It is safe to work around sewage so long as the sewage is excluded from the mouth and is kept away from cuts, mucous membranes and abrasions of the skin, and asphyxiating and toxic gases are avoided.

The beneficial organisms in sewage are those on which dependence is placed for the biological methods of treatment.

15–25. Biological analyses, sewage bacteria, and microscopic organisms. Analyses of sewage for the study of biologic life include

[29] G. E. Symons and others, *Water Works and Sewerage*, August, 1938, p. 789.

bacteriological and microscopic examinations. Standard sanitary bacteriological analyses are seldom made in the study of sewage, because it is known that intestinal bacteria are present; that the concentration of bacteria is high; and that bacterial counts are not a guide to interpretation of strength, to the selection of a method of treatment, or to the control of treament processes. The absence of bacteria may be interpreted as an indication of the presence of a bactericide such as an industrial waste.

Bacteriological analyses are used in stream-pollution and self-purification studies. Either the standard method or the membrane-filter technique [30] may be used. A high, positive correlation is said to exist between the results of the two methods.[31] Some authorities [32] recommend the latter test because of "simplicity, ease, convenience, precision, and speed, and because evidence points to a greater selectivity in indicating coliforms."

Sometimes microscopical and macroscopical analyses for the study of algae, fungi and the lower forms of animal life are made to aid in the determination of the progress of stream pollution and the condition of sand filters and trickling filters. Such analyses have no significance in the study of sewage characteristics.

A microscopical inspection of sewage may be expected to show the presence of bacilli, cocci, and the filamentous bacterium *Sphaerotilus natans*. Fungi, algae, protozoa, metazoa, vermes, and arthropoda are not ordinarily present in raw sewage except possibly as spores, encysted cells, or larvae. They are found, however, in parts of sewage-treatment plants, and in bodies of polluted water where they may play an important part in the sewage-treatment process, and in the self-purification of streams.

The total number of bacteria in a sample of sewage has little or no significance in the interpretation of its analysis. In a normal sewage the number may be between 2,000,000 and 20,000,000 per ml, and because of the extreme rapidity of the multiplication of bacteria, a sample showing a count of 1,000,000 per ml on the first analysis may show three or four times as many a few hours later. A bacterial

[30] See also L. W. Slanter and others, *Public Health Rept.*, January, 1955, p. 67; L. W. Slanetz and C. H. Bartley, *Applied Microbiology*, January, 1955, p. 46; J. A. McCarthy, *Am. Jour. Public Health*, December, 1955, p. 1569; and R. Eliasen, *Water and Sewage Works*, December, 1955, p. 523.

[31] See W. Litsky and others, *Am. Jour. Public Health*, August, 1955, p. 1049.

[32] See A. M. Rawn and F. R. Bowerman, *Water and Sewage Works*, January, 1956, p. 36.

analysis of sewage is ordinarily of little or no value because pathogenic organisms are almost certain to be present, there is no interest in the harmless organisms, and the helpful nitrifying and aerobic bacteria will not grow on ordinary bacteriological laboratory media. Occasionally the presence of certain bacteria may indicate the presence of industrial wastes. In general, the total bacterial count, as sometimes reported, represents only the number of bacteria that have grown under the conditions provided. It may bear no relation to the number of bacteria in the sample.

The presence of organic life in sewage is of importance because many methods of sewage treatment depend on biologic action for their effect. Sewages that do not contain deleterious industrial wastes, contain, or will support, the biological life necessary for their successful treatment.

15–26. Trends in sewage characteristics. Increasing economy in the use of water, the disposal of waste food with sewage, increased use of sewers for the collection of industrial wastes, and other conditions are tending to increase the strength of municipal sewages and the loads on municipal sewage-treatment plants. The widespread use in the home of detergents other than soap is having a marked effect on treatment processes.

15–27. Decomposition of sewage. If a glass container is filled with sewage and allowed to stand open to the air, a black sediment will appear after a short time, a greasy scum may rise to the surface, and offensive odors will be given off. This condition will persist for several weeks, after which the liquid may become clear and odorless. The sewage has been decomposed and is now in a more stable condition. The decomposition of sewage is brought about by bacterial metabolism, the exact nature of which is not thoroughly understood.

The decomposition of sewage may be divided into anaerobic and aerobic stages. These conditions are usually, but not always, distinctly separate. The growth of certain forms of bacteria is concurrent, while the growth of some other forms is dependent on the results of the life processes of other bacteria in the early stages of decomposition.

When sewage is fresh it may contain some oxygen. This oxygen is quickly exhausted, so that the first important step in the decomposition of sewage is carried on under anaerobic conditions. It may be accompanied by the creation of foul odors of compounds containing sulfur, particularly hydrogen sulfide; odorless gases such as carbon dioxide and methane; and other, more complicated organic compounds. An exception to the rule that putrefaction takes place only in the absence of oxygen is the production of foul-smelling substances by the putrefactive activity of obligatory and facultative anaerobes. Hydrogen sulfide can be produced, apparently, in the presence of oxygen, the action that takes place not being thoroughly understood.

The biolysis of sewage is the term applied to the changes through which its organic constituents pass owing to the metabolism of bacterial life. Organic matter is composed almost exclusively of the four elements carbon, oxygen, hydrogen, and nitrogen (COHN); sometimes sulfur and phosphorus are also present. The organic constituents of sewage can be divided into proteins, carbohydrates, and fats. The proteins are constituents principally of animal tissue, but they are found also in the seeds of plants. The chief distinguishing characteristic of the proteins is the possession of 15 to 16 per cent of nitrogen. To this group belong the albumens and casein. The carbohydrates are organic compounds in which the ratio of hydrogen to oxygen is the same as in water, and the number of carbon atoms is 6 or a multiple of 6. To this group belong the sugars, starches, and celluloses. The fats and salts are formed, together with water, by the combination of the fatty acids with the tri-acid base glycerol. The more common fats are *stearin, palmarin, olein,* and *butyrine.* The soaps are mineral salts of the fatty acids formed by replacing the weak base glycerol with some of the stronger alkalies.

The first state in the biolysis of sewage is marked by the rapid disappearance of the available oxygen present in the water mixed with the organic matter to form sewage. In this state the urea, ammonia, and other products of digestive putrefactive decomposition are partially oxidized, and in this oxidation the available oxygen present is rapidly consumed, the conditions in the sewage becoming anaerobic. The second state is putrefaction in which the action is under anaerobic conditions. The proteins are broken down to form urea, ammonia, the foul-smelling mercaptans, hydrogen sulfide, and so forth, and fatty and aromatic acids. The carbohydrates are broken down into their original fatty acid, water, carbon dioxide, hydrogen, methane, and other substances. Cellulose is also broken down but much more slowly. The fats and soaps are affected somewhat similarly to the hydrocarbons and are broken down to form the original acids of their make-up, together with carbon dioxide, hydrogen, methane, and so forth. The bacterial action on fats and soaps is much slower than on proteins, and the active biological agents in the biolysis of the hydrocarbons, fats, and soaps are not so closely confined to anaerobes as in the biolysis of the proteins. The third state in the biolysis of sewage is the oxidation or nitrification of the products of decomposition resulting from the putrefactive state. The products of decomposition are converted to nitrites and nitrates, which are in a stable condition and are available for plant food.

15–28. Cycles of organic matter. Organic matter passes through a cycle, illustrated graphically in Fig. 15–4, sometimes called the cycle of life and death, the nitrogen cycle, or by the name of the organic substance depicted in the sketch. The nitrogen cycle may be described somewhat as follows: on the death of a plant or animal, decomposition sets in, accompanied by the formation of urea, which is broken down into ammonia. This is known as the *putrefactive* stage of the nitrogen cycle. The next stage is *nitrification,* in which the compounds of ammonia are oxidized to nitrites and nitrates and are thus prepared for plant food. In the state of *plant life* the nitrites and nitrates are denitrified so as to be available as a plant or animal food. The highest state of the nitrogen cycle is *animal life,* in which

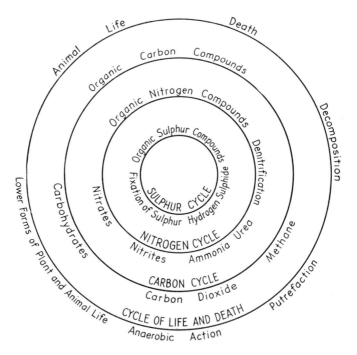

Fig. 15–4. Hypothetical organic cycles.

nitrogen is a part of the living animal substance or is changed from protein to urea, ammonia and so forth, by the functions of life in the animal. On the death of the animal the cycle is repeated. The nitrogen cycle, like the cycle of life and death, is purely an ideal condition because, in nature, there are many short circuits and back currents, which prevent the continuous progression of the cycle. The conception of this cycle is an aid in understanding biological processes in sewage treatment because these processes follow, in a general way, the cycle of life and death.

Chapter 16

The disposal of sewage

16–1. Methods of disposal. Methods of sewage disposal include its discharge into bodies of water or watercourses and on or beneath the surface of the ground. The sewage may be disposed of either with or without preliminary treatment, depending on the ability of the water or land to carry the load placed on it without resulting in a nuisance. Disposal into water, the most common method, is referred to as disposal by dilution. Disposal on land surface is known as broad irrigation or, sometimes, as sewage farming, depending on the aim in the method of disposal. Subsurface or underground disposal is applicable, primarily, to small amounts of sewage and is not commonly practiced. Underground disposal of raw sewage into drainage wells is widely condemned as a menace to the quality of ground water. The use of properly treated sewage-plant effluents to restore diminishing ground-water levels is practiced, however, apparently without detrimental effects on the public health.

16–2. Disposal by dilution. Disposal of sewage by dilution is the discharge of raw sewage or the effluent from a treatment plant into a body of water of sufficient size to prevent offense to the senses and to avoid danger to the public health. A knowledge of the conditions required for successful disposal by dilution is essential to the understanding of the aim of all processes of sewage treatment. If raw sewage could be disposed of in any stream, sewage treatment would not be necessary. Limitations on the characteristics of liquid pollutants that may be discharged into natural waters are not uniform but, in general, where there is no health hazard, sewage should receive at least primary treatment to reduce suspended solids to a maximum of 100 to 150 mg/l and BOD to less than 100 mg/l.

Among the desired conditions for successful disposal by dilution are adequate currents to prevent sedimentation and to carry the sewage away from habitations before putrefaction sets in, or sufficient diluting water high in dissolved oxygen to prevent putrefaction and to maintain fish and other life; a fresh or non-septic sewage; and absence of back currents or quiet pools favorable to sedimentation in the stream into which disposal is taking place. The conditions that should be prevented are offensive odors due to sludge banks, the rise of septic gases, deposits on shores, excessive oxygen depletion, unsightly discoloration, pollution of shellfish and the killing of other fish, and unsightly floating or suspended matter. In most instances pathogenic organisms must be prevented from entering surface waters to avoid the dissemination of disease. It is unwise to draw water supplies, without treatment, from a stream receiving a sewage effluent, no matter how careful or thorough the treatment of the sewage. The treatment of the sewage is a safeguard and lightens the load on the water-purification plant, but under no considerations can it be depended on to protect the community consuming the diluted effluent.

16–3. Permissible pollution. The degree to which it is permissible to pollute a body of water depends on its subsequent use. Usages available as measures of permissible pollution are: (1) natural state, (2) drinking-water, (3) preservation of fish, (4) safety for agricultural use, as stock watering and irrigation, (5) industrial, (6) recreational, (7) freedom from nuisance, and (8) commercial use, such as navigation.

The principal considerations in the promulgation of standards of permissible stream pollution should be health, esthetics, and economics.[1] None should be considered alone. For example, the existence of a small community may depend on the operation of a paper mill that pollutes the stream flowing by the community. The enforcement of the "natural state" standard would close the mill and wipe out the community.

Many authorities have promulgated standards of stream pollution.[2] Most of them have taken into consideration the ultimate use of the water. For example, Imhoff and Fair[3] classify receiving waters as shown in Table 16–1. Others have limited the BOD, suspended solids, dissolved oxygen, and sometimes the turbidity of effluents discharging into the receiving water.[4]

[1] See also E. C. Borgeson, *S. and I.W.*, March, 1953, p. 325.

[2] See G. Feller and J. Newman, reprint from *Industry and Power,* June, 1951.

[3] K. Imhoff and G. M. Fair, *Sewage Treatment,* 2nd edition, John Wiley and Sons, 1956.

[4] See also *Public Health Eng. Abstracts,* November, 1955, p. 19.

Table 16–1

CLASSIFICATION OF STANDARDS FOR POLLUTED WATER

Class	Use	Standard
A	Drinking water after chlorination.	Without filtration, bacterial standard less than 50 *B. coli* per 100 cc.
B	Bathing, recreation, and shellfish culture.	No visible sewage matters. Bacterial standard less than 100 *B. coli* per 100 cc.
C	Fishing.	Dissolved oxygen content not less than 3, and preferably 5, ppm. Carbon dioxide not more than 40, and preferably 20 ppm.*
D	Rough industrial uses and irrigation.	Absence of nuisance, odors, and unsightly suspended floating matters. Dissolved oxygen present.

The following are Tri-state Standards of Connecticut, New York, and New Jersey, for 1936, applicable to tidal waters in New York City area:

A	Primarily for recreational purposes, shellfish culture, and development of fish life.	Full removal of floating solids.† At least 60 per cent removal of suspended solids. Probable number of *B. coli* not to exceed 100 per 100 cc. Average of dissolved oxygen saturation not less than 50 per cent during any week of the year.
B	All other waters.	Full removal of floating solids.† At least 10 per cent removal of suspended solids plus additional removal if needed to prevent sludge deposits. Average dissolved oxygen saturation not less than 30 per cent during any week of the year. No *B. coli* requirement.

* The report of the Ohio Valley Water Sanitation Committee, *S. and I.W.*, March, 1955, p. 321, points out that it is hard to set tolerance limits for any substance because of the different susceptibilities of various species and the little known toxicity of mixtures.

† Sewage-treatment plant performance.

The Ohio River Valley Sanitation Commission has expressed its standards, as paraphrased by Thomas,[5] as follows:

(a) The arithmetic mean density, m, of coliforms should not exceed 5,000 per 100 ml.

(b) MPN's (most probable numbers) of no more than 20 per cent of samples in any month may be greater than 5,000 per 100 ml, nor may more than 5 per cent of samples be greater than 20,000 per 100 ml.

Thomas points out that such standards may be useful in large rivers but in smaller streams wider fluctuations may be expected to occur. The use of MPN as a basis for stating coliform concentrations is approved in *Standard Methods*.

A bioassay may be used in limiting the concentration of a toxic substance. A bioassay is made by measuring the concentration of the toxic substance which will kill a predetermined proportion of an aquatic species in a fixed time and at a fixed temperature.

16–4. Preliminary investigations. Before adopting disposal of sewage by means of dilution a study should be made of the nature of the sewage or effluent and of the body of water into which the sewage or effluent is to be discharged. This study should include measurement of the quantity of water available at all seasons of the year for wet and dry years; analyses of the diluting water to determine particularly the available dissolved oxygen; a hydrographic survey to determine channels and shoals, the velocity and direction of currents, and the effect of winds and tides; and a study of the effect on water supplies and bathing beaches, aquatic life, and so forth. Good judgment aided by proper interpretation of such information should lead to the most desirable location of the sewer outlet. (See also Sect. 6–26.) If sewage treatment is found to be necessary tests should be made to determine the extent and thoroughness of the treatment required.

16–5. Preliminary treatment. If the sewage to be disposed of by dilution contains unsightly floating matter, oil, or grease, or is high in settleable solids, no amount of oxygen in the diluting water will prevent a nuisance to sight or the formation of putrefying sludge banks. Under such conditions it will be necessary to introduce screens or sedimentation basins, or both, in order to remove the floating and the settleable solids. Biologic or other methods of treatment may be necessary for the removal of other undesirable conditions.

[5] H. A. Thomas, *S. and I.W.*, February, 1955, p. 212.

All methods of sewage treatment, with but few exceptions, are preliminary to the disposal of sewage by dilution.

16–6. Protection of aquatic life. The food value of fish and of shellfish in our coastal waters is a natural resource demanding conservation. The cost of sewage treatment must be measured against the value of the fish in the body of water into which the sewage is to be discharged. Limiting concentrations of toxic and other substances that can be endured by aquatic life, as measured under one condition, may not be correct under other conditions because of the synergistic action of some substances which, when combined with others, greatly increase their harmful effects.[6] Fish life may be benefited by a slight amount of pollution that supplies food but, if the turbidity is so increased that light is excluded and the oxygen content of the water is dangerously reduced, fish life is inhibited.

Conditions affecting fish life in water[7] include temperature, light, color, dissolved and settleable solids, chlorides, fluorides, and dissolved oxygen. Other interrelated factors are species of fish, their age, and the concentrations of toxic materials. For example, a fish may resist some pollution when there is a high level of dissolved oxygen present but be killed by the same substance when there is a deficiency of oxygen. At a dissolved-oxygen saturation below about 70 per cent, fish life begins to disappear and at 40 per cent in warm water only lower forms of life remain. In general, the dissolved-oxygen content for warm-water fish habitats should not be less than 5 mg/l for more than 8 hours in any 24-hour period, and at no time less than 3 mg/l.[8]

The shellfish industry is seriously affected by pollution because shellfish are conveyors of intestinal disease, and the taking of shellfish from polluted waters is prohibited wherever health authorities have jurisdiction.

16–7. Protection of recreational facilities. The recreational facilities for bathing, boating, and fishing furnished by our streams should be preserved even though no monetary value can be placed on them. Public support for a campaign for sewage treatment is easier to obtain in the hope of preserving recreational resources as

---

[6] P. Doudoroff and others, *S. and I.W.*, July, 1953, pp. 802 and 840.

[7] Ohio Valley Water Sanitation Commission Report, *S. and I.W.*, June, 1956, p. 678.

[8] See also Committee Report, Ohio River Valley Water Sanitation Commission, *S. and I.W.*, March, 1955, p. 321.

well as through the expectation of protecting health. The Joint Committee on Swimming Pools and other Public Bathing Places of the American Public Health Association has stated:

. . . it is very desirable that the bathing waters at public bathing places on natural streams, lakes, and tidal waters, should be on the same standard of bacterial quality as is required for swimming pools. It is recognized, however, that the strict application of swimming-pool standards to all public bathing waters would probably not be practical at present.

Among the bacterial criteria for the quality of water at bathing places is that proposed by Winslow and Moxon [9] which provides, in effect, that the *coli-aerogenes* index of water in a safe area should not exceed an average of 100 per 100 cc, or a maximum of 1,000 per 100 cc. "Other observers, notably Mallman, have suggested . . . the density of certain types of streptococci is a more significant index of sanitary quality."

16–8. Self-purification of streams. The self-purification of streams is due to dilution, sedimentation, reduction, oxidation, and sunlight. The actions are physical, chemical, and biological.

Temperature, turbulence, and the hydrography of the stream are important physical factors affecting its self-purification. They greatly affect the action of all the previously mentioned factors, except dilution. Sedimentation, oxidation, and the effect of sunlight, together with physical, chemical, and biological activities, are increased by rising temperatures.

When putrescible organic matter is discharged into water the offensiveness of the organic matter is diminished by its dispersion through the diluting water. If the dilution is sufficient it alone may prevent nuisance. As surface tributaries and underground streams join the main stream the increased dilution further disperses the sewage solids, effecting self-purification through dilution.

discharge into the diluting water, owing to the growth and activity
The oxidation of organic matter commences immediately upon its
of oxidizing organisms and, to a slight degree, to chemical reaction. As long as sufficient oxygen is present in the water, septic conditions will not exist and offensive odors will be absent. When the organic matter is completely nitrified or oxidized there will be no further demand on the oxygen content of the stream and the stream will be said

[9] See H. W. Streeter, "Disposal of Sewage in Inland Waterways," *Modern Sewage Disposal*, Federation of Sewage Works Associations, 1938, p. 200.

to have purified itself. The most important condition for the successful self-purification of a stream is an initial quantity of dissolved oxygen to oxidize all the organic matter contributed to it, or the addition of sufficient oxygen subsequent to the contribution of sewage to complete the oxidation. Oxygen may be added through the dilution received from tributaries, through aeration over falls and in whitewater rapids, by the action of the wind, by quiescent absorption from the atmosphere, or by the action of microscopic organisms. A stream that will absorb air (oxygen) rapidly will stand more pollution than an equally pure water not reaerating rapidly.

Reduction occurs when organic matter is hydrolyzed, either chemically or biologically, to form liquids or gases and to put some solids into solution.

Sunlight is effective in self-purification through its sterilizing effect on certain bacteria, through its bleaching powers, and through photosynthesis, by which chlorophyll-bearing organisms take energy from the sun and convert it into food for other forms of life, absorbing carbon dioxide and giving off oxygen in the process.

Biological forces include bacteria, which attack organic matter and convert it into simple chemical substances; algae, which depend on photosynthesis to utilize carbon dioxide and produce oxygen; protozoans some of which prey on bacteria whereas others act like algae; rotifers and crustaceans, which consume algae and protozoans; large aquatic plants, which act similarly to algae; and macroscopic animals, which work over mud deposits and live on plankton and insect larvae.

The rapidity of self-purification depends on the kind of organic matter, the presence of available oxygen, the rate of reaeration, temperature, sedimentation, and the velocity of the current. Sluggish streams are more likely to purify themselves in a shorter distance than rapidly flowing, turbulent streams, whereas the latter are more likely to purify themselves in a shorter time, other conditions being equal. The absorption of oxygen is more rapid in a stream whose surface is broken than in a stream with unbroken surface. However, the growth of algae, other biological activity, and the effect of sunlight and of sedimentation may be more potent factors than a broken surface in self-purification. Little or no self-purification may be expected in an ice-covered stream. It is frequently more advantageous to discharge sewage into a swiftly moving stream, regardless of the conditions of self-purification, as the undesirable conditions which may result occur far from the point of disposal and may be offensive to no one.

16–9. Zones of pollution.   A polluted stream undergoing self-purification has been divided into four zones [10] as follows:

First, the *zone of degradation,* in which pollution has recently occurred and oxygen is reduced to about 40 per cent. The water is turbid; sunlight is excluded; algae are dying or gone. Fish life may be present, feeding on the fresh organic matter. Sludge deposits are commencing and the typical bottom worms *Limnodrilus* and *Tubifex* appear, together with sewage fungi such as *Sphaerotilus natans.*

Second, the *zone of active decomposition,* in which the oxygen lies between 40 per cent and zero and rises again to 40 per cent. In this zone there is no fish life; the water is grayish and darker than in the preceding zone; septic conditions may have set in; and the organisms of active organic decomposition are at work. Methane, hydrogen, nitrogen, hydrogen sulfide, and other odorous gases may be given off, and scum may form on the surface. As the active decomposition diminishes the oxygen content rises. Where pollution is intensive and decomposition is extremely active the transition into the next zone may be delayed.

Third, the *zone of recovery,* in which the oxygen content increases from 40 per cent, macroscopic aquatic life reappears, the water is clearer, fungi diminish, and algae reappear. Nitrates, sulfates, phosphates, and carbonates may be found.

Fourth, the *zone of cleaner water,* in which the dissolved oxygen is close to saturation and natural stream conditions are restored.

Some conditions in the four zones are summarized in Table 16–2.

16–10. Self-purification of lakes.   Sewage may be disposed of into lakes with as great success as into running streams if conditions favorable to self-purification exist. However, the discharge of sewage or sewage-treatment plant effluents into a lake will add nutrients to the water which will support and may encourage the growth of aquatic flora and fauna.[11] If sufficient nutrient is added to support damaging growth the lake may be lost, as a source of water supply, for recreation, and for other purposes. The approach to this condition may be detected through routine observations of the aquatic life in the lake. The situation may be avoided by: (1) stopping the dis-

[10] See also G. C. Whipple, *The Microscopy of Drinking Water,* 4th edition, John Wiley and Sons, 1927.

[11] See also R. L. Smith and W. Subby, *Public Works,* February, 1955, p. 91. C. N. Sawyer, *Jour. New Eng. Water Works Assoc.,* Vol. 61, 1947, p. 109; R. O. Sylvester and others, in *The Trend in Engineering,* published at the University of Washington, April, 1956, p. 8.

Table 16-2

LIVING INDICES OF STREAM POLLUTION AND SELF-PURIFICATION

Zone	Typical Organisms
Degradation	Fish and green algae declining.
	Littoral forms of green and blue-green algae trailing from frequently wetted stones. These include *Stigeoclonium*, *Oscillatoria*, and *Ulothrix*.
	Bottom forms in sludge: reddish worms (Tubificidae) similar to earthworms, such as *Tubifex* and *Limnodrilus*.
	Water fungi typically white, olive green, putty gray, rusty brown. *Sphaerotilus natans*, *Leptomitus*, *Achlya*.
	Ciliated Protozoa or Ciliata, such as *Carchesium*, *Epistylis*, and *Vorticella*.
Active decomposition	Bacteria flora flourishing, anaerobes displacing aerobes, which reappear toward the lower end of the zone.
	Protozoa follow course of aerobic bacteria, first diminishing and then reappearing.
	Fungi follow a similar course, disappearing under true septic conditions and then reappearing. Organisms are thread-like and develop pink, cream, and grayish tints.
	Algae present to a very slight extent at the lower end of the zone.
	Tubifex present only at the upper and lower ends of the zone.
	Maggots and *Psychoda* (sewage fly) larvae present in all but the most septic stage.
Recovery	Protozoa, rotifers, crustaceans appear.
	Fungi are present to a limited degree.
	Algae appear in the following order: Cyanophyceae, Chlorophyceae, and diatoms.
	Large plants: sponges, bryozoans, etc., appear.
	Bottom organisms include *Tubifex*, mussels, snails, and insect larvae.
	Carp, suckers, and more resistant forms of fish.
Cleaner water	Normal conditions, characterized particularly by game fish.

charge of the effluent into the lake, (2) control of the growth of the algae in the water by the use of algacides or by the introduction of predatory flora or fauna, (3) changing the regimen of the lake to create a different environment, or (4) by treating the waters of the lake to remove the aquatic life. However, as has been pointed out by

Hasler: [12] "Once complete eutrophication has taken place, the lake may never regain its former state even though the nutrient source in the form of sewage has been removed."

Lakes and rivers purify themselves from the same causes, but the currents in lakes are less pronounced or may be non-existent. In shallow lakes (20 ft or less in depth) dependence must be placed on horizontal currents and the stirring action of the wind to keep the water in motion in order that the sewage and the diluting water may be mixed. In deeper water, currents induced by the wind are helpful, but full dependence may not have to be placed on them. The drag of the wind has been found to induce surface currents from 3 to 6 per cent of the wind velocity and to reach to depths of 45 to 60 ft in the Great Lakes. Vertical currents and the seasonal turnovers in the spring and fall completely mix the waters of a lake in which the temperature of the bottom water never rises higher than 4° C.

In the early winter the cold air cools the surface water of a lake. The cooling increases the density of the surface water, causing it to sink and allowing the warmer layers below to rise and become cooled. After the temperature of the entire lake has reached 4° C the vertical currents induced by temperature cease, as continued cooling decreases the density of the surface water, which now remains at the surface. In the spring, as the temperature of the surface water rises to 4° C, the water becomes heavier and drops through the colder strata below, causing vertical currents. These phenomena are known as the fall and spring turnovers and are restricted almost entirely to the temperate zone. The former is usually more pronounced. These turnovers are effective in assisting the self-purification of deep lakes.

Since turbulence, currents, dilution, and the proportion of surface area to volume of a lake exposed to reaeration and sunlight are less than in a flowing stream, it is to be expected that the pollution load which can be carried per unit volume of lake and the rate of self-purification will be less than in a stream.

16–11. Indices of self-purification. Progress in the self-purification of a stream can be observed through physical, chemical, and biological changes. Physical measurements include color and turbidity. Both will be highest in the zone of active decomposition. Turbidity will be diminished by sedimentation, and color by the action of sunlight.

---

[12] A. D. Hasler, *Ecology*, Vol. 28, No. 4, October, 1947. See also C. N. Sawyer, *Jour. New Eng. Water Works Assoc.*, Vol. 61, 1947, p. 109.

Chemical indices of self-purification are highly significant. In the order of their relative importance they are: (1) dissolved oxygen, (2) BOD, and (3) suspended solids. Less significant indices include chlorides and the various nitrogen determinations. pH is recognized as a poor criterion for expressing toxicity of acids or alkalies.[13]

At any stage in the decomposition and stabilization of a polluted stream the predominating organisms are those best suited to the environment. Anaerobes and fungi are present during septicization, and game fish appear in the zone of cleaner water. Nocturnal deficiencies in dissolved oxygen often determine the distribution of organisms in a stream.[14] Hence, the character of life present may be used as an index of the progress of sewage treatment and the self-purification of a body of water.

The biotic index proposed by Beck [15] depends on the preceding principle. It is written in the form

$$BI = 2nA + nB \qquad (16\text{--}1)$$

where A represents organisms that will not tolerate appreciable organic pollution, number per ml.

B represents the organisms that will do so but cannot exist under aerobic conditions, number per ml.

n is the number of microscopic organisms per ml.

A biological survey [16] may be valuable and legally useful in revealing the pollutional history of a stream. A summary of various types of organisms typifying various zones [17,18] is shown in Table 16–2, and data on changes in plankton and bacteria in the Illinois River are shown in Table 16–3.

16–12. Bacterial changes. Bacterial changes in the progress of stream pollution and self-purification have been studied intensively, and it is known that their growth and death follow the expression $B = K/10^{kt}$ where B is the density of coliforms per liter, K and k are

[13] Committee Report, Ohio Valley Water Sanitation Commission, *S. and I.W.*, March, 1955, p. 321.

[14] See also A. R. Gaufin and C. M. Tazewell, *Public Health Rept.*, 1952.

[15] W. M. Beck, Jr., *S. and I.W.*, October, 1955, p. 1193.

[16] See also R. Parker, *S. and I.W.*, February, 1953, p. 211.

[17] See also P. J. A. Zeller, *Proc. 19th Texas Water Works Short School*, 1937; and F. E. Giesecke and P. J. A. Zeller, *Bull.* 47, Texas Engineering Experiment Station, 1939.

[18] See W. C. Purdy, *Ohio Conference on Sewage Treatment*, 1932, p. 21.

Table 16–3

SUMMARY OF PLANKTON AND BACTERIAL DATA ON INVESTIGATIONS
OF THE POLLUTION OF THE ILLINOIS RIVER

Plankton data in cubic standard units per cubic centimeter; gelatin counts
of bacteria per cubic centimeter. Averages for 11 months, October, 1921, to
August, 1922. From *Pub. Health Bull.* 198, 1930.

Miles below Lake Michigan	Stream Flow, thousands of second-feet	Time of Flow from Station 41, hours	Plankton			Total* Plankton	Bacteria
			Pollutional †	Cleaner †		
35	8.69	...	107	51	105	49	687	1,913,100
39	8.69	...	154	49	158	51	673	1,148,780
41	9.21	0	152	60	103	40	637	1,106,500
64	15.46	12.0	276	65	145	35	881	681,100
100 (LS)	17.73	36.0	179	58	132	42	722	219,050
131 ‡	21.14	80.3	142	45	172	55	932	69,620
148	19.97	135	123	36	221	64	793	38,230
161	20.2	178	88	20	360	80	923	15,015
205 (H)	21.6	222	111	20	446	80	1,245	25,192
302	32.4	291	39	16	213	84	1,072	13,486

* This total includes "indifferent" organisms, and also those of unknown
sanitary significance.
† Per cent is shown in this column.
‡ For 6 months only.
LS = La Salle.   H = Havana.

constants, and t is time in days.[19, 20]   Values of constants can be determined from observations of average numbers of bacteria after
times t under different temperatures of storage in the laboratory.
Since the trend of the major portions of the river curves is similar to
curves derived from the laboratory-stored samples, it is "inferred
that the mechanism, and the rates of satisfaction of BOD under
natural stream conditions are about the same, in the supernatant
stream water, as under conditions of the ordinary laboratory test." [20]

16–13. Quantity of diluting water.   In a large majority of the
problems of the disposal of sewage by dilution it is not necessary to

[19] See also Gunnar Akerlindh, *Water and Sewage Works,* September, 1954,
p. 412.
[20] See also *Sewage Works Jour.,* March, 1934, pp. 208 and 233.

add sufficient dilution water to oxidize completely all organic matter present. Ordinarily it is sufficient to prevent putrefactive conditions until the flow of the stream, lake, or tidal current has reached some large body of diluting water or a place where putrefaction is no longer a nuisance. It is never desirable to allow the dissolved oxygen content of a stream to be exhausted, since putrescible conditions will exist locally before exhaustion is complete.

Since the amount of oxygen needed is dependent on the amount of organic matter in the sewage rather than on the total volume of sewage, and since the amount of organic matter is closely proportional to the population, the amount of diluting water required has sometimes been expressed in terms of population. Experience has indicated that where raw sewage is being put into a body of water, 4 to 7 cfs per 1,000 population is required to prevent nuisance. Between a minimum limit of 2 and a maximum of 8 cfs of diluting water per 1,000 population the success of disposal by dilution is uncertain. Above the higher limit the avoidance of septic conditions is practically assured, and below the lower limit a nuisance can be expected. These limitations refer only to dissolved oxygen conditions and have no bearing on the creation of sludge banks, unsightly floating matter, or other undesirable conditions. It is possible by means of the de-oxygenation-reoxygenation, or the oxygen-sag, curve to compute the approximate amount of diluting water required to maintain any reasonable minimum of dissolved oxygen or BOD in a stream.

If it is desired to determine the volume of diluting water necessary to mix with sewage to assure a minimum dissolved oxygen content in the stream or at some predetermined point below the point of pollution, the following observations must be made: (1) rate of discharge of sewage or effluent into the stream, (2) temperature of the sewage or effluent, (3) its BOD, (4) BOD of diluting water, (5) temperature of the stream, (6) oxygen initially dissolved in the stream, (7) the time required to flow to the predetermined point, (8) the permissible dissolved oxygen at the predetermined point, (9) the oxygen initially dissolved in the sewage or effluent, and (10) the reaeration constant of the stream. When all of these conditions are known the amount of diluting water required may be determined through the use of the information in Sect. 16–16.

16–14. Dilution in sea water. The oxygen content in sea water is about 20 per cent less than in fresh water at the same temperature. The greater quantity of dissolved matter in sea water reduces its capacity to absorb many sewage solids. This, together with the chemical reactions that occur when sewage mixes with sea water, serves to precipitate some of the sewage solids, giving a milky appearance to the water and forming sludge banks. Such sludge banks are particularly offensive as there is a greater tendency to form hydrogen sulfide in sea water than in fresh water. When sewage is mixed with sea water the greater specific gravity and the lower temperature of the sea water cause the lighter, warmer sewage to rise and to spread out in a thin film or sleek. On a calm day this sleek may be noticeable for great distances from the sewer outfall.

The reaeration of salt water is less rapid than that of fresh water in proportion to the respective solubilities of oxygen in the two waters; and still less, but to an unknown amount, by reason of the greater viscosity and consequent small value of the diffusion coefficient. The evidence of the action which takes place in the absorption of oxygen from the air by sea water and its effect on dissolved sewage solids is conflicting, but, in general, fresh water is a better diluent than salt water.

16–15. The oxygen balance. The oxygen balance has been variously defined.[21] Streeter [22] has defined it as the difference between the dissolved oxygen content and the total first-stage BOD at a point in the stream, and he has defined the net reaeration as the change in oxygen balance between two points. He shows that the oxygen balance can be expressed as $O_a - L_a$ or $O_b - L_b$, where O_a and O_b are the dissolved oxygens, and L_a and L_b are the total oxygen demands at the two points, A and B, respectively, in the stream. This method gives accurate results only when $L_a - L_b$ affords a true measure of the total oxygen demand exerted on the stream between the two points.

16–16. Deoxygenation and reoxygenation. When a polluted stream is exposed to the air, deoxygenation and reoxygenation proceed simultaneously so that the amount of dissolved oxygen present at any instant can be determined through knowledge of the combined rates of the two phenomena. Such knowledge is of value in predicting the oxygen content in a polluted stream at any point, or in the estimation of dilution or sewage-treatment requirements when the conditions of pollution are known. In most dilution problems it is possible to measure or estimate all but one of the parameters in formula 16–2, and to solve for the unknown parameter. This formula has limitations similar to those applicable to formula 15–3.

[21] *American Sewerage Practice,* McGraw-Hill Book Co., Vol. III, 1935, p. 162.
[22] H. W. Streeter, *Modern Sewage Treatment,* Federation of Sewage Works Associations, 1938, p. 191.

The formula for the oxygen-sag curve is expressed as

$$D = \frac{K_1 L_a}{K_2 - K_1} (10^{-K_1 t} - 10^{-K_2 t}) + D_a(10^{-K_2 t}) \qquad (16\text{-}2)$$

where D = dissolved oxygen deficit after time t. D is expressed in mg/l.

t = time of incubation, or of flow downstream, in days.

D_a = initial dissolved oxygen deficit, in mg/l. This is the amount below saturation.

L_a = initial BOD (first stage) in mg/l.

K_1 = coefficient of deoxygenation, 0.1 at 20° C.

K_2 = coefficient of reoxygenation.

$D_a = (D_o - D_p)$, in which D_o is the dissolved oxygen in mg/l at 100 per cent saturation at the temperature of the liquid, and D_p is the actual dissolved oxygen present, in mg/l, at the same temperature.

Whenever sewage and water are mixed the resulting temperature, dissolved oxygen content, BOD, etc., of the mixture can be computed from the general expression

$$C_m = \frac{C_s Q_s + C_w Q_w}{Q_s + Q_w} \qquad (16\text{-}3)$$

in which C_m = the particular characteristic of the mixture desired, e.g., temperature.

C_s = the corresponding characteristic of the sewage or effluent.

C_w = the corresponding characteristic of the diluting water.

Q_s = the quantity of sewage or effluent in the mixture.

Q_w = the quantity of diluting water in the mixture.

The coefficient of reoxygenation, K_2, varies with the temperature according to the expression

$$(K_2)_T = (K_2)_{20}(1.0159^{T-20}) \qquad (16\text{-}4)$$

in which $(K_2)_T$ = the coefficient of reoxygenation at any temperature T, in degrees centigrade.

$(K_2)_{20}$ = the coefficient of reoxygenation at 20° C.

A logarithmic form of the expression has been devised by Orford and Ingram [23] as:

[23] H. E. Orford and W. T. Ingram, *S. and I.W.*, May, 1953, p. 566, with preceding articles in *ibid.*, April, 1953, pp. 419 and 424.

$$D = \frac{0.15a(1.25S)}{k_2 - 0.15a} (10^{-0.15at} - 10^{-k_2t}) + D_a 10^{-k_2t} \qquad (16\text{--}5)$$

in which the nomenclature is the same as in formulas 15–3 to 15–6. The derivation of this formula is based on graphical and statistical studies of the results given by formula 16–2 and its results are within an equal degree of precision. Neither deoxygenation nor reoxygenation can be expected to follow these mathematical expressions with better than fair correlation, because the natural, physical phenomena cannot be expected to follow chemical laboratory conditions on which formula 16–2 is based.

It has been shown by Akerlindh [24] that the oxygen deficiency in a lake, where there is no flow at a state of equilibrium, is in direct proportion to the added pollution assuming a constant rate of reaeration, or

$$k_2D = RL_a \qquad (16\text{--}6)$$

where R is a numerical constant.

The rate of reoxygenation is affected by a complexity of natural conditions so that the coefficient at $20°$ C cannot be expressed as a constant but must be expressed in terms of the natural conditions. Observations on the rate of reoxygenation or reaeration in long stretches of the Illinois and Ohio rivers during warm weather have shown the value of $(K_2)_{20}$ to be in the neighborhood of 0.24, but observations of a turbulent, shallow portion of the highly polluted Des Plaines River below Joliet, Ill., during cold weather gave values of $(K_2)_{20}$ averaging 2.57. Approximate values of K_2 are as follows: [25]

	K_2 at $20°$ C
Small ponds and backwaters	0.05–0.10
Sluggish streams and large lakes	0.10–0.15
Large streams of low velocity	0.15–0.20
Large streams of normal velocity	0.20–0.30
Swift streams	0.30–0.50
Rapids and waterfalls	0.50 and higher

It is obvious that the rate of reaeration under a coat of ice will be zero.

A curve drawn in accordance with formula 16–2 is shown in Fig.

[24] Gunnar Akerlindh, *Water and Sewage Works,* August, 1954, p. 412.

[25] *Rept. of Eng. Board of Review,* Sanitary District of Chicago, Part III, Feb. 21, 1925, Appendix I.

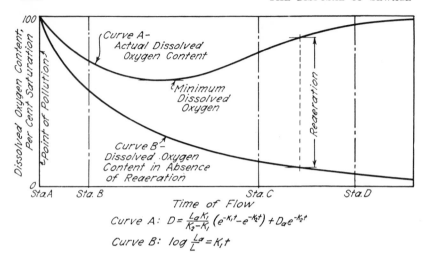

Curve A: $D = \frac{L_a K_1}{K_2 - K_1}\left(e^{-K_1 t} - e^{-K_2 t}\right) + D_a e^{-K_2 t}$

Curve B: $\log \frac{L_a}{L} = K_1 t$

Fig. 16–1. The oxygen-sag curve, showing change in dissolved oxygen in a stream below an assumed point of pollution. (From *Report of Eng. Board of Review*, Sanitary District of Chicago, Part III, Feb. 21, 1925, Appendix I.)

16–1.[26] The appearance of the curve gives the name "the oxygen-sag curve." The formula does not hold if the time of flow from Station A to Station D is greater than the period of first-stage deoxygenation, or if the dissolved oxygen content falls below zero, because the formula is based on the hypothesis of first-stage deoxygenation and the presence of oxygen at all times.

16–17. Minimum dissolved oxygen point. Knowledge of the minimum dissolved oxygen point is of importance in stream-pollution control. This point can be determined graphically by plotting the dissolved-oxygen sag curve for the desired conditions, in the form shown in Fig. 16–1.[27]

Another method has been devised by Le Bosquet and Tsivoglou.[28] Using the nomenclature of formulas 15–3 to 16–4 inclusive, with D_c equal to the dissolved oxygen deficit at the critical point, and with Q equal to the rate of flow in the stream in cubic feet per second, then D_c varies inversely with Q where D_a is zero and a steady pollution

[26] *Rept. of Eng. Board of Review*, Sanitary District of Chicago, Part III, Feb. 21, 1925, Appendix I.

[27] See also Gunnar Akerlindh, *Water and Sewage Works*, September, 1954, p. 412.

[28] M. Le Bosquet, Jr., and E. C. Tsivoglou, *S. and I.W.*, August, 1950, p. 1054.

load is introduced into the stream in which Q is the rate of flow; that is, $QD_c = C_3$. They have shown also that

$$D_c = L_a C_2 \qquad (16\text{-}7)$$

where

$$C_2 = \frac{K_1}{K_2 - K_1} (10^{-K_1 t} - 10^{-K_2 t}) \qquad (16\text{-}8)$$

and that

$$(DO)_c = S' - C_3(1/Q) \qquad (16\text{-}9)$$

where $(DO)_c$ = minimum dissolved oxygen in stream, mg/l.
$\quad S'$ = dissolved oxygen saturation value, mg/l.
$\quad C_3 = C_1 \times C_2$

If $1/Q$ is plotted against $(DO)_c$ a straight line is obtained from which other values of $(DO)_c$ and $1/Q$ can be determined.

Example. The average value of $(DO)_c$ at $25°$ C in the Cincinnati Pool in the Ohio River was found to be 4.0 mg/l for a flow of 10,500 cfs. (*a*) What would be the value of $(DO)_c$ when $Q = 25,000$ cfs?

Solution. $(DO)_c = S - C_3(1/Q)$; therefore, $4 = 8.38 - C_3(1/10,500)$. Hence

$$C_3 = \frac{8.38 - 4.90}{1/10,500} = 46,100$$

$$(DO)_c = 8.38 - (46,100)(1/25,000) = 8.38 - 1.85 = 6.53 \text{ mg/l}$$

16–18. A statistical method. A statistical method has been devised [29] for predicting the maximum reduction in oxygen concentration in a polluted stream which is based on the expression

$$y = a - b_1 x_1 - b_2 x_2 - b_3 x_3 \qquad (16\text{-}10)$$

where y = dissolved oxygen drop, mg/l.
$\quad x_1$ = 5-day BOD at station x_1.
$\quad x_2$ = water temperature at station x_2 in $°$C.
$\quad x_3$ = stream-discharge factor, cfs.
$\quad a, b_1, b_2,$ and b_3 are constants derived from observed data.

After the values of the constants have been determined by a statistical analysis of data collected by observations of stream constants the formula is applicable to unknown conditions in that stream. In collecting data the most useful observations will be those made in the range between average and critical conditions of oxygen deficiency.

16–19. Reaeration. Reaeration depends largely on such physical factors as time, temperature, turbulence, depth, sunlight, and the

---

[29] M. A. Churchill and R. A. Buckingham, *S. and I.W.*, April, 1956, p. 517.

rate of deoxygenation of the liquid. In most problems of practical importance it is necessary to compute the coefficient of reaeration by direct observations of dissolved oxygen and BOD at various critical points and to compute the value of K_2, the coefficient of reaeration, from the results. Predictions of future conditions are based, then, on the results of these observations.

The instantaneous rate of reaeration, called r, can be expressed as $-(dD/dT) = 2.3K_2D$. The value of r is a maximum when D is equal to the oxygen saturation for any given temperature, and $r_{max} = -2.3K_2D_{max}$. The effect of temperature on r_{max} has been expressed by Streeter[30] as

$$r_{max} \text{ at } T_2 \text{ (degrees)} = r_{max} \text{ at } T_1 \text{ (degrees)} \times 1.016^{(T_2-T_1)}$$
$$(16\text{--}11)$$

where T_1 and T_2 are different temperatures in degrees centigrade.

The average rate or reaeration r_m between two stations, A and B,[31] can be expressed as

$$r_m = x_t + (O_b - O_a) = (L_a - L_b) + (O_b - O_a) \quad (16\text{--}12)$$

$$= x_t + (D_a - D_b) = (O_b - L_b) + (O_a - L_a) \quad (16\text{--}13)$$

in which O_a and O_b represent dissolved oxygen content, D_a and D_b represent dissolved oxygen deficiencies, L_a and L_b are the BOD at points A and B, respectively, and x_t is the total oxygen demand exerted on the stream between A and B.

The rate of reaeration in the highly polluted Illinois River between Lockport and Chillicothe has been reported by the United States Public Health Service as between 2 and 16 lb of oxygen per day per 1,000 sq ft of water surface, the variation being explicable on the basis of the preceding factors.

The rate of absorption of oxygen by water from air and from plants is shown in Fig. 16–2.[32] With knowledge of the rate of deoxygenation, or the oxygen demand of a stream, it is possible to predict, with the aid of Fig. 16–2 or with known values of K_2, the coefficient of reaeration, the rate of oxygen recovery in a stream. The results obtained by the use of the figure may not be exact because factors of turbulence,

[30] H. W. Streeter, *Modern Sewage Treatment,* Federation of Sewage Works Associations, 1938, p. 197.

[31] See also *Sewage Works Jour.,* May, 1935, pp. 534 and 539.

[32] See also *Sewage Works Jour.,* September, 1932, p. 892.

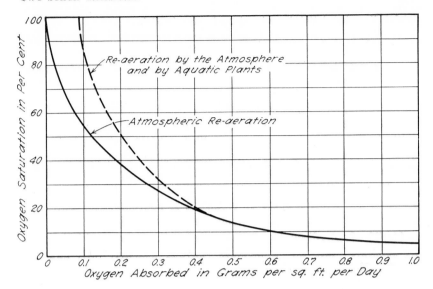

Fig. 16–2. Oxygen absorbed by water of different degrees of oxygen saturation when exposed to the air or to the oxygen produced by aquatic plants. (From *Sewage Works Jour.*, September, 1932, p. 892.)

depth, etc., are not considered. Another important factor may be the concentration of nitrites and nitrates, the oxygen of which is available and is used chemically and biologically in reoxygenation.

16–20. Two-stage oxidation. Adeney [33] showed that natural oxidation occurs in two stages: first, the carbonaceous matter, and second, the nitrogenous matter. Under some conditions all the carbonaceous matter may be oxidized before the nitrogenous matter is attacked. Streeter [34, 35] has formulated the following discontinuous equation as expressing two-stage oxidation when only *positive* values of $t - a$ are considered: [36]

$$Y = L_c(1 - 10^{-k_c t}) + L_n(1 - 10^{-k_n (t-a)}) \qquad (16\text{--}14)$$

[33] W. E. Adeney, *The Principles and Practice of the Dilution Method of Sewage Disposal,* 1926.

[34] H. W. Streeter, *Sewage Works Jour.,* March, 1935, p. 251.

[35] H. W. Streeter, *Sewage Works Jour.,* May, 1935, p. 534, and March, 1936, p. 282.

[36] *Ibid.,* p. 273.

where Y = total BOD oxidized up to any time t.

L_c and L_n are total first- and second-stage BOD, respectively.

k_c and k_n are corresponding specific rates of oxidation.

a is a "lag" constant indicating the time at which second-stage oxidation begins.

Values of k_c and k_n were reported by Streeter [37] for Illinois River conditions as 0.103 and 0.031, respectively.

Studies of an extensive series of 40-day BOD tests made by the Sanitary District of Chicago on the Illinois River show that the point of inflection or change from first stage to second stage occurs in about 9 or 10 days. It is shown also that at 20° C the specific rate of second stage or nitrification stage of oxidation is approximately one-third the rate of the first or carbonaceous stage of oxidation.

16–21. Immediate oxygen demand. First-stage oxidation can be separated into an "immediate" oxygen demand, (k_i), and the usual BOD, (k_b), which exists concurrently with it. An expression can be written [34,35] in the form

$$X_t = L_b(1 - 10^{-k_b t}) + L_i(1 - 10^{-k_i t}) \qquad (16\text{–}15)$$

where X_t = total oxygen demand satisfied up to any time, t.

L_b, L_i = total initial BOD and immediate BOD, respectively.

If a sample of river water were incubated at 20° C the value of k_b should approximate 0.1 and that of k_i about 1.6, with t in days. At other temperatures the relation would follow formula 16–4. About 97.5 per cent of the immediate oxygen demand should be satisfied in 24 hours at 20° C. If the 1-day and 5-day 20° BOD of a sample were measured, the ratio of 1-day to 5-day BOD should be about 0.3. From this fact we can estimate roughly the reduction in total oxygen, including the "immediate" demand, that would be expected to occur at any time during the first stage according to the above equation. [For an illustrative example see *Sewage Works Jour.*, March, 1935, p. 269.]

16–22. Sludge deposits. Sludge deposits in a body of water are important in affecting its oxidation. For example, the Engineering Board of Review of the Sanitary District of Chicago [38] found the total oxygen demand of the sludge in the Illinois River between La Salle and Chillicothe to be 0.282 lb per capita per day. This is

[37] *Ibid.*, p. 251.

[38] Page 171 of reference in footnote 26.

more than the 20-day oxygen demand of the sewage in the same stretch of the river.

As a result of research at Harvard University, Baity [39] has concluded:

There appears to be no correlation between the rate of oxygen demand and the amount of available dissolved oxygen in the supernatant water.

A period of septicity of a sludge deposit has no appreciable effect upon the resumption of aerobic activity when oxygen is again available.

The rate of oxygen demand is not a direct function of the depth of sludge deposit, the increase in rate being smaller than the increase in depth. The relation can be formulated as

$$Y = 2,700X^{0.485} \qquad (16\text{--}13)$$

in which Y is the rate of oxygen demand in milligrams per day per square meter of sludge deposit surface. X is the sludge depth in centimeters.

Oxygen does not appear to diffuse in a sludge deposit to a greater depth than 1 cm.

Other conclusions are drawn by Baity with respect to the effect of light, temperature, salinity, and biologic life on the oxidation of sludge deposits.

The oxygen demand by sludge deposits has been formulated by Streeter [30] as

$$L_d = \frac{p_d}{2.3k'} (1 - 10^{-k't'}) \qquad (16\text{--}17)$$

where L_d = cumulative BOD in pounds or kilograms in time t' in days.
   p_d = BOD added to the deposit in pounds or kilograms, per day.
   k' = specific rate of oxidation of the deposit.

Where k' equals 0.03 to 0.05, the value of L_d tends to become stabilized within 30 to 40 days so that the amount of BOD oxidized daily is about equal to p_d, the amount added to the deposit.

Where the period of sludge accumulation is relatively long, so that the rate of oxidation becomes substantially equal to the rate of sludge addition, the total rate of oxidation in a given stretch of a river, including that of the stream proper, the settling sludge and the deposited sludge, should approach very closely the observed rate of decrease in the average BOD between the upper and lower terminals of the stretch (i.e., $L_a - L_b$), the latter being first corrected for the effects of intermediate flow.[30]

[39] H. G. Baity, *Sewage Works Jour.*, May, 1938, p. 539.

Disposal on Land

16–23. Irrigation or farming.[40] Broad irrigation is the discharge of sewage upon the surface of the ground, from which a part of the sewage evaporates and through which the remainder percolates, ultimately to escape in surface drainage channels. Sewage farming is broad irrigation practiced with the object of raising crops. Broad irrigation can be accomplished successfully without the growing of crops, but it is seldom attempted, as some return and sometimes even a profit can be obtained from the crops raised. Broad irrigation and sewage farming differ from intermittent sand filtration in the intensity of the application of the sewage, the method of preparing the area on which the sewage is to be treated, and the care in operation. In broad irrigation and intermittent sand filtration the paramount consideration is successful disposal of the sewage. In sewage farming the paramount consideration is the growing of crops. In general, irrigation and farming return no profit except under unusual conditions.[41]

The change that occurs in the characteristics of sewage due to its filtration through the ground is the same as occurs in aerobic filtration, and the character of the water drained from beneath the soil is similar to that from an intermittent sand filter. It can be discharged into a dry watercourse without causing a nuisance. Studies have indicated that sewage irrigation is neither specially beneficial nor specially injurious to soils.[42]

The sewage farms at Paris, Berlin, and Melbourne are examples of the successful disposal of sewage by farming. Sewage farming in the United States has not been widely successful except in the Southwest, where the climate, the soil, and the need for water combine to make favorable conditions.[43] It has been practiced in other parts of the country with indifferent success.[44] One of the early sewage farms [45] in the United States was located at Pullman, Ill., in 1880. Its spectacular failure has since been a deterrent to similar experiments in unfavorable regions.

[40] See also *Sewage Works Jour.*, July, 1944, p. 729.
[41] See also B. P. Skulte, *S. and I.W.*, January, 1956, p. 36.
[42] See also E. W. Steel and E. J. M. Berg, *S. and I.W.*, November, 1954, p. 1325.
[43] See also B. P. Skulte, *S. and I.W.*, January, 1953, p. 1297.
[44] See *Tech. Bull.* 675, U. S. Department of Agriculture, 1939; and *S. and I.W.*, February, 1953, p. 244.
[45] See *Eng. News,* June 17, 1882, p. 203, and Jan. 12, 1893, p. 26.

Even under the most favorable conditions there are few cities that can show a profit from the use of sewage for farming. The water value of some sewages may, on a few farms, give a financial return, and the income from the farm may be helpful in defraying the cost of using the sewage on it.

16–24. Irrigating and fertilizing values of sewage. Raw sewage has but slightly more, if any, fertilizing value than water. It contains about 20 mg/l of nitrogen of which 50 per cent is available for plant food. Treated sewage usually contains less than this and, to prevent clogging of the soil, some treatment is usually necessary. The amounts of nitrogenous material in sewage is shown in Table 15–1. A highly nitrified trickling-filter effluent may contain up to 10 mg/l of nitrates and about 0.5 mg/l of nitrites. An activated-sludge effluent may contain up to 7 to 8 mg/l of nitrates and about 0.5 mg/l of nitrites. It can be expected that normal domestic sewage with about 250 mg/l of suspended solids will contain about 5 mg/l of phosphoric acid and about 20 mg/l of potassium.

A committee of the American Society of Civil Engineers [46] has concluded that the cost of reclaiming water from sewage and the unfavorable attitude of the public towards crops irrigated with reclaimed water will greatly limit the use of such water for irrigation in the United States for many years.

16–25. Irrigation preparation and practice.[46] A porous, sandy soil on a good slope and with good underdrainage is most suitable for broad irrigation. Impervious clay or gumbo soils are unsuitable and should not be used. They become clogged at the surface, forming pools of putrefying sewage, or in hot weather form cracks, which may permit untreated sewage to escape into the underdrains.

The sewage may be distributed to the irrigated area in any one of five ways, which are known as: (1) flooding, (2) surface irrigation, (3) ridge-and-furrow irrigation, (4) spray irrigation, (5) filtration, and (6) subsurface irrigation. In each of these methods the sewage is distributed intermittently, with relatively long periods intervening between applications. In broad irrigation and in sewage farming sewage is not applied to the land continuously. It is undesirable to convey sewage in open, unprotected ditches because of the danger of its use by cattle or unsuspecting persons for purposes to which the sewage is unsuited. Chlorination, signs, fences, and patrols, if adequate, may give some protection. Another factor to be guarded against in exposed pools of sewage is the danger from the breeding

---

[46] See also B. P. Skulte, *S. and I.W.*, January, 1956, p. 36.

of mosquitoes. Sewage may offer them a favorable environment that is unfavorable to fish, their natural enemies.

In application to land by *flooding*, sewage is distributed to a level area surrounded by low dikes. The depth of the dose may be from 1 in. to 2 ft. In *surface irrigation* the sewage is allowed to overflow from a ditch over the surface of the ground into which it sinks or over which it flows into another ditch placed at a lower elevation. This ditch conducts the sewage to a point of disposal or to another area requiring irrigation. *Ridge-and-furrow irrigation* consists in plowing a field into ridges and furrows and filling the furrows with sewage while crops are grown on or between the ridges. In *spray irrigation* primary effluent is sprayed from large nozzles over the ground in a rain-like spray. The soil should contain sufficient cover crop or growth to prevent erosion. Rates up to 100 ft per year have been used satisfactorily.[47] In *filtration* the sewage is distributed in any desired fashion onto the surface and is collected by a system of underdrains after it has filtered through the soil. In *subsurface irrigation* the sewage is applied to the land through a system of open-joint pipes laid immediately below the surface, similarly to a system of underdrains. Combinations of and modifications of these methods are sometimes made. Underdrains may be used in connection with any of these forms of distribution.

The preparation of the ground consists in constructing ditches or dikes, where required; grading to prevent pooling; laying underdrains; and grubbing and clearing the land. The main carriers, in open channels, may be excavated in open earth or earth lined with an impervious material. The distribution from the main carriers to groups of laterals may be controlled by hand-operated stop planks. If the soil has a tendency to become water-logged, it may be relieved by underdrains installed at depths up to 3 to 6 ft, and 40 to 100 ft apart. The tile underdrains may discharge into open ditches excavated for the purpose, which serve also to drain the land. Drains should be used where the ground water is within 4 ft of the surface, and the open ditches should be cut below the drains to keep the ground water out of them. Four- or 6-in. open-joint farm tile may be used for the underdrains. The porosity of the soil will be increased by cultivation.

Before being turned on to the land, sewage should be screened and heavy-settling particles should be removed. The rate of application

[47] See C. D. Henry and others, *S. and I.W.*, February, 1954, p. 123; N. H. Sanborn, *S. and I.W.*, September, 1953, p. 1034; and J. W. Bell, *Public Works*, September, 1955, p. 111.

may be increased as the intensity of the preliminary treatment is increased. The rate at which sewage may be applied is dependent also on the nature of the soil, and may vary between 4,000 and 30,000 gal per acre per day, although higher rates have been used with the effluent from treatment plants and on favorable soil. The sewage should be applied intermittently in doses, the time between doses varying between one day and two or three weeks or more, dependent on the weather and the condition of the soil. The methods of dosing vary as widely as the rates. The dose may be applied continuously for one or two weeks with correspondingly long rests, or it may be applied with frequent intermittency alternated with short rests, interspersed with long rest periods at longer intervals of time. The rate of application of the dose to the land, between rest periods, is about 10,000 to 150,000 gal per acre per day. This is between 2½ and 5 times as fast as the average rate of filtration. The rate of the application of the sewage is also dependent on the weather and may vary widely between seasons. It is obvious that a rain-soaked pasture cannot receive a large dose of sewage without danger of undue flooding. One of the principal difficulties with the treatment or disposal of sewage by broad irrigation is that the greatest load of sewage must be cared for in wet seasons when the ground is least able to absorb the additional moisture.

16–26. The crop. From a sanitary viewpoint no crops which come in contact with sewage should be cultivated on a sewage farm. Such products as lettuce, strawberries, asparagus, and potatoes should not be grown. Grains, fruits, and nuts are grown successfully so long as they do not come in contact with sewage. Italian rye grass and other forms of hay are grown with the best success as they will stand a large amount of water without injury. The raising of stock is advisable for sewage farms where hay and grain are cultivated. The stock should be fed on the fodder raised on the irrigated lands and should not be allowed to graze on the crops during the time that they are being irrigated. This restriction is due as much to the danger of injury to the distributing ditches and the formation of bogs by the trampling of cattle as to considerations for the health of the cattle.

16–27. Oxidation ponds, stabilization ponds, or lagoons.[48] A stabilization pond, oxidation pond, or lagoon is a pool or pond constructed and maintained under specified conditions for the treatment

[48] See also C. R. Griffith, *S. and I.W.*, February, 1955, p. 180. P. J. A. Zeller, *Proc. 19th Texas Water Works Short School*, 1937. F. E. Giesecke and P. J. A. Zeller, *Bull.* 47, Texas Engineering Experiment Station, 1939. *Sewage Works*

of sewage, industrial wastes, treatment-plant effluents, or sludge. Treatment in a lagoon depends on such conditions as sunlight, algae, evaporation, percolation, sedimentation, and oxidation. It results in the biological stabilization of the influent, oxidation, nitrification, and possibly the reduction of liquid volume. Treatment in an oxidation pond may produce an effluent that will not require further dilution for its disposal. Satisfactory experience with lagoons was reported early in the South and Southwest of the United States.[49] Favorable experiences have been reported subsequently from northern [50] and midwestern states, from Canada,[51] and from world-wide sources of information.[52] A result has been an increase of interest in oxidation ponds and an accelerating trend towards their use.

Advantages of the use of lagoons include: successful disposal of waste liquids; evaporation of some liquid and possibly percolation of other portions; effectiveness as an equalizing basin to absorb rapid fluctuations in quantity of flow and in quality of waste; low first cost where conditions are favorable; suitability of lagoon contents for use in some industrial processes, such as coke quenching or condenser cooling; and, under favorable conditions, the provision of a wildlife refuge. Among the disadvantages may be included: a potential hazard to the public health, comfort, or decency, under conditions unfavorable for the use of a lagoon; possible high cost of maintenance; and possible pollution of underground water and adjacent surface water. Pollution of surface waters may result from wildlife activities or from overflow or flooding of the lagoon. Under some conditions silting, overnitrification, overgrowth of algae, weeds, or other life, and the breeding of mosquitoes or other flying insects may result.

Jour., May, 1946, p. 433, and November, 1948, p. 1025. G. J. Hopkins and J. K. Neal, *Proc. 11th Ind. Wastes Conf.*, Purdue University, May, 1956, p. 197. W. W. Towne and others, *S. and I.W.*, April, 1957, p. 377. See also Sect. 24-15.

[49] See P. J. A. Zeller, *Proc. 19th Texas Water Works Short School*, 1937; and F. E. Giesecke and P. J. A. Zeller, *Bull.* 47, Texas Engineering Experiment Station, 1939.

[50] See also W. W. Towne and others, *S. and I.W.*, April, 1957, p. 377, with bibliography.

[51] One was recommended for Regina, Sask., Canada, population 90,000.

[52] See D. E. French, *Water and Sewage Works*, December, 1955, p. 538, and June 15, 1956, p. R-261. *Public Works*, February, 1956, p. 136. W. Van Heuvelen and J. H. Svore, *S. and I.W.*, June, 1954, p. 771; and 7th edition of this book, p. 356. See also *S. and I.W.*, June, 1955, p. 752; and R. J. Ellison and R. L. Smith, *Public Works*, March, 1954, p. 89.

Putrefactive odors are sometimes controlled, and treatment is made effective, by the addition of sufficient sodium nitrate to care for about 20 per cent of the BOD in the effluent. The breeding of flying insects, especially of mosquitoes, may be prevented or controlled by breeding top-feeding minnows in the lagoon when there is sufficient oxygen dissolved in the water.

Results from the lagooning of sewage or plant effluent may include: a biologically stabilized effluent saturated, or nearly saturated with oxygen; loss by evaporation of 15 to 20 in. of water annually, depending on the climate; and loss by percolating, in rare instances, of 100 ft or more, of water annually.[53] The effluent should be low in settleable solids.

16–28. Design of oxidation ponds. Oxidation ponds may be classified as those which: (1) absorb needed oxygen directly from the air, or (2) receive their oxygen primarily through biological activity and photosynthesis. Rates of oxygen absorption in the first type can be computed on the basis discussed in Sect. 15–10. The rate of oxygen absorption by photosynthesis has been formulated rationally by Oswald and Gotaas[54] as

$$D = \frac{d \times h \times C_c}{1,000S \times F \times T_c} \tag{16–18}$$

$$= \frac{d \times h \times L_t}{1,000S \times F \times P \times T_c} \tag{16–19}$$

where S = insolation in gm calories per sq cm per day.
A = surface area exposed to light.
D = detention period, days.
$E_s = SAD$ = total light energy, usually in langleys.
C_c = concentration of algae.
L_t = first-stage BOD.
d = depth of pond; = $(\log_e I_i)/(\alpha\, C_c)$ (16–20)
T_c = temperature coefficient.
F = efficiency of light utilization.
h = heat of combustion of algae.
$P = L_t/C_c$.
I_i = incident light intensity.
α = specific absorption coefficient.

[53] C. D. Parker and others, *S. and I.W.*, June, 1950, p. 760.
[54] W. J. Oswald and H. B. Gotaas, "Photosynthesis in Sewage Treatment," *Proc. Am. Soc. Civil Engrs.*, Vol. 81, Paper 686, May, 1955.

An example will illustrate the application of the formula.

Find the required depth of a lagoon, depending on photosynthesis, if the sewage has a BOD of 125 mg/l; $I_i = 1,500$ ft candles; $P = 1.25$; and $\alpha = 1.2 \times 10^{-3}$.

Solution.
$$d = \frac{\log_e 1,500}{1.2 \times 10^{-3} C_c} = \frac{6,000}{C_c} \text{ (approx.)}$$

but
$$C_c = L_t/P = 125/1.25 = 100$$

then
$$d = 6,000/100 = 60 \text{ cm or 2 ft (about)}$$

Among features to be considered in the design of an oxidation pond are: (1) location of the pond at a distance of one-half mile or more to leeward of a residence; (2) a minimum holding period for a Type 1 pond of about four months in extreme cold weather; (3) depths of liquid not less than 2 ft, and preferably not less than 3 ft to discourage protuberant weeds; depths greater than 5 ft may inhibit oxidation; and (4) a surface area of one acre per 100 population, which is equivalent to a BOD load of about 17 lb per day per acre. Heavier loading is sometimes permitted with a retention period of at least 20 days in Type 1 ponds, or not more than 60,000 gal or 50 lb BOD per acre per day. Primary treatment, usually including anaerobic digestion, is often necessary preceding lagooning, to prevent the deposition of sludge, the sealing off of percolation, or the formation of scum. Practical considerations in the design of Type 2 ponds have indicated that regardless of the showings by the formulas, detention periods should not be less than one day for summer periods nor more than six days for winter conditions. It may be calculated that under summer conditions Type 2 ponds should operate successfully as far north as beyond the Arctic Circle.

16–29. Fish and water fowl.[55]   The cultivation of fish in dilute sewage-plant effluents can be done successfully. The possibilities of growing water fowl have been suggested. It is significant that the food value of fish and fowl that can be produced in sewage-fed ponds may exceed the food value of vegetables or grain that can be cultivated on the same area. The nature of the effluent from some treatment processes is such as to be more available for fish than for plants, and some algae that are nourished by the sewage provide food for fish.

Requisite conditions for success are settled sewage in a pond not

[55] See also *Sewage Works Jour.*, January, 1936, p. 150; V. E. Davison, *Farmers' Bull.*, U. S. Department of Agriculture, 1938; and S. F. Snieszko, *A Symposium on Hydrobiology*, University of Wisconsin, 1940, p. 227.

more than about 6 ft deep, adequate diluting water equal to two or three times the volume of sewage, and, under some conditions, turbulence to maintain dissolved oxygen. It is desirable to permit diluting water to enter at a number of places to assure adequate distribution and mixing of the sewage solids. It is essential to maintain an oxygen content of at least 4 mg/l, and to exclude toxic substances, oily wastes, and materials that might clog gills or wings. The ponds must be kept free from sludge deposits. It is estimated that the treated sewage from 1,000 to 2,000 persons per acre can be cared for provided the dilution and reaeration are adequate. The utilization of sewage in a fish pond, like its utilization in farming, is not to be considered as a method of treatment nor as a method of disposal. It is, however, a method for the recovery of some value from sewage.

16–30. Hygienic aspects of raw sludge disposal.[56]   The hygienic aspects of the disposal of sewage and of sludge (see also Sect. 24–5) on land are of importance to the public health. Properly managed sewage farms have been operated successfully without reported effect on the farm workers or neighboring residents. All that seems to be necessary is the exercise of care to avoid the ingestion of sewage or of sewage-contaminated material or contact with open cuts, sores, or mucous membrane, and to practice the principles of good personal hygiene. Successful experience abroad does not confirm the misgivings expressed in the United States.[57]   Even in this country liquid digested sludge and dried sludge are spread on farm lands in some regions,[58] but the spreading of wet, raw sludge or septic-tank sludge is not considered to be good practice.[59] The picture must not be painted too brightly, however, as a badly operated farm may be an abomination, dangerous and noisome to surrounding areas. Stagnant pools may offer breeding places for mosquitoes, and improperly drained land may pollute water supplies.

Mom and Schaeffer [60] have reported that typhoid bacteria are to be found in sewage and in digested sludge from an Imhoff tank. No typhoid fever organisms were found in sludge after drying. Where the irrigant has a high coliform count the vegetables have exhibited high coliform flora.[61]   Chlorine residuals, as normally maintained in

[56] See also *Sewage Works Jour.*, May, 1945, p. 650.

[57] See also A. M. Rawn, *Proc. 18th International Congress of Agric.*, Dresden, 1938.

[58] See also *S. and I.W.*, December, 1952, p. 1546.

[59] See L. W. Van Kleeck, *Water and Sewage Works,* November, 1952, p. 463.

[60] C. P. Mom and C. O. Schaeffer, *Sewage Works Jour.*, July, 1940, p. 715.

[61] N. N. Norman and P. W. Kabler, *S. and I.W.*, May, 1953, p. 605.

sewage-treatment practice, are reported as insufficient to yield an effluent free from tubercle bacilli.[62] Insufficient information is available to show that poliomyelitis is, or is not, conveyed by sewage or sludge.[63]

A Committee of the American Society of Civil Engineers recommended that: [64]

(a) Raw sewage or its untreated solids content, or the soil which has recently been irrigated, shall not come in contact with foodstuffs designated for human consumption; nor shall livestock graze on pasture irrigated therewith.

(b) Forage crops which are to be harvested and cured may be irrigated with the untreated effluent from adequate subsidence tanks.

(c) For use in the cultivation of human foodstuff, particularly that to be eaten raw, the water reclaimed from sewage must be well oxidized and thoroughly sterilized at all times, and

(d) Sewage solids to be used as fertilizer must be digested and dried, or if undigested may be kiln-dried at temperatures which will destroy all inimical pathogenic organisms.

The findings of Rudolfs [65] and others after a survey of the literature on the survival of pathogenic organisms in soil and in sludges, and after an investigation of the contamination and decontamination of vegetables grown in polluted soil, do not conflict with the preceding statements except possibly in the following: ". . . if sewage irrigation or night-soil application is stopped one month before harvest, the fruit, if eaten raw, would not be likely vectors for the transmission of human bacterial enteric diseases."

16–31. Subsoil irrigation. The application of septic-tank effluent, or a better effluent, to subsurface sand filters is widely practiced in unsewered areas. A suggested layout for a rural residence disposal plan is shown in Fig. 16-3.[66, 67] The rate of filtration recommended by various authorities [68] is about 1 gal per sq ft of sand surface per day, using sand with an effective size of 0.25 to 0.50 mm and a uniformity coefficient not greater than about 4.0.

[62] See *Sewage Works Jour.*, September, 1950, p. 1123.

[63] See V. W. Langworthy, *S. and I.W.*, March, 1953, p. 290.

[64] *Trans. Am. Soc. Civil Engrs.*, October, 1942, p. 1652.

[65] W. Rudolfs and others, *S. and I.W.*, October, 1956, p. 1261 ff.

[66] See also J. E. Kiker, Jr., *Bull.* 23, Florida Engineering Experiment Station, 1948.

[67] See also *S. and I.W.*, September, 1950, p. 1147.

[68] See also J. A. Salvato, Jr., *S. and I.W.*, August, 1955, p. 909.

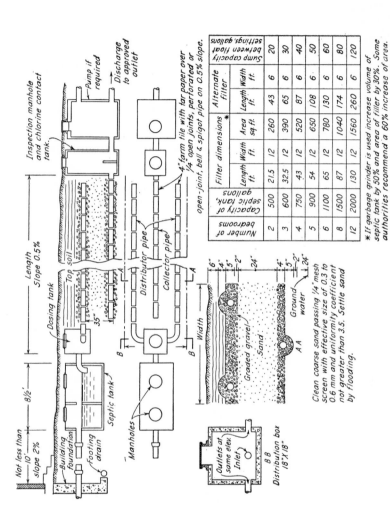

Number of bedrooms	Capacity of septic tank, gallons	Filter dimensions			Alternate filter		Sump capacity between float settings, gallons
		Length ft.	Width ft.	Area sq ft.	Length ft.	Width ft.	
2	500	21.5	12	260	43	6	20
3	600	32.5	12	390	65	6	30
4	750	43	12	520	87	6	40
5	900	54	12	650	108	6	50
6	1100	65	12	780	130	6	60
8	1500	87	12	1040	174	6	80
12	2000	130	12	1560	260	6	120

* If garbage grinder is used increase volume of septic tank by 50% and area of filter by 30%. Some authorities recommend a 60% increase of area.

Clean coarse sand passing ¼" mesh screen with effective size of 0.3 to 0.6 mm and uniformity coefficient not greater than 3.5. Settle sand by flooding.

Fig. 16-3. Suggested layout for residential, subsurface disposal plant. (Based on J. A. Salvato, Jr., in *S. and I.W.*, August, 1955, p. 909.)

Conditions affecting the size and length of subsurface distribution pipe and percolating trenches are the rate of sewage flow and the absorptive characteristics of the soil. Kiker [66] recommends 4-in. agricultural drains in an 18-in. trench for a percolation coefficient of less than 0.4; 24-in. for a coefficient between 0.4 and 1.0; and 30-in. for a coefficient between 1.0 and 2.3. The *percolation coefficient* is the reciprocal of the rate, in gallons per day per square foot of trench bottom, at which the sewage may be safely applied to the field. It can be computed from the expression

$$C = (t + 6.24)/29 \qquad\qquad (16\text{--}21)$$

where C = percolation coefficient.

t = maximum time required for water to fall 1 in. during percolation tests in saturated soil, minutes.

Some coefficients given by Kiker are: coarse sand or fine gravel, 0.3; fine sand or light loam, 0.3 to 0.16; sandy clay or heavy loam, 0.6 to 1.3; medium clay, 1.3 to 2.0; and tight clay or rock, above 2.0. Quenelle [69] suggests the determination of the rate of absorption by a different method involving observations of the rate at which water must be poured into an 8-in. diameter hole containing a 6-in. depth of 1-in. or 2-in. diameter gravel, in order to maintain a constant depth of about 6 in. of water in the hole.

In laying distribution tile it is desirable that the slope be between 0.1 and 0.3 per cent to give both adequate distribution and adequate time for percolation of water through the joints in the line. Where the length of underdrain is more than 200 to 300 ft a dosing tank is recommended to assure filling of the entire length of the tile.

16–32. Ground-water replenishment. In some suitable areas sewage-treatment effluents have been used for the replenishment of ground water.[70] Tests of five different soils showed variations in rates of infiltration after 60 days of continuous tests, from 26 ft to 0.75 ft per day.

[69] O. G. Quenelle, *Public Works,* April, 1954, p. 79.

[70] See G. T. Orlob and R. G. Butler, *Jour. San. Eng. Sect.,* American Society of Civil Engineers, Paper 1002, June, 1956.

Chapter 17

Screening

17-1. Purpose. The first step in the treatment of sewage is coarse screening in order to remove the larger particles of floating or suspended matter. Screens and sedimentation basins are used to prevent the clogging of sewers, channels, and treatment works; to avoid the clogging of and injuries to mechanical equipment; to overcome the accumulation of sludge banks; to minimize the absorption of oxygen in diluting water; and to intercept unsightly floating matter.

Fine screening may take the place of sedimentation where insufficient space is available for tanks and it is desired to remove only a small portion of the suspended matter. Recent practice in the United States has tended to restrict the field of fine screening to treatment requiring less than 10 per cent removal of suspended matter, thus eliminating screens from the field covered by plain sedimentation tanks. Settled sewage is of better quality than screened sewage, and the improvement in quality may be secured more economically by sedimentation than by screening.

17-2. Types of screens. The definitions of some types of screens, as proposed by the American Public Health Association, follow: A *bar screen* or *rack* is composed of parallel bars. A *mesh screen* is composed of a fabric, usually wire. A *grating* consists of two sets of parallel bars in the same plane in sets intersecting at right angles. A *band screen* consists of an endless perforated band or belt which passes over upper and lower rollers. A *perforated-plate screen* is made of an endless band of perforated plates similar to a band screen. A *wing screen* has radial vanes uniformly spaced which rotate on a horizontal axis. A *disk screen* consists of a circular, perforated disk, with or without a central truncated cone of similar material mounted in the center. Allen [1] gives the following definitions: A *drum screen*

---

[1] K. Allen, *Trans. Am. Soc. Civil Engrs.*, Vol. 78, 1915, p. 880.

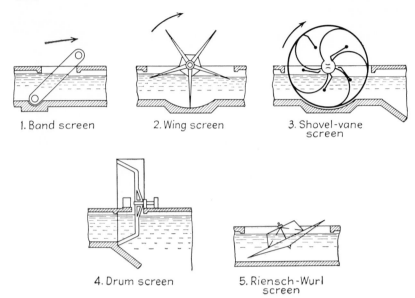

1. Band screen   2. Wing screen   3. Shovel-vane
                                                   screen

4. Drum screen   5. Riensch-Wurl
                           screen

Fig. 17–1.   Moving screens.   (From K. Allen, *Trans. Am. Soc. Civil Engrs.*,
Vol. 78, 1915, p. 880.)

is a cylinder or cone of perforated plates or wire mesh which rotates
on a horizontal axis.   A *shovel-vane* screen is similar to a wing screen
with semicircular wings.   Some screens are shown in Fig. 17–1.   Bar
screens are shown in Figs. 17–2 and 17–3.   A *cage screen* consists of
a rectangular box with the sides made up of parallel bars with the
upstream side of the cage or box omitted.   The bottom and the top
may be either a solid or perforated steel plate.   Bars are undesirable
in the bottom and the top because of difficulty in cleaning.

Screens can be classified as fixed, movable, or moving.   Fixed
screens are permanently set in position and must be cleaned by rakes
or teeth that are pulled between the bars.   Movable screens are stationary when in operation but are lifted from the sewage for the
purpose of cleaning.   Moving screens are in continuous motion when
in operation and are cleaned while in motion.   Fixed bar screens may
be set either vertical or inclined.   They are rarely set horizontal.

Movable screens with a cage or box at the bottom are sometimes
used.   The bottom should be of solid material to prevent the forcing
of screenings through it when the screen is being raised for cleaning.
A mesh screen should be used only under special circumstances be-

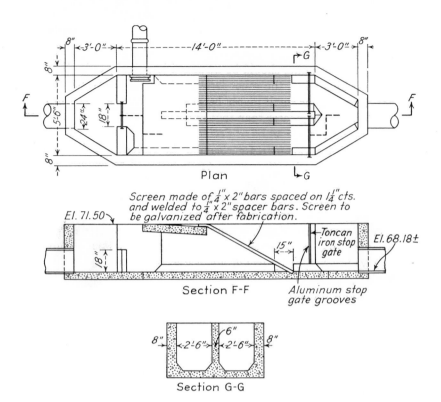

Plan

Screen made of $\frac{1}{4}$" x 2" bars spaced on $1\frac{1}{4}$" cts. and welded to $\frac{1}{4}$" x 2" spacer bars. Screen to be galvanized after fabrication.

El. 71.50

18"

Toncan iron stop gate

El. 68.18±

15"

Section F-F

Aluminum stop gate grooves

8" | 2'-6" | 6" | 2'-6" | 8"

Section G-G

Fig. 17–2. Screen chamber at Mendota, Ill.

Fig. 17–3. Bar screen and grit chamber at Calumet sewage-treatment plant, Sanitary District of Chicago.

399

cause of the difficulty in cleaning. Screens that must be raised from the sewage for cleaning should be arranged in pairs in order that one may be working when the other is being cleaned. Movable screens are not desirable for small plants because the labor involved in raising and lowering is greater than that in cleaning with a rake and such screens are more likely to be neglected. In a large plant rakes operated by hand are too small for cleaning the screens. A fixed screen is sometimes cleaned with moving teeth fastened to endless chains. The teeth pass between parallel bars and comb out the screenings. If the screen chamber in a small plant is too deep for accessibility a movable cage or box screen may be used.

Moving screens are usually of fine mesh or perforated plates. They are kept moving in order to allow continuous cleaning. They are cleaned by brushes, or by jets of air, water, or steam.

The word *screen* is not strictly applicable to a set of parallel bars, which is more properly called a *rack*. Unfortunately, however, the term *screen* has been adopted in sewerage practice and is applied to racks as well as mesh screens and grids.

17–3. Basic details of bar-screen design. Extracts from recommendations of the Joint Committee (see Sect. 5–2) concerning bar-screen design are:

Clear openings between bars should be from 1 to 2 in.

Clear openings for mechanically cleaned screens may be as small as $\frac{5}{8}$ in.

For hand-raked bar screens the screen chamber should be designed to provide a velocity through the screen of 1 f.p.s. at average rate of flow. Maximum velocities during wet-weather periods should not exceed 2.5 f.p.s. for mechanically cleaned screens.

The effective velocity shall be determined by considering a vertical projection of the screen openings . . . from a point on the screen level with the invert of the channel up to the flow line at the screen design flow.

The screen channel invert shall be 3 to 6 in. below the invert of the incoming sewer.[2]

Hand-cleaned screens, except for emergency use, should be placed on a slope of 30° to 45° with the horizontal.

The channel preceding and following the screen shall be filleted to prevent stranding and sedimentation of solids.

All mechanical units that are operated by timing devices should be provided with auxiliary float controls which will set the cleaning mechanisms in operation at predetermined high water marks. These auxiliary controls should operate independently of the regular controls.

[2] It is not always possible to meet this requirement for small sewers. An example is shown in Fig. 17–2.

17–4. Sizes of openings. The area or size of the opening of a screen is dependent on the kind of sewage to be treated and the objective to be attained.

Large screens with openings between 1½ in. and 6 in. protect pumps, dosing devices, conduits, and valves from large objects, such as pieces of timber and dead animals. The amount of material collected on large screens is variable and is usually small.

Medium-size screens with openings ¼ in. to 2 in. prepare sewage for passage through pumps, dosing devices, and treatment devices.

Fine screens usually have openings in the shape of slots ¼ in. to 1/16 in. wide and ¼ in. to 2 in. long. They can remove solids preparatory to the disposal of sewage by dilution; protect trickling filters, complex dosing apparatus, and sewage farms; prepare sewage for the activated-sludge process; and diminish possible difficulties with scum in digestion tanks.

17–5. Coarse screens or racks. Racks are commonly made of long, parallel, rectangular or modified trapezoidal shaped bars placed on a slope of 30° to 60° from the horizontal. The flatter angle is sometimes preferred to make cleaning easier and to give better velocities through the screen and through the screen chamber. Racks of this type are shown in Figs. 17–2, 17–3, and 17–4.

The shape of the bar in a bar screen depends on the unsupported length of the bar and the assumed load to be supported on it. The stresses in the bar are a result of impact and bending, caused by blows in cleaning and by the depth of sewage backed up when the screen is clogged. Head losses up to 2½ ft may be allowed in operation and provided for in design. A generous allowance should be made in addition for the indeterminate stresses in cleaning. The screen should be supported only at top and bottom, since intermediate supports in a bar screen are undesirable unless they are so arranged as not to interfere with the teeth of the cleaning devices.

The bars are placed with the small dimension transverse to the direction of flow of sewage. Occasionally the bars are made trapezoidal in transverse cross section, the longer axis being parallel to the flow of sewage and the smallest side downstream. The effect is to create an opening that is self-cleaning. It is desirable that the bar be placed on a slope in order to obtain a low velocity through the screen and to cause the screenings to accumulate near the surface of the sewage. The slope is limited since the smaller the slope the longer the bars must be and the greater the difficulty of hand cleaning. Small

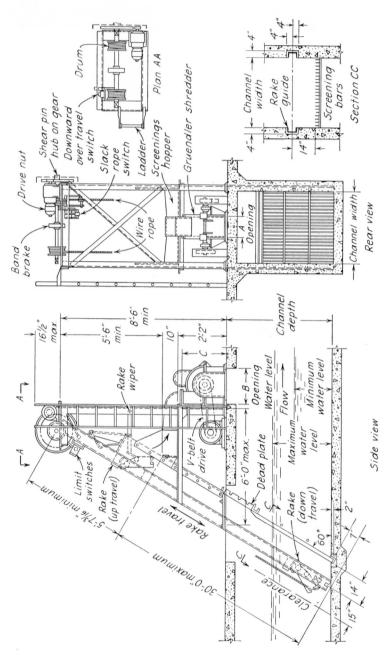

Fig. 17–4. Mechanically cleaned bar screen. (Courtesy Link Belt Co.)

slopes will tend to make the screens self-cleaning. As the screen clogs, the increasing head of sewage will push the accumulated screenings up the screen. Flat screens in a vertical position are not desirable because of the difficulty of cleaning and the accumulation of material at inaccessible points. If a screen is placed in a horizontal plane with the flow of sewage downward cleaning is difficult, solid matter is forced through the screen, and loss of head is increased. An upward flow through a horizontal screen is undesirable as the material is caught in a position inaccessible for cleaning. Movable screens are more easily handled when placed in a vertical plane.

The horizontal velocity through a screen chamber should not fall below 2 fps for grit-bearing sewage, or below 1 fps for other sewage, to avoid undesirable sedimentation in the screen chamber. Recommended velocities through the openings in a screen are stated in Sect. 17–3. Higher velocities tend to force undesirable solids through the screen. The submerged area of the surface of a screen, including bars and openings, should be about 200 per cent of the cross-sectional area of the approach sewer for separate sewers, and 300 per cent for combined sewers.

In the design of a screen, conditions to be considered to meet area, velocity, depth, and other requirements include: rates and depths of flow, width of channel, slope of screen and velocity through it, and dimensions of bars and of openings between them. These factors will affect the performance of the screen, the head loss through it, and the frequency of cleaning required. A net submerged screen area of not less than 2 sq ft per mgd should be allowed for separate sewers, and 3 sq ft per mgd for combined sewers. An example of the design of a screen chamber is given in Sect. 17–7.

In large plants it may be desirable to construct two or more screens in parallel to care for the fluctuations of flow, to provide better velocities through the screens, and to permit cleaning or repairs to one while the other is in operation.

17–6. The screen chamber. The length and width of the screen are fixed to give desirable dimensions to the screen chamber and to provide the necessary opening in the screen. The width of the screen chamber and the screen should be the same. The screen chamber should be sufficiently long to prevent eddies around the screen. If the dimensions permit an undesirable velocity in the chamber they should be changed. A sufficient length of screen should be provided to project above the sewage for the accumulation of screenings. The bars may be carried up and bent over at the top to simplify the removal of screenings.

Coarse screens are usually placed upstream from other parts of a treatment works. They may be followed by grit chambers or finer screens. Coarse screens are sometimes placed as a protection above medium or fine screens. In sewage containing grit the finer screens may be placed downstream from the grit chamber. Provision should be made for bypassing the screen chamber to permit cleaning and repairs. Screen chambers are sometimes designed in duplicate to allow the cleaning of one while the other is in operation, and to care for high rates of flow. Where a plant bypass is to be installed the entrance to it may be placed immediately upstream from the screen chamber.

17–7. Screen-chamber design. Conditions involved in a screen-chamber design include: (1) the rate of flow, Q, (2) the dimensions and spacings of the bars, (3) the velocity of flow normal to the screen, V_s, (4) the velocity of flow through the screen chamber, V_c, (5) the width of the screen openings, W_s, (6) the width of the screen chamber, W_c, (7) the angle of the screen with the horizontal, α, (8) the submerged length of the screen, l_s, and (9) the depth of flow in the screen chamber, d_c. All of these factors are interrelated so that the assumption of the magnitude of two or more may fix the magnitude of the others without fixing all of them. In design, therefore, assumptions are made concerning controlling factors and those that are dependent on them are computed. If not within proper limits new assumptions are made and dependent parameters are computed until a satisfactory design is attained.

Example. Let it be desired to design a bar screen chamber through which maximum, average, and minimum rates of flow are, respectively, 15, 7.5 and 3 cfs; the screen is such that there is one more space than there are bars; the outlet is controlled by a proportional weir such that depth of flow is directly proportional to rate of flow; and design dimensions must conform to requirements in Sects. 17–3 and 17–5.

Solution. Assume $\alpha = 30°$; $V_s = 1.0$; and that there are 20 bars each $\frac{1}{4} \times 2$ in. on $1\frac{1}{4}$-in. centers.

Then
$$W_c = 21 \times 1 + 20 \times \frac{1}{4} = 26 \text{ in. or } 2.17 \text{ ft}$$
and
$$W_s = 21 \times 1 = 21 \text{ in. or } 1.75 \text{ ft}$$
Then
$$\text{max } l_s = Q_{max}/(W_s \times V_s) = 15/(1.75 \times 1) = 8.56 \text{ ft}$$

Then

$$\text{max } d_c = 8.56/2 = 4.28 \text{ ft}$$

and

$$\text{max } V_c = 15/(2.17 \times 4.28) = 1.61 \text{ fps}$$

Since the depth varies with the rate of flow, velocities will remain constant for all rates of flow and conditions remain within the specified limits.

17–8. Hand-cleaned racks. Fixed racks, cleaned by hand, are constructed so that the teeth of a specially designed rake will fit between the bars of the rack without striking the bar supports and spacers, and so that the operator can pull the material up and toward him to dump it on the floor at the top of the screen, as indicated in Figs. 17–2 and 17–3. The floor on which the screenings are deposited should be provided with drainage either by a grid through which water can drop back into the sewage, or a flat, perforated iron plate with a drainage channel beneath it which can be easily cleaned. Facilities must be provided also for prompt removal and disposal of the screenings.

17–9. Mechanically cleaned racks.[3] Mechanically cleaned racks consist of fixed racks that are cleaned by moving rakes attached to an endless chain, and other forms of mechanisms. The rakes discharge the screenings into a receptacle in which they may be carried to disposal, or they may be dropped from the rakes into a comminutor which returns the ground screenings to the plant influent. One type of mechanically cleaned rack is shown in Fig. 17–4. A float-controlled device is available that operates the screen mechanism automatically when sufficient screenings accumulate to build up a predetermined head differential above and below the screen.

Continuous operation of the cleaning mechanism keeps the screen clean and avoids the fluctuations in flow otherwise caused by clogging of the screen. It consumes more power, however, and causes greater wear of the mechanism. Intermittent operation automatically controlled is common practice.

17–10. Fine screens. Most fine screens are patented, mechanically cleaned devices that include four types: the Riensch-Wurl, the Dorrco, the Tark, and the Rex. The Riensch-Wurl screen and a special type of Dorrco drum screen are shown in Fig. 17–1. The Tark or Link-Belt screen is of the drum type, the sewage passing through the perforated surface of a cylindrical drum turning slowly

---

[3] See also F. L. Flood, *Water and Sewage Works*, May, 1954, p. R-219.

with its horizontal axis at right angles to the direction of flow of the sewage. The screenings are carried to the top of the drum from which they are swept by brushes mounted on an endless chain and traveling parallel to the axis of the drum. The sewage that has passed into the drum leaves it through one end and at right angles to its original direction of flow. The Rex screen is a band screen consisting of sections of screening plates fastened to an endless chain. The plates, in turn, are cleaned by revolving brushes.

If fine screens are to be installed they should be purchased on specifications fixing the materials, strength, durability, and performance with guarantees of power-consumption limits and head loss through the screen.

17–11. Micro-screens. Micro-screens consist of very fine-mesh wire cloth supported on a hollow cylinder into which the liquid flows through the meshes of the cloth. Such screens have been used in a few cases in place of secondary or final sedimentation tanks to remove settleable solids from secondary treatment plant effluents. One such screen is reported [4] to be made of stainless steel fabric with one million holes per square inch, each with a nominal opening of 0.045 mm. The capital cost of such a screen, at Lufton, England,[5] is reported as less than that of sand filters. It is reported to have reduced suspended matter 66 per cent, BOD 36 per cent, and COD 20 per cent.

17–12. Grinding of screenings.[6] The grinding of screenings and their return to the sewage for subsequent treatment is widely practiced. Difficulties resulting from such treatment include increased scum troubles and possibly a tendency towards acid fermentation in digestion tanks. A common grinder for large installations is of the hammer mill type, some capacities of which are stated in Table 17–1. A triturator is a grinder that depends on cutting knives for shredding the screenings.

To avoid nuisances from odor, moisture, and other causes the grinder should be completely enclosed and the ground screenings should be returned to the sewage through a pipe. The Griductor,[7] the Comminutor,[8] and the Barminutor are proprietary devices, the first

[4] See *Water and Sewage Works,* June, 1953, p. 239, and August, 1954, p. 356.

[5] See also S. C. Evans and F. W. Roberts, *The Water and Sanitary Engineer* (Br.), December, 1952, p. 286.

[6] See also F. L. Flood, *Water and Sewage Works,* May, 1954, p. R-219.

[7] See *Sewage Works Jour.,* September, 1942, p. 1188.

[8] See also *Mun. San.,* August, 1936, p. 275; and *Sewage Works Jour.,* January, 1941, p. 145.

Table 17–1

CAPACITIES OF JEFFREY SWINGING-HAMMER SCREENINGS GRINDER

(H. J. N. Hodgson, *Sewage and Trade Wastes Treatment,*
Adelaide, Australia, 1938.)

Size of Machine, in.	Overall Dimensions, Not Including Motor	Size of Motor, hp	Capacity, lb of wet screenings per hr
20 × 12	3 ft 9½ in. × 29 in.	29	1,800
24 × 18	4 ft 9 in. × 33 in.	40	3,500
30 × 24	5 ft 10½ in. × 39½ in.	50	4,500

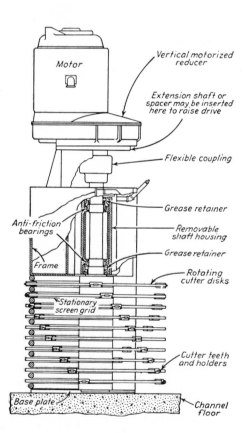

Fig. 17–5. Sectional view of a Griductor. (Courtesy Infilco.)

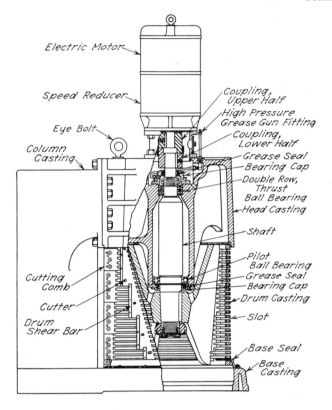

Electric Motor

Speed Reducer

Eye Bolt

Column Casting

Coupling, Upper Half
High Pressure Grease Gun Fitting
Coupling, Lower Half
Grease Seal
Bearing Cap
Double Row, Thrust Ball Bearing
Head Casting
Shaft
Pilot Ball Bearing
Grease Seal
Bearing Cap
Drum Casting
Slot

Cutting Comb
Cutter
Drum Shear Bar

Base Seal
Base Casting

Fig. 17–6. Sectional view of a Comminutor. (Courtesy Chicago Pump Co.)

two being shown in Figs. 17–5 and 17–6, respectively. The Comminutor is an almost completely submerged, slotted drum that rotates in the channel, grinding solids to pass $\frac{3}{16}$-, $\frac{1}{4}$-, or $\frac{3}{8}$-in. slots, without removing them from the sewage. All such proprietary screenings grinders obviate the need for screens.

17–13. Quantity of screenings. The amount of materials removed by screens varies between 0.5 and 30 cu ft, more or less, per million gallons of sewage screened, depending on the character of the sewage and the sizes of the screen openings. The screenings collected on different-size openings are reported in Fig. 17–7.[9] The nature of the sewage and the type and size of screen openings so greatly affect the quantity of screenings collected that general state-

[9] See also *Sewage Works Jour.*, April, 1931, p. 223.

ments may be of little value in the estimation of screenings to be expected. However, twenty-two municipal screening plants handling raw sewage show the following: on racks with openings 1 to 2 in., 4.7 to 0.3 cu ft per million gal, weighing about 50 to 60 lb per cu ft; on fine screenings with openings $\frac{3}{64}$ to $\frac{1}{8}$ in., 32.5 to 5.2 cu ft per million gal, weighing about 55 to 65 lb per cu ft and containing 70 to 90 per cent volatile matter in dry solids.

The coarse screening of sewage has little or no effect on the results of the standard suspended-solids test between the raw and the screened sewage, primarily because the method of sampling does not properly collect the larger particles removed by the screens. With very fine screens there may be a reduction of 20 to 30 per cent of the suspended solids from ordinary domestic sewage.

17–14. Nature of screenings. Screenings before drying contain 75 to 90 per cent moisture and weigh 40 to 60 lb per cu ft. The dry

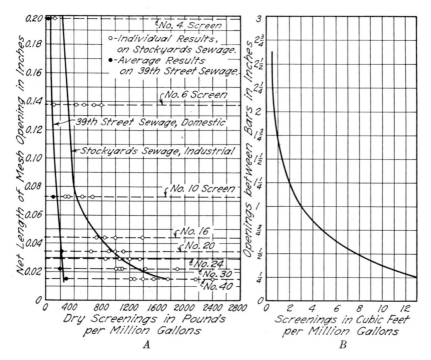

Fig. 17–7. Amount of screenings collected on different size openings. (*A*) From Report on Industrial Wastes Disposal, Union Stock Yards District, Chicago, Ill., to the Sanitary District of Chicago, 1921. (*B*) From Report by H. G. N. Hodgson, Adelaide, Australia, 1938.

weight of screenings collected varies between about 10 and 400 lb per million gal of sewage screened. Screenings consist of fecal matter, cloth, paper, rubber, particles of waste food, and other highly putrescible organic matter necessitating prompt removal and disposal.

17–15. Disposal of screenings. Screenings may be burned, buried, digested, dumped into large bodies of water, or shredded and returned to the sewage. Burial is attempted only at smaller plants and is not always satisfactory. Burial with quicklime or with chlorinated lime has been reported. Screenings must be buried sufficiently deep to avoid odors and shallow enough to permit bacterial activity. A cover of 12 to 18 in. of porous earth will probably be found to give the best results.

Screenings digestion has been attempted at a few plants with insufficient success to encourage the general adoption of the method.[10] In some plants attempts have been made to digest ground screenings in digestion tanks with sewage sludge.

Burning or incineration has been found to be a highly satisfactory method for the disposal of screenings.[11] Before the screenings are incinerated water is partially removed by compressing the screenings with a roll or a hydraulic press, under a pressure of about 325 psi, that may reduce the moisture content to 60 to 65 per cent, or the screenings can be centrifuged to about the same percentage of moisture. Screenings can be incinerated at about 1,250 to 1,400° F in gas, oil, or coal furnaces either with or without a mixture of oil or coal. About 2,000 to 3,500 Btu of additional heat will be required per pound to incinerate screenings containing 65 to 70 per cent moisture. The mechanical equipment required for the incineration of screenings varies from a 55-gal oil drum to a complete, municipal-type refuse incinerator.

[10] See *Sewage Works Jour.*, March, 1933, p. 363.
[11] See also *Mun. San.*, January, 1937, p. 37.

Chapter 18

Sedimentation

18–1. Purposes of sedimentation. Sewage is treated by sedimentation to reduce the content of settleable solids in order to prevent the formation of sludge banks, to reduce the BOD in diluting water, to prepare sewage for subsequent treatment or for final disposal into water or onto land, and for other purposes. Removal of settleable or suspended solids and other characteristics may be accomplished by plain sedimentation or it may be accelerated, and some suspended and dissolved solids may be made to settle by biological processes known as bioprecipitation.

18–2. Types of sedimentation basins and methods of operation. Sedimentation basins may be operated on the fill-and-draw principle, sedimentation taking place during the period that the basin stands full, or they may be operated continuously. Fill-and-draw basins are rarely used, partly because of their relative inefficiency, greater cost, and greater head loss in operation when compared with continuous-flow basins. In continuous-flow basins the liquid is allowed to flow slowly and continuously through the basin, sedimentation taking place as the liquid passes through the basin.

Basins are either rectangular or circular in plan. A type of horizontal-flow, rectangular basins is shown in Fig. 18–1, and of a radial-flow, circular basin in Fig. 18–2. Deep, hopper bottoms are sometimes used, as shown in Fig. 20–3. The relative advantages of longitudinal-flow rectangular tanks and of radial flow circular tanks are controversial.[1] Conditions favoring long, narrow, and relatively shallow tanks include freedom from short circuiting; a high ratio of settling zone to inlet and outlet zone, and hence, a lesser importance of inlet and outlet devices; and a lessened effect of horizontal and vertical currents. However, the cost of construction and of cleaning may be greater than in circular or in relatively wide rectangular

[1] See also E. B. Fitch, *S. and I.W.*, January, 1956, p. 1.

411

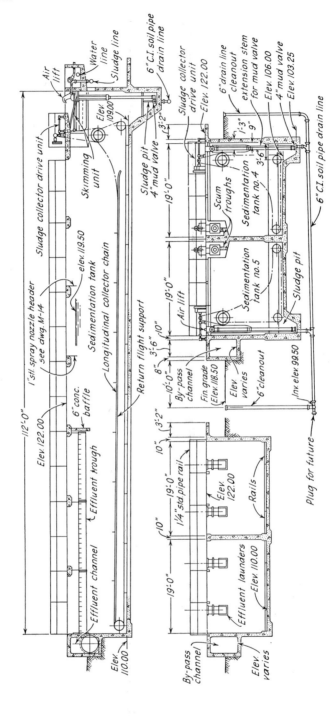

Fig. 18-1. Rectangular sedimentation basin at Central Contra Costa, Calif. (Courtesy Brown and Caldwell, Engineers.)

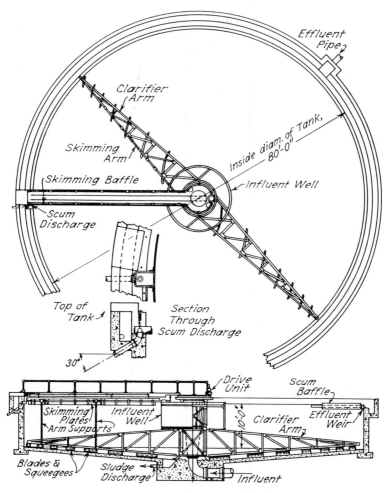

Fig. 18–2. Dorr clarifier. (Courtesy Dorr-Oliver Co.)

shapes. Vertical flow tanks were more commonly found in early sewage treatment practice but they are now more commonly used in water purification practice. The upward, vertical velocity may be made progressively slower as the liquid ascends so that a blanket of sludge is suspended in the liquid. Such a basin is shown in Fig. 18–3. The sludge blanket acts as a screen or filter which aids in removing solids from the rising liquid. Heavy sludge falls to the bottom and passes continuously from the tank through the sludge pipe shown in

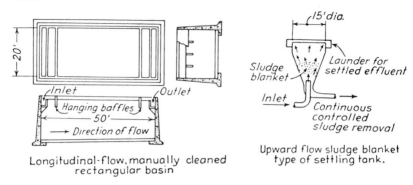

Longitudinal-flow, manually cleaned
rectangular basin

Upward flow sludge blanket
type of settling tank.

Fig. 18–3.   A horizontal-flow and a vertical flow sedimentation tank.

the figure.   Many types of these basins, used primarily in water
works practice, are patented.

Sedimentation basins may be cleaned either manually or mechanically, the latter being more common.   Mechanically cleaned basins
are shown in Figs. 18–1, 18–2, and others.   Sludge can be removed
continuously from both basins by controlled, continuous flow through
the sludge pipe.   Manually cleaned basins must usually be taken out
of service to be cleaned.   Mechanically cleaned basins, with continuously operated scrapers, need not be shut down for cleaning, and
little or no allowance for sludge accumulation need be made in their
design.

A grit chamber is a special type of sedimentation basin designed
to remove the heavier, non-putrescible inorganic matter, of 0.2-mm
diameter or larger, known as grit.   This material is difficult to handle
with the lighter, putrescible organic matter collected in sedimentation
basins and is troublesome in other treatment devices, pumps, and
equipment.   Grit is removed by controlling the velocity of flow
through the basin to cause the grit to settle, but the velocity is made
high enough to prevent the settling of lighter material.

A detritus tank is designed to collect both grit and putrescible material.   Sedimentation tanks are not often designed for this dual
purpose, but a grit chamber or a sedimentation tank can become a
detritus tank through faulty operation.   Some operators prefer to
remove detritus from a grit chamber than to remove grit from a
sedimentation basin or a sludge digestion tank.

Among unique forms of sedimentation basins suggested but not

Table 18–1

SOME RESULTS OF PLAIN SEDIMENTATION

Location of Plant	Flow, mgd	Susp. Solids			BOD			Data from S. and I.W.
		Influent, mg/l	Effluent, mg/l	Per Cent Removal	Influent, mg/l	Effluent, mg/l	Per Cent Removal	
Papillion Ck., Omaha, Nebr.	4.85	610	130	78	300	82	73	July, 1957, p. 828
Easterly, Cleveland, Ohio	108.3	267	142	47	178	109	39	Nov., 1952, p. 1424
Racine, Wis.	21.3	157	85	47	134	83	38	Dec., 1952, p. 1538
Muskegon, Mich.	7.13	160	71	55	175	133	24	Sept., 1953, p .1108
Aurora, Ill.	8.07	162	72	56	76	60	21	Jan., 1953, p. 96
Detroit, Mich.	388	217	115	47	125	74	41	Jan., 1953, p. 98
Greece, N. Y.	0.76	231	189	42	257	208	42	Jan., 1952, p. 101
Muskegon Heights, Mich.	1.75	238	157	34	247	182	26	Jan., 1952, p. 102
Minneapolis-St. Paul, Minn.	122.3	310	80	74	210	130	38	March, 1952, p. 334
Toledo, Ohio	41.1	214	108	49	243	178	23	June, 1955, p. 748

widely adopted in practice is the multiple-tray clarifier.[2] It consists of a series of trays, one but a small distance above the other, in a circular sedimentation basin, each tray equipped with a revolving arm that scrapes the accumulated sludge from the tray to a central point of concentration. This device invokes a basic principle in sedimentation by increasing the surface area in contact with the settling particles in the liquid. Apparently the combination of cost and performance has not justified the adoption of such a device in practice.

18–3. Results and costs of sedimentation. Results of sedimentation may be expressed as the percentage removal of characteristic constituents of the influent. Some results are shown in Table 18–1. The period of retention and the settling rate are important in affecting settling basin performance, as shown in Fig. 18–4. The figure shows the small gain in efficiency for increased retention periods be-

[2] See *Proc. Am. Soc. Civil Engrs.*, April, 1944, pp. 457 and 472.

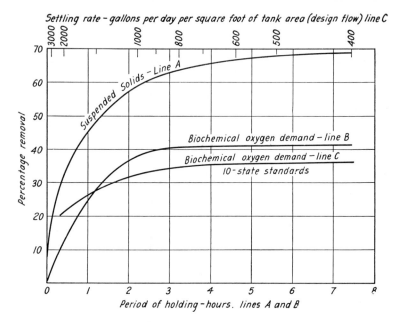

Fig. 18–4. Probable performance of sedimentation basins.

yond 2 to 3 hr, and very little increase in efficiency of BOD removal at a settling rate less than about 600 gpd per sq ft of tank area. It is to be expected that the higher the concentration of suspended solids in the influent the greater will be their percentage removal.

Mechanically cleaned basins are more commonly constructed since, for equal performance, they have lower first cost and are relatively low in operating cost. Some cost figures, compiled by Schroepfer,[3] based on a retention period of 2½ hr, are shown in Table 18–2. It is to be noted that these figures are of value primarily for comparative purposes. Their application to present conditions is discussed in Sect. 28–7.

18–4. Principles of sedimentation.[4] Gravity is the principal force causing matter to settle in water. No formula, theoretical or

---

[3] G. P. Schroepfer, *Proc. Am. Soc. Civil Engrs.*, April, 1938, p. 737.

[4] The references listed here will lead to numerous authoritative publications on the theory of sedimentation: W. E. Dobbins, *Trans. Am. Soc. Civil Engrs.*, Vol. 109, 1944, p. 629; T. R. Camp, *Proc. Am. Soc. Civil Engrs.*, Vol. 71, 1945, p. 445; L. B. Escritt, *Surveyor*, Vol. 111, 1952, p. 203; A. C. Ingersoll and others, *Proc. Am. Soc. Civil Engrs.*, Vol. 81, Separate No. 590, 1955; C. N. H. Fischer-

Table 18–2

CONSTRUCTION AND OPERATION AND MAINTENANCE COSTS
OF SEDIMENTATION PLANTS OF VARIOUS CAPACITIES

(From G. P. Schroepfer, *Proc. Am. Soc. Civ. Engrs.*, April, 1938, p. 737.)

Plant Capacity or Sewage Treated, mgd	Construction Cost			Operation and Maintenance Cost		
	Usual Lower Cost	Estimated in This Analysis	Usual Higher Cost	Usual Lower Cost	Estimated in This Analysis	Usual Higher Cost
10	$ 240,000	$ 325,000	$ 400,000	$ 17,000	$ 23,000	$ 29,000
25	550,000	725,000	900,000	38,000	50,000	62,000
50	980,000	1,300,000	1,600,000	68,000	90,000	110,000
75	1,350,000	1,800,000	2,250,000	94,000	125,000	160,000
100	1,720,000	2,300,000	2,900,000	120,000	155,000	200,000

See Sect. 28–7.

empirical, has been devised that is applicable in practical sedimentation-basin design because of the widely varying conditions occurring during operation. Among these conditions are:

1. Sizes of particles. The greater the size the more rapid is the rate of settling. Coalescence, peptization, solution, and precipitation affect particle size during sedimentation.

2. Specific gravity of settling particles.

3. Concentration of suspended matter.[5] The higher the concentration the more efficient is the removal of suspended matter.

4. Temperature. The higher the temperature the lower is the viscosity of the liquid and the more rapid the rate of sedimentation.

5. Period of retention. The longer the period, within limits, the higher is the efficiency of sedimentation. See Fig. 18–4.

6. Depth, shape, baffling, and operation of the basin.

7. Velocity and length of flow through the basin.

8. Wind blowing on the surface of the liquid in the basin.

9. Biological, electrical, and other forces.

Where there is no interference, other than the viscosity of the liquid, spherical particles of granular matter will settle at the rates indicated in Table 18–3.

strom, *Proc. Am. Soc. Civil Engrs.*, Vol. 81, Separate No. 687, May, 1955; and D. E. Bloodgood and others, *Jour. San. Eng. Div.*, American Society of Civil Engineers, Paper 1083, October, 1956. See also Sect. 18–5.

[5] See also *Sewage Works Jour.*, May, 1940, p. 513.

Table 18–3

RATE OF SETTLING OR HYDRAULIC VALUES
OF SETTLING PARTICLES IN SEWAGE

Millimeters per Second

Diam-eter, mm	Hydraulic Value Specific Gravity		Diam-eter, mm	Hydraulic Value Specific Gravity		Diam-eter, mm	Hydraulic Value Specific Gravity		Diam-eter, mm	Hydraulic Value Specific Gravity	
	2.65	1.20		2.65	1.20		2.65	1.20		2.65	1.20
1.00	100	12.0	0.20	21.0	2.2	0.04	1.1	0.15	0.006	0.025	0.003
0.90	92	10.5	0.15	15.0	1.5	0.03	0.62	0.08	0.005	0.017	0.0021
0.80	83	9.5	0.10	7.4	0.8	0.02	0.28	0.035	0.004	0.011	0.0013
0.70	72	8.4	0.09	5.6	0.75	0.015	0.155	0.020	0.003	0.0062	0.75*
0.60	63	7.7	0.08	4.8	0.58	0.01	0.069	0.0084	0.002	0.0028	0.35*
0.50	53	6.2	0.07	3.7	0.45	0.009	0.056	0.0068	0.0015	0.00155	0.20*
0.40	42	4.9	0.06	2.5	0.35	0.008	0.044	0.0054	0.001	0.00069	0.084*
0.30	32	3.8	0.05	1.7	0.26	0.007	0.034	0.0041	0.0001	0.00007	0.00085*

* Divide by 1,000.

Settling rates of particles between 0.1 and 1.0 mm are found empirically. Rates for smaller particles are expressed in accordance
with Stokes' law which is in the form

$$V = \frac{\gamma_s - \gamma_w}{18\mu} d^2 \qquad (18\text{--}1)$$

where V = velocity of sedimentation, mm per sec.
  γ_s = unit weight of settling particle, specific gravity.
  γ_w = unit weight of water, specific gravity.
  μ = viscosity of liquid, in poises.
  d = diameter of particle, mm.

Flocculent matter with a specific gravity approximately that of
water is so greatly affected by the conditions listed on the preceding
page that its settling rate is uncertain and "density currents" exist
as explained in Sect. 23–41. In addition to these effects the flocculent
particles coalesce and, growing larger, settle more rapidly.

In the design of sedimentation basins in which the particles of matter settle at a uniform rate it is hypothetically possible to assume that clear water can be skimmed from the surface at the rate of the settling of the smallest particle to be removed. Hence, hypothetically, the depth of the tank is of no significance. All that is necessary is that the rate of flow through the basin shall equal the product of the surface area and the settling velocity of the smallest particle to be removed.

18–5. Practical considerations in design.[6] Depth is an important consideration in practical sedimentation-basin design. It takes time for a settling particle to reach the bottom. The time is provided by retarding the velocity of flow and making the length of flow, or period of retention, such that the particle will reach the bottom before reaching the outlet. It would seem that the shallower the basin the shorter would be the necessary period of retention and the shorter the necessary length of the basin. In fact, the absurd conclusion is reached that a basin without depth and without length would be the most desirable. Experience must, therefore, be depended on in practical design.

Attempts have been made to formulate mathematical expressions that would be applicable to the determination of the dimensions of sedimentation basins. Notable among these attempts are those of Hazen,[7] Slade,[8] Camp,[9] and Carpenter and Speiden.[10, 11] In view of the large number of conditions involved and the unknown "constants" in most of the formulas, it continues to be customary to base the design of sedimentation basins on experience.

In the design of sedimentation basins the flowing-through velocity is assumed to be q/A, where q is the rate of flow and A is the cross-sectional area normal to the direction of the velocity of flow. The period of retention is assumed to be Q/q, where Q is the volume of the contents of the basin. The flowing-through period is the time required for a dye or other indicator to flow through the basin without diffusion. The retention efficiency is the ratio of the flowing-through period to the retention period, multiplied by 100. The flowing-through period is determined by observing the time required for

[6] See also T. R. Camp, *S. and I.W.*, January, 1953, p. 1.
[7] Allen Hazen, *Trans. Am. Soc. Civil Engrs.*, Vol. 73, 1904, p. 43.
[8] J. J. Slade, Jr., *Trans. Am. Soc. Civil Engrs.*, Vol. 102, 1937, p. 289.
[9] T. R. Camp, *Sewage Works Jour.*, September, 1936, p. 742.
[10] L. V. Carpenter and H. W. Speiden, *Sewage Works Jour.*, March, 1935, p. 200.
[11] See also G. M. Fair and J. C. Geyer, *Water Supply and Waste-Water Disposal*, John Wiley and Sons, 1954.

Table 18-4

GRIT CHAMBER RESULTS

Place	Flow, mgd	Grit, cu ft per mg	Data from S. and I.W.		
Cranston, R. I.	2.46	2	Oct., 1952, p. 1315		
Easterly, Cleveland, Ohio	108.3	3.04	Nov., 1952, p. 1424		
Aurora, Ill.	8.87	0.89	Jan., 1953, p. 96		
Worcester, Mass.	21.8	4.5	Jan., 1952, p. 100		
Greece, N. Y.	0.76	8.28	Jan., 1952, p. 101		
Port Washington, N. Y.	1.4	0.72	June, 1955, p. 750		
Kenosha, Wis.	... *	0.35	June, 1953, p. 734		
Toledo, Ohio	41.1	0.72	June, 1955, p. 748		
Minneapolis-St. Paul, Minn.	122.3	4.6	March, 1952, p. 334		
Austin, Texas †	2.0	0.06	0.85 ‡	29.0 §	
Baltimore, Md.	81.5	0.2	3.1	56.0	
Berea, Ohio	0.4	0.5	4.6	50.4	

* Population 55,000.

† All data on and below this line are for washed grit from detritor installations, courtesy of the Dorr Co. The data are from D. E. Bloodgood, "Grit Chambers," *Water and Sewage Works*, December, 1955.

‡ Per cent putrescible on a dry basis.

§ Per cent of volatile in putrescible matter.

dye, chemical solution, or radioactive tracer to flow through the tank, with allowance for diffusion of the indicator.[12]

Some details of sedimentation basin design are discussed in Sects. 18–11 to 18–17.

18–6. Grit chambers.[13] A grit chamber is an enlarged channel, or a tank, in which the velocity of flow through it is so controlled that only the heavier solids, such as grit and sand, with a size of 0.2 mm or larger, are deposited while the lighter organic solids are carried forward in suspension. The removal of grit is necessary to prevent the clogging of sewers, to protect pumps and moving-part appurtenances, and to protect equipment in sewage-treatment works. Grit

[12] See also Wm. Seaman, *S. and I.W.*, March, 1956, p. 296; and John Finch, *Water and Sewage Works*, October, 1953, p. 418.

[13] See also D. E. Bloodgood, *Water and Sewage Works*, December, 1955, p. 545.

chambers are necessary on most sewers whether storm, sanitary, or combined.

Many conditions affect the amount of grit that may be expected. Amounts between 1 and 12 cu ft per million gal may be expected, with a maximum of as high as 80 reported.[14] In a study of sixty plants Thoman [15] reported a variation from 0.5 to 10 cu ft in combined sewers and from 0.76 to 4.8 cu ft per million gal in separate sewage. Some further information is given in Table 18–4.

The deposited material usually contains sufficient putrescible matter to cause some nuisance in final disposal unless it is spread on land in the open, or is used as fill in a dry place. After adequate washing and drying it has been used as a filling material, for roads, for sludge-drying beds, or for similar purposes as a substitute for sand.

To remove gritty material by sedimentation without depositing organic matter, the horizontal velocity of flow through a rectangular grit chamber should be between 0.5 and 1 fps. The higher velocity is preferred. The velocity required to start the movement of non-uniform and sticky material, such as grit, that has settled in a grit chamber is given by Bloodgood [16] as

$$V_c = 500(S - 1)D \qquad (18\text{–}2)$$

where V_c = critical velocity, fps.

S = specific gravity.

D = diameter of particle, ft.

Grit chambers are cleaned manually, mechanically, and hydraulically. Manual cleaning is described in Sect. 29–15. Mechanical cleaning includes clamshell buckets and mechanical conveyers; [17] and hydraulic ejectors or high-velocity jets constitute hydraulic methods.

Kivell and Lund [18] point out that the capacity of a grit chamber is in direct proportion to the surface area regardless of the relation of width, depth, and velocity, and that a "grit chamber may be made of any shape desired, so long as the (surface) area is sufficient." Surface areas recommended are given in Table 18–5. Many grit chambers are rectangular in plan, with a cross-section similar to that shown in Fig. 18–7.

---

[14] See G. P. Schroepfer, *Proc. Am. Soc. Civil Engrs.*, April, 1938, p. 737.

[15] J. R. Thoman, *S. and I.W.*, September, 1951, p. 1110.

[16] D. R. Bloodgood, *Water and Sewage Works,* December, 1955, p. 545.

[17] See also J. M. Symons, *Water and Sewage Works,* November, 1954, p. 500.

[18] W. A. Kivell and N. B. Lund, *Water Works and Sewerage,* June, 1941, p. 144.

Table 18–5

SURFACE AREAS OF GRIT CHAMBERS

Diameter of Particles to Be Removed, mm	Approximate Screen Mesh Number	Rate in 1,000 Gallons per Day per Square Foot of Surface Area
0.79	35	73
0.36	48	51
0.28	65	38
0.17	100	25

In the design of a grit chamber q, the rate of flow, and V, the average velocity of flow, are usually known. Assuming a rectangular cross-sectional area with w the width, d the depth, l the length, then

$$wd = q/V \quad \text{and} \quad wl = A$$

where A is the surface area taken from Table 18–5.

There are thus two equations with three unknowns: w, d and l. Any one of these may be selected to give reasonable dimensions of the chamber. Periods of retention recommended by most states vary between 30 and 60 seconds.

Continuous removal and washing of deposited grit particles is desirable for satisfactory performance. Proprietary mechanisms [19] such as the Dorr Company's Detritor, shown in Fig. 18–5, Link Belt's Straightline,[20] Circuline equipment, and Jeffrey Manufacturing Company's Jigrit are available for this purpose. Where high lift is involved a clamshell bucket may be suitable. Water jets often give trouble due to clogging of the nozzle.

Although the maintenance of a constant velocity through any grit chamber is desirable, it is especially so in chambers from which the grit is not removed continuously. Under such conditions two or more chambers should be used in parallel. In times of high flow both chambers will be in use. Multiple channels are required for hand-cleaned chambers. Single channels are permissible where mechanical collection devices are used. Where cleaning is not continuous it may be necessary to await a low-flow period and divert all flow through one channel while the other channel is cleaned. A uniform, constant velocity through a grit chamber is obtained by the use of multiple

[19] See also F. L. Flood, *Water and Sewage Works*, May, 1954, p. R-219.
[20] *Sewage Works Jour.*, September, 1943, p. 1014.

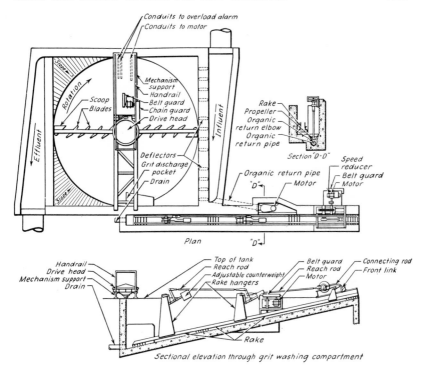

Fig. 18–5. Dorr detritor and grit washing equipment. (Courtesy Dorr-Oliver Co.)

chambers in parallel, by the use of special inlet and outlet devices, or by both means.

18–7. Inlet and outlet devices for grit chambers. The efficiency of a grit chamber is greatly affected by the location of the inlet pipe and the direction of the incoming velocity. For the best results the inlet pipe should be located on the center line of the grit-chamber channel and the incoming velocity should be along the axis of the chamber. Although this condition is most desirable it is sometimes difficult to attain, particularly where there are two or more chambers in parallel. For example, the middle chamber in Fig. 17–3 has the most ideal situation for the inlet.

The depth of water in the chamber is controlled by the outlet device. Camp [21] suggests that the maximum water level should cause as much

[21] T. R. Camp, *Sewage Works Jour.*, March, 1942, p. 368.

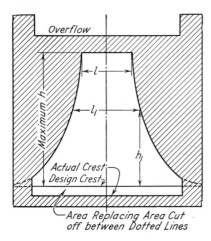

Fig. 18–6. Proportional-flow weir.

backwater in the sewer at maximum flow as is permitted by sewer velocity considerations. So long as there is no backwater at minimum flow there should be no trouble from deposits in the sewer, but, at the same time, the elevation of the water in the chamber must be such that there is no "shooting flow" into the chamber at minimum flow.

Although some grit chambers discharge over a standard overflow weir, or through a submerged pipe, the most satisfactory type of discharge control is one that will permit an unchanging velocity of flow through the chamber, regardless of the rate of flow. Such devices include the proportional-flow weir, the Venturi or Parshall flume, the Bushee flume,[22] the Camp flume,[21, 23] the Palmer-Bowlus flume mentioned in Sect. 6–20, and the control flume described in Sect. 18–9.

18–8. Proportional-flow weir.[24] A proportional-flow weir consists of a combination of a weir and an orifice, somewhat as shown in Fig. 18–6. In proportional-flow weirs the orifice has a straight, horizontal edge which comprises the weir. The sides of the orifice are so curved that the cross-sectional area of the orifice diminishes as the three-halves power of the increasing depth of flow over the weir. Hence, the rate of flow over the weir, or through the orifice, will vary directly with the head on the weir.[25]

Unfortunately such a device will not result in a uniform veloc-

[22] R. J. Bushee, *Water Works and Sewerage,* June, 1944, p. R-169.

[23] See L. B. Escritt, *Surveyor,* Oct. 6, 1945, p. 635.

[24] See also *Eng. News-Record,* July 29, 1943, p. 72, and Nov. 12, 1936, p. 679.

[25] See also R. L. Gordier, *Water and Sewage Works,* March, 1956, p. 118.

ity throughout the cross-section of the grit chamber. This non-
uniformity is due to two conditions: (1) the velocity along the
bottom of the chamber will be greater than near the top; and (2) the
edge of the weir must be some finite distance above the bottom of
the grit chamber, usually about 12 in. The less this distance the
more nearly will the *average* velocity be constant but the greater
may be the maximum velocity which will occur at the bottom of the
chamber, sweeping out deposited material. An additional objection
to such weirs is the fact that they cannot function as submerged
weirs but necessitate the loss of head of the full depth of water over
the crest of the weir.

The flow through an orifice of this type is given by the expression: [26]

$$Q = C \times 1.57 \sqrt{2g}\,(l\sqrt{h})h$$

or, if $C = 0.6$,

$$Q = 7.5(lh^{\frac{1}{2}})h \qquad\qquad (18\text{--}3)$$

In order that Q may vary as h it is necessary that $lh^{\frac{1}{2}}$ be a constant, or

$$lh^{\frac{1}{2}} = K = l_1 h_1^{\frac{1}{2}} \qquad\qquad (18\text{--}4)$$

where Q = rate of discharge over the weir, cfs.
     l = width of opening at height h, ft.
    K = a constant.

Procedure in design is: (1) with known velocity of flow and dimensions of the grit chamber, select the maximum value of h; (2) compute
l for this value of h by formula 18–3; (3) compute K from formula
18–4; (4) compute other corresponding values of h_1 and l_1, using the
value of K from the preceding step, thus determining the shape of
the side curves. For values of h less than 1 in. the side curves are
terminated vertically to the weir crest, without allowance for the
area cut off because it is of no practical significance. If cut off at a
height of less than 1 in. the corners are more likely to clog. If they
are cut off at much more than 1 in. the actual weir crest should be
lowered below the design crest to compensate for the loss in capacity
at low heads.

18–9. Constant-velocity grit chamber and control flume. *The
grit chamber.* It is possible to design a grit chamber and a control
flume without curved surfaces so that there is but little variation of
velocity of flow through the grit chamber between maximum and

[26] See also *Eng. News,* June 25, 1914, p. 1409.

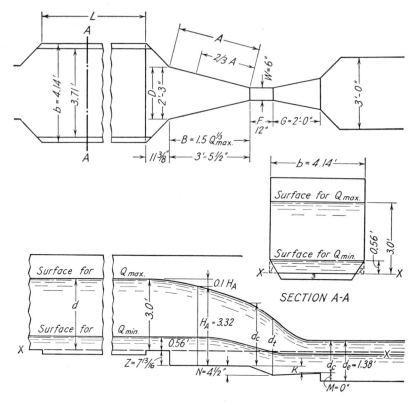

Fig. 18–7. Parshall flume for grit-chamber control.

minimum rates of flow. If a Parshall flume [27] is used for velocity control [28] it can be shown that

$$Q = 4.1 W H_A{}^{3/2} \tag{18-5}$$

$$d + Z = 1.1 H_A \tag{18-6}$$

$$\frac{Q_{\min}}{Q_{\max}} = \frac{[1.1(Q_{\min}/4.1W)^{2/3} - Z]}{[1.1(Q_{\max}/4.1W)^{2/3} - Z]} \tag{18-7}$$

$$V_0 = \frac{2.6(1 - K^{1/3})^{1/2}(K^{1/3} - K)}{(1 - K)^{3/2}} \tag{18-8}$$

[27] See R. L. Parshall, *Bull.* 336, Colorado Experiment Station, Fort Collins, Colorado, and *Trans. Am. Soc. Civil Engrs.*, Vol. 89, 1926, p. 841; and C. G. Richardson, *Jour. New Eng. Water Works Assoc.*, March, 1934.

[28] See R. L. Parshall, *Farmers' Bull.* 1683, U. S. Department of Agriculture, 1941.

where Q is the rate of flow in cfs; Q_{min} = minimum rate of flow; Q_{max} = maximum rate of flow; V_0 is the velocity at the greatest deviation from the desired velocity. Other dimensions, to be used in feet, are shown in Figs. 18–7 and 18–8.

The method of applying these formulas in design is illustrated by the solution of the following example:

Example. Let it be desired to design a grit chamber and control flume, with flat surfaces and Parshall flume for velocity control, in which the maximum rate of flow is 8 mgd, the minimum is 1.5 mgd, and the velocities at maximum and at minimum rates of flow are to be 1 fps.

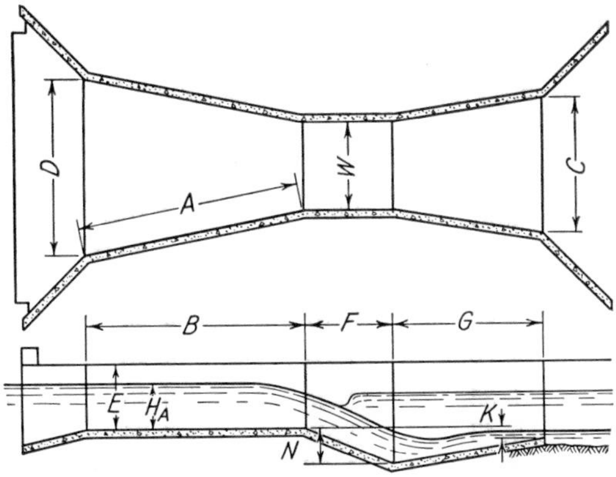

W, ft in.	*A*, ft in.	⅔*A*, ft in.	*B*,* ft in.	*C*, ft in.	*D*,† ft in.	*F*, ft	*G*, ft	*K*, in.	*N*, in.
3	1 6⅜	1 0¼	1 6	0 7	0 10³⁄₁₆	½	1	1	2¼
6	2 0⁷⁄₁₆	1 4⁵⁄₁₆	2 0	1 3⅝‡	1 3⅝	1	2	3	4½
9	2 10⅝	1 11⅛	2 10	1 3	1 10⅝	1	1½ ‡	3	4½
1 0	4 6	3 0	4 4⅞	2 0	2 9¼	2	3	3	9
1 6	4 9	3 2	4 7⅞	2 6	3 4⅜	2	3	3	9
2 0	5 0	3 4	4 10⅞	3 0	3 11½	2	3	3	9
3 0	5 6	3 8	5 4¾	4 0	5 1⅞	2	3	3	9
4 0	6 0	4 0	5 10⅝	5 0	6 4¼	2	3	3	9
6 0	7 0	4 8	6 10⅜	7 0	8 9	2	3	3	9
8 0	8 0	5 4	7 10⅛	9 0	11 1¾	2	3	3	9

* Let $B = 1.5Q_{max}^{1/3}$, but not less than figure shown in this column.

† Ratio of D/B is to be the same as the ratio of the values in this table, regardless of the magnitude of B.

‡ *Sic*, as given by Parshall.

Fig. 18–8. Dimensions for Parshall flume.

Solution. 1. Select, from the dimensions shown in the table in Fig. 18–8, a flume that will give desirable depths of flow in the grit chamber. In this problem a flume with a 6-in. throat will be selected.

2. Determine the value of Z, from formula 18-7

$$\frac{1.5}{8} = \frac{[1.1(2.32/2.05)^{2/3} - Z]}{[1.1(12.4/2.05)^{2/3} - Z]} = \frac{1.20 - Z}{3.64 - Z}$$

$$Z = 0.64 \text{ ft.}$$

3. Determine the depths of flow in the grit chamber, for various rates of flow. These depths, computed by the expression

$$d = 1.1 \left(\frac{Q}{4.1W}\right)^{2/3} - Z \tag{18–9}$$

are recorded in column 3 of the accompanying table of computations.

COMPUTATIONS IN DESIGN OF GRIT CHAMBER

Rate of Flow, mgd	Rate of Flow, cfs	Depth of Flow, ft	Grit Chamber, Vertical Sides Cross-Sectional Area, sq ft	Velocity, fps
1.5	2.32	0.56	2.32	1.000
2.0	3.10	0.81	3.35	0.925
2.5	3.88	1.04	4.30	0.902
3.0	4.65	1.25	5.18	0.897
3.5	5.43	1.46	6.04	0.900
4.0	6.20	1.66	6.86	0.904
6.0	9.30	2.36	9.76	0.954
8.0	12.40	3.00	12.40	1.000
1	2	3	4	5

4. Compute the width of the grit chamber from the expression

$$b = \frac{Q_{max}}{d_{max}V} = \frac{Q_{min}}{d_{min}V} = \frac{12.4}{3 \times 1} = \frac{2.32}{0.56 \times 1} = 4.14 \text{ ft.}$$

5. Compute the velocities of flow at various depths, from the expression, $V = Q/(4.14d)$. Results are shown in column 5. These velocities show a 10.3 per cent variation between maximum and minimum velocity.

Other dimensions of the grit chamber are determined by the desired period of retention, the methods of cleaning proposed, and other conditions. If it is desired to place cleaning mechanisms in the grit chamber it may be necessary to narrow the bottom and to use fillets, as indicated in the cross-section shown in Fig. 18-7. The distribution of velocity in the grit chamber will be unaffected, between maximum and minimum rates of flow, if the following conditions are met: (1) elevation of line XX represents the bottom of the rectangular grit chamber for which velocities have been computed; (2) the height of the fillets above line XX does not bring them above the surface at minimum rate of flow; and (3) area 1 + area 2 = area 3.

Dimensions of grit chamber and flume closely satisfying these conditions are shown in Fig. 18–7.

The control flume. The practicability of the preceding design depends on the design of a control flume through which the rate of flow will conform to equation 18–5. Such conditions exist in a Parshall flume only under conditions of "free flow," that is, when the depth d_c, in Fig. 18–7, is not affected by downstream conditions. Under such conditions

$$d_t + \left(\frac{Q}{d_t W}\right)^2 \frac{1}{2g} \gtreqqless H + N \tag{18–10}$$

where H = total energy at the section where depth of flow is d_c. If loss of energy due to friction is neglected

$$H = d + Z \tag{18–11}$$

and, from equation 18–6,

$$H = 1.1 H_A \tag{18–12}$$

then, from equations 18–5 and 18–12, and substituting in 18–10,

$$\frac{d_t}{H_A} + 0.26 \left(\frac{H_A}{d_t}\right)^2 - 1.1 \gtreqqless \frac{N}{H_A} \tag{18–13}$$

Now it can be shown, by the calculus, that the limiting maximum rate of flow for free-flow conditions occurs when

$$H_A \gtreqqless 10N \tag{18–14}$$

and

$$\frac{d_t - N}{H_A} \gtreqqless 0.7 \tag{18–15}$$

and

$$Q_{\max} = 4.1 W (10N)^{3/2} \tag{18–16}$$

$$Q_{\max} = 130 W N^{3/2} \tag{18–17}$$

When these equations are applied to the illustrative example it is seen that $Q_{\max} = (4.1)(0.5)(10 \times 0.375)^{3/2} = (130)(0.5)(0.375)^{3/2} = 15$. Since this rate of flow is larger than the maximum rate of 12.4 in the example, free-flow conditions will exist.

Consideration must also be given to tail-water conditions. It can be seen from Fig. 18–7 that, to prevent submergence,

$$d_c + K > d_c' \quad \text{and} \quad d_c' + M \gtreqless d_e$$

When $Q = 12.4$, d_c = critical depth = 2.68 ft, $d_c' = 1.42$ ft, and $d_e = 1.38$ ft. Hence

$$d_c + K = 2.68 + 0.25 = 2.93 > 1.38$$

$$d_c' + M = 1.42 + 0 > 1.38$$

When $Q = 2.32$, $d_c = 0.875$, $d_c' = 0.46$, and $d_e = 0.43$

$$d_c' + M = 0.46 + 0 > 0.43$$

Since all conditions for free flow are fulfilled the design is satisfactory.

Other control flumes. Bushee [29] and Camp [30] have offered methods for the design of grit chambers giving approximately constant velocities of flow. Camp's design, involving a parabolic cross-section, is patented and is controlled by American Well Works.

18–10. Detritus tanks and aerated grit chambers. A detritus tank may be considered to be a grit chamber in which the velocity of flow is such that an appreciable amount of organic matter may settle out with the grit. If the tank is designed to permit this action, the organic matter may be separated from the grit by controlling the velocity with baffles or by controlled aeration of the flow through the tank.[31] The rising air bubbles are depended on to separate lighter organic matter from the descending grit. The organic matter may pass from the chamber with the effluent. The grit may be removed continuously by scrapers or by other means. Among the advantages of an aerated grit chamber are the lack of need for careful velocity control; variations in rate of flow have little effect on grit removal; the grit removed is clean enough for disposal without further washing; and the removal of grit and the flotation of grease can be combined in the same chamber.

Clean, washed grit may be expected to contain between 1 and 5 per cent of putrescible matter.

[29] R. J. Bushee, *Water Works and Sewerage,* June, 1944, p. R-169.

[30] T. R. Camp, *Sewage Works Jour.,* March, 1942, p. 368.

[31] See also N. Grant, *Eng. News-Record,* April 28, 1949, p. 57; S. E. Kappe and J. B. Neighbor, *S. and I.W.,* September, 1951, p. 833; and F. C. Roe, *S. and I.W.,* September, 1951, p. 825; D. R. Bloodgood, *Water and Sewage Works,* June 15, 1956, p. R-251; and H. Blunk, translated by C. P. Edwards, *Sewage Works Jour.,* May, 1953, p. 509.

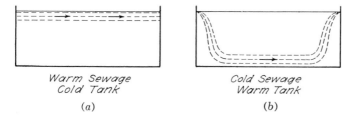

Warm Sewage   Cold Sewage
Cold Tank   Warm Tank
(a)   (b)

Fig. 18–9. Effect of temperature on distribution of currents in sedimentation basins.

18–11. Design of sedimentation basins. In the design of primary sedimentation basins of the longitudinal, continuous-flow type, the quality of the suspended matter affects the principles to be applied. The settleable material is of a nature not so readily affected as flocculent matter by "gravity currents" and temperature currents but, nevertheless, these must be guarded against. An effect of temperature on the distribution of currents is illustrated in Fig. 18–9.

The following conditions control, in general:

Retention period, 1 to 3 hr. The longer period is used where there is to be no subsequent treatment and the highest efficiency is desired. Too long a period may induce septicization. Shorter periods may be used where only coarse solids are to be removed.

Depth, which should not be more than 10 ft, exclusive of storage space. Mechanically cleaned basins should be as shallow as practical but not less than 7 ft. Final clarifiers for activated sludge should not be less than 8 ft.

Velocity of flow, about 1 fpm, although 5 fpm has been used in some large basins. Velocities as high as 12 to 18 fpm have been used.[32]

Practice and precedent control the design of primary sedimentation basins. Some data on basic design factors are summarized in Table 18–6.

As a result of analyses of sedimentation-basin costs, given in Table 18–2, Schroepfer[33] has concluded that, where the pressing need is the removal of solids, a retention period of 1 to 1½ hr is economical, and where higher BOD removal is desired, periods of 2½ to 3½ hr may be economical, or secondary treatment may be

[32] See T. R. Camp, *S. and I.W.,* January, 1953, p. 1.
[33] G. P. Schroepfer, *Proc. Am. Soc. Civil Engrs.,* April, 1938, p. **737**.

Table 18–6

BASIC DESIGN FACTORS FOR SETTLING TANKS MECHANICALLY CLEANED

(Compiled from data published in *Sewage Works Engineering*, March, 1948, p. 118, and by information given by the Joint Committee.)

From *Sewage Works Engineering*	From Joint Committee
Minimum detention period, hr:	Maximum permissible surface settling
Largest allowance by any state, 4	rates, gal per sq ft per day:
Most common allowance, 2.5; 2 to 3	Primary settling tanks not fol-
Smallest allowance by any state:	lowed by secondary treatment,
Preceding activated-sludge treat-	for total flow of 1 mgd or less,
ment, 1	600 (for large flows a higher
Primary, 1.5	settling rate is permitted)
Secondary, 2	Intermediate settling tanks, 1,000
Surface loading, gal per day flowing	Final settling tanks:
through, per sq ft of tank sur-	
face:	
Largest, 900	
Most common, 900	
Smallest, 600	

Type of Treatment	Size of Plant, mgd	Gal per Sq Ft per Day
Std trickling filter	...	1,000
High-rate trickling filter	...	800
Activated sludge	2 or less	800
Activated sludge	over 2	1,000

better. Many installations of sedimentation basins have designed periods of at least 2½ hr preceding sand filters or trickling filters, and about 1½ hr preceding activated sludge treatment. Retention periods in warm climates may be shorter because of the higher efficiency of sedimentation at warmer temperatures.[34]

The load per square foot of surface area of the basin may be between 300 and 4,000 gal per day for granular solids; 800 to 2,000 for sewage solids; and 1,000 to 1,200 for flocculent material. Imhoff and Fair [35] suggest that the load in gallons per day per square foot

[34] See also T. de S. Furman, *S. and I.W.*, June, 1954, p. 745.

[35] K. Imhoff and G. M. Fair, *Sewage Treatment,* 2nd edition, John Wiley and Sons, 1956.

should be 180 times the tank depth, in feet, divided by the retention period, in hours. Although a relatively high ratio of tank surface to tank volume is desirable in a settling basin, too great an area is conducive to the creation of currents by wind. A wind of 20 mph might result in a surface velocity of 0.5 to 1.0 fps, piling the water up on one side of the basin and upsetting the basin's efficiency. The dimensions of a tank that is rectangular in plan and in cross-section must be computed with the following limitations in mind: The ratio of width to length should be as small as feasible and not greater than 1:5 or 1:4; with a maximum width of flowing-through channel of 20 to 25 ft; and a relation of depth to length such that the smallest particle of matter to be removed reaches the bottom during the retention period.

18–12. Inlet and outlet devices for sedimentation basins.[36] Successful performance by a sedimentation basin depends greatly on the inlet and outlet devices, which are intended to distribute the flow evenly across the basin. The shorter the basin, the more important is the effect of these devices on its performance. The minimum allowable distance between the inlet and outlet of a basin is 10 ft.

Methods of admitting sewage to rectangular sedimentation basins include: (1) inlet pipes evenly spaced across the end of the basin, either with upturned elbows or discharging horizontally against a hanging baffle, the pipes being submerged 1 to 3 ft below the surface; (2) perforated baffles; (3) submerged flow directed against the wall of the tank; and (4) an overflow weir. The last is commonly used.

Uniform distribution of flow among a number of tanks fed from the same pipe or open channel can be adjusted through the independent pipes or channels to each tank, the rate of flow being controlled by manipulation of a valve or gate on the respective pipe or channel.

A typical overflow weir for the inlet of rectangular tanks is shown in Fig. 18–3. In non-mechanical, radial-flow, hopper-bottom final clarifiers the inlet should be in the center at least 6 ft below the water surface and 5 ft above the bottom of the hopper. All types of inlets should be protected by baffles hanging about 2 or 3 ft in front of them to distribute the currents. It is to be noted that intermediate baffles are used only in non-mechanically cleaned sedimentation tanks. The overflow weir is probably the most common form of inlet device and is used almost universally as an outlet device.

[36] See also *Sewage Works Jour.*, July, 1943, p. 609.

Outlets from sedimentation basins are commonly designed as over-flow weirs or troughs, sometimes called launders, of the type illustrated in Figs. 18–1, 18–2, and 23–13. The location and length of these weirs in relation to the rate of flow through the basin affect its performance. In primary sedimentation basins, to remove sewage solids the outlet weir may be placed opposite the inlet, or on the periphery of a circular tank with its inlet at the center. If flocculent material is to be removed, the launder may be placed somewhere between the inlet and the wall of the basin. To minimize surges in the basin the rate of flow per foot length of the outlet weir, in rectangular basins, should not exceed about 200,000 gal per day, and should preferably be less than one-fourth of this. On circular tanks the weir should be equivalent in length to a weir extending around the periphery of the tank; weir loadings are not to exceed 10,000 gal

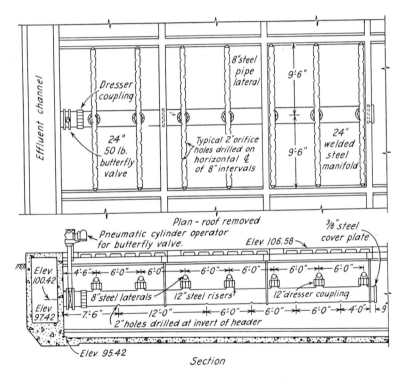

Fig. 18–10. Sedimentation basin at Central Contra Costa sewage-treatment plant, California, showing special effluent collection provisions. (Courtesy Brown and Caldwell, Engineers.)

per day per linear foot of weir for plants designed for average flows of 1 million gal per day; and not more than 15,000 gal per day for other tanks, except under special conditions. To obtain such lengths of outlet weirs in rectangular basins it may be necessary to arrange the weirs as indicated in Figs. 18–1, 18–10, and 23–13. It is often desirable to make most or all the length of the weir vertically adjustable in order to place better control of the basin in the hands of the operator. It is important that the edge of the weir is level. If it is not an uneven distribution of flow will probably occur. V-notches cut in the edge of the weir will tend to overcome some of the difficulties caused by only a slight slope in a weir's edge.

18–13. Baffling. Adequate baffling is essential for proper distribution of currents and for preventing the movement of floating material. Complicated baffling is undesirable. Too much baffling, resulting in the concentration of currents, is as bad as too little, and, unfortunately, baffling that may be satisfactory at one condition may be unsatisfactory under other conditions. For example, a hanging baffle in Fig. 18–9a would break up the surface current. It would be useless in Fig. 18–9b.

Inlets may be protected by baffles hanging 2 or 3 ft in front of the weir and submerged 18 to 24 in. Around-the-end baffles parallel to the direction of the flow of the current and extending from the bottom of the basin to slightly above the surface are used to decrease the width of the flowing-through channel and to increase the ratio of length to width. Two or three submerged overflow baffles placed normal to the direction of flow and extending upwards from the bottom for a few feet may be used to separate sludge storage space into compartments and to break up bottom currents. A skimming baffle should be placed ahead of the outlet weir.

The tops of all submerged structural features should be finished with slopes adequate to prevent the accumulation of sludge on them. A minimum slope of 1.7 vertical to 1 horizontal is recommended.

18–14. Facilities for cleaning. The cleaning of rectangular, flat-bottomed sedimentation basins, other than by mechanisms that are designed as a part of the tank, is facilitated by the location of a central gutter in the bottom of the basin, into which the sludge may be pushed with squeegees when the sewage has been removed. The slope of the bottom of the basin towards the gutter should not be less than 1:80 to 1:25 and may be steeper. A pipe, 2 in. or larger in diameter, containing water under pressure, with hose connections at frequent intervals, is a useful adjunct in flushing sludge from the sedimentation basins. Pyramidal sludge hoppers in shallow, non-mechanically cleaned tanks should have a minimum slope of 1.7 vertical to 1 horizontal. Conical tanks may have a minimum slope of 1.5 to 1. Where possible, sludge should be removed by hydrostatic pressure and the hoppers should be accessible for sounding and for cleaning.

Deep, cylindrical vertical-flow tanks are more expensive and difficult to construct than the shallower, rectangular type, but they are advantageous in that sludge may sometimes be removed by gravity or by pumping without interrupting the operation of the tank. They will also operate with shorter periods of retention and higher velocities. Sewage is admitted to these tanks slightly above the tank bottom and rises to flow over a skimming trough placed around the periphery of the tank. Such tanks are not common in the United States. The upward velocity should not be greater than the settling velocity of the smallest particle to be removed.

Pipes or channels through which sewage or sludge is to flow should be laid in straight alignment and on as steep a grade as possible. Round-bottom channels are preferable to flat bottoms, which are more conducive to the collection of deposits and are cleaned with greater difficulty. Slopes above 2 to 3 per cent should provide adequate velocities. It is desirable to leave all sludge channels open on top to permit inspection, or to use removable covers over the channels. If sludge pipes must be closed, openings should be left at every change of direction, and it is desirable to have such openings equipped for connection, by means of a hose, to a high-pressure water supply, to permit flushing of the sludge pipe. No such connection should be made to a potable water supply. Sludge pipe lines should be laid out to avoid unvented vertical bends in which gas may accumulate and result in the air-locking of the pipe.

Facilities for scum removal should be placed ahead of the outlet weir on primary settling basins and should be considered for final sedimentation basins following trickling filters; the equipment should be automatic and should provide for easy scum removal; and it should discharge to a sludge well for pumping to a digester.

18–15. Mechanically cleaned basins. Among the advantages of the mechanical cleaning of sedimentation basins may be included better control of operation, no need for sludge storage in the basin, and a self-flocculating [37] effect that improves the efficiency of the

[37] See also *Sewage Works Jour.*, September, 1941, pp. 1040, 1058, 1066, and 1069, and September, 1943, p. 1013.

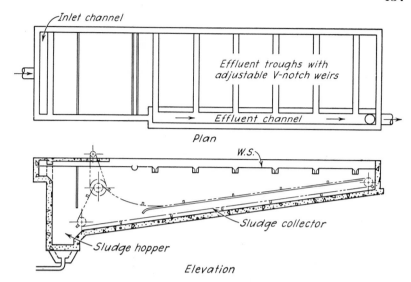

Fig. 18–11. Section of rectangular sedimentation tank with radically sloped bottom. (From H. A. Thomas and J. L. Dallas, *Jour. Boston Soc. Civil Engrs.*, October, 1952, p. 354.)

removal of suspended solids as much as 50 per cent. In basin design a 2-hr retention period, a maximum depth of 8 ft, and an overflow rate of 600 gal per day per sq ft of surface area for flows of less than 1 mgd, and somewhat higher for larger plants, are good practice.

Mechanically cleaned sedimentation basins [38] are built either square, rectangular, or circular in plan and are equipped with a mechanism that continuously or intermittently cleans the tank, concentrating the deposited material at one end or in the center of the tank. Many proprietary devices are available involving unique features.[37] The manufacturing field is highly competitive and specifications must be carefully written.[39]

A circular tank with revolving arms is shown in Fig. 18–2 and a straight-line, mechanically cleaned tank is shown in Figs. 18–1 and 18–11. The mechanism in circular tanks may be carried on a turntable supported on a central column. Mechanisms with enclosed power units are operated with ⅓- to 1½-hp motors for a 100-ft diameter mechanism. One-hp motors have been found sufficient for

[38] See also F. L. Flood, *Water and Sewage Works*, May, 1954, p. R-219.
[39] See also F. L. Flood, *ibid.*, May, 1953, p. R-144.

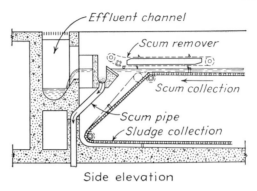

Side elevation

Fig. 18–12.   Effluent end of mechanically cleaned sedimentation chamber, with mechanical scum remover.

driving the mechanism in 60-ft-long rectangular tanks. The speed of travel of the scraper mechanisms is usually limited to about 1 ft per min to avoid disturbing the sludge.

18–16. Skimming of sedimentation basins. Mechanically operated skimming devices,[40] as illustrated in Fig. 18–12, remove scum from sedimentation basins by pushing it into the overflow trough. In circular tanks one type of skimmer floats on the surface and rides with the revolving collector arm.

18–17. Roofs. It is not ordinarily necessary to place a roof on a sedimentation basin, as the odors created are not strong and difficulties from ice are seldom serious. Basins are, however, sometimes roofed to avoid such difficulties, to landscape the grounds, or for other reasons. A roof has the advantage of preserving a quiescent surface, undisturbed by wind or rapid temperature changes, and thus increases the efficiency of the basin.

18–18. Preaeration. Preaeration of strong, raw sewage may be practiced to reduce the load on subsequent treatment devices. The aeration period, with either air diffusion or mechanical agitation, should be about 30 min, and never less than 20 min. Longer aeration periods are desirable, up to 45 min, if appreciable BOD reduction is to be effected. The rate of application of air should be adjustable.

18–19. Grease and oil removal.[41] Grease and oil are most commonly removed from sewage for the protection of sewers, pumps, and

[40] F. L. Flood, *Water and Sewage Works,* May, 1954, p. R-219.
[41] See also *Mun. San.,* January, 1938, p. 27; *Civil Eng.,* March, 1935, p. 138; *Sewage Works Jour.,* July, 1942, p. 799, and May, 1944, pp. 482 and 495.

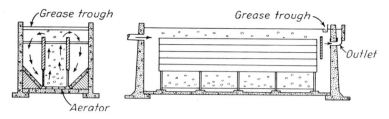

Fig. 18–13. Aerated grease-removal tank.

sewage-treatment processes. Normally the amount and quality of grease in domestic sewage will not repay the cost of its recovery, but profit has resulted through the recovery of grease from such industrial wastes as wool washing and packing houses. Sewage grease may be converted into soap, lubricants, pitch, candles, and other non-edible products.

Fales and Greeley [42] state that grease in sewage includes fats, waxes, free fatty acids, calcium and magnesium soaps, mineral oils, and other non-fatty materials. Sometimes the liquid portions are called oil and the solid portions grease. The term grease is applied generally to materials whether of animal or of vegetable origin.

Grease and oil can be removed from sewage either as a scum or as sludge. As scum, grease may be removed by hand skimming or mechanically. The formation of an easily removable greasy scum is encouraged by passing the greasy sewage through a diffused-air aeration tank with diffusers similar to those described in Sect. 23–18, and as shown in Fig. 18–13. Some of these grease particles may be adsorbed on the surface of the bubbles, forming a greasy scum on the water surface. Unfortunately, under some conditions so much greasy material may remain in solution or in colloidal suspension as to make this an undesirable method for its removal. It has been found that the turbulence in sewers, causing aeration, has increased the amount of greasy scum to be handled in some sewage-treatment plants.

Imhoff and Fair [43] suggest that the surface area of the tank should be computed by the expression

[42] A. L. Fales and S. A. Greeley, *Trans. Am. Soc. Civil Engrs.*, October, 1943, p. 507.

[43] K. Imhoff and G. M. Fair, *Sewage Treatment*, 2nd edition, John Wiley and Sons, 1956.

$$A = 1{,}110q/V_r \qquad\qquad (18\text{-}18)$$

where A = surface area of tank, sq ft.

q = rate of flow of sewage, mgd.

V_r = minimum rising velocity, in. per min.

The rising velocity is the rate of rise of particles as observed in a glass cylinder in the laboratory. In practice the magnitude of V_r is of the order of 10. Usually a retention period of about 3 min, and about 0.03 cu ft of air per gal of sewage is sufficient in this type of tank. In the design of such tanks [44] the ratio of length to depth of channel should be about 2 or $1\frac{1}{2}$ to 1. Proprietary tanks [45] that combine various stages in the process of the removal of grease in a single tank are available.

The addition of chlorine to the air to be diffused, the rate of application being about $1\frac{1}{2}$ mg/l of the sewage treated, has been found to increase the effectiveness of grease removal two to four times. Other materials that promote flotation and foaming may be added to the sewage. These materials include oil, grease, resin, and glue. On the other hand acids and the metallic salts inhibit foaming and are objectionable in skimming tanks which depend on skimming of foam.

Grease is now removed from sewage by vacuum flotation. The sewage is subjected to a vacuum of several inches of mercury for 10 to 15 minutes. The addition of coagulants will further increase the removal of solids.[46] The scum may be removed continuously by revolving skimmer arms, which sweep it to the outlet trough. A proprietary device, the Vacuator [47] is available for this purpose.

Mahlie [48] reports the removal of oil by an electric process in which the sewage flows through a series of pipes. An electric current is passed through the sewage, oil separating and collecting at the anodes. The process is patented.

Grease may be removed by the addition of chemicals, principally sulfuric acid, although lime and aluminum sulfate have been used. Most of the chemical methods for the removal of grease are protected by patents, although sulfuric acid has been used for years. The

[44] See also *Water Works and Sewerage*, February, 1945, p. 37.

[45] See also *Sewage Works Jour.*, September, 1942, p. 1194.

[46] See also *Sewage Works Jour.*, March, 1944, p. 287.

[47] See *Sewage Works Jour.*, September, 1942, p. 1178, and September, 1943, p. 1000.

[48] *Sewage Works Jour.*, May, 1940, pp. 202 and 527.

addition of chemicals, including chlorine, breaks the greasy emulsion, setting grease free to come to the surface.

Unwanted grease that has been removed from sewage may be disposed of in the same manner as screenings, as described in Sect. 17–15. Grease or vegetable oils, but not mineral oil, may be placed in sludge-digestion tanks.

18–20. The effect of detergents on sewage treatment.[49]   A detergent is any cleaning agent such as water or soap. Technically, synthetic detergents are understood to be substances, other than soap, used as cleaning agents such as alkylaryl sulfonates, alkylphenoxy polyglycols, and derivatives of high-molecular-weight polyethylene glycols, which may be classified as anionic or nonionic. They are widely used as substitutes for soap, and are sold under proprietary names.[50]

The use of synthetic detergents, sometimes called syndets, in the place of soap is increasing to such an extent in domestic cleansing and washing that the effect is becoming noticeable in sewage treatment.[51]   Some detergents require special treatment and some cannot be treated biologically. This is due, partly, to the character of the ionic charge [52] on the active molecule.

Some effects that have occurred include:

1. Curdy precipitate, formed by soap in hard water, is absent. The effect is noticeable, particularly in hard-water regions.

2. Formation of suspended solids and their removal in primary tanks are reduced.

3. BOD of sewage is likely to be less than where soap is used.

However, since the BOD test is affected by detergents, conclusions based on it must be carefully drawn.[53]

4. Volume of digester gas is less.

5. Grease tends to emulsify and carry over into secondary treatment.

6. Frothing may be excessive where air and sewage are mixed, as in the activated-sludge process.

[49] See Review of Literature for bibliography in *Proc. Am. Soc. Civil Engrs.*, Vol. 81, Paper 594, January, 1955, p. 22.

[50] See also R. H. Bogan and C. N. Sawyer, *S. and I.W.*, September, 1954, p. 1069.

[51] See *S. and I.W.*, March, 1953, pp. 245 ff.

[52] See also W. R. Gowdy, *S. and I.W.*, January, 1953, p. 15; and S. D. Faust, *Water and Sewage Works*, June, 1953, p. 242.

[53] See W. D. Sheets and G. W. Maloney, *S. and I.W.*, January, 1956, p. 10.

7. Bacterial growth may be inhibited.

8. No evidence of deleterious effect on septic action or sludge digestion.[54]

Although a method for the measurement of anionic detergents in sewage has been devised,[55] treatment-plant operators are more or less dependent on trial and experience to cope with the trend towards increasing amounts of detergents in sewage.

[54] See J. E. Fuller, *S. and I.W.*, July, 1952, p. 844.
[55] See J. Longwell and W. D. Maniece, *The Analyst*, March, 1955.

Chapter 19

Chemical treatment

19-1. The process. Chemical precipitation consists in adding to the sewage such chemicals as will, by reaction with one another and with the constituents of the sewage, produce a flocculent precipitate and thus hasten sedimentation. Sewage containing large quantities of substances that will react with a small amount of added chemicals to produce the required precipitate is the most favorable for this form of treatment. The results, as measured by BOD reduction, are better than plain sedimentation but are not so good as biological treatment. The process is particularly suitable where only seasonal treatment is required, as in a summer resort, or as a supplement to other methods of treatment, or for industrial wastes under favorable conditions. The process is quickly adjustable to changing conditions and is especially suitable for industrial plants using chemical processes of manufacture.

The advantages of this process over plain sedimentation are a more rapid and thorough removal of the suspended matter. Its disadvantages include the accumulation of a large volume of sludge, the necessity for skilled attendance, the expense of chemicals, and the temptation of an unsympathetic or disinterested administration to fail to provide funds for its operation.

A diagram representing typical steps in the process is shown in Fig. 19-1. In the process dry chemical is fed into a mixing device in which the chemical goes into solution or suspension. The solution is then fed into the sewage which has previously passed through a coarse or medium screen or has been subject to preliminary sedimentation. The mixture flows into the flocculator, where it is stirred gently to induce good coagulation and flocculation. The treated sewage flows from the flocculator to the sedimentation tank or clarifier where the supernatant liquid and the sludge are separated, and the process is complete except for the problem of sludge and effluent disposal.

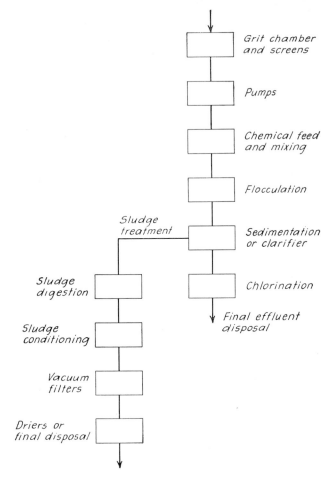

Fig. 19–1. Flowing-through diagram of a chemical treatment plant.

Factors and steps entering into the design of a plant to treat sewage chemically include aeration, stirring, retention time, presettling, return of sludge, and the various mechanical flocculators and clarifiers. Some basic design factors recommended by various state boards of health are listed in Table 19–1.

19–2. Status of the process. Historically the chemical treatment of sewage is one of the first processes that was attempted. It reached a peak in England between 1880 and 1890. Its renaissance has occurred in the United States since about 1935. In 1933 there

Table 19–1

BASIC DESIGN FACTORS FOR CHEMICAL PRECIPITATION RECOMMENDED
BY VARIOUS STATE DEPARTMENTS OF HEALTH

(From Staff Report, *Sewage Works Eng.*, March, 1948, p. 120.)

State	Minimum Average Mixing Period, min	Minimum Average Flocculation Period	Minimum Average Settling Period	Surface Settling Rate, gal per sq ft per day
Alabama	1	15–30 min	2 hr	
Connecticut		Rapid mixing		
Colorado	Mixing and flocculation, 2 hr			1,000
Illinois	Rapid	Gentle agitation	2.5 hr for mixing and settling	1,000
Idaho	Rapid	Gentle agitation	2.5 hr for mixing and settling	1,000
New Jersey	1	20 min	2 hr	
Oregon	1	10–30 min	2 hr	

were only three full-scale plants in this country. Statistics available in 1950 [1] show 197 plants serving 5.25 million persons in 1945.

The decline of the chemical-treatment process was due to the development of biological processes that secured better results at lower costs. Its renaissance may be attributed partly to the increased availability of better chemicals at low cost, mechanical equipment for handling the chemicals, better knowledge of the chemistry of the process, and adequate methods of handling the sludge produced.

19–3. Results and limitations. [2] Chemical treatment is useful in reducing suspended solids and BOD, and in clarifying and reducing the color of sewage. Dissolved solids are affected but slightly, if at all; some colloidal matter, turbidity, and color remain in the effluent. "The process is inferior to biological oxidation in the degree of removal of B.O.D., organic nitrogen, organic carbon, and ammonium compounds." [3]

Percentages of reduction of BOD as high as 95 have been obtained

[1] J. R. Thoman, *Public Health Repts.*, Supplement 213, 1950.

[2] See also W. Donaldson, *Modern Sewage Disposal,* Federation of Sewage Works Associations, 1938, p. 85.

[3] See *Sewage Works Jour.*, November, 1935, p. 997.

on a strong sewage with a heavy dose of chemical, but such high reduction cannot be expected under ordinary, routine operation. With reasonable dosages of chemical the suspended solids removal varies between 60 and 85 per cent, and the BOD reduction between 35 and 60 per cent.[4]

Although the reduction of turbidity is not an object in chemical treatment, it has been found [5] that the turibidity measurement, together with pH determinations of influent and effluent, are easy tools with which to control the process and to regulate the chemical dosage.[6] Information given by Donaldson [7] shows the cost of chemicals for eight plants in 1936 and 1938 varying between $5.79 and $8.75 per million gallons.[8]

Since no dissolved oxygen or nitrate is added in the process of chemical treatment to aid in the satisfaction of the BOD, the putrescibility of a chemically precipitated effluent is higher than that from activated-sludge or trickling-filter effluent. None of the chemicals used has proven deleterious to subsequent sludge digestion, and the effect of some, for example activated carbon, has been beneficial.

19–4. Chemistry of the process. The purpose of adding chemicals to sewage is to form an insoluble, flocculent precipitate. The success of the method depends, to a great extent, on the quantity and quality of the floc formed, and this, in turn, depends on the kind and quality of chemicals used and the method of adding them to and mixing them with the sewage. Among the chemicals used in sewage treatment, either alone or in combination, may be included alum, lime, copperas, ferric sulfate, chlorinated copperas, sulfuric acid, ferrous chloride, ferric chloride, sodium silicate,[9] and sulfur dioxide. Some less widely used chemicals [10] include Sulfacar, an aluminum hydroxychlorosulfate $[Al_2Cl_2SO_4(OH)_2]$, and Ferrigel, a compound made from ferric chloride and gelatin, glue, or certain proteins. When any of these chemicals, either alone or in proper combination, or in conjunction with chlorine, air, or a biological floc, is added to sewage, a reaction takes place to form an insoluble precipitate that adsorbs

---

[4] See *ibid.*, March, 1945, p. 134.

[5] See *ibid.*, March, 1936, p. 195.

[6] See *Mun. San.*, May, 1937, p. 279.

[7] W. Donaldson, *loc. cit.*

[8] Information concerning cost index values is given in Sect. 28–7.

[9] See also *Sewage Works Jour.*, May, 1940, p. 562.

[10] See also *ibid.*, November, 1940, p. 1051.

and precipitates colloidal and suspended solids, carrying them down with the floc in its descent through the contents of the tank.

Hypothetical reactions that occur when the more commonly used chemicals are added to sewage are shown in Table 19–2. Each of the chemicals or coagulants reacts with a reagent in the sewage or with one added with the primary coagulant. For example, lime may

Table 19–2

CHEMICAL REACTIONS IN SEWAGE TREATMENT

(*Sewage Works Jour.*, November, 1935, p. 997.)

Chemical	Reaction *
Alum	$Al_2(SO_4)_3 + 3Ca(HCO_3)_2 \rightleftharpoons 3CaSO_4 + 2Al(OH)_3 + 6CO_2$ S (342) S (486) S (408) I (156) S (264)
Copperas and lime	$FeSO_4 \cdot 7H_2O + Ca(HCO_3)_2 \rightleftharpoons Fe(HCO_3)_2 + CaSO_4 + 7H_2O$ S (278) S (162) $S\text{-}I$ (178) S (136) (126) $Fe(HCO_3)_2 + 2Ca(OH)_2 \rightleftharpoons Fe(OH)_2 + 2CaCO_3 + 2H_2O$ $I\text{-}S$ (178) $I\text{-}S$ (148) $I\text{-}S$ (90) $I\text{-}S$ (200) (36) $4Fe(OH)_2 + O_2 + 2H_2O \rightleftharpoons 4Fe(OH)_3$ $S\text{-}I$ (359.6) 32 36 I (427.6)
Ferric sul- fate and lime	$Fe_2(SO_4)_3 + 3Ca(OH)_2 \rightleftharpoons 3CaSO_4 + 2Fe(OH)_3$ S (400) $I\text{-}S$ (222) S (408) I (213.8)
Chlorinated copperas	$6FeSO_4 \cdot 7H_2O + 3Cl_2 \rightleftharpoons 2FeCl_3 + 2Fe_2(SO_4)_3 + 42H_2O$ S (1036.8) (106.5) S (324.4) S (800) (756)
Ferric chloride	$FeCl_3 + 3H_2O \rightleftharpoons Fe(OH)_3 + 3H^+ + Cl^-$ S (162.1) (54) I (74.8) (3) (35) $3H^+ + 3HCO_3^- \rightleftharpoons 3H_2CO_3$
Ferric chloride and lime	$3FeCl_3 + 3Ca(OH)_2 \rightleftharpoons 3CaCl_2 + 2Fe(OH)_3$ S (486.6) $I\text{-}S$ (222) S (333) I (149.6)
Lime	$Ca(OH)_2 + H_2CO_3 \rightleftharpoons CaCO_3 + 2H_2O$ $I\text{-}S$ (74) S (62) $I\text{-}S$ (100) (36) $Ca(OH)_2 + Ca(HCO_3)_2 \rightleftharpoons 2CaCO_3 + 2H_2O$ $I\text{-}S$ (74) S (162) $I\text{-}S$ (200) (36)
Ferrous chloride †	$4FeCl_2 + 4Ca(OH)_2 + O_2 + 2H_2O \rightleftharpoons 4Fe(OH)_3 + 4CaCl_2$ S (507.2) $I\text{-}S$ (296) (32) (36) I (427.6) S (444)

* S = soluble I = insoluble $I\text{-}S$ = partly soluble

     The figure in parentheses is molecular weight

† Not in reference.

Table 19–3

Some Characteristics of Chemical Coagulants

Chemical	Remarks
Ferric chloride	*a.* Preferable for sludge conditioning in activated sludge.
	b. Most economical for plants requiring more than 7 tons of iron annually, with facilities for handling it.
	c. Available as anhydrous, solid, lump, or aqueous solution.
	d. Can be made locally of chlorine and iron or steel scrap.
	e. Floc forms satisfactorily at all temperatures.
	f. Suitable for oxidizing H_2S with high pH.
	g. Highly corrosive and difficult to handle.
	h. Solution must be stored and handled in rubber-lined containers and pipes.
	i. Useful in odor and corrosion control, forming iron sulfide with H_2S, and is not absorbed by organic matter. Cheaper than chlorine for the purpose.
	j. Coagulates best with pH below 7.0, optimum at 5.5.
	k. Generally considered the best coagulant available.
	l. Anticipated percentage removal S.S.* = 90 to 95; BOD = 80.
	m. Dose at optimum pH = 2.0 to 2.5 gr. per gal.
Chlorinated copperas	*a.* Good for sludge conditioning in activated sludge.
	b. Economical for plants requiring more than 7 tons of iron annually, with facilities for handling it.
	c. Poor at pH 7.0; good at 5.5 and 9.0 to 9.5 with dose of 2.5 to 5.9 gr. per gal.
	d. Per cent reduction S.S. = 80 to 90 and BOD = 70 to 80.
Ferrous sulfate (copperas)	*a.* pH greater than 7.7 favors oxidation to ferric hydroxide.
	b. Dry feeders not easily used because of caking but are used.
	c. Tendency for cheaper grades to cake during storage.
	d. First cost is relatively low.
	e. Widely available as waste product from steel mills.
	f. Optimum pH about 9.0 with dose 2.5 to 5.0 gr. per gal.
	g. Overdose results in undesirable after-precipitation.
	h. Can be fed in solution form.
Ferric sulfate (ferrisul)	*a.* More efficacious than copperas or chlorinated copperas when used with lime.
	b. pH best about 8.0 to 8.5 with dose about 2.5 gr. per gal.
	c. Per cent reduction S.S. = 80 and BOD = 60.
	d. Can be fed dry or as a liquid.
Alum	*a.* Not yet widely used in sewage treatment.
	b. Economical and conveniently handled.
	c. Can be used with dry feeder.
	d. pH range from 6.0 to 8.5; above 7.0 most practical.
	e. Dose 5–6 gr. per gal with per cent reduction S.S. = 80 and BOD = 60.
Clay and other inert materials	*a.* Not yet tried on plant scale.
	b. Dosages of 100 ppm in lab. have given excellent results.
Bentonite clay, sand, asbestos fiber, paper, etc. †	*c.* Bentonite flocs readily over wide pH range with natural alkalinity.
	d. Materials other than bentonite not yet developed practically.
Lime CaO = quick $Ca(OH)_2$ = hy- drated	*a.* Can be dry-fed.
	b. Non-corrosive.
	c. Commonly used for upward adjustment of pH.
	d. Quicklime must be stored in dry, steel tanks and must be hydrated (slaked) before use. Dry hydrated lime can be stored in any dry place.
Sodium carbonate (soda ash)	*a.* Non-corrosive.
	b. Can be fed dry.
Chlorine	*a.* Corrosive and toxic. Can be stored in cast iron, lead, glass, or rubber.
	b. Requires special dosing equipment.
	c. Useful in odor and concrete-corrosion control and to control flies and ponding on filters.
Aluminum chloride	*a.* Optimum pH 5.5 and 9.0; gr. per gal at 9.0 = 5, and at pH of 5.5 = 2.5 to 5.0.

* S.S. = Settleable solids.
† See also R. D. Hoak, *Water and Sewage Works*, June 1, 1955, p. R-315.

be mixed with all the chemicals in the preceding list except with alum, sulfuric acid, or sulfur dioxide.

The formation of the most effective floc is the mark of the successful operator. Its formation depends on a variety of conditions, such as pH, flocculation, mixing, period of settling, and circulation of sludge. For any particular sewage and chemical these must be adjusted by laboratory tests and by experience based on operation records.

19–5. Choice of chemicals. Factors to be considered in the choice of chemicals include cost, quantity required, handling, storing, and feeding requirements, and effectiveness in producing desired results. No chemical best fills all requirements under all conditions. The advantages and disadvantages of various chemicals are summarized in Table 19–3.[11]

19–6. Quantity of chemicals. The amounts of the different chemicals that are required can be computed hypothetically from equations given in Table 19–2, but the actual amounts required can be determined with precision only as a result of tests.[12]

19–7. Handling chemicals. Experience with chemicals in water-works practice has been followed in sewage treatment as far as it is applicable. This fact holds true particularly with the solution-feed and dry-feed devices and in the storage of chemicals. However, for ferric chemicals, that are not widely used in the water-works field, a special technique has been developed for handling and dosing in sewage treatment.

Ferric chloride is the most widely used ferric chemical. Some of the characteristics of this chemical are listed in Table 19–3. Some data on the commercial forms of iron salts available as coagulants are given in Table 19–4.

19–8. Chemical-feed devices. Chemical-feed devices, either manually or automatically controlled, are available for feeding chemicals as a gas, a liquid, a slurry, in solution, or as a dry solid. Chlorine and sulfur dioxide are about the only chemicals applied in gaseous form. The methods and equipment perfected in water-works practice are used in the application of chlorine. An isometric view of the chlorine-dosing installation at Vallejo, Calif., is shown in Fig. 19–2. Liquid or solution feeders depend on various principles for their control. A common type controls the head on an orifice, submerged hose, or siphon, by means of a float-feed valve. Variations

[11] See also *Water Works and Sewerage*, September, 1943, p. 347.
[12] See also *ibid.*, Vol. 81, 1934, p. 358.

Table 19-4

CHARACTERISTICS OF COMMERCIAL IRON SALTS

(*Sewage Works Jour.*, November, 1935, p. 997.)

Coagulant	Formula	Per Cent Iron	Form	Container
Ferric chloride (anhydrous) *	$FeCl_3$	34.4	Powder	150-lb steel drum
Crystal ferric chloride †	$FeCl_3 \cdot 6H_2O$	20.6	Lump	435-lb barrel
Liquid ferric chloride ‡	$FeCl_3$ + water	5	Solution	4,000- and 8,000-gal tank cars
Ferric sulfate (anhydrous) §	$Fe_2(SO_4)_3$	27.9	Granular	180-lb and 380-lb bags
Chlorinated copperas ‖	$FeSO_4 \cdot 7H_2O + Cl_2$	17.8	Granular + liquid	200-lb bag and 400-lb bbl.¶
1	2	3	4	5

* Commercial chemical approximates 98% $FeCl_3$.
† 60% $FeCl_3$.
‡ Commercial shipments vary from 39 to 45%.

§ Commercial chemical about 90% $Fe_2(SO_4)_3$.
‖ 88.7 lb $FeSO_4 \cdot 7H_2O$ + 11.3 lb Cl_2 = 100 lb.
¶ Also in cylinders, drums, and tank cars.

of flow can be effected by change of head or size of orifice, either manually or automatically. Other devices are controlled by reciprocating pumps or motor-driven equipment carrying small cups, siphons, and so forth, which are adjustable to feed at a uniform rate or at a rate proportional to the flow of sewage. The rate of feeding is controlled by dropping the chemical from a hopper on to a screw conveyor, a grooved or slotted disk, a reciprocating plunger, or other device whose rate of motion is adjustable. In some feeders the hopper is vibrated to avoid arching of the chemical. A device of this type is illustrated in Fig. 19-3. The rate of dosing may be automatically controlled by the mechanism, the desired rate being set on the micrometer scale shown.

19-9. Chemical mixers. Chemicals should be well mixed in solution before being applied to the sewage, in order to secure the best results. The mixing is accomplished by violent agitation in a "flash mixer" of the type illustrated in Fig. 19-4, in an aerated mixing tank, or in some other device. Too long a mixing period is undesirable as subsequent floc formation may be injured. The period in the mixing device should lie between 30 and 180 seconds.

19-10. Use of activated carbon. The use of activated carbon in the treatment of sewage has been found to be advantageous in the control of odors; in the adjustment of pH in sludge digestion; in improving sludge digestion and the quality of sludge and its drying characteristics; in preventing the production of scum in sludge-diges-

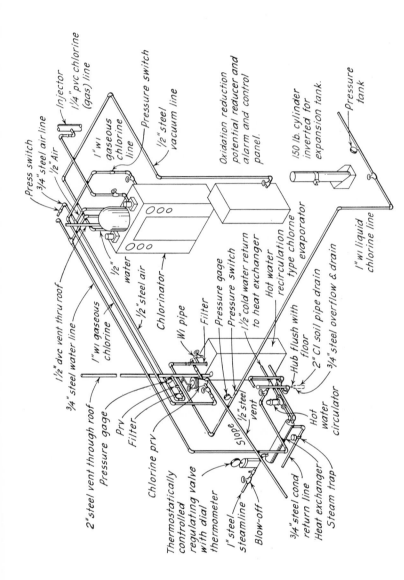

Fig. 19-2. Arrangement of chlorine-dosing equipment at Vallejo, Calif. (Courtesy Brown and Caldwell, Engineers.)

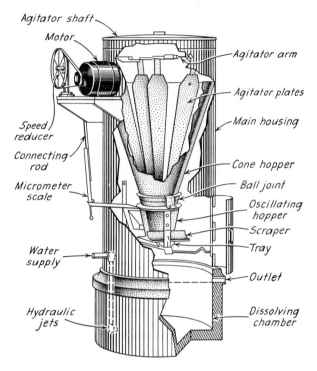

Fig. 19–3. Dry-chemical feeder. (Courtesy Builders Iron Foundry.)

tion tanks and on Imhoff tanks; and in controlling the bulking of sludge.

The peculiar properties of activated carbon are due, in part, to the adsorptive properties of its particles, which expose an extremely large surface area to colloidal matter in the sewage that is adsorbed by the carbon particles.

Activated carbon is used in the form of a powder that may be applied by a dry-feed machine directly to the sewage or sludge to be treated. Practically all the benefits claimed for activated carbon can be obtained by applying a dose of 35 to 50 lb of carbon per million gal of sewage treated. In general, the carbon should be added just after the coarse screens have been passed, although other points of application have been used with satisfactory results.

19–11. Return of sludge. The recirculation of sludge or of effluent from the clarifier to the influent of the flocculator has been found to aid in coagulation and to reduce the amount of chemical

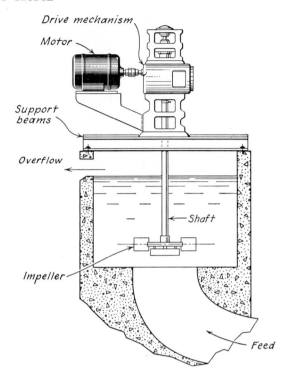

Fig. 19–4. A flash mixer. (Courtesy Dorr-Oliver Co.)

required. In an investigation of the effect of the return of sludge Rudolfs and Gehm [13] have concluded:

1. Returned alum, ferric chloride, and ferric chloride plus lime sludges have a definite clarifying value, although the same effect can usually be obtained with from 1 to 5 mg/l of the coagulant.

2. The amount of returned sludge necessary with ferric chloride or alum to obtain maximum clarification is lower than when lime-coagulated sludge is used.

3. The order of addition of return sludge and coagulant does not seem to be important.

4. Partially treated sludges are less effective than fully treated, and over-treated sludges are no more effective than fully treated ones.

5. Acid sludges have no clarifying values, but lower slightly the pH values of raw sewage.

6. Increasing the ferric coagulant dosage decreases the effectiveness of return sludge in clarification.

[13] W. Rudolfs and H. W. Gehm, *Sewage Works Jour.*, January, 1937, p. 22.

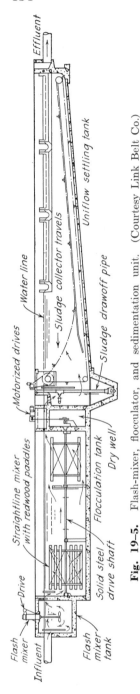

Fig. 19-5. Flash-mixer, flocculator, and sedimentation unit. (Courtesy Link Belt Co.)

There is a certain optimum amount of return sludge to produce the best results. Depending on the nature of the sewage, this will occur with a suspended-solids content of 2,000 to 3,000 mg/l in the mixed liquor.

19–12. Flocculation. Flocculation is the formation of flocs of settleable matter with a large surface area relative to the weight of the particle of floc. As the floc settles through the liquid it sweeps other settleable particles down with it, increasing the efficiency of removal of settleable matter and decreasing the time required therefor. Flocculent particles may be formed by chemical, mechanical, or biological means, or by combinations thereof.

Chemical flocculation, either with or without mechanical aid, is the most common procedure in flocculation. In chemical flocculation the chemical should be thoroughly mixed with the sewage before entering the flocculation basin. Whether or not the flocculator contains mechanical aids, the period of retention in it should be from 20 to 60 min, preferably between 30 and 40 min, to allow sufficient time for the formation of floc. The velocity of flow through the flocculator should be greater than 3 to 5 fpm to prevent sedimentation in the flocculator. After the floc has been formed the effluent should go to the sedimentation tank or clarifier where sedimentation takes place and from which sludge is removed.

A combined chemical mixer, flocculator with mechanical aids, and clarifier is illustrated in Fig. 19-5. It consists of a long, narrow, rectangular tank containing two to four mechanical paddles with their shafts at right angles to the direction of the flow of sewage. The peripheral speed of the paddles should be between 1½ and 2½ fps in order to maintain solids in suspension. The paddles should revolve with their tops slightly below the surface of the sewage. The paddles near the influent may revolve somewhat faster than those near the effluent end of the flocculator. The paddles may be spaced so that the minimum distance between them, when in a horizontal position, is not greater than 2 to 3 ft. Other proprietary devices, such as Infilco's Accelator,[14] combine the process of mixing, flocculation, and sedimentation in one tank.

Other types of flocculators include a tank in which the paddles revolve with the axis parallel to the direction of flow; a tank through which air is diffused while the sewage flows through it in a helical path; and a tube in which flocculated sewage and chemically treated sewage are mixed, part of the mixture being sent to the clarifier and the remainder being returned to the flocculating tube. Air blown gently through the sewage has also been used successfully in flocculation.

In the design of flocculators, outlet disturbances in the flocculator and inlet disturbances into subsequent settling tanks should be minimized because of the fragile nature of the floc. In the design of channels leading to the clarifier care must be taken to avoid corners and dead spaces conducive to sedimentation. Flocculated sewage should not be pumped nor allowed to flow through channels between the steps of flocculation and sedimentation. The flocculation chamber should be an integral part of the settling basin, as shown in Fig. 19–5.

Mechanical flocculation alone is the coalescence of finely divided suspended matter primarily under the influence of physical forces, usually gentle stirring, and in the absence of biologically active slime. Bioflocculation involves similar action, but primarily under the influence of biologically active slimes.[15] By stirring gently with mechanical paddles, diffused air, or other mechanical means, for 20 to 60 min, a natural self-flocculation will occur that will be helpful in subsequent treatment. Mechanical flocculation [16] has been shown to aid in the removal of both non-settleable and colloidal solids from the effluents of secondary sewage-treatment processes such as trickling-filter effluent and activated-sludge effluent. Some results

[14] See also *Water Works and Sewerage*, February, 1941, p. **70**; and *Sewage Works Jour.*, September, 1942, p. 1188.

[15] See also *Sewage Works Jour.*, May, 1941, p. **506**.

[16] See *ibid.*, March, 1940, p. 280.

Table 19-5

RESULTS OF FLOCCULATION

Type of Treatment	Suspended Solids in Effluent after Quiescent Settling, mg/l	Suspended Solids in Effluent after Continuous Settling, mg/l	Characteristic Affected *	Per Cent Removal by Flocculation	
				Without Chemicals	With Chemicals
Plain settling	60	80	BOD	10–15	25–35
Plain settling and filtration	30	50	Suspended solids	5–10	20–30
Flocculation and settling	50	56	Settleable solids	4– 5	4– 5
Flocculation, settling, and filtration	20	35			
Chemical precipitation	15	30			
Chemical precipitation and filtration	4	15			

* From L. G. Rice, *Water and Sewage Works*, December, 1950, p. 519.

reported by Fischer and Hillman [16] in a Dorrco flocculator are summarized in Table 19-5.

In general, where chemicals are added before flocculation, greatly increased efficiency results, more than sufficient to justify the added cost of the combination of flocculating methods.

19–13. Proprietary chemical processes. The chemical treatment of sewage has been fruitful in the production of patented devices and processes. Sixty-four United States patents granted between 1873 and 1935 are listed in the report of a committee of the American Public Health Association.[17] The proprietary processes most widely known include the Scott-Darcey, the Guggenheim, and the Laughlin.

19–14. Scott-Darcey process. The principal feature of this process is the inclusion in it of the manufacture of ferric chloride by the action of chlorine on scrap iron.[18] A chlorine solution is passed

[17] See *Sewage Works Jour.*, November, 1935, p. 997.
[18] See also *Mun. San.*, June, 1938, p. 298.

through a chamber containing scrap iron and comes out as ferric chloride, ready for application to the sewage. If the concentration of the chlorine in the solution is above 3,000 mg/l, ferric chloride should be formed. When the chlorine falls below this, or contact with iron is too prolonged, ferrous chloride is formed.

19–15. Guggenheim process.[19] This process consists essentially of the aeration of chemically flocculated sewage for about $1\frac{1}{2}$ hr, followed by sedimentation with the return of sludge from the clarifier to the aeration tank. It differs from the activated-sludge process because it operates on chemically flocculated sewage, the coagulant used being ferric iron salt, and because the detention and aeration periods are shorter. Tests reported by a committee of the American Public Health Association [20] indicate a higher BOD reduction than can be obtained by ordinary chemical precipitation.

19–16. Laughlin process. In this process ferric chloride and lime are normally used as coagulants, followed by sedimentation and filtration of the effluent through magnetite filters. The magnetite filter is cleaned automatically, the magnet being set into action as the depth of water rises over the filter.

19–17. Putnam process. In the Putnam process coagulants used include lime, carbon, a ferric salt, return sludge, and mechanical flocculation. The effluent is filtered in a rapid sand filter of the water-works type. It is claimed that 99 per cent of the suspended solids and 89 per cent of the BOD are removed. The process includes the disposal of sludge that is first dewatered on a vacuum filter and is then distilled by heat.

19–18. Sludge production and disposal. The weight of sludge to be expected in chemical treatment can be predicted approximately by adding the amount of chemical precipitants, as computed from hypothetical reactions, to the estimated weight of suspended solids that will be precipitated. Chemical sludge is compact, and that resulting from ferric coagulants digests rapidly and dries quickly so that the difficulties of sludge handling, in so far as the qualities of the sludge are concerned, are less than indicated by the fact that the added chemicals tend to increase the weight of the sludge. The disposal of chemical sludge offers no problems different from the disposal of sludge from biological processes.

[19] See also *Sewage Works Jour.,* September, 1944, p. 973, and January, 1942, p. 104.

[20] *Sewage Works Jour.,* November, 1935, p. 997.

The volume of sludge to be handled does not constitute a major disadvantage to the process. At Indianapolis, Ind.,[21] primary, dried solids amounted to about 900 lb of dry solids per million gal of sewage, with a moisture content of about 95 per cent. If the sewage were treated with 500 lb of lime, the solids would be increased to 2,165 lb. With the ordinary moisture content the total sludge weight should be about 2,400 lb more per million gal of sewage than from plain sedimentation, or about 2½ times as much. Buswell[22] has stated:

(1) . . . one would expect twice as much organic matter in sludge from chemical precipitation, (2) Sludge of 10 per cent more solids may be expected from chemical precipitation. On this basis the total volume of sludge obtained by chemical precipitation would be somewhat less than that obtained by plain sedimentation.

Disinfection and Chlorination [23]

19–19. Methods and purposes. Sewage may be disinfected by various means, but chlorination is used almost exclusively in practice. Laboratory studies[24] have demonstrated the effectiveness of gamma radiation from radioactive substances but field experiences are not yet widely reported.

Sewage is disinfected to protect public water supplies, shellfish, and bathing beaches; to prevent the spread of disease; to aid in the control of corrosion; to prevent growths in sewers; to keep down odors; to kill filter flies and keep down odors on trickling filters; to prevent putrefaction in sludge thickening; to aid in grease removal; to aid in some industrial-waste treatment; to reduce BOD; to delay the putrefaction of sewage or treatment-plant effluent so that a fresher substance may be available for subsequent dilution or treatment; to decrease BOD load on receiving waters; to control digester foaming; and for other purposes.

Sterilization is the destruction of all bacterial life, including spores. Ordinarily even the most destructive agents do not accomplish complete sterilization. Chlorine and its compounds are practically the

[21] See *Sewage Works Jour.*, May, 1936, p. 475.

[22] See *Sewage Works Jour.*, November, 1935, p. 1063.

[23] See *Water and Sewage Works*, May, 1949, p. R-137, March, 1951, p. 130, and June 1, 1955; and W. N. Grune, *Water and Sewage Works*, August, 1955, p. 350. See also procedures recommended by Joint Committee, *S. and I.W.*, October, 1953, p. 1235; and L. W. Van Kleeck, *Wastes Eng.*, 1956, pp. 268, 320, and 371.

[24] See *Wastes Eng.*, July, 1955, p. 363.

only ones used for the disinfection of sewage. The lime in chemical precipitation, the acid in grease flotation, and the aeration in the activated-sludge process all serve to disinfect sewage, but they are not used primarily for that purpose. Copper sulfate has been used as an algicide, but never on a large scale as a bactericide. Heat has been suggested, but its high cost has prevented its practical application to the disinfection of sewage.

19–20. Some characteristics of chlorine.[25] Among the characteristics of chlorine that affect the manner in which it is handled and the amount that is used in sewage treatment may be included: (1) It is toxic. The odor of chlorine is detectable at 3.5 volumes in one million volumes of air; it produces throat irritation at 15 volumes; coughing at 30 volumes; exposure for more than 30 minutes is dangerous at 40 volumes; and it is fatal at 1,000 volumes. (2) It is about 2.5 times the weight of air so that leaking gas descends and ventilation must be provided with this in view. (3) It is neither combustible nor explosive. (4) It is highly corrosive at temperatures above 195° F, and at normal room temperature when moist.

Chlorine is normally used in liquid form in sewage treatment. It is shipped in steel containers holding from 150 lb to more than one ton. It is available also in other forms such as chlorinated lime, HTH, and chlorine dioxide. Chlorinated lime contains 33 per cent, by weight, of chlorine, and HTH (high test hypochlorite) contains 67 per cent. The amount of chlorine "available" in these compounds and the oxidizing power of other disinfectants vary so widely that the term *available chlorine,* analogous to chlorine equivalent, has been developed. The per cent of chlorine equivalent is a measure of the oxidizing power of a compound in terms of chlorine. It is possible for a compound to have more than 100 per cent equivalent chlorine as, for example, $HOCl$ which has 134.5 per cent available or equivalent chlorine.

19–21. Bactericidal effect of chlorination.[26] Chlorine, when added to sewage, forms chlorinous compounds including $HOCl$, OCl,

[25] See also *Jour. Am. Water Works Assoc.,* October, 1953, p. 1060. *Chlorine,* a technical brochure, Pittsburgh Plate Glass Co., 1948. "Liquid Chlorine," *Bull.* 7, Solvay Technical and Engineering Series, 1949. "Chlorination of Sewage and Industrial Wastes," *Manual 4,* Federation of Sewage and Industrial Wastes Associations. R. V. Day and others, *Ind. and Eng. Chem.,* May, 1953, p. 1001. A. E. Griffin, *Public Works,* October, 1949, p. 10. L. F. Warrick, *Water and Sewage Works,* April, 1951. *S. and I.W.,* October, 1953, p. 1235.

[26] See also E. W. Moore, *Water and Sewage Works,* May, 1953, p. R-197.

and chloramines. The germicidal effect is due, probably, to the reaction of these compounds, especially of HOCl, with essential enzymes of the bacterial cell stopping the metabolic process. Among the conditions affecting germicidal value are pH, temperature, time, and germicidal concentration. pH affects germicidal power through its relation to the formation of HOCl which is many times more effective than OCl. For example, at $20°$ C and a pH of 5.0 or less, the ratio of HOCl to OCl is 0.997 or more and at pH of 10 or more the ratio is 0.005 or less. The effect of temperature on germicidal value, within normal limits of sewage treatment, is unimportant. The effect of time, expressed by Chick's Law, is

$$\log (N_1/N_2) = kt \tag{19-1}$$

where N_1 is the number of organisms present at start.
N_2 is the number present at the end of time t.
k is a constant.

Each value of k is applicable to constant, ideal conditions and to one specific organism. Germicidal effects are directly proportional to the concentration of disinfectants. However, since methods of determining residual chlorine are interfered with by other compounds, equal chlorine dosages in different sewages do not always indicate equal killing power. Likewise, since some chlorine is consumed by organic matter, an increase in applied chlorine is not a direct measure of increased germicidal effect.

19–22. Amount of chlorine. The amount of chlorine used depends on the quality of the sewage to be treated, the stage of decomposition of organic matter, the desired degree of disinfection, the period of contact, the pH, and the temperature. A relationship between the amount of chlorine applied and results desired in disinfection has been suggested by Hess [27] as:

$$\frac{1}{\log MPN} = a + bR \tag{19-2}$$

where a and b are constants and R is the total chlorine residual. Grune [28] recommends the control of chlorination by the maintenance of a fixed chlorine residual after a specified contact period preceded by adequate mixing. Some figures showing approximate chlorine requirements for adequate disinfection are given in Table 19–6. Most

[27] S. G. Hess, *S. and I.W.*, July, 1953, p. 751.
[28] W. N. Grune, *Water and Sewage Works*, August, 1955, p. 350.

Table 19–6

CHLORINE REQUIRED FOR DISINFECTION

Sewage or Effluent	mg/l *	mg/l †
Raw sewage	6–12	20–25
septic	12–25	. . .
Settled sewage	5–10	15–20
septic	12–40	
Chemical precipitation	3– 6	20
Trickling filter, standard, normal	3– 5	12–15
standard, poor	5–10	
High-rate trickling filter	. . .	15–20
Activated sludge, normal	2– 4	5–15
poor	3– 8	
Sand filter, normal	1– 3	5–10
poor	3– 5	
Odor control, etc.	. . .	10–20

* From L. H. Enslow, *Modern Sewage Disposal*, Federation of Sewage Works Associations, 1938, p. 98; and W. N. Grune, *Water and Sewage Works*, August, 1955, p. 350.

† From L. G. Rice, *Water and Sewage Works*, October, 1950, p. 436.

state boards of health require a residual of 0.5 mg/l and a contact period of 30 min, although only 15 min is required by a few states, when sewage effluents are being treated.[29] Warrick [30] states that with strongly septic, raw sewages it may take as much as 40 ppm. For BOD reduction 1 ppm of chlorine may reduce the BOD by 2 ppm.[31]

Groff and Ridenour [32] as a result of study of breakpoint chlorination of sewage, concluded that:

Chlorination to the breakpoint did not result in increased B.O.D. reduction over that obtained by the low dosages of chlorine commonly used, but the reduction was permanent; the B.O.D. of a chlorinated sewage varies directly with the residual chlorine beyond the first mg/l of chlorine added; and the B.O.D. reduction obtained with low dosages of chlorine in amounts sufficient to give a slight residual was not permanent but lasted only shortly after the beginning of the second stage of oxidation.

[29] See *Sewage Works Eng.*, March, 1948, p. 120.

[30] *Water and Sewage Works*, April, 1951, p. 179.

[31] See also *Water and Sewage Works*, May, 1949, p. R-137, March, 1951, p. 130, and June 1, 1955, p. R-277. W. N. Grune, *Water and Sewage Works*, August, 1955, p. 350.

[32] G. Groff and G. M. Ridenour, *Sewage Works Jour.*, September, 1943, p. 847.

The application of insufficient chlorine to create a residual, sometimes known as *subresidual chlorination,* has been found to be efficient in the use of chlorine but not always adequately effective in disinfection.[33]

The removal of bacteria is usually only apparent or temporary because many of them, encased in the solid matter of the sewage, escape the effect of the chlorine and are not detected in the bacterial analysis. Strong and old sewages, high temperatures, and short periods of contact will require more chlorine to produce satisfactory results. A septic effluent requires more chlorine than a raw sewage because of the greater oxygen demand by the effluent.

19–23. Method of application.[34] Chlorine is applied to flowing sewage ordinarily in the form of either gas or liquid, following standard water-works practice and using similar equipment. The chlorine-dosing apparatus is placed in a separate, heated, and well-ventilated room. A vent near the floor is desirable since chlorine is heavier than air. A gas mask resistant to chlorine should be accessible and in a convenient location *outside* of the chlorine room.

Chlorine is normally fed in an aqueous solution requiring about 17 gal of water per lb of chlorine gas at 68° F. Special equipment is usually required to feed the chlorine solution into a closed line or an open channel and to obtain satisfactory dispersion. At least four types of feeders are available in practice. In the solution-feed type a high-strength, aqueous solution of chlorine is fed into the sewage; in direct or dry-feed chlorine gas is fed under pressure, directly into the sewage. In the semi-vacuum feeder the system is maintained under a vacuum during the time the eductor is in operation. In the full-vacuum feeder an ejector is employed into which the gas is drawn to provide solution feed and create the vacuum. This type of feeder is used frequently because of its safe operation. Chlorine will not feed unless there is enough vacuum to induce flow. There are four basic methods for controlling the rate of flow of chlorine. These vary between a fixed rate of flow controlled manually to a "program control" involving automatic variation of rate of solution flow in proportion to the rate of flow of sewage.

The chlorinating equipment should have a capacity to apply at least 18 mg/l of chlorine to sedimentation tank effluent; 12 mg/l to trickling filter effluent, and 6 mg/l to intermittent sand effluent.

[33] See also *S. and I.W.,* August, 1950, p. 1004.
[34] See also Joint Committee Report on the Handling of Chlorine, *S. and I.W.,* October, 1953, p. 1235; and *Water and Sewage Works,* June 1, 1955, p. R-83.

Chlorine may be applied in a solid form in emergencies or temporarily because of the greater ease of applying a solid to tanks or placing it on filters. Chlorine is available in solid form as chloride of lime ($CaOCl_2$) or calcium hypochlorite containing, when freshly made, 33 per cent, by weight, of chlorine; as high-test hypochlorite (HTH), a non-hygroscopic powder containing about 66 per cent chlorine; and as sodium hypochlorite.

To obtain effective disinfection of sewage with chlorine the contact period should not be less than 15 minutes, on the basis of the average flow, and there should be residual chlorine after disinfection, of not less than 0.1 to 0.5 mg/l. In some treatment processes the chlorine dose may be less and no residual is required as only a partial satisfaction of the chlorine demand is desired.

Prechlorination is preferable to post-chlorination in connection with plain sedimentation because: (1) the longer period of contact results in better bacterial kill; (2) odors are controlled better; (3) algal growths are reduced; (4) septic action and the formation of hydrogen sulfide are delayed or avoided; (5) no post-chlorination chamber is needed; and (6) undesirable effects of variations in rate of flow of sewage are minimized.

Two-stage application, i.e., application at two points well separated in reference to the raw sewage and the plant effluent, may produce equal results with less chlorine.[35]

19–24. Results of chlorination. The application of chlorine to sewage reduces the bacterial count temporarily and reduces the BOD from 10 to 35 per cent, depending on the condition and stage of decomposition of the sewage.[36] Spores and bacteria protected in organic matter not penetrated by the chlorine escape its sterilizing effect. Bacteria surviving chlorination, including intestinal forms, may multiply rapidly thereafter, finding a favorable environment free from natural enemies, the result being an increase in the total bacterial count as compared with that preceding chlorination.

Effects of the addition of chlorine in sewage treatment processes are to reduce nitrates in the effluent, to diminish carbon dioxide production, to increase turbidity, and to affect the oxidation-reduction potential. E_h-residual chlorine[37] curves approach an asymptote

[35] See also D. M. Pierce, *S. and I.W.*, August, 1952, p. 929.

[36] See also *Water and Sewage Works*, May, 1949, p. R-137; March, 1951, p. 130, and June 1, 1955, p. R-277. W. N. Grune, *Water and Sewage Works*, August, 1955, p. 350; and R. V. Day and others, *Ind. and Eng. Chem.*, May, 1953, p. 1001.

[37] E_h signifies electrical potential, usually expressed in millivolts, mv.

Table 19–7

SOME RESULTS OF CHLORINATION

Place	Population, 10^3	Rate of Flow, mgd	Cl Is Applied to	Cl Applied, mg/l	Cl Residual, mg/l	Reference in *S. and I.W.*
Cranston, R. I.	27.8	2.46	Sed. tank after aeration	3.0	0.6	Oct., 1952, p. 1315
Cleveland, Ohio Easterly,	...	108.3	Final sed. after A.S.*	3.8	0.8	Nov., 1952, p. 1424
Westerly,	...	38.0	Imhoff tank, pre and post	13.6	1.4	Nov., 1952, p. 1427
Muskegon, Mich.	61 †	7.13	Settled raw	8.3	0.6	Sept., 1953, p. 1108
Greece, N. Y.	13.8	0.76	A.S. sed. tank	5.1	0.6	Jan., 1952, p. 101
Detroit, Mich.	2,700	444	Primary sed.	3.7	1.0±	Sept., 1955, p. 1095
Niles, Mich.	14	2.9	Primary sed.	4.2	0.5	Aug., 1953, p. 975
Racine, Wis.	73	21.3	Primary sed.	3.6 ‡	...	

* A.S. indicates activated sludge.
† Population equivalent.
‡ Chlorine demand.

where E_h is slightly less than 1,400 mv.[38] The application of as much as 15 mg/l of chlorine to sewage before biological treatment does not interfere measurably with the treatment process because the relatively small amount of chlorine added is quickly absorbed by the organic matter. Some results of the chlorination of sewage are shown in Table 19–7.

19–25. Decontamination factor. The expression of the effectiveness of disinfection as percentage removal, P, may be unsatisfactory because of the closeness of the figures to 100. The decontamination factor, F, may be more significant where

[38] From C. E. Keefer and J. Meisel, *S. and I.W.*, July, 1953, p. 759.

$$F \text{ is } \log \left(\frac{100}{100 - P} \right)$$

For example, where P is 99 F is 2, and when P is 99.9 F becomes 3. The following solution, based on an example by Thomas [39] illustrates an application of the decontamination factor:

Example. In a primary sewage-treatment plant receiving raw sewage with 10^7 coliform bacteria per 100 ml: (*a*) 50 per cent are removed by sedimentation, (*b*) 99 per cent of the remainder by chlorination, (*c*) the effluent is diluted 10:1 in the receiving stream, and (*d*) the die-away is 75 per cent per day. The time of flow to a water-works intake is 1.5 days. What overall percentage removal of bacteria will be necessary at the water-works to meet the U. S. Public Health Service standard of not more than 1.0 coliform per 100 ml?

Solution. The values of F for each stage of sewage treatment are, respectively: (*a*) 0.3, (*b*) 2.0, (*c*) 1.0, (*d*) $1.5 \times 0.6 = 0.9$. Hence $\Sigma E = 4.2$, or 99.994 per cent reduction.

19–26. Electrolytic treatment.[40] Attempts to treat sewage by electrolytic means have proved to be impracticable. With the exception of the Landreth direct-oxidation process [41] and electrodialysis, electrolytic methods have depended on the solution of a metal anode, usually iron, the formation of the hydroxide of this metal, and the flocculating value of the hydroxide on the sewage.

The direct-oxidation process combined electrolysis with the application of lime. Experience has resulted in the conclusion that it is uneconomical and impracticable, the lime being more effective than the electricity.[41] Electrodialysis [40] is "electrolysis with the separation at the electrodes of the ions of the soluble salts or the products of their discharge."

19–27. Disinfection by gamma radiation.[42] The coliform index in sewage effluents has been reduced as much as 99 per cent by a dose of 50,000 reps,[43] and the total count reduced 99 per cent by 100,000

---

[39] H. A. Thomas, *S. and I.W.,* November, 1955, p. 1236.

[40] See also *Sewage Works Jour.,* September, 1942, p. 1021, and November, 1942, p. 1281.

[41] See *Eng. News-Record,* Sept. 18, 1919, p. 541.

[42] G. M. Ridenour and E. H. Armbruster, *Jour. Am. Water Works Assoc.,* June, 1956, p. 611.

[43] A *rep* (roentgen equivalent physical) is a unit of absorbed dose of 93 ergs per g. A *rad* is an absorbed dose of 100 ergs per g. The difference is negligible

reps disinfection with gamma radiation.   Unlike chlorine as a disinfectant gamma radiation disinfection is unaffected by pH over a range between 5 and 8.5.   As a comparable figure 1 to 3 million reps are required to sterilize most foodstuffs.   Gamma irradiation of settled sewage and of sewage sludge has shown 100 per cent kill with 5 million to 2 million rads.[43]

in estimating the permissible limits of dosage.   The rad, a newer unit, is preferable to the rep. See U. S. Bureau of Standards, *Handbook* 59, September, 1954.

Chapter 20

Septic tanks
and Imhoff tanks

20-1. The septic process. Septic action or septicization is a natural, biological process in which bacteria and other microscopic and submicroscopic forms of life, acting in the absence of oxygen, reduce organic substances to lower oxidized forms, some solids are dissolved or liquefied, and gas containing principally carbon dioxide, methane, and sometimes a small amount of hydrogen sulfide and traces of other gases, are given off. The biological process in the septic tank represents that portion of the cycle of life and death in which complex organic compounds are reduced to a simpler condition to be available as food for low forms of plant life. The treatment of sewage by septic action, when introduced, promised the solution of all problems in sewage treatment. Septic action is now better understood, and it is known that some of the early claims were unfounded.

The principal advantage of septic action in sewage treatment is the relatively small amount of sludge that must be cared for compared to that produced by plain sedimentation or by chemical precipitation. The sludge from a septic tank may be 25 to 30 per cent or even 40 per cent less in weight, and 75 to 80 per cent less in volume, than the sludge from a plain sedimentation tank. The most important results of septic action and the greatest septic activity occur in the deposited organic matter or sludge. The biologic changes due to septic action that occur in the liquid portion of the tank contents are of little or no importance. Among other advantages are the comparative inexpensiveness of the tanks and the small amount of attention and skilled attendance required.

The septic tank is not widely used in municipal practice because of the better results obtained by other processes, the occasional dis-

467

charge of effluent worse than the influent, and the occasional discharge of sludge in the effluent caused by violent septic boiling. It is, however, widely used by isolated institutions and for schools, residences, and small establishments where sewers are not available. Occasionally the odors given off by the septic process are highly objectionable and are carried for a long distance. Over-septicization must be guarded against, as an over-septicized effluent is more difficult of further treatment or of disposal than a comparatively fresh, untreated sewage. An over-septicized or stale sewage is indicated by the presence of large quantities of either free or albuminoid ammonia, frequently accompanied by hydrogen sulfide and other foul smelling gases. The oxygen demand in an over-septicized sewage is greater than that in a fresh or more carefully treated sewage.

20–2. The septic tank.[1] A septic tank is a horizontal, continuous-flow, one-story sedimentation tank through which sewage is allowed to flow slowly to permit settleable matter to settle to the bottom where it is retained until anaerobic decomposition is established, resulting in changing some of the suspended organic matter into liquid and gaseous substances, and in a reduction of the quantity of sludge to be disposed of.[2] The purpose of the septic tank is to store the sludge for such a period of time that partial liquefaction of the sludge may take place, and thus minimize the difficulty of sludge disposal. For this reason the sludge-storage capacity of a septic tank is ordinarily greater than is required in a plain sedimentation tank. It is to be noted that in a septic tank the rate of flow of the effluent must equal the rate of flow of the influent at all times. Tanks holding stagnant, household sewage are called *cesspools.* The use of septic tanks and cesspools is confined almost exclusively to household and similar small installations.

Septic and sedimentation tanks differ only in the period of retention and the frequency of cleaning. The period in a septic tank is longer and the tank is cleaned less often. The results obtained by the two processes differ. A septic tank can be converted into a sedimentation tank, or vice versa, by changing the method of operation, no constructional features requiring change.

[1] See also S. R. Weibel and others, *Studies on Household Sewage Disposal Systems,* Housing and Home Finance Agency, Washington, D. C., 1949. *Manual of Septic Tank Practice,* U. S. Public Health Service Publication **526**, 1957.

[2] Definition proposed by the American Public Health Association.

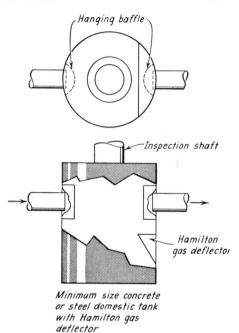

Fig. 20–1. Circular, household septic tank.

20–3. Household or domestic septic tanks.[3] The simplest form of septic tank for a household may be either a single-compartment tank, cylindrical or rectangular in shape, somewhat as shown in Fig. 20–1. Recommended capacities of septic tanks are shown in Table 20–1 and Fig. 16–3. A household tank should not contain less than about 500 gal of sewage with an allowance for the accumulation of about 20 gal of sludge annually or between cleanings for each person using the tank. In a two-compartment tank the first compartment should hold not less than 500 gal. Two-compartment tanks, such as shown in Fig. 20–2, in which the capacity of the first compartment is two-thirds to one-half of the entire tank, serve longer between cleanings than a single-compartment tank of the same total capacity. Further compartmentation serves no useful purpose.

[3] See S. R. Weibel and others, *Studies on Household Sewage Disposal Systems,* Part I, 1949; Part II, 1950; and Part III, 1954, U. S. Public Health Service. *Manual of Septic Tank Practice,* U. S. Public Health Service Publication 526, 1957.

Table 20-1

RECOMMENDED CAPACITIES OF SEPTIC TANKS *

Dwellings						Day Schools †				
Bed-rooms	Max Persons Served	Tank Capac-ity, gal	Dwellings Length × Width × Depth, ft			Maxi-mum Persons Served	Tank Capac-ity, gal	Day Schools † Length × Width × Depth, ft		
2 or less	4	500	6	3	4	60	1,000	8½	4	4
3	6	600	7	3	4	120	2,000	11	5	5
4	8	750	7½	3½	4	180	3,000	13½	6	5
5	10	900	8½	3½	4	240	4,000	18	6	5
6	12	1,100	8½	4	4½	300	5,000	18	7½	5
7	14	1,200	9	4	4½	360	6,000	20	8	5
8	16	1,500	10	4½	4½	420	7,000	20	8½	5½
						480	8,000	23	8½	5½

* Tank capacities in this table are based on 50 gal per capita in dwellings, 25 in camps, and 17 in day schools. It is assumed that the liquid capacities will provide enough volume for a 2-yr accumulation of sludge.

† Add 50 per cent to tank capacity for persons served in camps.

Some desirable features in the design of household septic tanks include:

1. The material used should be watertight and corrosion resistant. Concrete, large-diameter vitrified tile pipe with the axis vertical, and well-protected metal have been used.

2. The natural ventilation provided should be adequate. Ordinarily the open ends of the inlet and outlet will be adequate, or an open shaft, leading to the ground surface will be sufficient. The upper end of the open shaft should be shielded to prevent the dropping of objects into the tank, or to prevent access to it by small animals.

3. A manhole should be provided, as shown in Fig. 20-2, to permit inspection and cleaning.

4. Baffles should be limited to one hanging baffle at the inlet to prevent high surface velocities, and a hanging baffle in front of the outlet to prevent the escape of scum. The inlet baffle may extend 12 in. below the liquid surface, and the outlet baffle about 18 in. below the surface.

5. The escape of gas and sludge into the effluent pipe may be diminished by a gas deflector [4] beneath the outlet pipe, as shown in the circular tank in Fig. 20-1.

[4] See E. R. Baumann and H. E. Babbitt, *Bull.* 409, Engineering Experiment Station, University of Illinois, February, 1953; and *Water and Sewage Works,* March, 1954, p. 132.

The time between cleanings of a household septic tank depends on the number of persons using it, the quantity and quality of sewage discharged into it, and other conditions, so that no number of days can be stated as applicable to all tanks. This time may be a year or longer, under normal conditions and where no garbage is put into the tank, if the sizes recommended in Table 20–1 are used. The normal quantity of disinfecting substances used in housekeeping should have no undesirable effect on the operation of the tank. No attempt should be made to disinfect the tank during its normal operation.

Septic tanks are cleaned by pumping out or draining supernatant liquor, and pumping, bailing, draining, or otherwise removing the sludge. It is neither necessary nor desirable to remove all of the sludge when the tank is cleaned, but deposits of grit and non-digestible matter should be removed.

20–4. The Imhoff tank. An Imhoff tank is a two-story sedimentation and septic tank combining sedimentation in the upper compartment and sludge digestion in the lower compartment. The entire tank is filled with sewage since the compartments are connected by

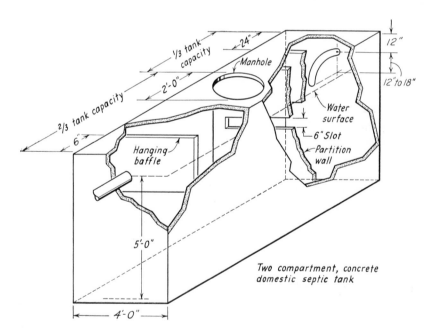

Fig. 20–2. Two-compartment, rectangular, household septic tank.

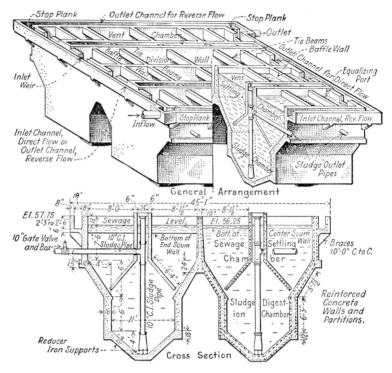

Fig. 20–3. Imhoff tank at Cleburne, Texas. (*Eng. News,* Vol. 76, p. 1029.)

an opening in the partition between them. A deflector between the two compartments deflects the downward passage of settling particles from the upper to the lower compartment, but it prevents the upward flow of gases into the sedimentation compartment, diverting the gas into the scum compartment from which it escapes to the air. A section through an early Imhoff tank in the United States is shown in Fig. 20–3 and through a Spiragester,[5] a more recent type applicable to moderate-size installations, in Fig. 20–4.

The three compartments of the Imhoff tank are the upper called the *sedimentation* or *flowing-through chamber;* the lower called the *digestion chamber;* and the intermediate compartment, open to the air, called the *scum chamber.* Sedimentation of settleable solids occurs in the sedimentation chamber causing them to pass through an opening, commonly called the *slot,* in the bottom of the sedimentation

[5] A proprietary device of the Lakeside Engineering Corporation.

chamber, into the digestion chamber. In the latter chamber solids
are humified and gasified by septic action. The generated gases
escape from the digestion chamber through the scum chamber and
into the atmosphere. The distinctive features of the Imhoff tank
are the gas-trapped slot that prevents gas from the digestion compartment from passing through the sedimentation compartment, and
the absence of a flowing-through current in the digestion compartment. Three types of these tanks have been built: radial flow,
longitudinal flow with circular or conical digestion compartments, and
longitudinal flow with rectangular digestion compartments. The last
has been the most common in the United States.

   20–5. Status of the Imhoff tank. The Imhoff tank was introduced into the United States from Germany by Dr. Karl Imhoff, in
1907. It was a patented device, the patents for which have now
expired in this country. Imhoff tanks were installed widely throughout the United States shortly after their introduction, the last of the

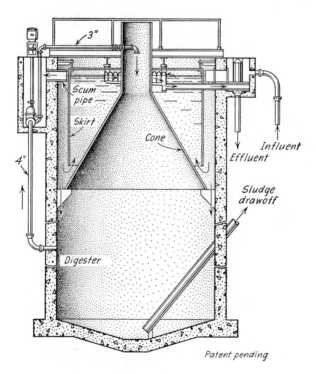

Fig. 20–4. The Spiragester. (Courtesy of the Lakeside Engineering Corp.)

large installations being at the West Side plant in Chicago, with a capacity of 472 mgd. The tank was widely used for preliminary treatment preceding trickling filtration. Of late years the number of installations of Imhoff tanks has steadily decreased, their adoption being confined mainly to small plants serving less than about 1,000 persons. The factors that have led to this situation include: better sludge digestion is obtained in heated, separate digestion tanks; the cost and the results of separate digestion are more attractive; separate digestion tanks are easier to operate, and more gas can be obtained from them; scum, foaming, and other operating difficulties are more easily controlled in separate digestion.

20–6. Sedimentation compartment. The velocity of flow, the period of detention, and the quantity of sewage to be treated determine the dimensions of the sedimentation chamber, as in other forms of tanks. Where ordinary domestic sewage is being treated, minimum periods of detention allowed by various state health departments [6] vary from 1½ to 4 hr, 2½ hr being common. About 1 to 1½ hr is sufficient before activated-sludge treatment, 2 hr preceding trickling filters or sand beds, and 2 to 3 hr if the sole treatment. All these are based on dry-weather flow rates. It may be necessary occasionally to bypass an Imhoff tank during storm conditions where a short detention period for the average flow becomes too brief during maximum rates of flow. The velocity of flow should not exceed 1 fpm. A greater velocity results in less efficient sedimentation. A longer period than the approximate limits set may result in a septic or a stale effluent, and a shorter period may result in loss of efficiency of sedimentation. The settling rate should be about 600 gal per day per sq ft of tank surface area, but may be increased to 900 gal preceding activated-sludge treatment or where recirculation is used. The bottom of the sedimentation chamber should slope not less than 5 vertical to 4 horizontal, in order that deposited material will descend into the sludge-digestion chamber. Provision should be made for cleaning these sloping surfaces by placing a walk on the top of the tank from which a squeegee can be handled to push down accumulated deposits. It is desirable to make the material of the sides and bottom of the sedimentation chamber as smooth as possible to assist in preventing the retention of sludge in the sedimentation chamber. Wood, glass, and concrete have been tried. Concrete is the most common and has been found to be satisfactory. The ratio of length to width may be

[6] See *Sewage Works Eng.*, March, 1948, p. 118.

between 5:1 and 3:1, with the depth to the slot approximately equal to the width. The length of the compartment should not exceed about 100 ft. Short lengths are desirable in order to provide good sludge distribution. The width of the chamber is fixed by considerations of economy and convenience. It should not be made so great as to permit cross currents. In general, a narrow chamber is desirable. Satisfactory chambers have been constructed at depths between 5 and 15 ft. The depth should be sufficiently shallow so that the particles have time to fall to the slot before reaching the end of the flowing-through compartment. Experience and practice dictate that the total depth of the tank should be made as great as possible, up to a limit of 30 to 35 ft, with due consideration of the difficulties of excavation.

Two or more sedimentation chambers are sometimes used over one sludge-digestion chamber in order to avoid the depths called for by the sloping sides of a single sedimentation chamber. An objection to multiple-flow chambers is the possibility of interchange of liquid from one chamber to another through the common digestion chamber.

The inlet and outlet devices should be so constructed that the direction of flow in the tank can be reversed in order that the accumulated sludge may be more evenly distributed in the hoppers of the digestion chamber. The sewage should leave the sedimentation chamber over a long weir in order to minimize fluctuations in the level of sewage in the tank. The freeboard, or vertical distance from top of tank wall to water surface, should be between 18 and 24 in. The gases in the digesting sludge are sensitive to slight changes in pressure. A lowering of the level of sewage will release compressed gas, which will too violently disturb the sludge in the digestion chamber. Gentle stirring action of rising gas bubbles is desirable, however, since it brings the fresh sludge more quickly under the influence of the active bacterial agents. Hanging baffles, submerged 12 to 16 in. and projecting 12 in. above the surface of the sewage, should be placed in front of the inlet and outlet, and in long tanks intermediate baffles should be placed to prevent the movement of scum or its escape into the effluent. An Imhoff tank that is operating properly should not have any scum on the surface of the sewage in the sedimentation chamber.

20–7. The slot. The *slot* or opening at the bottom of the sedimentation chamber should not be less than 6 in. between lips as measured along the slope of the hopper. Wider slots are preferable but too wide a slot will involve too much loss of volume in the digestion chamber. The lower lip should project 6 to 8 in. horizontally under the upper lip, to prevent the return of gas into the sedimentation compartment, or a triangular beam may be used as a deflector beneath the slot. The beam has the advantage' of decreasing the depth of tank required to provide the necessary sludge storage.

20–8. The digestion chamber. The *digestion chamber* should be designed to store sludge 6 to 12 months, the longer periods being for the small installations. In warm climates the shorter periods may be satisfactory. The amount of sludge that will be accumulated is as uncertain as in other forms of sewage treatment.

Recommendations or requirements of various state boards of health (see Sect. 5–2) show capacities from 2 to 6.5 cu ft per capita, with 3 to 3.5 most common, as shown in Table 20–2. The required capacity may be less in warm climates and where shorter periods between sludge withdrawals are possible. The trend in temperate climates has been to increase the sludge-digestion volume above those capacities considered satisfactory in the 1930's and 1940's.

The effective capacity of the chamber is measured as the entire volume of the chamber approximately 6 in. below the lower lip of

Table 20–2

CAPACITIES OF DIGESTION TANKS

From Recommendations of the Joint Committee *			Based on a Study by L. G. Rice, *Water and Sewage Works*, October, 1950, p. 436		
Type of Plant	Heated Tank, cu ft per capita	Unheated Tank, cu ft per capita	Type of Plant	Heated Tank, cu ft per capita	Unheated Tank, cu ft per capita
Imhoff tanks	...	3– 4	Primary treatment only	2 –3	3 –5
Primary tanks	2–3	4– 6	Primary treatment with chemicals and floccula-		
Primary tanks plus standard trickling filter	3–4	6– 8	tion	4.0	6.0
Primary tanks plus high-rate trickling filter	4–5	8–10	Complete treatment with trickling filters	2.5–4.0	4 –6
Activated sludge	4–6	8–12	Complete treatment with high-rate filters	3.0–4.0	4.5–6.0
			Activated sludge alone	4.0–6.0	6.0–8.0
			Complete treatment using activated sludge	3.5–6.0	5.0–8.0

Note. The capacities should be increased by allowing for the suspended-solids population equivalent of any industrial wastes in the sewage, and may be reduced if the sludge is dewatered mechanically. Volumes should be calculated on the basis of the bottom having planes sloping 30° from horizontal upward from the end of the withdrawal pipe unless sludge-moving equipment is installed. For populations of 5,000 or less, the larger values should be considered.

* See Sect. 5–2.

the slot, with the bottom of the sludge compartment adequately sloped. It may be stated as a general principle that the sludge compartment must be large enough so that offensive sludge need not be withdrawn during cold weather when biologic action is slow.

The digestion chamber usually consists of one, two, or three inverted cones or pyramids called hoppers, with side slopes about 2 horizontal to 1 vertical and preferably steeper, without necessitating too great a depth of tank. The purpose of the steep slope is to concentrate the sludge at the bottom of the hopper thus formed. Concrete is ordinarily the material of construction, as a smooth surface can be obtained by proper workmanship. Where slopes are flat, a water pipe perforated at intervals of 6 to 12 in. may be placed at the top of the slopes, and water may be admitted for a short time to move the sludge when the tank is being cleaned. If more than one hopper is used, it should be connected well below the level that will be reached by the top of the sludge so that the sludge may be evenly distributed in the hoppers and so that no hopper may be overloaded.

A cast-iron pipe, 6 to 8 in. in diameter, is supported in an approximately vertical position with its open, lower end about 12 in. above the lowest point in the digestion chamber. This is used for the removal of sludge. A straight pipe from the bottom of the tank to a free opening in the atmosphere is desirable in order to allow the cleaning of the pipe or the loosening of sludge at the start, and to prevent the accumulation of gas pockets. The sludge is led off through an approximately horizontal branch so located that from 4 to 6 ft of head are available for the discharge of the sludge. A valve is placed on the horizontal section of the pipe. A sludge pipe is shown in Fig. 20–3. Under such conditions, when the sludge valve is opened the sludge should flow freely. The hydraulic slope to insure proper sludge flow from an Imhoff tank should not be less than 12 to 16 per cent. An air lift may be used if it is necessary to lift the sludge after it has been drawn from the tank.

20–9. The scum chamber. The volume of the *scum* chamber should be equal to about one-half that of the digestion chamber. The surface area of the scum chamber exposed to the atmosphere should be 25 to 30 per cent of the horizontal projection of the top of the digestion chamber; no vent should be less than 18 in. wide, and at least one vent should be 24 in., or more, wide. The freeboard should be 18 to 24 in. Some tanks have operated successfully with only 10 per cent, but troubles from foaming can usually be anticipated unless ample area for the escape of gases has been provided.

All portions of the surface of the tank should be made accessible in order that scum and floating objects can be broken up or removed. The gas vents should be made large enough so that access can be gained to the sludge chamber through them when the tank is empty.

Precautions should be taken against the wrecking of the tank by high ground water when the tank is emptied. With an empty tank and high ground water there is a tendency for the tank to float. The flotation of the tank may be prevented by building the tank of massive concrete with a heavy concrete roof, by underdraining the foundation, or by the installation of valves which will open inwards when the ground water is higher than the sewage in the tank. If it is possible for the tank to be drained by gravity, entire dependence for its safety should not be placed on the attendant to keep the tank full during periods of high ground water.

Roofs are not essential to the successful operation of Imhoff tanks. They are used sometimes, as for septic tanks, to assist in controlling the dissemination of odors, to protect the sewage against freezing, and to aid in bacterial activity. In the construction of a roof, ventilation must be provided as well as ready access to the tank for inspection, cleaning, and repairs.

20–10. Sludge withdrawal. In most Imhoff tanks sludge is withdrawn by gravity under a hydrostatic head of not less than about 6 ft. The sludge-withdrawal pipe should not be less than 8 in. in diameter unless the sludge is to be pumped from the tank, when a 6-in. pipe may be used. The sludge is discharged into a channel beside the tank. It then flows by gravity through the channel, or is pumped to the drying beds or to other points of disposal. Sludge is a difficult substance to handle as it may not start to flow readily, but once well started it may flow as readily as water, provided that the velocity is in the hydraulically turbulent region. In the installation of sludge pipes and channels there should be as few changes in direction as possible; a cleanout should be placed at each change in direction; and provision should be made for injecting water under pressure into the sludge pipe, without creating a cross connection with a potable-water supply. Perforated water pipes to aid in starting the flow of sludge are sometimes placed at the bottom of the digestion compartment, near the sludge pipe.

20–11. Imhoff-tank results. The Imhoff tank has the advantage over the septic tank that it will not deliver sludge in the effluent, except under unusual conditions. The Imhoff tank serves to digest sludge better than a septic tank, and it will deliver a fresher effluent than a plain sedimentation tank. Imhoff sludge is more easily dried and disposed of than the sludge from either a septic or a sedimentation tank. This is because it has been more thoroughly humified and contains about 90 to 95 per cent of moisture. As it comes from the tank it is almost black, flows freely, and is filled with small bubbles of gas which expand on the release of pressure from the bottom of the tank, thus giving the sludge a porous, spongelike consistency which aids in drying. When dry it has an inoffensive odor like garden soil, and it can be used for filling waste land without further putrefaction. It has not always been successful as a fertilizer.

Offensive odors are occasionally given off by Imhoff tanks, even when properly operated. They also have a tendency to "boil" or foam. The boiling may be quite violent, forcing scum over the top of the gas vent and sludge through the slot in the sedimentation chamber, thus injuring the quality of the effluent. The scum on the surface of the transition chamber may become so thick or so solidly frozen

Table 20–3

RESULTS OF OPERATION OF IMHOFF TANKS *

	Urbana-Champaign, Ill. (1)	Fitchburg, Mass. (2)	Worcester, Mass. (3)	Chicago West Side (4)	Cleveland Westerly (5)	Cleveland Southerly (6)
Average flow, mgd	4.63	3.1	23.3	413.4	28.5	31.6
Detention period, hours	1.58	...	2.5	...	...	
Suspended solids, ppm:						
Raw sewage:						
Total	223	231	285	181	262	270
Volatile	190	185	...	...	...	...
Effluent:						
Total	86	41	102	96	160	170
Volatile	67	26.5	...	...	...	...
Removal, per cent:						
Total	61 †	82 †	64 †	47	38.9	37 †
Volatile	65 †	86 †	...	...		...
BOD, ppm:						
Raw sewage	272	215	167.9	126	245	204
Effluent	141	81	103.7	77	182	113
Removal, per cent	48.2	62 †	38 †	38.9	25.7	44.6 †

* See Table 28–2 for more recent Imhoff tank results.

† Computed from reported information.

(1) For year ending April 30, 1944. From Annual Report. (2) For year 1943. *Sewage Works Jour.*, November, 1944, p. 1294. (3) For year 1942. *Sewage Works Jour.*, March, 1945, p. 363. (4) For year 1943. *Sewage Works Jour.*, November, 1944, p. 1235. (5) For year 1940. *Sewage Works Jour.*, January, 1943, p. 108. (6) For year 1940. *Sewage Works Jour.*, January, 1943, p. 114.

as to prevent the escape of gas, with the result that sludge may be driven into the sedimentation chamber.

Some chemical analyses of Imhoff-tank influents and effluents are given in Table 20–3. It is to be noted that the nitrites and nitrates are still present in the effluent, whereas they are seldom present in the effluent from septic tanks. The Imhoff-tank sludge has a lower percentage of moisture than septic-tank sludge, and its specific gravity is higher. It is heavier and more compact because of the longer time and the greater pressure it has been subjected to in the digestion chamber of the Imhoff tank.

20–12. Limitations of Imhoff tank installations. No preliminary treatment need be given to sewage entering an Imhoff tank other than coarse screening and grit removal. The tanks function best in warm climates or where the sludge digestion compartment is warm, and where the character of the sewage is such that acid conditions will not develop in the digestion compartment. Imhoff tank construction is difficult in quicksand or in rock, and care must be taken in design and in operation, where the ground-water table is high, to prevent the tank from floating or collapsing if it is dewatered. The tanks are most suitable for small cities and for communities and institutions where constant and skilled attention is not required and the character of the effluent will meet requirements to prevent stream pollution. The use of the tanks has not been found desirable in larger communities where sedimentation and digestion are more satisfactorily performed in separate structures.

Chapter 21

Sewage filtration

21–1. Theory of filtration. The cycle through which the elements forming organic matter pass from life to death and back to life again has been described in Chapter 15. Septic action occupies that portion of the cycle in which the combinations of these elements are broken down or reduced to simpler forms and the lower stages of the cycle are reached. The action in the filtration of sewage builds up the compounds again in a more stable form and almost complete oxidation is attained, depending on the thoroughness of the filtration. In the filtration of sewage only the coarsest particles of suspended matter are removed by mechanical straining. The success of the filtration is dependent on life that exists on the surface of the filtering material. The smaller the particles of filtering material the greater is the surface area and, hence, the greater is the amount of organic matter present. Difficulties from filter clogging and the inhibition of aeration limit the minimum size of the filtering material.

The desirable form of life in a filter is the so-called nitrifying bacteria that live in the interstices of the filter bed and feed on the organic matter in the sewage. Anything that injures the growth of these bacteria injures the action of the filter. In a properly constructed and operated filter, all matter that enters in the influent leaves with the effluent, but some of it is in a different molecular form. A slight amount may be lost by evaporation and gasification, but this is more than made up by the nitrogen and oxygen taken from the atmosphere. The nitrifying action in sewage filtration is shown by the reduction of the content of organic nitrogen, free ammonia, and oxygen consumed and the increase in nitrites and nitrates.

The theory of filtration may serve to explain, in part, the results obtained from contact beds, trickling filters, and sand filters.

21–2. Contact beds. A contact bed is a watertight tank filled with coarse material, the tank being alternately filled, allowed to stand full, emptied, and allowed to stand empty while the solids in the sewage are deposited on the contact material and subsequently oxidized during the period of standing empty. Interest in contact filters is mainly historical since the beds mark a transition in the development of sewage treatment from sand filters to trickling filters. During the "contact period," when the filter is standing full, fresh suspended matter is deposited on the contact material and is worked on by anaerobic organisms. At the next contact period the material that has been exposed to the air and has been oxidized during the period of standing empty may be washed off the contact material and carried out with the effluent on the next emptying of the tank.

The rate of treatment on contact beds, being about 60 gal per cu yd per day, is relatively slow in consideration of the quality of the effluent produced. Attempts to increase this rate by distributing the sewage over the surface of the bed and allowing it to trickle through the contact material led to the production of the trickling filter.

The outstanding advantages of contact beds over trickling filters are the relatively small amount of head consumed by the contact bed, freedom from filter (*Psychoda*) flies, and the possibility of operating the bed without exposing the sewage to view. The odors from contact beds will probably be less than from trickling filters, but without very careful operation the quality of the effluent from the contact bed will not be so good. Preliminary treatment in the form of screens or tanks or both is desirable. The contact bed may be placed in a crowded residential district.

As a result of the success of the trickling filter and other more satisfactory methods of treatment, contact beds are no longer in common use.

Trickling Filters, Standard Rate

21–3. Description. A trickling filter is a bed of coarse, rough, hard, impervious material over which sewage is sprayed, or otherwise distributed through the air, after which the sewage trickles downward through the filter in contact with the air. The action of the oxygen in the air is an essential part of the process of trickling filters. The treatment of sewage in a trickling-filter plant involves three stages: preliminary or primary treatment, filtration, and final sedimentation. The heart of the plant is the filter. The other two steps are essential, however, to the successful functioning of the plant.

Fig. 21–1. Standard-rate trickling filter with spray nozzles, at Bloomington, Ind. The dosing tank for the filter, and the glass-covered, sludge-drying beds are shown in the background. (Courtesy Pacific Flush Tank Co.)

A trickling filter is a bed of coarse, rough, hard material over which sewage is sprayed, or otherwise distributed; it is then allowed to trickle slowly through in contact with the air. A general view of a trickling filter, with fixed nozzles for distribution, is shown in Fig. 21–1. The action of the filter is due to oxidation by organisms attached to the material of the filter. The solid organic matter of the sewage deposited on the surface is worked over and oxidized by the aerobic bacteria and is discharged in the effluent in a highly nitrified and flocculated condition. At times the discharge of suspended matter becomes so great that the filter is said to be unloading. The action differs from that in a contact bed in that there is no period of septic or anaerobic action and the filter, in normal operation, does not stand full of sewage. The term *trickling filter* is now used to include all forms of filters through which sewage trickles over the filtering material. Two types are generally recognized: the standard-rate filter and the high-rate filter, the differentiation depending on the rate of dosing and the method of operation.[1]

21–4. Advantages and disadvantages. Among the advantages of a trickling filter may be included its relatively high nitrifying effect; its dependability to give a good effluent under wide variations of influent quality; a relatively low operating cost; its ability to function under extreme weather conditions, particularly in low temperatures; and a satisfactory efficiency in reduction of BOD and suspended solids from unfavorable influents.

A disadvantage of the installation of a trickling filter at many plants is the head that is lost through the filter. This may vary

[1] See F. W. Mohlmann, *Water and Sewage Works,* May 1, 1955, p. R-261.

between 5 and 11 ft, in addition to the depth of the filter which may be between 6 and 10 ft. Other disadvantages include odor and fly nuisance, the large area required, and the relatively high construction cost. Sedimentation of the effluent is usually necessary to remove the settleable solids. During the period of secondary sedimentation the quality of the filter effluent may deteriorate. In winter the formation of ice on the filter results in an effluent of inferior quality, but since the diluting water can usually care for such an effluent at this season the condition is usually not objectionable. The filters sometimes give off offensive odors in hot weather, and flying insects may breed in the filter in sufficient quantities to become a nuisance if preventive steps are not taken. If the filters are constructed to permit it they can be filled with sewage, which is usually successful in killing the flying insects. The dissemination of odors is especially marked during treatment of a stale or septic sewage. The treatment of a fresh sewage seldom results in the creation of offensive odors.

Trickling filters are not suitable for sites in built-up districts because of odors. The head required for their operation may require pumping; constant attention is required for success; and preliminary treatment through screens and tanks is necessary. The effluent is of high quality.

Raw sewage cannot be treated successfully on a trickling filter. Coarse solid particles should be screened and settled out, in order that the distributing devices or the filter may not become clogged. The effluent from most primary treatment processes, except from the septic tank, will probably prove to be a satisfactory influent for a trickling filter. A septic-tank effluent may prove to be so stale as to be detrimental to the biological action in the filter.

21–5. Status. Since its inception at Salford, England, about 1893,[2] the trickling filter has gained steadily in favor until it is now recognized as a standard method of secondary treatment. The recent development of the high-rate filter has added popularity to the trickling filter as an effective method of sewage treatment.

21–6. Rate of filtration and loading. The rates and loadings to be allowed in the design of trickling filters are usually expressed in million gallons per day per acre of filter surface, and on an organic loading usually expressed in pounds of BOD per unit of filter volume.

[2] See W. E. Stanley, *Modern Sewage Disposal,* Federation of Sewage Works Associations, 1938, p. 51.

Units of expression are being revised,[3] but as of Jan. 1, 1958, they have not been universally accepted. Rates of loading, expressed in units commonly used are: (1) 200,000 to 600,000 gal per acre-foot per day; (2) 2 to 3 million gal per acre of surface area, per day; (3) 250 to 400 lb BOD per acre-foot per day, without recirculation, and 250 to 600 lb with 1:1 recirculation; and (4) 10 to 20 lb BOD per day per 1,000 cu ft of filter material. In the new recommended units [3] the rates are 5 to 15 ft [4] of liquid per day.

The rates based on organic loading are the most logical, although all the rates are approximately equal. The higher rates are suitable for warmer climates. Furman [5] states that 7.5 to 20 million gal per acre per day can be used without recirculation and with 2½- to 3-in. size of filtering material. Forced ventilation, discussed in Sect. 21–24, in filters up to 12 ft deep permits rates of surface application up to 20 mgad with settled sewage containing 200 mg/l BOD, without recirculation.

Roughing filters, designed for the pretreatment of unusually strong sewage, may be loaded in excess of 100 lb BOD per 1,000 cu ft of filter material.

Recirculation rates of 1:1 of final settling tank effluent is recommended to maintain satisfactory filter results. The additional cost involved is the principal objection to recirculation.

21–7. Pretreatment. Special methods of treating sewage before trickling filtration include: partial purification by the activated-sludge process, chemical treatment, and preaeration. These methods are not to be confused with the ordinary primary processes of treatment such as sedimentation or septicization. Both bioflocculation and chemical pretreatment are useful mainly in the treatment of sewage containing industrial wastes. Preaeration may be useful in domestic waste pretreatment to increase BOD removal in primary sedimentation and in keeping the liquid aerified until it reaches the filtration process.

21–8. Partial purification. If the progress of the treatment of sewage in an aeration tank is studied it is found that almost 60 per cent of the total work done in 6 hours is accomplished in the first hour. About 15 per cent more is accomplished in the next hour, and only 10 per cent in the third hour. The greatest amount of treatment occurs, then, in the first hour. The amount which takes place in the

[3] See *S. and I.W.,* February, 1957, p. 134.
[4] Measured vertically.
[5] T. de S. Furman, *S. and I.W.,* May, 1954, p. 686.

last 5 hours in the aeration tank is no greater than that which takes place in the short time required to pass through a trickling filter. Because of this fact attempts have been made, by the aeration of sewage for only a short time in the presence of activated sludge, to produce an effluent from the aeration tank that could be treated on a trickling filter at a rate faster than may be used for normal primary-treatment effluents.

Such treatment is called partial purification. Experience with it has shown that the retention period in the aeration tank has been greatly reduced, resulting in the need for a smaller tank and the use of less power than would be required for complete treatment, and the trickling filters have operated successfully with the increased load.

Hatfield,[6] as a result of his experience at Decatur, Ill., stated: "Pre-aeration . . . allowed filter dosage rates to be increased to 3.0 to 3.3 m.g.a.d., which corresponds to a 5-day BOD loading from 2,000 to 4,000 pounds per day on a 6-foot depth filter. . . . It has also been noted that preaeration has cured filter pooling."

Among disadvantages of the process is that the quantity of sludge produced is only about 25 per cent of that produced by complete activated-sludge treatment. It has been found that the effluent from a "partial-purification" tank, when applied to a trickling filter that has become clogged because of overloading, will clear it up and restore it to an excellent condition.

Reaeration of the activated sludge produced in the aeration and settling tanks is required because of the too-short period in the aeration tank. The amount of power required for reaeration is an important item of the cost which detracts somewhat from the advantages of the process. The sludge produced is not in so good a condition as that from complete treatment by the activated-sludge process. It will not settle so readily and it is more difficult to dry. The process of partial purification is useful principally where the disposal of sludge is not difficult and where the nature of the effluent is such that either sufficient dilution is possible or sufficient filter area is available to care for the effluent from the aeration tank.

The construction of a partial-purification plant on the activated-sludge principle, followed by trickling filtration, is undesirable as it is improbable that such a plant will be either economical or as successful as a complete activated-sludge plant. Partial purification by activated sludge, followed by trickling filtration, has been attempted principally to relieve the load on overloaded trickling filters.

[6] W. D. Hatfield, *Sewage Works Jour.*, October, 1931.

Table 21-1

DESIGN FACTORS FOR TRICKLING FILTERS

(From *Sewage Works Eng.*, March, 1948, p. 119.)

| Authority [1] | Pounds of BOD per day per 1,000 cu ft of filtering material | |
	Standard-rate filters	High-rate filters
Alabama	10	
California	10	66.5 * for 1st stage, and 44.5 for 2nd stage
Connecticut	9.2 *	69 *
Colorado	9.2 *	92.5 *
Florida	13.8 *	69 *
Illinois [2]	9.2 *	
Iowa [2]	8.1 *	
Idaho	9.2 *	
Kansas	9.2 *	
Minnesota [2]	9.2 *	
Missouri [2]	8.1 *	
New Jersey [3]		
New York [2]		55.5 *
Oregon	9.2 to 12 *	55.5 * to 74
South Carolina [4]		
South Dakota	5.7 *	
Texas	10.3 *	47 *
Ten-State Standards [5]	15	110 †

[1] State Board of Health except for Ten-State Standards.

[2] These states are in the Upper Mississippi Valley group, but their standards were higher as published in 1948.

[3] 630,000 gpd per acre-ft.

[4] 3,000 persons per acre-ft.

[5] See Sect. 5-2.

* Units converted to pounds per 1,000 cu ft.

† Where BOD in effluent is not more than 30 mg/l.

21-9. Design of trickling filters. In the design of trickling filters the new approach [7] begins with consideration of the loading to be used.[8] Some basic design data are given in Table 21-1. The

[7] See W. T. Ingram, *Jour. San. Eng. Div.*, American Society of Civil Engineers, Paper 999, 1956.

[8] See also J. M. Farrall, *S. and I.W.*, September, 1956, p. 1069.

filtering material may be selected on the basis of the available satisfactory supply and the principles outlined in Sect. 21–10. The depth of the bed is fixed, in part, by the topographical conditions, which may limit the head that can be used. When the preceding features of the filter have been determined, the design of the functional features follows, with the selection of: (1) the method of distribution; (2) the dosing tanks or dosing systems; (3) the distribution system or equipment; (4) the underdrains; and (5) the method of ventilation. Technical publications by the Pacific Flush Tank Company [9] will be found helpful in the design of fixed-nozzle distribution systems.

21–10. Filtering material. The Committee on Filtering Materials of the American Society of Civil Engineers [10] recommended that:

Material for filter media should be sound, hard pieces with all three dimensions as nearly the same as possible, clean and free from dust, screenings, and other fine material. It should be of as nearly uniform size as possible, and the material should not disintegrate under service conditions, either by breaking into smaller pieces, or by crumbling into fine material.

It is further recommended by the Committee [11] that:

A satisfactory material for a trickling filter should be free from fines . . . and should be substantially sound as determined by the sodium sulfate soundness test. The selection of the general type of material to be utilized should be determined for each proposed project in the light of all local data.

In general, those sizes of filtering materials found to give the best results have ranged between 1 in. and 3 in., with uniform size of material from top to bottom, or possibly with a layer of 6 in. or less of larger material immediately above the underdrains. Finer materials in the body of the bed are conducive to clogging, and coarser materials to a poorer quality of effluent so far as BOD reduction is concerned.

There is no choice between gravel, broken stone, slag, or other hard, durable substance. Anthracite coal has been used in some plants.

21–11. Depth of bed. Considerable variation is found in the depths of filter beds in the United States, between a minimum of about 6 ft and a maximum of 10 ft. Clark,[12] as a result of tests on four filters with depth of 4, 6, 8, and 10 ft, respectively, concluded

[9] See Pacific Flush Tank Co., *Sprinkling Filter Data Book* 130, 1953.
[10] *Proc. Am. Soc. Civil Engrs.*, December, 1936, p. 1543.
[11] *Manual of Practice* 13, American Society of Civil Engineers, 1937.
[12] H. W. Clark, *Ind. and Eng. Chem.*, April, 1927.

Fig. 21–2. High-rate trickling filter with revolving distributor arms. Louisiana State Mental Hospital, Jackson, La., Barnard and Burk, Engineers. (Courtesy Yeomans Bros. Co.)

that the 10-ft filter depth could be operated successfully with 8 to 10 times the load on a 4-ft filter. With deeper filters difficulties may be met from inadequate ventilation and from pooling on the surface with the increased surface rate required by the additional depth of filter. The Joint Committee (see Sect. 5–2) limits acceptable depths of filtering material between 5 and 7 ft.

Forced ventilation [13] permits the use of deep filters and high rates of dosing. This method has the advantage of reducing the surface area of filter required, but it increases the depth of the filter and, hence, the head loss through the filter.

21–12. Distribution of sewage on a trickling filter. Sewage is distributed over the surface of a trickling filter by spray nozzles, somewhat as shown in Fig. 21–1, by reaction-jet arms, as shown in Fig. 21–2, and rarely by other miscellaneous means. Revolving arms are most commonly used, the use of spray nozzles being confined more to climates where freezing will interfere with the operation of the revolving arms.

The use of revolving-arm distributors is restricted to circular beds not more than 150 to 200 ft in diameter. Fixed nozzles may be used for large beds and for beds other than circular in plan. However the sewage is distributed on the bed, it should be passed through a 1-in., or smaller, rack or screen before going to the nozzles. Where

[13] This is discussed also in Sect. 21–24.

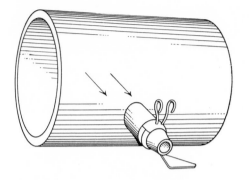

Fig. 21–3. Reaction-type jet nozzle, with splash plate. (Courtesy Pacific Flush Tank Co.)

feasible a piping arrangement that will permit recirculation of the effluent and the flooding of the filter is desirable.

21–13. Rotary distributors. A rotary distributor consists of two or more hollow, radial arms supported by a column in the center of a circular filter bed. These arms revolve in a horizontal plane about the central, vertical column, at a rate of about one revolution in 10 to 15 minutes or less. The use of four arms may be advantageous since two of them may be disconnected when not needed, as in freezing weather. Provision should be made for the drainage of all liquid from the arms, when desired. The arms, when revolving, should clear the surface of the bed by 6 in. or more, where icing is anticipated. The arms consist of pipes perforated on one side, from which the sewage flows in horizontal jets as the arms revolve, impelled by the jet reaction, or by a motor. Two types of jets are used, film and round. The film jet is created by allowing a round jet issuing from a hole in the distributor arm to impinge on a flat plate below the orifice, as shown in Fig. 21–3. In some devices a mercury seal is necessary between the revolving parts of the central riser pipe. No seal is required by the device shown in Fig. 21–4a because of the elevation of the overflow flange. A dosing tank is needed where the revolving arms are driven by jet reaction, since without the dosing tank the rate of flow of liquid would be insufficient to drive the arms during periods of minimum flow, if there is no recirculation. Positively driven arms require no dosing tank and have the advantage of greater freedom from wind resistance. A jet-reaction distributor is shown in Fig. 21–2. The central column of a motor-driven distributor is shown in Fig. 21–4b.

Most rotary distributors are proprietary devices, the details of which are unique with each manufacturer. The plant designer may specify types and performance, but is usually not called on to design the details.

Advantages of the rotary distributor over the fixed-nozzle distributor include lower head losses, varying between 2 and 5 ft when jet driven, and less when motor driven; simplification or elimination of dosing equipment and pipe-distribution systems; and more even distribution of the sewage. Among the disadvantages are difficulties with ice and snow, and the restriction to a circular shape of filter.

21–14. Distribution systems for fixed nozzles. The method of distributing sewage onto relatively small filters by fixed nozzles is indicated in Fig. 21–5. Two separate nozzle fields, each with its own dosing tank, are generally to be desired over a common nozzle field with a single dosing tank. Where fixed nozzles are used, sewage enters the dosing tank, which, when filled, is automatically and quickly emptied through the air-locked dosing siphon into the distribution system. In small plants an intermediate tank, as shown in Fig. 21–5, may be desirable to simplify the design of the main dosing tank and siphon. Twin dosing tanks for larger plants are illustrated in Fig. 21–9.

Since the discharge head diminishes as the tank empties, the shape of the tank is so adjusted that an approximately equal amount of sewage is applied per unit area on the surface of the filter. Because of the time required to fill the dosing tank the flow through the nozzles is not continuous. In practice the dosing cycles vary between 5 and 15 min, the nozzles being in operation somewhat more than half the time. The design should be based on a maximum rest period of 5 min for the average rate of sewage flow into the filter. The ideal cycle is apparently one that will give a continuous discharge from the underdrains of the filter, with practice tending towards continuous sprinkling of the surface.

In the determination of dosing-tank capacities, siphon sizes, number of nozzles, nozzle spacings, and other details of fixed-nozzle layouts empirical coefficients and available "commercial" sizes must be used. Publications of the Pacific Flush Tank Company will be found useful in such design.

21–15. Distribution pipes. The pipes in the distribution system are properly laid out in such a manner that the head loss from the dosing tank to all nozzles is as nearly uniform as practicable. When the nozzles are placed at the apices of equilateral triangles, as shown in Fig. 21–5, satisfactory distribution will be given. In some filters the bed is sloped to compensate for the head losses in the distribution

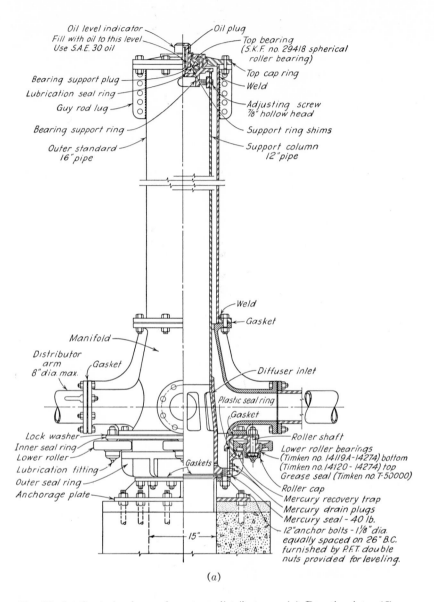

Oil level indicator
Fill with oil to this level
Use S.A.E. 30 oil

Oil plug

Top bearing
(S.K.F. no. 29418 spherical
roller bearing)

Top cap ring

Weld

Bearing support plug

Lubrication seal ring

Guy rod lug

Bearing support ring

Adjusting screw
⅞" hollow head

Support ring shims

Outer standard
16" pipe

Support column
12" pipe

Weld

Gasket

Manifold

Distributor
arm
8" dia. max.

Gasket

Diffuser inlet

Plastic seal ring

Gasket

Lock washer
Inner seal ring
Lower roller
Lubrication fitting
Outer seal ring
Anchorage plate

Gaskets

Roller shaft

Lower roller bearings
(Timken no. 14119A-14274) bottom
(Timken no. 14120 - 14274) top
Grease seal (Timken no. T-50000)

Roller cap
Mercury recovery trap
Mercury drain plugs
Mercury seal - 40 lb.
12" anchor bolts - 1⅛" dia.
equally spaced on 26" B.C.
furnished by P.F.T. double
nuts provided for leveling.

15"

(a)

Fig. 21–4. Central columns for rotary distributors. (a) Reaction-jet. (Courtesy Pacific Flush Tank Co.) (b) Motor-driven. (Courtesy American Well Works.)

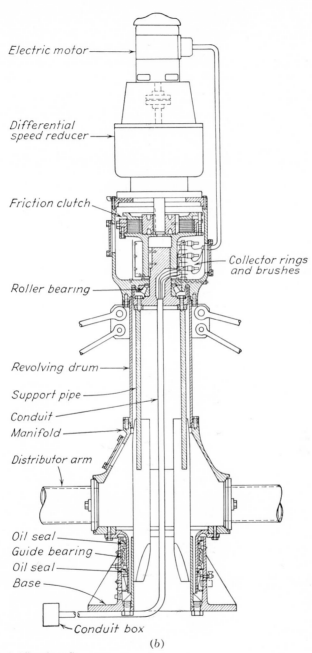

Electric motor

Differential
speed reducer

Friction clutch

Collector rings
and brushes

Roller bearing

Revolving drum

Support pipe

Conduit

Manifold

Distributor arm

Oil seal
Guide bearing
Oil seal
Base

Conduit box

(b)

Fig. 21–4 (*Continued*).

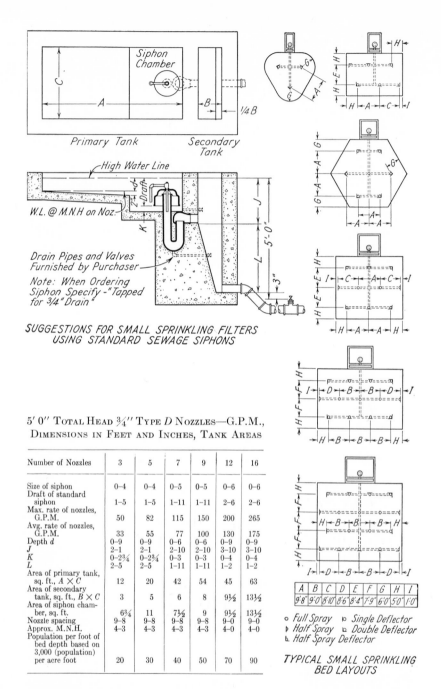

SUGGESTIONS FOR SMALL SPRINKLING FILTERS
USING STANDARD SEWAGE SIPHONS

5′ 0″ Total Head ¾″ Type *D* Nozzles—G.P.M.,
Dimensions in Feet and Inches, Tank Areas

Number of Nozzles	3	5	7	9	12	16
Size of siphon	0–4	0–4	0–5	0–5	0–6	0–6
Draft of standard siphon	1–5	1–5	1–11	1–11	2–6	2–6
Max. rate of nozzles, G.P.M.	50	82	115	150	200	265
Avg. rate of nozzles, G.P.M.	33	55	77	100	130	175
Depth *d*	0–9	0–9	0–6	0–6	0–9	0–9
J	2–1	2–1	2–10	2–10	3–10	3–10
K	0–2¾	0–2¾	0–3	0–3	0–4	0–4
L	2–5	2–5	1–11	1–11	1–2	1–2
Area of primary tank, sq. ft., $A \times C$	12	20	42	54	45	63
Area of secondary tank, sq. ft., $B \times C$	3	5	6	8	9½	13½
Area of siphon chamber, sq. ft.	6¾	11	7½	9	9½	13½
Nozzle spacing	9–8	9–8	9–8	9–8	9–0	9–0
Approx. M.N.H.	4–3	4–3	4–3	4–3	4–0	4–0
Population per foot of bed depth based on 3,000 (population) per acre foot	20	30	40	50	70	90

A	B	C	D	E	F	G	H	I
9′8″	9′0″	8′0″	8′6″	8′4″	7′9″	6′0″	5′0″	1′0″

o Full Spray ▷ Single Deflector
▷ Half Spray ▣ Double Deflector
▣ Half Spray Deflector

TYPICAL SMALL SPRINKLING
BED LAYOUTS

Fig. 21–5. Dosing tank, dosing siphon, and suggested layouts for small trickling filters. (*Sprinkling Filter Data Book* 130, Pacific Flush Tank Co.)

494

pipes, but the expedient is somewhat objectionable because of the dribbling of the sewage from the lower nozzles after the dosing tank is emptied, and because of the utilization of the highest head in the dosing tank to fill the distributing pipes between doses. The dribbling can be minimized by proper design of the distribution system, and the wasting of the maximum head available can be diminished by increasing the surface area of the dosing tank.

One successful form of distribution system consists of a main or header leading down the center of the bed with branches at right angles to the main. The spray nozzles are spaced along these branches. The pipes should be larger than would be demanded by considerations of economy alone, both for the purpose of reducing head losses and for ease in cleaning. Larger pipes, with resulting slower velocities of sewage flow, may be used with settled than with unsettled sewage. Velocities higher than 30 fpm are desirable to avoid clogging of the pipes.

21–16. Pipe location and support. The pipes are placed far enough below the surface of the filling material so that the top of the spraying nozzle is 6 to 12 in. above the surface of the filter. If the pipes are placed near the surface they are accessible for repairs but are exposed to temperature changes. If the pipes are large their presence near the surface may seriously affect the distribution of the sewage through the filter. If the distributing pipes are placed near the bottom of the filter they are inaccessible for repairs and the nozzles must be connected to them by means of long riser pipes.

Wherever they are placed, the pipes may be supported by columns extending to the foundation of the filter bed, there being a column at every pipe joint with such intermediate supports as may be required; in some plants the pipes are supported by the filtering material. The latter method is probably the more common as it is satisfactory and less expensive. It has the disadvantages, however, that settling of the filter material may break the pipe or cause leaks, and, if the bed becomes clogged, removal of the material is made more difficult. Valves should be placed in the distribution system in such a manner that different sets of nozzles can be cut out at will, thus resting some portions of the filter and permitting repairs without shutting down the entire filter.

It is desirable to place threaded plugs in the end of all distribution pipes to permit flushing, and provision should be made to permit complete drainage of the distribution system to prevent freezing in the event of shutdown in cold weather.

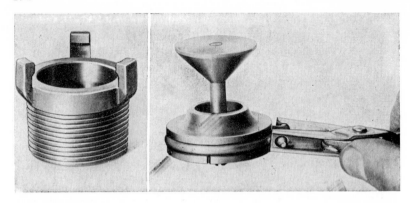

Fig. 21–6. Fixed nozzle for trickling filters. (Courtesy Pacific Flush Tank Co.)

21–17. Types of fixed nozzles. A commonly used type of fixed sprinkler nozzle is shown in Fig. 21–6. Nozzles that will throw sprays other than circular are now rarely used. One type of reaction-jet nozzle is shown in Fig. 21–3. An impingement nozzle discharges onto a saucer-like bowl, producing a cavitation effect which is said to improve the aeration of the liquid.

21–18. Automatic dosing devices. These are used to supply sewage to contact beds, trickling filters, and intermittent sand filters. They can be placed in two categories: those with moving parts and those without moving parts. Moving-part devices are now practically obsolete. Those without moving parts operate as air-locked devices, are less liable to disorders, and are nearer foolproof than any device depending on moving parts for its operation. The simplest form of these devices is the automatic siphon used for flush tanks, the operation of which is described in Sect. 6–11.

21–19. Two alternating siphons. In the operation of sand filters, sprinkling filters, or other forms of treatment where there are two or more units to be dosed, it is desirable that the dosing of the beds be done alternately. A simple arrangement for two siphons operating alternately is shown in Fig. 21–7. They operate as follows: With the dosing tank empty at the start water will stand at bb' in siphon 2 and at aa' in siphon 1. As the water enters through the inlet on the left the tank fills. When the water rises sufficiently, air is trapped in the bells, and as the water continues to rise in the tank, surfaces a' and b' are depressed an equal amount. When b' has been depressed to d, a' has been depressed to c'. Air is released from siphon 2 through the short leg, and siphon 2 goes into operation. Surface c' rises in siphon 1 as the tank empties, and when the action of siphon 2 is broken by the admission of air when the bottom of the bell is uncovered the water in siphon 1 has assumed the position of bb' and that in 2 is at aa'. The conditions of the two siphons are now reversed from that at the beginning of the operation, and as the tank refills siphon 1 will go into operation. It is to be noted that these siphons are made to alternate by weakening the seal of the next one to discharge and by strengthening the seal of the one which has just discharged.

21–20. Three or more alternating siphons. An arrangement for the alternation of three or more siphons is illustrated in Fig. 21–8. At the commencement of the cycle it will be assumed that all starting wells are filled with water except well 1, and that all main and all blow-off traps are filled with water. The following description of the operation of the siphons is taken from the catalog of the Pacific Flush Tank Company:

The liquid in the tank gradually rises and finally overflows into the starting well No. 1 and the starting bell being filled with air, pressure is developed

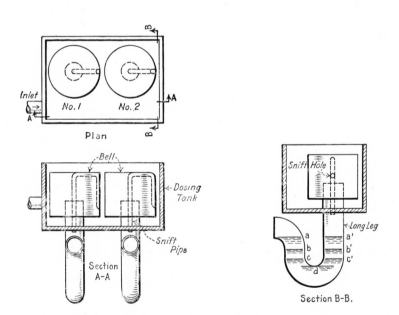

Fig. 21–7. Two alternating siphons, establishing principle of weakening seal of trap to cause it to discharge next.

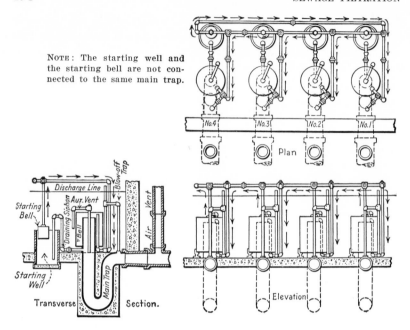

Fig. 21–8. Miller plural alternating siphons, establishing principle of starting well to cause siphons to discharge. (Courtesy Pacific Flush Tank Co.)

which is transmitted, as shown by the arrows, to the blow-off trap connected with siphon No. 2. When the discharge line is reached, sufficient head is obtained on the starting bell to force the seal in blow-off trap No. 2, thus releasing the air confined in siphon No. 2 and bringing it into full operation.

During the time that siphon No. 2 is operating, siphonic action is developed in the draining siphon connected with starting well No. 2 and as soon as the level in the tank is below the top of the well it is drained down to a point below the bottom of starting bell No. 2. It can now be seen that after the first discharge starting well No. 2 is empty, whereas the other three are full. . . . Therefore when the tank is filled the second time, pressure is developed in starting bell No. 2, which forces the seal of blow-off trap No. 3, thus starting siphon No. 3.

This alternation can be continued for any number of siphons. Other arrangements have been devised for the automatic control of alternating siphons, but these principles of the air-locked devices are fundamental.

21–21. Alternating twin dosing tanks. In the operation of the twin, air-locked dosing tank shown in Fig. 21–9, sewage enters at the point marked "inlet" and flows through the siphon marked "feed" to enter tank A. The sewage does not enter tank B because the feed siphon to tank B is filled with air which is trapped in the top of the feed by the sewage in channels C and D. When the level in tank A rises to the maximum discharge line, sewage falls into the chamber marked "compression dome A" and the air compressed in this dome is forced into "feed" A, locking the feed and stopping the flow into tank A. A slight rise of the level of the sewage in channel C causes water to fall into starting well A and to release the air locks in main siphon A and "feed" B by compressing the air in the corresponding starting bell. Sewage now flows from tank A and through "feed" B

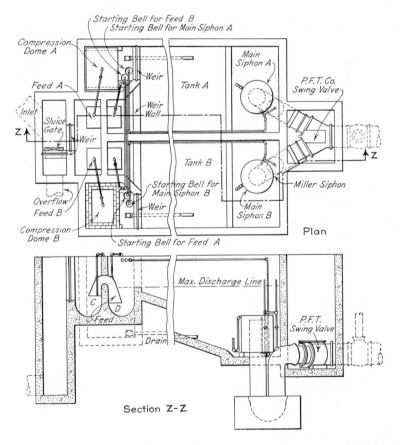

Fig. 21–9. Twin dosing tanks for trickling filters. (Courtesy Pacific Flush Tank Co.)

into tank *B*. When tank *B* is filled, the flow is reversed into tank *A* in a similar manner.

21–22. Timed siphons. In the operation of a number of contact beds, not only must the dosing of the tanks be alternated, but also some method is needed by which the beds shall be automatically emptied after the proper period of standing full. To fulfill this need the principle of the timed siphon must be employed in conjunction with the alternating siphons. In operation water flows from the main siphon chamber into the timing chamber at a rate determined by a timing valve. The contact bed is held full during this period. As the timing chamber fills with water, air is caught in the starting bell and the pressure is increased until the seal in the main blow-off trap is blown and the main siphon is put into operation. As the water level in the main siphon chamber descends, water flows from the timing chamber into the main siphon through the draining siphon and the timing chamber is emptied ready to commence another cycle.

21–23. Ventilation of trickling filters. Trickling filters have been designed with provision for supplying air to, or the ventilation of, the lower portions of the filter, in the belief that the presence of a plentiful supply of oxygen was necessary for successful filtration. A supply of about 0.1 cu ft of air per min per sq ft of filter surface [14] may be sufficient. A 5° F difference in temperature between the applied sewage and the surrounding air will supply this rate to a 6-ft depth of filter by natural draft. Natural-draft ventilation may be provided by building the filters above the ground surface with open sides or by leaving the ends of the underdrains open or connecting them to a chimney to draw air through them. An objection to such an arrangement in cold climates is, however, the possibility of freezing in the bed.

21–24. Forced ventilation of filters. Forced ventilation of trickling filters involves the forcing of air vertically through the filter by the use of fans or other mechanical equipment. The procedure is used in deep filters and in high-rate filters.[15] It resembles, to some extent, the controlled filtration process described in Sect. 21–35. In high-rate filters the beds may be completely enclosed by a fixed roof with a central hood from which a fan supplies 40 volumes of air per volume of sewage, at a pressure of 20 mm of water. The air passes down through the filter. An average dosage rate is 3 to 4

[14] See also W. K. Johnson, *S. and I.W.*, February, 1952, p. 135.
[15] See H. J. N. Hodgson, *Sewage and Trades Wastes Treatment*, Adelaide, Australia, p. 165, 1938.

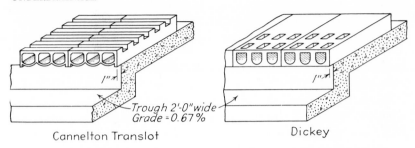

Cannelton Translot   Dickey

(From G. S. Russell, *Sewage and Ind. Wastes Eng.*, May, 1950, p. 258.)

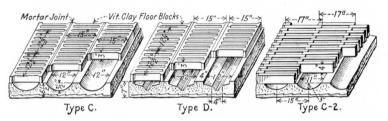

Type C.   Type D.   Type C-2.

Fig. 21–10. Underdrain blocks for trickling filters. (From *Eng. News,* Vol. 74, 1915, p. 5.)

volumes of sewage to 1 volume of filter stone. The filters are free from odors and flies and produce a satisfactory effluent, but it is assumed that there may be difficulty from freezing in a cold climate. The introduction of air through a perforated bottom in a trickling filter, causing the air to pass upwards through the filter either by induced or by forced draft, is practicable. The rate of ventilation may be in the neighborhood of about 1 cu ft of air per min per sq ft of filter surface area.[16] Filters up to 12 ft in depth, with forced ventilation, treating sewage with a BOD up to 200 mg/l, at a surface load of 20 mgad without recirculation, are said to have been successful in Germany.

21–25. Underdrainage.[17] The underdrainage of a trickling filter should consist of some form of false bottom such as is shown in Fig. 21–10. Where possible the underdrains should be open at both ends for the purpose of ventilation and flushing. It is desirable that the drains should be arranged so that a light can be seen through them

[16] See also A. Rumpf, *S. and I.W.*, March, 1956; and W. T. Ingram, *Jour. San. Eng. Div.*, American Society of Civil Engineers, Paper 999, June, 1956.

[17] See *Sewage and Industrial Wastes Eng.*, May, 1950, p. 257.

in order that clogging can be located easily. The drains should be placed on a slope of approximately 2 in 100 towards a main collector, and their capacity should be sufficient to carry a hydraulic load at about one-half full depth. The total inlet area into the underdrains should be at least 5 per cent of the surface area of the filter. Velocities in the underdrains should exceed about 2 fps.

21–26. Covers. Covers have been provided for some trickling filters in cold climates. Sprinkling nozzles have been found to work satisfactorily in extremely cold weather, and it is generally accepted that the covering of filters may not be necessary if the filter is not shut down during the cold weather.

21–27. Results. The effluent from a trickling filter may be expected to be dark, odorless, and sometimes high in visible suspended matter. The unloading of the filter may occur at any time, but it is most likely to occur in the spring or in a warm period following a period of low temperatures. Unloading causes more suspended matter in the effluent than in the influent and may render the effluent putrescible. The action is marked by the discharge of solid matter that has sloughed off the filter material, increasing the turbidity of

Table 21–2

RESULTS OF TRICKLING-FILTER OPERATION

(From D. E. Dreier, *Water and Sewage Works*, May, 1953, p. R–186.)

Plant No.	Pop., 1,000's	Type of Sewer	Average Flow, mgd	Average BOD, mg/l Raw	Average BOD, mg/l Primary Effluent	Average BOD, mg/l Filter Effluent	Depth, ft	Filtering Medium Type	Filtering Medium Size, in.	Load BOD, lb per acre-ft Avg	Load BOD, lb per acre-ft Max	Filtering Material, cu ft per lb BOD	Nitrate in Effluent, mg/l Avg	Nitrate in Effluent, mg/l Min
1	4.27	S	0.46	...	...	...	7	...	...	...	...	...	...	...
2	6.0	C	0.52	360	220	16	5	L	2½–4	...	...	...	...	...
3	35	S₁	4.82	248	139	50	10	D	1 –1½	279	434	174	7.0	3.2
4	34	C	4.57	128	94	46	8	1	1½–3	264	330	165	6.7	2.0
5	325	S	34.4	227	137	46	7.5	S₂	1½	515	772	85	4.6	1.14
6	51	C	7.77	117	72	22	6	L	1½–2	192	867	227	6.35	2.8
7	275.5	S₁&C	47.9	269	207	67	10	L	1½–2½	590	703	74	1.32	0.16
8	23	S	2.42	751	547	145 [2]	8	3	2½	1,741 [4]	3,078 [4]	25	7.9	0.9
9	40	C	4.2	160	70	12 [5]	8	L	2	188	313	232		
10	160	C	15.3	200	...	41 [5]	7	GS	1½–3	324	...	135		

Notes: [1] Granite for top 14 in., remainder is L. [2] Effluent from second-stage filters. [3] Two filters L, and 2 granite. [4] First-stage filters. [5] Final effluent

L. Limestone. D. Dolomite. S₁. Separate. S₂. Slag. GS. Gravel, stone. C. Combined.

Plants: (1) Plymouth, Wis. (2) Litchfield, Ill. (3) Madison, Wis. (4) Elgin, Ill. (5) Dayton, Ohio. (6) Aurora, Ill. (7) Akron, Ohio. (8) Fort Dodge, Iowa. (9) Bloomington-Normal, Ill. (10) Des Moines, Iowa.

Table 21-3

RESULTS OF TRICKLING-FILTER OPERATION

(From F. W. Mohlmann, *Water and Sewage Works*, May 1, 1955, p. R-261.)

Number of Plants	Group Designation	Range of BOD Loading, lb per acre-ft	BOD of Effluent from Filter and Secondary Settling, mg/l	Per Cent Overall BOD Reduction
4	No deep recirculation	253– 429	86.9	92.2
4	With deep recirculation	245–1,170	85.7	90.8
8	2-stage	192– 930	66.5	90.2
4	With shallow recirculation	792–2,320	81.8	88.1
4	With deep recirculation	1,100–1,950	78.7	87.5
3	No deep recirculation	720–2,130	75.7	82.8
3	With deep recirculation	2,530–5,750	70.3	78.3
4	With shallow recirculation	2,370–8,250	70.1	74.8

the effluent. When the diluting water is insufficient to care for the solids so carried in the effluent, they can be removed by a period of sedimentation that must not be prolonged until the material becomes septic. The nitrogen in the effluent is almost entirely in the form of nitrates, and the percentage of saturation with dissolved oxygen is high. The effluent is more highly nitrified than that from a contact bed, and its relative stability is also higher, so that it demands a smaller volume of diluting water. The degree of nitrification in the effluent can be partly controlled through adjustment of the rate of dosing of a high-rate filter.

Some trickling-filter operating results are shown in Tables 21–2 and 21–3.

High-Rate Filters [18]

21–28. Description. A high-rate trickling filter resembles the standard trickling filter in its design, except that the rate of application of liquid to the surface of the filter is higher, greater capacity must be provided in the dosing and in the underdrainage systems, and adequate ventilation must be considered.[19] An almost universal feature of all high-rate filters is the continuous application of the

[18] See also *Sewage Works Jour.*, May, 1950, p. 257.
[19] The ventilation of high-rate filters is discussed in Sect. 21–24.

dose. This is a necessary feature of operation in order that accumulated organic matter may be carried away continuously.

High capacity, rather than high rate, is a term sometimes applied to highly loaded, continuously dosed filters using little or no recirculation and relatively low surface-dosing rates. The term high rate is understood, in general, to include both types of filters. High-rate filters may operate alone, in two stages, or even in three stages, with or without intermediate sedimentation between stages. Multiple stages are used on strong sewages or where a high quality of effluent is desired. The filter may be considered to act as a biological colloider, precipitating activated floc from the sewage.

A process in which a high-rate filter acts to pretreat the influent to an activated-sludge plant, the bioactivation process,[20] has been developed. It is claimed that the process produces an excellent effluent, and that the operation of the activated-sludge plant is freed from the deleterious effects due to sudden changes in the quality of the influent.

Since its introduction [21] in 1936 the advantages of the high-rate filter have resulted in the installation of an increasing number of such plants.

21-29. Advantages. Among the advantages [22] of the high-rate filter may be included: simplicity in operation; rugged resistance to shock loads; relatively low operating costs for equivalent performance as compared with standard filters; and low construction costs for satisfactory performance. Information about construction costs is shown in Tables 28-4 and 28-6. There is also good control of effluent quality, particularly the nitrate content; and the filter-fly problem is minimized.

21-30. Types of high-rate filters. Montgomery [23] has classified trickling filters as shown in Table 21-4. It is to be noted in the table that three of the high-rate filters are patented, the Aero-filter,[24] the Accelo filter,[25] and the Bio-filter.

Flowing-through diagrams for high-rate filters with combinations of clarifiers and of recirculation are shown in Fig. 21-11.

21-31. Dosing rate and filter load. Rates of applying influent load to a high-rate trickling filter in acceptable use are: (1) 10 to 30

---

[20] See also *Sewage Works Jour.*, September, 1941, p. 1025.

[21] See also *Sewage Works Jour.*, September, 1941, p. 895.

[22] See also F. L. Flood, *Water and Sewage Works,* July, 1952, p. 280.

[23] J. A. Montgomery, *Sewage Works Jour.*, September, 1941, p. 905.

[24] See *ibid.*, p. 1064.

[25] See *ibid.*, September, 1943, p. 1009.

Table 21–4

CLASSIFICATION OF TRICKLING FILTERS

(J. A. Montgomery, *Sewage Works Jour.*, September, 1941, p. 905.)

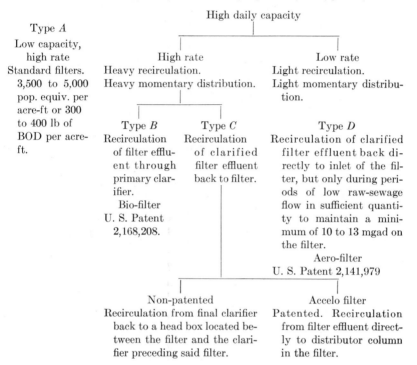

High daily capacity

Type *A*

Low capacity, high rate
Standard filters.
3,500 to 5,000 pop. equiv. per acre-ft or 300 to 400 lb of BOD per acre-ft.

High rate
Heavy recirculation.
Heavy momentary distribution.

Low rate
Light recirculation.
Light momentary distribution.

Type *B*
Recirculation of filter effluent through primary clarifier.
Bio-filter
U. S. Patent 2,168,208.

Type *C*
Recirculation of clarified filter effluent back to filter.

Type *D*
Recirculation of clarified filter effluent back directly to inlet of the filter, but only during periods of low raw-sewage flow in sufficient quantity to maintain a minimum of 10 to 13 mgad on the filter.
Aero-filter
U. S. Patent 2,141,979

Non-patented
Recirculation from final clarifier back to a head box located between the filter and the clarifier preceding said filter.

Accelo filter
Patented. Recirculation from filter effluent directly to distributor column in the filter.

million gal per acre per day; (2) 1,000 to 3,000 lb BOD per acre-ft per day; or (3) 55 to 75 lb BOD per day per 1,000 cu ft of filter material. Some discussion of filter loading is given in Sect. 21–6. Recirculation may result in a rate of application of liquid to the filter surface up to seven times the influent rate, as indicated in Table 21–5. The rate of loading the filter depends, in part, on the degree of treatment desired. As the load is increased an increase in the BOD of the effluent and a decrease of nitrification can be expected.[26] The filter load is considered as the work which the filter is expected to perform in changing the characteristics of the sewage entering the plant. Thus two filters with the same load may be subjected to

[26] See also *Sewage Works Jour.*, May, 1940, p. 477.

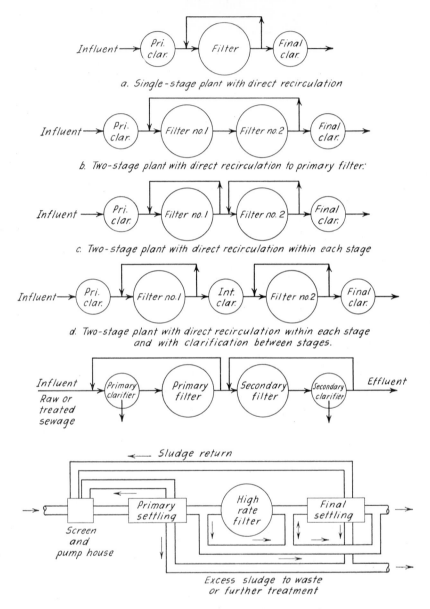

a. Single-stage plant with direct recirculation

b. Two-stage plant with direct recirculation to primary filter.

c. Two-stage plant with direct recirculation within each stage

d. Two-stage plant with direct recirculation within each stage
and with clarification between stages.

Fig. 21–11. Flowing-through and recirculation diagrams for high-rate, trickling filters.

Table 21–5 *

RECOMMENDED RECIRCULATION RATES FOR HIGH-RATE FILTERS

Raw Sewage BOD, ppm	Recirculation †			Factors to Be Used in Determining Size of Clarifier When Recirculation Is Used (Types *B* and *C* Filters, Table 21–4) ‡	
	Single Stage		Two Stage		
	Inter-mediate Treat-ment	Com-plete Treat-ment	Each Stage	Single Stage	Two Stage
Up to 150	1.0	0.75	0.5	1.75	1.5
150 to 300	2.0	1.5	1.0	2.5	2.0
300 to 450	3.0	2.25	1.5	3.25	2.5
450 to 600	4.0	3.0	2.0	4.0	3.0
600 to 750	5.0	3.75	2.5	4.75	3.5
750 to 900	6.0	4.5	3.0	5.5	4.0

* Compiled from data by Bachmann (*Sewage Works Jour.*, September, 1941, p. 895) and Montgomery (*ibid.*, p. 905).

† The figures in these three columns show the ratio of flow in the recirculation pipes to the rate of flow of raw sewage. The rate of flow onto the surface of the filter, in terms of raw sewage, is shown in the last two columns of this table, except for single-stage, intermediate treatment.

‡ For example, with a raw sewage BOD of 150 to 300 mg/l, high-capacity, high-rate filters (Types *B* and *C* in Table 21–4) require 1.5 of recirculation to 1 of raw sewage in single-stage operation. Therefore, the size of the clarifier through which recirculation is carried on must be 2½ times that which is required if no recirculation is being used. In two-stage operation, based on 150 to 300 mg/l of BOD, 1 part of recirculation is paralleled with 1 part of raw sewage. Therefore, the clarifiers through which recirculation is carried on must be twice the size they would be if no recirculation were used. For Type *D*, Aero-filters, the size of the clarifier is based on the rate of flow of raw sewage without recirculation, unless the BOD of the raw sewage is in excess of 450 mg/l.

markedly different dosing rates, depending on the strength of the incoming sewage and the rate of recirculation.

The relation between the momentary or maximum rate of application and the average rate of application is another consideration. Where sewage is fed to the bed continuously and evenly in a rainlike spray over the entire surface of the bed, the momentary rate will equal the average rate. Where the dose is not evenly distributed, as when applied by distributor arms, the momentary rate of application may be high.

The dosing rate must be sufficient to maintain a continuous rate of flow of liquid through the filter to keep all parts of the filter, throughout its depth, wet at all times, to maintain a continuous unloading of solids from the filter, to discourage fly breeding, and to avoid surface ponding. Within a momentary minimum application rate of 4 to 8 mgad and a maximum of 125 mgad the momentary dosing rate seems to have little effect on the filter performance.[27]

21–32. Design factors. Some design factors for high-rate filters are given in Table 21–1. Some additional recommendations of the Ten-State Standards are: (1) A controlled recirculation system should be provided to maintain continuous dosing at a rate always equal to or in excess of 10 million gal per acre per day. (2) The rest period during which any unit area receives no sewage should not be in excess of 15 sec. (3) The use of high-rate filters Types A and B will be considered where a settled effluent with a BOD of 30 mg/l or more is acceptable, and where the applied load, recirculation included, does not exceed 110 lb of BOD per 1,000 cu ft of filter media per day. Type A filters are those used with conventional primary settling tanks, and the recirculation is such that the BOD of the influent to the filter, recirculation included, shall not exceed 3 times the BOD of the required settled effluent. Type B filters are used after fine screens. The BOD of the influent shall not exceed, recirculation included, 3.33 times the BOD of the required settled effluent.

Some interesting requirements, particularly with respect to the terms used, are:

Condition	Average	Flow Maximum	Minimum
Minimum coefficient of area *	0.96	0.96	0.96
Maximum coefficient of distribution †	1.65	2.00	
Maximum dosing ratio ‡	2.0	2.0	2.0

* *Coefficient of area* . . . ratio of that filter surface receiving sewage to the total filter surface area.

† *Coefficient of distribution* . . . sum of those filter areas, expressed in per cent of the filter surface receiving sewage, on which the flow deviates from the average dosing rate by 100 per cent or more, 75 per cent or more, 50 per cent or more, 25 per cent or more, and 0 per cent or more; this sum divided by 100.

‡ *Dosing ratio* . . . maximum dosing rate on any unit area of the filter divided by the average dosing rate on that area of the filter receiving sewage.

These requirements are not now accepted as standard.

[27] See also *ibid.*, September, 1941, p. 895.

It has been shown by a study of the performance of trickling filters [28] that:

For filters without recirculation

$$n = 1.102(V'/Q)^{-0.322}; \qquad \bar{r} = 0.55; \qquad \bar{s} = 0.234$$

or

$$n = 0.1062L^{0.302}; \qquad \bar{r} = 0.52; \qquad \bar{s} = 0.34$$

For filters with recirculation

$$n = 2.065 \left(\frac{V'(1 + R)}{Q} \right)^{-0.444}; \qquad \bar{r} = 0.739; \qquad \bar{s} = 0.23$$

For all data

$$n = 1.157 \left(\frac{V'(1 + R)}{Q} \right)^{-0.396}; \qquad \bar{r} = 0.705; \qquad \bar{s} = 0.22$$

where n = fraction of 5-day BOD in settled sewage remaining in following clarifier effluent.

V' = gross volume of filter media, in 1,000's of cu ft.

Q = volume of raw sewage, mgd.

$\bar{r}$ = adjusted coefficient of correlation for logarithmic form of equation.

L = organic loading, pounds of 5-day BOD in settled, raw sewage per 1,000 cu ft of filter media, per day.

$\bar{s}$ = standard error of estimate, for logarithmic form of equation.

R = recirculation ratio.

21–33. Filter details. A depth of 3 ft is recommended [29] for the Bio-filter [30] and of 5 to 6 ft for the Accelo filter,[31] although 3 ft is permissible if local conditions are favorable. A minimum of 5 ft is recommended [32] for Aero-filters for single-stage operation, and 3 ft for 2-stage operation, with a maximum depth of 8 ft. Forced ventilation is discussed in Sect. 21–24. The Ten-States Authority (see Sect. 5–2) recommends a minimum depth of 5 ft and a maximum of 6 ft. In New England most of the high-rate filters are single stage with a 6-ft depth of stone.

Filter stone may be of uniform-size, angular, screened trap rock with 95 per cent passing a 3½-in. screen, not over 15 per cent passing

[28] J. M. Fairall, *S. and I.W.*, September, 1956, p. 1069.

[29] See *Sewage Works Jour.*, September, 1941, p. 895.

[30] See *Sewage Works Jour.*, September, 1941, p. 918.

[31] See *Sewage Works Jour.*, October, 1940, p. 481.

[32] See *Sewage Works Jour.*, September, 1941, p. 905.

a 2¼-in. screen, and less than 5 per cent passing a 1¼-in. screen.[33]

21–34. Recirculation. Recirculation is considered advantageous in high-rate filtration because it brings activated particles of flocculent material produced in the filters in contact with the incoming sewage. However, in a few plants where the quality of the influent and the effluent do not require it, recirculation is not practiced.

Recirculation ratios, that is the ratio of the volume of filtered sewage to the volume of settled sewage applied to the filter, vary between 1 and 10, or even higher. However, for ratios above 2 the increased beneficial effect may be small and the economy questionable. Unless other conditions control, recirculation should provide continuous dosing at a minimum surface rate of 10 mgad. This rate should be sufficient to apply an influent to the filter, recirculation included, not to exceed 3 times the BOD required in the settled effluent where the influent has passed through primary tanks, or 3.3 times when it has passed through fine screens only. Recommended rates of recirculation are shown in Table 21–5.

21–35. Controlled filtration. Ingram[34] states that the process of controlled filtration includes the following essentials: (1) a trickling filter of sectional design, as shown in Fig. 21–12; (2) means for the introduction and distribution of controlled quantities of sewage to each section of the filter; (3) means for the introduction of controlled quantities of air under each section of the filter; (4) means for maintaining influent reaching and passing through the filter at about the same temperature and preferably between 15 and 30° C; (5) a non-absorbing filter medium sized to some degree of uniformity to provide medium surface and ample void space, that is a filter-stone size of 1½ to 3 in.; (6) means for removing effluent from the sections.

Design conditions recommended include: (1) rates of flow up to 12.4 mg per acre-ft per day, or 200 mg per acre per day; (2) organic loads up to 13,800 lb per acre-ft per day, or 200,000 lb per acre per day; (3) ratio of organic to hydraulic rates from 500 to 1,800 lb per mg; (4) air supply not exceeding 2 cu ft per gal of filter influent for extreme organic loadings and, in general, about one-half of this for influents having 50 to 130 mg/l of BOD; (5) filter water temperature

[33] The stone may be tested also according to standards C-88-39T of the American Society for Testing Materials.

[34] W. T. Ingram, *Jour. San. Eng. Div.*, American Society of Civil Engineers, Paper 999, June, 1956.

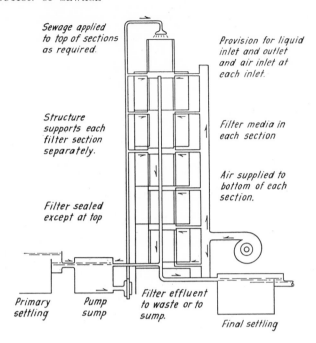

Sewage applied
to top of sections
as required.

Provision for liquid
inlet and outlet
and air inlet at
each inlet.

Structure
supports each
filter section
separately.

Filter media in
each section

Air supplied to
bottom of each
section.

Filter sealed
except at top

Primary
settling

Pump
sump

Filter effluent
to waste or to
sump.

Final settling

Fig. 21–12. Diagram of controlled filtration with a sectional filter. (From Wm. T. Ingram, *Proc. Am. Soc. Civil Engrs., Paper* 999, June, 1956.)

between 17 and 25° C; (6) sectional application of settled sewage to 1, 2 or 3 sections as sewage strength increases; (7) sectional application of air; (8) depth of filled sections 18 to 24 ft; and (9) sectional distribution of organic surface loading as follows:

	Sect. 1	Sect. 2	Sect. 3
1 section application, per cent	100		
2 section application, per cent	65–70	Up to 35	
3 section application, per cent	55–60	Up to 30	Up to 15

21–36. Distribution of sewage. Sewage may be distributed over the bed through fixed nozzles in a rainlike spray, by a revolving-disk distributor in a similar manner, or by rotary distributors. Most high-rate filters are equipped with four-arm, rotary distributors, with two of the four arms equipped with weir boxes or siphonic overflows on the influent to provide satisfactory operation under considerable range of flow rates. A diagram and data suggested by Montgomery

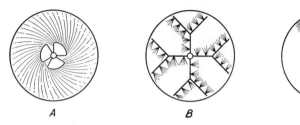

A   B   C

Fig. 21–13. Distributors for high-rate filters.

Table 21–6

CLARIFIERS FOR HIGH-RATE FILTERS

(From *Sewage Works Jour.*, September, 1941, p. 901.)

Clarifier	Single-Stage Treatment		Two-Stage Treatment
	Intermediate	Complete	
Primary clarifier			
Maximum overflow rate, gallons per square foot per day	800–1,000	1,200–1,500	1,200–1,500
Minimum detention period, hours	2.0	1.5	1.5
Secondary clarifier			
Maximum overflow rate, gallons per square foot per day		800–1,000	1,200–1,500
Minimum detention period, hours		1.5	1.5

concerning principles of distribution of sewage on high-rate filters, are shown in Figs. 21–2 and 21–13 and Table 21–5. Since most high-rate filters are proprietary devices, the details of the distributor are unique with the manufacturer.

21–37. Sedimentation. Data concerning special types of clarifiers used in Bio-filters, suggested by Bachmann [35] are given in Table 21–6. The Ten-States Authority (see Sect. 5–2) recommends an overflow rate per square foot of water surface not to exceed 800 gal per day at the design flow for final sedimentation tanks, and 1,000 gal per day for intermediate tanks.

[35] See *Sewage Works Jour.*, September, 1941, p. 895.

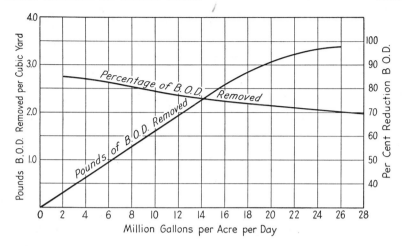

Fig. 21–14. Relation between dosing rate and BOD removal on high-rate filters.[36]

21–38. Results. The information in Fig. 21–14, from Gaillard,[36] shows the relation between dosing rate and BOD removal as a "conservative estimate of reasonable expectation." Bachmann [37] states that with normal-strength sewage and two-stage treatment, with a recirculation ratio of one in each stage, an overall reduction of BOD of 90 to 95 per cent can be expected with less than 10 ppm BOD remaining, together with the production of a well-nitrified effluent high in dissolved oxygen and low in suspended solids. Results reported by Mohlmann [38] indicate percentage removals of suspended solids up to 60 to 65 or more. Additional results [39] are shown in Table 21–7.

21–39. Final settling or humus tanks.[40] The effluent from trickling filters contains large quantities of settleable organic matter, particularly when the filter is undergoing the process of "unloading." This material is highly putrescible, has a relatively high oxygen demand, and is light and flocculent. It should, therefore, be removed. Final settling tanks for trickling filters are built in accordance with

---

36 *Sewage Works Jour.*, September, 1941, p. 918.

37 *Ibid.*, p. 898.

38 F. W. Mohlmann, *Water and Sewage Works*, May, 1950, p. R-133.

39 See also R. S. Rankin, *Proc. Am. Soc. Civil Engrs.*, Separate **336**, November, 1953.

40 See also *S. and I.W.*, November, 1950, p. 1428.

Table 21-7

RESULTS OF HIGH-RATE FILTRATION, PORT WASHINGTON, N. Y.

(From *S. and I.W.*, June, 1955, p. 750.)

Flow into Plant, mgd	Popu- lation	Grit, cu ft per million gal	Chlorine		Solids Digested, per cent		Digester Gas, cu ft per capita per day
			Applied, lb per million gal	Residual, mg/l	Dry	Volatile	
1.4	11,700	0.72	117	2.0	6.7	37	1.6

PORT WASHINGTON, N. Y. (*continued*)

Suspended Solids, mg/l				BOD, mg/l			
Raw Sewage	Settled Sewage	Final Efflu- ent *	Reduc- tion, per cent	Raw Sewage	Settled Sewage	Final Efflu- ent *	Reduc- tion, per cent
263	65	24	91.5	399	103	16	96

DALLAS–WHITE ROCK, TEXAS
AVERAGE FOR JUNE TO DECEMBER, 1954

(From *Public Works*, October, 1955, p. 100.)

Flow into Plant,† mgd	BOD in Settled Sewage, mg/l	Flow to Filters,‡ mgd	Dosing Rate, mgad	BOD Loading		BOD Efflu- ent, mg/l
				Pounds per Day	Pounds per Acre	
25.9	177	40.5	18.1	19,150	2,282	39.4

* From high-capacity filter.   † Population equivalent is 110,000.
‡ Includes recirculation ratio of 1.56 = 40.5/25.9.

Table 21–8

DETENTION PERIODS AND LOADINGS RECOMMENDED
FOR FINAL SETTLING TANKS

(From L. G. Rice, *Water and Sewage Works*, December, 1950, p. 519.)

Effluent from	Detention Period, hr	Settling Rate, gal per sq ft per day	Weir Overflow Rate, gal per lin ft per day
Standard trickling filter			
Average	1–2	600– 800	
Maximum	...	1,000–1,200	15,000
High-rate trickling filter			
Average	2–2½		
Maximum	...	800	
Activated sludge			
Average	2–2½	800–1,000	5,000
Maximum	...	...	15,000

the principles outlined for activated sludge in Sect. 23–41. Detention periods and rates of flow recommended by some state health authorities are given in Table 21–8. Thoman [40] has shown that about two-thirds of the sewage-treatment plants in the United States with standard trickling filters are equipped with final settling tanks. Most of the plants without such tanks are located in the west-south central group of states.

The period of detention should be in the neighborhood of 1 hour for the effluent from normal-rate filters, and 1½ hours for high-rate filters. The amount of material to be cared for is in the neighborhood of 2 to 4 cu ft per million gal of sewage treated. It is discharged from the filter at irregular periods, depending upon the weather and the condition of the filter. A change of temperature from cold or cool weather to warm weather is most conducive to unloading. The sludge collected in the final settling tanks may be disposed of by return to a sludge-digestion chamber, as it is usually not suitable for immediate disposal on a drying bed. The capacity of the digestion tank should be increased by about 25 per cent [41] to receive such sludge.

21–40. Comparison of high-rate and standard-rate trickling filters. A comparison of the features of the two types of filters is shown in Table 21–9.

[41] See *Sewage Works Jour.*, March, 1944, p. 324.

516

Table 21–9

COMPARISON OF STANDARD-RATE AND
HIGH-RATE TRICKLING FILTERS

(From G. T. Lohmeyer, *S. and I.W.*, January, 1957, p. 89.)

Trickling Filter

Feature	Standard-Rate	High-Rate
Hydraulic loading, mgad	Less than 4.0	From 10 to 30
Organic loading, BOD in pounds per acre-ft per day	600	3,000
per 1,000 cu ft per day	Less than 15	Over 30
per cu yd per day	Less than 0.4	Over 0.8
Dosing interval	Not more than 5 min, generally intermittent but can be continuous	Not more than 15 sec, must be continuous
Sloughing	Intermittent	Continuous
Secondary sludge	Black, highly oxidized, light fine particles	Brown, not fully oxidized, fine particles, tending to septicity
Effluent	Highly nitrified, into nitrate stage, 20 mg/l or less BOD	Not fully nitrified—generally only to nitrite stage, 30 mg/l or more BOD
Recirculation system	Generally not included but can be included if hydraulic loading is not exceeded	Always included, although in some types recirculation is used only during periods of low flow

Chapter **22**

Intermittent sand filters
and other filters

22–1. The intermittent sand filter. An intermittent sand filter is a specially prepared bed of sand, or other fine-grained material, on the surface of which sewage is applied intermittently, and from which the effluent is removed by a system of underdrains. A plan of such a filter is shown in Fig. 22–1. The preliminary treatment, an essential part of the process, may consist of primary treatment only, or more complete treatment may be provided before the dose is put onto the sand filter. The quality of the filter effluent is usually such that no subsequent treatment is needed unless it be, possibly, chlorination.

"The chief advances in this process, during its existence of 50 yr, were in drainage and methods of dosing, accompanied by an appreciation of the value of pre-settling to increase the rate of dosage and thereby decrease the required area."[1] A dry, temperate, or warm climate, a large area, and available filtering material are desirable for the installation of an intermittent sand filter.

Intermittent sand filtration requires large areas of land and considerable sand. The beds must be cared for intelligently, but the process does not require constant, skilled attendance. Preliminary treatment by screening is necessary and by sedimentation is desirable. This form of treatment is well suited to small cities where sand is available. It is suited also for isolated locations such as small motor courts, hotels, and hospitals where land and sand are available. The quality of the effluent can be better than that produced by any other process of treatment.

[1] C. G. Hyde, *Modern Sewage Disposal,* Federation of Sewage Works Associations, 1938, p. 7.

517

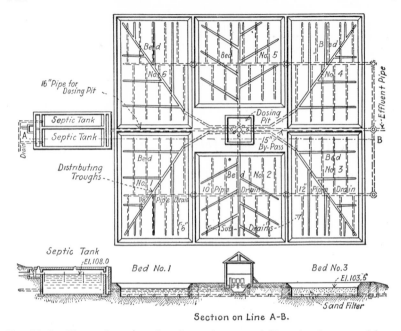

Section on Line A-B.

Fig. 22–1. Plan and section of an intermittent sand filter showing central location of control house.

22–2. Operating cycles, dosing, and maintenance.

In the operation of an intermittent sand filter one dose per day is considered the ordinary method of operation, although some plants operate with as many as four doses per day per filter, and others with one dose at long and irregular intervals. It is not necessary to rest the filter unless signs of overloading and clogging appear. The intermittent dosing action may be obtained by the action of automatic siphons as described in Sect. 21–18 ff., by other automatic devices, or by the manual operation of valves. The dose may be distributed on the beds as described in Sect. 22–6. The effluent is withdrawn from beneath the filter through a system of underdrains, into which it enters after its passage through the bed. There are no control devices on the outlet, since the rate of filtration is controlled by the dosing apparatus and the rate at which the dose is delivered to it. The dosing apparatus should respond quickly to variations in rate of flow of the influent. As doses are applied to a sand filter, a mat of organic matter or bacterial zooglea is formed on the surface of the bed. The mat is held together by hair, paper, and other tenacious materials. It may attain a thickness of $\frac{1}{4}$ to $\frac{1}{2}$ in. before it is necessary to remove it. So long as the filter is draining with sufficient rapidity this mat need not be removed, but if the bed shows signs of clogging the only cleaning that may be necessary will be the rolling up of this dried mat. It is believed that the greater portion of the action in the filter occurs in the upper 5 to 8 in. of the bed, but occasionally the beds become so clogged that it is necessary to remove $\frac{3}{4}$ in. to 2 in. of sand in addition to the surface mat, or to loosen up the surface by shallow plowing or harrowing. The necessity for such treatment may indicate that the filter is being overloaded and that the rate of filtration should be decreased or the preliminary treatment should be improved. The plowing of clogging material into the bed should be avoided, as such action makes the final condition of the bed worse than its condition when trouble was first observed.

In winter the surface of the bed should be plowed up into ridges and valleys. The freezing sewage forms a roof of ice which rests on the ridges, and the subsequent applications of sewage find their way into the filter through the valleys under the ice. In a properly operated bed the filtering material will last indefinitely, without change, except for the necessary restoration of the sand lost in cleaning the bed. If a filter is operated at too high a rate, however, although the quality of the effluent may be satisfactory, it will be necessary at some time to remove the sand and restore the filter.

22–3. Results.[2] Some results of sand filtration are shown in Table 22–1. A distinctive feature of the intermittent sand filter is the quality of its effluent. In a properly designed and operated plant the effluent is clear, colorless, odorless, and sparkling. It is completely nitrified, is stable, and contains a high percentage of dissolved oxygen. It contains no settleable solids except at widely separated periods when a small quantity may appear in the effluent. The efficiency of removal of bacteria is between 98 and 99 per cent, of BOD about 90 per cent, and of suspended solids over 75 per cent. The dissolved solids, the remaining bacteria, and the antecedents of the effluent are the only differences between it and potable water. An effluent from an intermittent sand filter is the most highly purified effluent delivered

---

[2] See also *Sewage Works Jour.*, November, 1949, p. 1002; and T. de S. Furman and others, *S. and I.W.*, March, 1955, p. 261.

Table 22–1

RESULTS OF SEWAGE TREATMENT AT MUSKEGON HEIGHTS, MICHIGAN—
ACTIVATED SLUDGE, ROCK FILTERS, SAND FILTERS

(From T. de S. Furman and others, *S. and I.W.*, March, 1955, p. 261.)

Population 20,000; flow, mgd, 1.63

Sewage and Effluents	Milligrams per Liter		
	BOD	Suspended Solids	Dissolved Oxygen
Raw	230	242	
Primary	170	134	
Activated sludge	51	67	
Rock filter	35	62	3.6
Sand filter	8	8	5.7

by any form of sewage treatment. The effluent can be disposed of without dilution, on account of its high stability. The treatment of sewage to so high a degree is seldom required, so that the use of intermittent sand filters is not common. Drawbacks to their use are the relatively large area of land necessary and the difficulty of obtaining good filter sand in all localities; in some localities the high nitrification in the effluent may induce an objectionably large algal growth.

22–4. Load and rate of filtration. The rate of filtration depends on the nature of the influent, the desired quality of the effluent, and the depth and character of the filtering material. Filters can be found operating at rates of 20,000 gal per acre per day, and others at many times this rate. A 3-ft depth of sand with an effective size of 0.25 mm and a uniformity coefficient not greater than 4.0 has been used. The Ten-States Authority (see Sect. 5–2) allows 165 lb of BOD or 125,000 gal per acre per day for strong, settled sewage, and limits the maximum liquid rate to less than 50,000 gal per acre per day. The loading for trickling-filter effluent is limited to a maximum of 500,000 gal per acre per day. It is recommended further that the filter be made up of 3 layers of gravel: the lowest $1\frac{1}{2}$ to $\frac{3}{4}$ in., the intermediate between $\frac{3}{4}$ and $\frac{1}{4}$ in., and the smallest or upper layer from $\frac{1}{4}$ to $\frac{1}{8}$ in. A depth of sand not less than 24 in. is recommended, with an effective size between 0.36 and 0.6 mm, and a uniformity coefficient not greater than 3.5.

The Committee on Filtering Materials of the American Society of Civil Engineers [3] recommended the following, expressed in gallons per acre per day for the effective size of sand indicated:

1. Raw sewage: 0.20 mm., 55,000; 0.3 mm., 65,000; 0.4 mm., 72,000.
2. Septic sewage: 0.2 mm., 80,000; 0.3 mm., 100,000; and 0.4 mm., 120,000.
3. Fresh settled sewage: 0.2 mm., 120,000; 0.3 mm., 140,000; and 0.4 mm., 160,000.

Furman [4] recommended, for Florida conditions, 125,000 gad on a 0.25-mm sand and 150,000 on a 0.45-mm sand.

22–5. Filtering material. The Committee on Filtering Material of the American Society of Civil Engineers [3] recommended the following specifications for filter material:

a. Homogeneity. The sand as placed should be free from strata or veins of material of varying grades of fineness.

b. Uniformity. The uniformity coefficient should not exceed 5.0.

c. Size. The effective size of the sand should not exceed 0.2 mm. to 0.5 mm.

d. Cleanliness. The total organic matter should be less than 1 per cent. The total acid-soluble matter should be less than 3 per cent. The sand should be practically free from clay, loam, soft limestone, or other materials which may be disintegrated by the sewage liquid, or which may have a tendency to cement the particles of sand.

e. Shape of Grains. The sand grains should be rounded or oval rather than sharp, and crushed flint or quartz gravel should not be used.

f. Material. A siliceous sand should be specified generally with a minimum of calcareous or argillaceous material. However, in certain areas, this might be undesirable economically as the available local material may include considerable calcareous material.

Within the limits mentioned in the specifications no careful attention need be paid to the size of the material. Sand found in place has been underdrained and used successfully for sewage treatment. The size of sand is fixed by the rate of filtration rather than by the bacteriological action of the filter. A coarse sand will permit the sewage to pass through the bed too rapidly, and a fine sand may hold it too long or the bed may become clogged. A uniform size of material should be used throughout the sand bed. The gravel layers, about 6 to 12 in. thick, graded from small sizes to stones just passing a 2-in. ring, should be used beneath the sand to facilitate drainage.

The thickness of the sand layer should not be less than 30 in. to

[3] See *Proc. Am. Soc. Civil Engrs.*, December, 1936, p. 1543.
[4] T. de S. Furman, *S. and I.W.*, June, 1954, p. 745.

insure complete treatment of the sewage. In shallower beds the sewage might trickle through without adequate treatment. Ordinarily beds are made 30 to 36 in. deep, but when deeper layers of sand are found in place there is no set limit to the depth which may be used. The shape and overall dimensions of the bed should conform to the topography of the site and the rate of filtration adopted. Single beds are seldom made greater than 1 acre in area.

22–6. Distribution system. The influent may be distributed onto the bed through a system of pipes terminating in outlets at the bed surface. Each outlet may be surrounded by a flat, concrete slab not over 18 in. to 2 ft in diameter to prevent erosion of the sand surface. Such outlets should be spaced not more than 30 to 60 ft apart. The piping system should be designed for velocities of not less than about 1 fps where the head is available, and all pipes should slope to one point to allow the draining of the system. Other details of the distribution system may follow trickling-filter standards. The use of a wooden trough on the filter surface for the distribution of sewage, as shown in Fig. 22–1, is becoming outmoded.[5]

The operation of automatic devices for dosing the bed is explained in Chapter 21. The dosing tank should have a capacity sufficient to cover the bed to a depth of about 1 to 3 in. at one dose, and the siphon should discharge at a rate of about 1 cfs for each 5,000 sq ft of filter area. A dose should disappear within 20 minutes to half an hour after it is applied to the filter. With the rate stated and two applications per day to a depth of 2 in. at each dose, the rate per acre per day will be 109,000 gal. In order to assure this intermittency of operation it is necessary to provide a number of units of filters in the design of an intermittent-sand-filter plant.

22–7. Underdrainage. Underdrains for intermittent sand filters usually consist of vitrified-clay pipe laid with open joints, the spigot being $\frac{1}{4}$ to $\frac{3}{8}$ in. from the shoulder of the hub. The joints should be carefully covered with graded gravel from 2 in. down to $\frac{1}{4}$ in. in size to prevent the entrance of sand into the drain. The underdrains should be laid not more than 15 ft apart. Smaller spacing is used with the fine filtering material or shallow beds. The bottom of the bed may be graded level, with the underdrains laid in rectangular trenches, or the bottom may be graded in ridges and furrows with an underdrain in the bottom of each furrow. If the underdrain is laid in a trench the drain should be surrounded with gravel to fill the entire

[5] See also *S. and I.W.*, July, 1950, p. 362.

trench, the top layer of gravel being ¼ in. or smaller in size. If the ridge-and-furrow type of bottom is used, the entire bottom of the bed may be covered with gravel laid level from the top of each ridge to a depth of 2 to 3 in. over the underdrains, or the underdrains may be surrounded with gravel to a thickness of 18 in. to 2 ft.

The underdrains should be laid on a slope sufficient to give a velocity of 3 to 4 fps when they are flowing full. The size of each drain is determined from the slope on which it is laid, the tributary area, and the maximum rate of flow through the filter. This rate of flow may be as high as 0.1 to 0.2 gal per min per sq ft of filter surface. Drains less than 6 in. in diameter are undesirable.

The underdrainage system should have a free outlet to permit ventilation of the sand bed, although filters with submerged underdrains have operated successfully.

22–8. Other filters. Among other filters that have been used in sewage treatment are rapid sand filters, the Hardinge sand filter and clarifier, the Dunbar filter, and the magnetite filter.

Rapid sand filters have been used to reclaim used water for other than potable purposes. They cannot be used successfully as a primary treatment device because of the rapid clogging of the sand.[6]

The Hardinge sand filter and clarifier differs from a mechanically cleaned circular clarifier principally in the layer of filter sand in the bottom of the clarifier and the porous underdrainage provided. The sand-cleaning mechanism is carried on a revolving arm similar to that in a clarifier. In operation the sand is submerged and continually cleaned, a small layer of sand and sludge being scraped to the center.

The Dunbar filter [7] is similar in construction and operation to an intermittent sand filter of coarse, graded material. It consists of materials graded from top to bottom from 0.04 in. to 6 in. In operation the surface of the bed is flooded at each dose, the process being repeated until the bed clogs. It is then removed from service to allow cleaning of the surface. Rates of operation may be up to 2 mgad, with 85 per cent reduction of BOD, in the applied sewage.

The magnetite filter, sometimes called a Laughlin filter, consists of a layer approximately 3 in. thick, of crushed magnetite sand sup-

[6] See also *Water Works and Sewerage,* August, 1940, p. 351; and A. E. J. Pettet and others, *S. and I.W.,* July, 1952, p. 835.

[7] See also E. W. Steel and P. J. A. Zeller, *Bull.* 37, Texas Engineering Experiment Station, 1928.

ported on a non-magnetic, metal-wire screen. Settled sewage is filtered through the sand until the head loss requires cleaning of the filter. Cleaning is done by forcing water upwards through the bed of sand at the same time that the sand is stirred by passing over it an electro-magnet that is alternately magnetized and demagnetized.[8] Such filters are obsolete and are mainly of historical interest.

[8] See also *Sewage Works Jour.*, May, 1937, p. 466; and September, 1941, p. 1047.

Chapter 23

Activated sludge

23-1. The process. The activated-sludge process of sewage treatment involves the aeration of screened, presettled, or otherwise primary-treated sewage, mixed with a small volume of activated sludge which has been collected in a sedimentation basin shortly before it has been mixed with the sewage preceding aeration.[1] The mixture in the aeration tank is known as *mixed liquor. Activated sludge* is "sludge settled out of sewage previously agitated in the presence of abundant atmospheric oxygen."[2] Buswell[3] states: "Activated sludge flocs are composed of a synthetic, gelatinous matrix, similar to that of *Nostoc* and *Merismopedia*, in which filamentous and unicellular bacteria are imbedded, and on which protozoa and some metazoa crawl and feed." A photomicrograph of an activated sludge is shown in Fig. 23-1. The presence of a large number of protozoans is indicative of good sludge.[4] Activated sludge differs from other sludges in appearance, physical characteristics, and biological composition. Good activated sludge has a distinctive musty, earthy odor when in circulation in the aeration basin. To the unaided eye it is a light brown, flocculent precipitate that settles rapidly in its mother liquor, leaving a supernatant liquid that is clear, colorless, odorless and sparkling.

A flowing-through diagram of the activated-sludge process and other information, when treating domestic sewage, are shown in Fig. 23-2. The difference between the activated-sludge process and the

[1] See R. E. McKinney and M. P. Horwood, *S. and I.W.*, February, 1952, p. 117, for a fundamental approach to the activated-sludge process.
[2] Definition by joint committee of the American Society of Civil Engineers and the American Public Health Association, 1928.
[3] A. M. Buswell and H. L. Long, *Jour. Am. Water Works Assoc.*, Vol. 10, 1923, p. 309; and *Eng. News-Record*, Vol. 90, 1923, p. 119.
[4] S. Bains and others, *S. and I.W.*, September, 1953, p. 1023.

Fig. 23–1. Photomicrograph of well-aerated activated sludge.

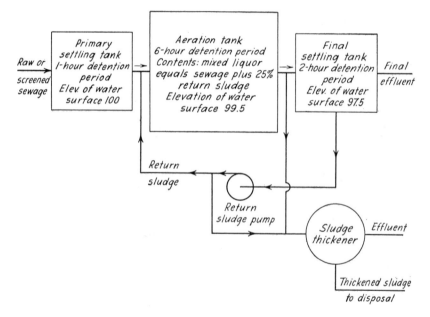

Fig. 23–2. Flowing-through diagram of a conventional, activated-sludge sewage-treatment plant. (Modified from drawing by W. N. Torpey and A. H. Chasick, *S. and I.W.*, November, 1955, p. 1217.) Elevations of water surfaces shown are relative only, and are approximate.

aeration of sewage is to be emphasized. The mixing of air with sewage is aeration. When activated sludge, recirculated from a final sedimentation tank, is added to incoming sewage to form a mixed liquor, which is subsequently aerated and from which activated sludge is later settled, the activated-sludge process is being used. The process is assumed to be biochemical [5] and is dependent on oxygen, although flocculation may occur with other gases. It has been found that satisfactory flocculation and clarification will occur only with adequate aeration and biological activity.[6]

23–2. Advantages and disadvantages. Some of the advantages of the process are a clear, sparkling, and non-putrescible effluent; freedom from offensive odors during operation; degree of nitrification controllable between limits; nature of the effluent variable to accord with the quantity and character of diluting water available; more than 90 per cent of the bacteria removed; approximately 90 per cent removal of BOD and settleable solids; relatively low installation cost as compared with trickling filters; and some commercial value in the sludge. The possibility of controlling the degree of nitrification is desirable, for, under certain conditions in the body of water receiving the effluent, nitrates in the effluent are conducive to troublesome algal growths.

The activated-sludge process is not suitable for adoption where constant, skilled attendance is not available because of the mechanical equipment that must be operated and maintained, and the chemical, biological, and physical characteristics of the process which must be understood. The amount of hydraulic head consumed and the surface area of plant required are less than the requirements of any process giving equal or better results. The quality of the effluent can be controlled, between limits, by manipulation of the process. The volume of sludge produced is greater than that produced by any other process, except possibly that of chemical treatment, and the sludge is difficult to treat. It may, however, have sufficient commercial value to repay a portion of the cost of its treatment.

Among the disadvantages of the process can be included uncertainty concerning the results to be expected under all conditions; sensitivity to changes in the quality of the influent; high cost of operation under some conditions; the necessity for constant, skilled attendance; and difficulty in dewatering and disposing of the large volume of sludge produced.

[5] See *Sewage Works Jour.*, January, 1942, pp. 3 and 32.
[6] See T. R. Haseltine, *S. and I.W.*, December, 1952, p. 1533.

Table 23–1

Fertilizing Values in Sludge

Results of Early Tests

Experimental Pot Number	Cultivating Medium, grams							Product					
	White Sand	Dolomite	Bone Meal	Potassium Sulfate	Activated Sludge	Activated Sludge *	Dried Blood	Number of Heads of Wheat	Number of Seeds	Weight of Seeds, grams	Bushels per Acre, calculated	Average Length of Stalk, inches	Weight of Straw, grams	Tons per Acre, calculated
1	19,820	60	6	3	0	0	0	14	85	2.38	6.20	19.4	2.25	0.18
2	19,820	60	6	3	0	0	8.61	15	189	5.29	13.6	23.0	8.25	0.68
3	19,820	60	6	3	20	0	0	22	491	13.75	35.9	35.4	26.75	2.23
4	19,820	60	6	3	0	20	0	23	518	14.50	38.7	37.1	26.21	2.18

Source: Eng. News, Vol. 73, 1915, p. 647; Eng. Record, Vol. 71, 1915, p. 421; and Jour. Am. Water Works Assoc., Vol. 3, p. 327.
* Extracted with ligroin.

23–3. Values in sludge. The principal value of activated sludge is as an aid in the manufacture of fertilizer. (See also Sect. 24–4.) In the activated-sludge process nitrifying bacteria abound, converting nitrogen to available plant food. An analysis of dried sludge [7] showed the following results, expressed in per cent, after the weight had been reduced 95.5 per cent by drying: nitrogen, 6.3; fat, 4.00; phosphorus, 1.44; volatile matter, 75. The effect of sludge on the rate of plant growth is shown in Table 23–1, from Bartow and Mohlmann.[7] Concentrations of some of the more common fertilizer constituents are shown in Table 23–2, from Rudolfs.[8]

23–4. Results. The effluent obtained from the activated-sludge process is commonly clear, sparkling, colorless, high in dissolved oxygen, low in BOD, and odorless or with an inoffensive odor. Its quality can be equalled only by the effluent from sand-filtration and it is the best that can be obtained continuously on a large scale from any treatment process. It can be expected, in general, that the effluent, regardless of the strength of a normal, domestic-sewage influent, will contain from 10 to 20 mg/l of suspended solids, and between 8 and 18 mg/l of BOD. The percentage removal is partly

[7] See Eng. News, Vol. 73, 1915, p. 647; Eng. Record, Vol. 71, 1915, p. 421; and Jour. Am. Water Works Assoc., Vol. 3, p. 327.
[8] W. Rudolfs, Water Works and Sewerage, December, 1940, p. 257.

Table 23–2

SOME CHEMICAL CONSTITUENTS IN SEWAGE SLUDGE

(W. Rudolfs, *Water Works and Sewerage*, December, 1940, p. 257.)

Constituent	Fresh Solids *	Digested Sludge *	Activated Sludge *
Total nitrogen, N	4.50	2.25	6.20
Phosphoric, P_2O_5	2.25	1.50	2.50
Potash, K_2O	0.50	0.50	0.75
Silica, SiO_2	13.80	27.60	8.50
Iron, Fe_2O_3	3.20	6.00	7.20
Aluminum, Al_2O_3	2.10	4.30	3.20
Calcium, CaO	2.70	5.70	1.70
Magnesium, MgO	0.60	1.00	1.40
Sulfur, SO_3	1.2	2.5	2.9
Chlorides, Cl	0.50	0.50	0.50
Sodium, Na_2O	0.80	1.50	1.00
Lead, PbO	0.10	0.20	0.20

* Percentage on dry basis.

Table 23–3

RESULTS OF ACTIVATED-SLUDGE PLANT OPERATION

Plant Number	Aeration Period, hr	Air, cu ft per gal	Raw Sewage Susp. Solids, mg/l	Raw Sewage BOD, mg/l	Return Sludge Per cent	Return Sludge Index	Final Sedimentation Tank Period, hr	Final Sedimentation Tank D.O., mg/l	Final Sedimentation Tank Susp. Solid, mg/l	Final Sedimentation Tank BOD, mg/l	Overall Op'n Cost, $ per cap. per year	Cu ft Air per Lb BOD Removed
1	6.1	0.87	...	114	36	376	...	5.6		9	1.59	0.87
2	...	0.8	...	178	...	99	...	3.9				
3	4.7	0.39	...	247	...	...	2.9					
4	7.0	0.85	238	195	...	...	...	4.9	16.4	15.5	0.93	
5	4.3	0.75	122	88	26.4	92	...	...	19.0	10.0	...	1.39
6	9.5	...	191	191	20	170	...	...	...	...	2.1	
7	4.54	0.46	356	140	38.3	106	...	3.5	11.0	6.3	0.95	1.44

No. 1. Boise, Idaho, from March, 1957,* p. 320; P = 36.3; Q = 6.2.
No. 2. Easterly, Cleveland, Ohio, Nov., 1952,* p. 1424; Q = 108.
No. 3. Muskegon Hts., Mich., Jan., 1952,* p. 102; P = 20; Q = 1.75.
No. 4. Fort Wayne, Ind., May, 1953,* p. 618; P = 130; Q = 18.8.
No. 5. Marion, Ind., Aug., 1953,* p. 976; PE = 21.2; Q = 5.07.
No. 6. Belvidere, Ill., July, 1953,* p. 855; PE = 9.7; Q = 1.4.
No. 7. Gary, Ind., Sept. 1952,* p. 1179; P = 819; Q = 160.3.
P = population, in thousands.   PE = population equivalent, in thousands.
Q = avg rate of sewage flow, mgd.
* Date of reference in *S. and I.W.*

Table 23-4

FERTILIZING INGREDIENTS IN SLUDGE, VARIOUS MANURES, AND ORGANIC NITROGENOUS MATERIALS *

(Per cent on dry basis)

Material	Nitrogen as N	Phosphoric Acid	Potash	Organic Matter	Moisture, per cent
Digested settled sludge	0.8–3.5	*1.63* †	*0.26* †	...	*6.4* † 70 ‡
Settled sludge	1.2–4.9				
Digested activated sludge	2.0–4.8	*2.10* †	*0.13* †		
Heat-dried activated sludge	4.0–7.0	1.7–2.5	0.13 §		*10*
Commercial pulverized					
Sheep manure	1.2–2.5	1.0–2.0	2.0–4.0	48	*64*
Cattle manure	1.6–2.1	1.0	1.0–2.2	66	*79*
Poultry manure	1.9–4.0	2.5–3.7	0.8–1.3	64	*68*
Blood	9–13	7–16			
Fish scrap	6.5–10.0	0.5–14			
Cottonseed meal	5–8	2–3	1–2		
Vacuum-filtered sludge ‖	3.2	2.26	0.28		

Note. The italicized figures are from Don R. Bloodgood, *Water and Sewage Works*, January, 1955, p. 44.

* See also H. A. Lunt, *Water and Sewage Works*, June 1, 1955, p. R-304.

† Dried.

‡ From drying beds.

§ From Milwaukee, Wis., sewage-treatment works.

‖ Ash 51.3 per cent and volatile 48.7 per cent, on dry basis. Grease 12.2 per cent.

dependent on the strength of the influent.[9] Some results of treatment by the activated-sludge process are shown in Table 23–3.

The volume of excess sludge resulting from the process is large because the moisture content is relatively high. The sludge is free from odor when fresh, but it becomes septic quickly, it is difficult to dewater, and it presents a difficult problem of disposal. Data on sludge qualities are given in Tables 23–2 and 23–4.

[9] See also W. N. Torpey and A. H. Chaswick, *S. and I.W.*, November, 1955, p. 1217.

23–5. Status. The introduction of the activated-sludge process was preceded by 30 years of experimentation in the aeration of sewage which, at times, closely approached the method known as the activated-sludge process.[10] The discovery of the process is generally credited to W. T. Lockett.[11] Since then the process has been studied extensively, improved, and refined. It has met such world-wide approval that activated-sludge works are to be found wherever sewage is extensively treated. The position of activated-sludge plants in 1950 is indicated by the figures given in Table 28–7.[12] The activated-sludge process is considered inapplicable to works with flows less than about one-half mgd, except under unusual circumstances, because of the mechanical equipment involved and the trained supervision required.

23–6. Pretreatment. It is generally considered desirable to give sewage some form of pretreatment before aeration in order to reduce the load on the aeration tank. The total cost of the process is less with pretreatment than without it. However, activated-sludge works have been operated without pretreatment.

Pretreatment may consist of sedimentation, either with or without the addition of chemicals, or fine screening. In the United States preliminary sedimentation is usually brief, being, in the newer plants, between 15 and 20 min in a mechanical clarifier, without chemicals. As a result of an analysis of the economics of the problem Schroepfer [13] has concluded that the economical period of presedimentation is between 30 and 60 min. English practice, with stronger sewages, calls for periods up to 6 to 8 hr.

23–7. Adsorption and oxidation. The activated-sludge process involves a balance between adsorption and oxidation. The former is controlled partly by the concentration of suspended solids in the mixed liquor and the latter by the dissolved oxygen in it. Among the causes of imbalance pointed out by Haseltine,[14] are: (1) inadequate oxygen supply, (2) presence of germicidal wastes, (3) excessive carbon dioxide, which may be diminished by the application of lime, (4) presence of septic sewage, or sludge, or high BOD in the influent, (5) excessive grease content of the influent, (6) inadequate aeration period, and (7) short circuiting in the aeration tank. The method

10 See E. Ardern and W. T. Lockett, *Jour. Soc. Chem. Ind.,* Vol. 33, 1914, p. 523.
11 See also *Trans. Am. Soc. Civil Engrs.,* October, 1941, p. 158.
12 See also *Water and Sewage Works,* July, 1950, p. 290.
13 See *Proc. Am. Soc. Civil Engrs.,* April, 1938, p. 737.
14 T. R. Haseltine, *Water and Sewage Works,* Part II, May, 1954, p. R-211.

of correction is obvious in some of the preceding difficulties. The success of treatment depends, to a great extent, on the maintenance of a proper balance between adsorption and oxidation.

23–8. Aeration of sewage. The rate of solution of oxygen through the surface of a quiescent body of water is so slow as to be practically negligible. A thin surface layer of the water becomes saturated immediately on exposure to the air; thereafter little oxygen is effectively transmitted through the surface layer. If the liquid is agitated the surface layer is broken up and the oxygen dissolved in it is carried into the body of the liquid.[15] A new surface layer becomes saturated, and it in turn is mixed with the body of the liquid so that the solution of the atmospheric oxygen is greatly expedited.[16] Violent agitation is unnecessary. It is desirable only to turn the body of the liquid rapidly and to mix it well so that all portions of the liquid may be exposed to the atmosphere in a short period of time.

Some basic conditions affecting aeration [17] include: (1) depth of aerator. Total absorption increases linearly with depth, within a practical range; (2) number of diffusers. An increase in the area of diffusers will decrease the bubble size, reduce coalescence, allow better lateral diffusion, favor increased oxygen adsorption, and diminish the rate of air flow per nozzle; and (3) increase of absorption. This is due to relative increase in bubble surface. The surface of a bubble varies as the square of its diameter, and bubble volume varies as the cube of its diameter. The rate of solution of oxygen from a rising bubble is slightly more rapid than from an equal area at the surface of the liquid. Although the rate of absorption of oxygen in water is known to be directly proportional to the oxygen deficiency, experience indicates that the average concentration of dissolved oxygen in a mixed liquor does not significantly affect the unit rate of oxygen utilization.[18] King [19] gives some empirical formulas for the rate of absorption of oxygen, such as

$$P = \frac{0.031H^{0.18}U^zS^{0.86}(1.024)^T}{d^{0.95}} \qquad (23\text{--}1)$$

[15] See also A. Pasveer, *S. and I.W.*, January, 1954, p. 28, January, 1956, p. 28, and October, 1955, p. 1130. A. M. Buswell, *S. and I.W.*, January, 1956, p. 33.

[16] See also A. Pasveer, *S. and I.W.*, November, 1953, p. 1253.

[17] From A. T. Ippen and C. E. Carver, Jr., *S. and I.W.*, July, 1954, p. 813.

[18] From D. B. Smith, *S. and I.W.*, July, 1953, p. 767.

[19] H. R. King, *S. and I.W.*, August, 1955, p. 894, and September, 1955, p. 1007.

where P = percentage of oxygen absorbed from the bubble.

U = oxygen deficiency of the water in mg/l at atmospheric pressure.

$z = 1/H^{0.13}$ where H is the water depth to the point where the bubble enters, ft.

S = bubble detention, or the rising time in the water, seconds. Usually about 10.

T = water temperature, degrees C.

d = diameter of bubble in inches. Restricted to the order of 0.1 to 0.3 in.

The application of the formula is limited to conditions normally met in the activated-sludge process, and to a dissolved-oxygen saturation of less than 50 per cent.

23–9. Preaeration of sewage.[20]   Preaeration is not a part of the activated-sludge process.   It is a preparatory treatment by aeration to separate grit, to remove gases, to add oxygen, to promote flotation of grease, and to aid in flocculation.   Roe [21] points out that preaeration reverses the oxidation-reduction potential, stopping the reduction of some solids, and attaining other objectives.   Since the primary use of air in preaeration is mechanical, the amount of air required cannot be expressed satisfactorily in terms of sewage strength.   Roe states that the amount required in preaeration will vary between 1 and 4 cu ft per lin ft of tank, the larger amounts being required by deep, wide tanks.   Air requirements may be formulated as:

$$A = 0.0021T + 0.041 \qquad (23\text{–}2)$$

where A = air, in cu ft per gal.

T = preaeration period, min.

23–10. Methods of aeration and design bases.   Sewage is aerated in the activated-sludge process by air bubbles blown through it from air distributors in the bottom of an aeration tank, or by agitation of the surface of the sewage, the tank contents being stirred by mechanical means so that air and sewage are intimately mixed.   The former method is known as air diffusion; the latter as mechanical agitation, or sometimes as bioaeration.   Air-diffusion methods are widely used, mechanical agitation being confined principally to

[20] See E. R. Baumann and others, *A Plant Scale Study of Preaeration in Sewage Treatment,* a bulletin of the Iowa Engineering Experiment Station, May 1, 1957.

[21] F. C. Roe, *S. and I.W.,* February, 1951, p. 127.

smaller plants. Roe [22] places the maximum economical size of mechanical agitation at about 1 mgd.

Some basic design factors in the two methods of aeration, recommended by the Ten-States Authority (see Sect. 5–2) are:

Limitations. Design data are presumed to achieve a removal of 90 per cent or more of BOD and suspended solids under normal conditions of load and operation.

Aeration tanks. Number of units. Two or more, capable of independent operation, where total capacity exceeds 5,000 cu ft.

Capacity. 7.5 hr detention for design flows from 0.2 to 0.8 mgd. In excess of 1 mgd detention period to be such that tank volume shall provide 30 cu ft per lb of BOD in aerator influent, exclusive of return sludge. Tank volumes for mechanical aeration shall be 50 per cent greater than for air diffusion. Appropriate adjustments are to be made where rate of sewage flow varies widely from 100 gal per capita daily and from 125 to 150 mg/l BOD.

Depths. Not less than 10 nor more than 15 ft.

Air supply. Must maintain at least 2 mg/l of dissolved oxygen, in all parts of aeration tanks except immediately beyond inlets. Normal requirements of air are 1,000 cu ft per lb BOD per day to be removed, with air equipment and piping designed 150 per cent in excess of this. Air shall have not more than 0.6 mg of dust per 1,000 cu ft of air. Air diffusers shall preferably be removable.

Waste sludge facilities. Control equipment and piping should have maximum capacity not less than 25 per cent of average rate of sewage flow and should function satisfactorily at rates of 0.5 per cent of average sewage flow or a minimum of 10 gpm, whichever is larger.

Air-Diffusion Aeration [23]

23–11. Period of aeration. A wide variation in aeration periods from about 3 to 18 hr is to be found in practice. The period of aeration depends on the degree of purification, the amount of nitrification sought,[24] and the strength of the raw sewage as measured by its BOD. High nitrification is not now generally desired since it has been found that non-nitrifying sludges make a plant more economical

[22] F. C. Roe and S. E. Kappe, *Sewage Works Jour.,* November, 1938, pp. 999 and 1007.

[23] See also "Air Diffusion in Sewage Works," *Manual of Practice* 5, Federation of Sewage and Industrial Wastes Associations, 1952.

[24] See *Sewage Works Jour.,* January, 1942, p. 15.

to operate, with shorter aeration periods and less air. Data presented by a committee of the American Public Health Association [25] show that the relation between period of retention and strength of sewage can be expressed as

$$BOD = 20(T + 1) \qquad (23\text{--}3)$$

where BOD is the BOD removal desired, in mg/l and T is the aeration period, in hours. Periods of aeration recommended by the Joint Committee (see Sect. 5–2) are:

Flows in mgd *	0.2–0.8	0.8–1.0	1.0+
Aeration period, hr	7.5	7.5–6.0	6

* Exclusive of return sludge.

An additional criterion is that the aeration tank shall have a minimum capacity of 30 cu ft per lb of BOD in the aerator influent. It has been found that nearly 60 per cent of the purification is accomplished during the first hour of a 6-hr aeration period, and only about 15 per cent in the last 3 hr. This fact and the relation between cost of plant and aeration have suggested to Schroepfer [26] that there may be a period of aeration that will produce desired results at the lowest cost, and that this period is about 4½ hr.

It is to be emphasized that, once the oxygen needs of the activated sludge have been satisfied, additional aeration, either through prolonged time of aeration, increased volume of air, or increased concentration of oxygen in the aerating atmosphere, will accomplish nothing more than to increase the cost.[27]

23–12. Aeration-tank dimensions. Aeration tanks are almost invariably constructed as long, relatively narrow, rectangular channels with a minimum ratio of length to width of 5:1, and designed to permit a net horizontal component of velocity of about 5 fpm. Such a velocity requires a channel 1,800 ft long to permit a detention period of 6 hr. Such lengths, as well as the longer ones required for longer detention periods, can be obtained by baffling the aeration chamber with round-the-end baffles. Equal or higher velocities, with shorter channels, can be attained by recirculating a portion of the aerated sewage. An objectionable condition that sometimes arises in long channels with recirculation is "short-circuiting," as a result of which

[25] See *ibid.*, p. 16.
[26] See *Proc. Am. Soc. Civil Engrs.*, April, 1938, p. 737.
[27] See *Sewage Works Jour.*, July, 1949, p. 643, and April, 1950, p. 490.

Fig. 23–3.   Interior view of preaeration tank at Washington, D. C. It is to be noted that diffuser plates had not been installed at the time this picture was taken.

underaerated sewage may be discharged from the tank. This can be partly overcome by operating two or more tanks in series.

The cross-sectional area of the channel is determined from the expression $q = AV$, in which q is the rate of flow of the mixed liquor, A is the cross-sectional area of the channel, and V is the horizontal component of velocity. No allowance is ordinarily made for the fact that the diffused air may occupy approximately 1 per cent of the volume of the tank. The channel width is fixed, to some extent, by the location of the diffuser plates, the greatest width being provided with spiral flow. Widths of channels normally used for spiral-flow tanks vary between 15 and 30 ft, with a depth of about 15 ft. With spiral-flow units a triangular, longitudinal baffle may be placed at the top of the side nearest to the diffuser plate, as shown in Fig. 23–3. No limit is placed on the width of ridge-and-furrow aeration tanks except that due to considerations of air-diffusion pipes.

Table 23-5

VALUE OF KUTTER'S n IN ACTIVATED-SLUDGE AERATION CHANNELS

(See *Proc. Am. Soc. Civil Engrs.*, January, 1934, p. 63.)

Velocity, fps	Ridge and Furrow	Spiral	Velocity, fps	Ridge and Furrow	Spiral
1.3	0.034 *	0.030	0.6	0.061	0.056
1.2	0.034 *	0.031	0.4	0.080	0.077
1.0	0.039 *	0.035	0.2	0.112	0.108
0.9	0.032 *	0.036	0.1	0.140	0.134
0.8	0.047	0.043	0.0	0.23 †	

* Observed.

† Asymptotic value found by extending curve.

The loss of head through an aeration tank can be computed from Kutter's or Manning's formula with values of n determined by Townsend and reported as in Table 23-5.[28]

23-13. Depth of tank. Practice and experience in the United States have led to the adoption of a depth of about 15 ft as representing an economical balance between structural cost and operating cost. A greater depth, to about 20 ft, would give greater efficiency of aeration,[29] but the cost of the tank would be increased, and the higher compression to which the air would be subjected would increase the operating cost. Tanks shallower than about 15 ft would decrease these items but the efficiency of aeration would be uneconomically reduced and the land area required would be proportionally increased.[30]

23-14. Quantity of air. A dissolved-oxygen concentration of at least 2 to 5 mg/l should be maintained in all parts of the aeration tank except possibly near the inlet. Under some unusual conditions the minimum may be permitted to fall to 1 mg/l. In order to maintain these concentrations it has been found necessary to apply from 0.2 to 1.5 cu ft of free air per gal of sewage treated, depending on the strength of the sewage and the design and control of the plant. Improved laboratory control and experience in operation have made possible a continued decrease in the quantity of air required, as indicated by the data in Table 23-6.

[28] See *Proc. Am. Soc. Civil Engrs.*, January, 1934, p. 63.

[29] See also *ibid.*, Vol. 64, 1938, p. 965.

[30] See also A. Pasveer, *S. and I.W.*, January, 1956, p. 28.

Table 23–6

AIR REQUIREMENTS IN DIFFUSED AIR AERATION

(From F. W. Mohlmann, "25 Years of Activated Sludge," *Modern Sewage Disposal*, p. 78.)

Plant		1930	1931	1932	1933	1934	1935	1936	1937
Chicago	Air, cu ft per gal	0.52	0.47	0.44	0.37	0.38	0.36	0.36	0.35
North Side	5-day BOD of effluent	8.5	8.4	9.7	13.1	14.1	10.1	8.5	9.2
Springfield,	Air, cu ft per gal	1.21	1.05	0.87	0.83	0.94	0.75	0.85	0.58
Ill.	5-day BOD of effluent	70	62	17	13	16	8	16	13

Since the air is used in reducing BOD it is more logical to express the volume of air used in terms of BOD removed. Normal requirements may be taken as 1,000 cu ft of air per day per lb of BOD removed from the primary effluent. Air-diffusion equipment, compressors, distribution pipes, and diffusers should be designed for 150 per cent over normal requirements.

23–15. Air compressors. Air is applied to the sewage at the bottom of the aeration tank at a pressure in the neighborhood of 5.5 to 6.0 psi, depending upon the depth of the sewage, the loss of head through the distributing pipes, and the rate of application. In different experimental plants the pressure has varied from 3 to 30 psi. Such pressures are on the line that divides the use of direct blowers for low pressures from turbo and reciprocating pressure machines for pressures above 10 psi. Positive-pressure blowers or direct blowers operate on the principle of a centrifugal pump, and because of the lower specific gravity of air they rotate at a high speed. Reciprocating compressors that operate similarly to water pumps are commonly undesirable because of the need for internal lubrication, which may result in pollution of the air, and the possibility of condensation of moisture in the air-distributing pipes.

For pressures up to about 10 psi the positive or Roots-type blower seems most desirable. It has a low first cost and the relatively high efficiency of about 75 to 80 per cent of the power input. No oil or dirt is added to the air to clog the distributing plates, as with the reciprocating machine. A disadvantage is the difficulty of varying the pressure or quantity of the output of the machine. As the required pressure and volume of air increase, the turbo blower becomes more and more desirable within the limits of pressure that are ordinarily used in this process. For small installations the best form of power is probably the electric drive, but when the capacity becomes such as to make turbo blowers advisable they should be driven by direct-connected steam turbines. Rotary blowers [31] of the positive-displacement dry type are used mostly for small and medium-size plants. They are used in units of less than 10,000 to 15,000 cfm. Centrifugal and turbo blowers are used in larger plants.

The positive or displacement blower delivers a constant volume of air at any fixed speed regardless of the discharge pressure. The rate of discharge is proportional to the speed. Since the compressor cannot operate against a closed discharge valve a bypass and relief valve should be provided. The pressure generated by the centrifugal blower is sensitive to speed and to air density and, therefore, to temperature.

Because of the noise and vibration connected with the operation of most blowers they should be located where they will cause the least annoyance. They should be insulated from their foundation to prevent the transmisson of vibration and noise to and through the building.

23–16. Power consumption. Usually power consumption is expressed in kilowatt-hours per million gallons of sewage treated, or in horsepower per million gallons per day. The former figure varies between about 300 and 1,000, and the latter between 16 and 60, for either air diffusion or mechanical aeration. Since the power consumption depends greatly on the degree of treatment effected, a more reasonable and expressive figure would be in units of work per pound of 5-day BOD removed. Some plant guarantees expressed in such a unit have been in the neighborhood of 0.35 kwh per lb of 5-day BOD removed or about 18 hp per million gal per day for fresh domestic sewage with 200 mg/l of BOD.[32] Power consumption is usually lower in terms of pounds of BOD removed when strong rather than weak sewage is treated.

23–17. Air pipes. The computation of the diameter of an air pipe is based on the expression $Q = AV$, that is, the rate of flow is equal to the product of the cross-sectional area of the pipe and the velocity of flow of fluid. The economical velocity of flow of compressed air through steel pipes is in the order of 2,000 to 3,000 fpm or faster. The computation of the loss of pressure due to friction may be based on fundamentals of fluid mechanics or by the use of empirical formulas.[33] The familiar basic Weisbach formula is

[31] See also D. L. Dowling, *Water Works and Sewerage*, August, 1940.

[32] See *Sewage Works Jour.*, November, 1938, p. 1007.

[33] See also A. A. Lemke, *S. and I.W.*, January, 1952, p. 24; and H. L. McMillan, *Eng. News-Record*, Vol. 91, 1923, p. 178.

$$h_f = f\,\frac{4LV^2}{D2g} \qquad (23\text{-}4)$$

where h_f = head loss in air pipe, ft of water, if formula shown below for f is used.

D = diameter of pipe, ft.

V = velocity of air flowing in air pipe, fps.

L = length of pipe, ft.

g = acceleration of gravity, 32.2 ft per sec per sec.

f = friction factor. For air, under normal conditions of temperature and moderate pressures met in the activated-sludge process, it is

$$(35 \times 10^{-7})\left(1 + \frac{1}{3D}\right) \qquad (23\text{-}5)$$

Example. Find the pressure loss, in inches of water, for 100 ft of 12-in. pipe carrying 4,000 cu ft of air.

Solution.

$$f = (35 \times 10^{-7})\left(1 + \frac{1}{3.3}\right) = 46.5 \times 10^{-7}$$

$$V = Q/A = (4,000 \times 4)/(\pi \times 1 \times 60) = 85 \text{ fps}$$

$$h_f = (46.5 \times 10^{-7})(400)(85^2)/(1 \times 64.4)$$

$$= 0.208 \text{ ft.} \qquad\qquad\qquad Answer.$$

It is to be noted that the application of the Weisbach formula, as shown in the example, is limited to flow of compressed air under isothermal conditions, at low pressure, and with relatively low head losses or pressure drop. These are the conditions normally met in the distribution of air in the activated-sludge process.

In designing the air pipes the layout should be such as to equalize pressure losses as nearly as possible. Piping should be above, or branch pipes should rise above, the liquid level in the aeration tanks to prevent backflow of sewage into the air piping, and all pipes should be sloped to permit the drainage of liquid from them. A pipe gallery is shown in Fig. 23–4.

Ordinary cast-iron or steel pipe should not be used for air pipes, because fine particles of scale, rust, or chips of lining may break loose to clog the diffusers. Where the temperature of the air in the pipes may become low enough to permit moisture to condense, or air pipes are too small for thorough inside cleaning, the material of the pipe should be non-corrodible, such as heavily galvanized iron,

Fig. 23–4. A pipe gallery in an activated-sludge, sewage-treatment plant.

copper, aluminum, or special corrosion-resistant alloys. Paints and similar protective linings are to be avoided.

23–18. Diffusers.[34] It is desirable to diffuse the air in small bubbles to provide the greatest possible efficiency in aeration. The bubbles are made by blowing air through porous diffuser material. This may be in the form of saran-wrapped tubes [35] or as porous ceramic tubes or plates. The use of the latter is more general. A type of flat plate commonly used is shown in Fig. 23–5.

"Aloxite" and "Norton" plate and tube diffusers are made of grains of crystalline aluminum oxide bonded with high-aluminum glass, with permeabilities up to 120. Plates are a foot square by an inch thick, and tubes are either 3 in. or $1\frac{3}{4}$ in. in diameter, $\frac{5}{8}$ or $\frac{3}{8}$ of an inch thick, respectively, and 24 in. long. Filtros plates are made of natural, pure silica sand bonded with synthetic silica. The plates are 12 x 12 x $1\frac{1}{2}$ in. and are available in porosities up to 60.

An advantage of such material for plates or pipes is that it is

[34] See *Mun. San.*, February, 1937, p. 129; and *Sewage Works Jour.*, January, 1936, p. 22.
[35] See J. H. Blodgett, *S. and I.W.*, October, 1950, p. 1290.

Fig. 23–5. Aloxite diffuser plates. (Courtesy Carborundum Co.)

sufficiently impermeable to prevent sewage from flowing through it into the air pipe when the air pressure is removed and it is sufficiently permeable to permit air to pass through it into the sewage without an excessive head loss.

The permeability of a diffuser plate is defined as the volume of air in cubic feet per minute that will pass through 1 sq ft of diffuser surface at 2-in. differential pressure, measured in height of water column, under standard conditions of temperature and humidity.[36] Permeabilities recommended [37] lie between 40 and 80, larger ratings tending to give uneven distribution. Grade 40 with a pore diameter of 0.012 in. is generally recommended where air supply is clean. Otherwise grades 60 to 80 (0.016 in. to 0.020 in.) may be suitable.

King [38] recommends the oxygen absorption rating as an important specification. This factor is defined as the volume of air required to produce a given amount of oxygen absorption in the liquid over the plate. Absorptions for new plates are in the range of 35 to 62.5 per hr per sq ft of plate surface. King [39] has given some empirical formulas for oxygen absorption rates in spiral-flow aeration tanks which are applicable to limited conditions.

Diffuser plates are fastened into place in the bottom of aeration tanks in metallic, usually cast-iron, or concrete supports by means of Portland cement, rubber gaskets, asphalt, and other substances. They may rest directly on the sides of the air channel formed in the tank bottom or they may be set in holders, as shown in Fig. 23–5. As many as 100 plates may be placed in a group on one air valve, although a smaller number will show more even air distribution and will allow more flexible control. Plates and tubes controlled by the

[36] See *Sewage Works Jour.*, January, 1942, p. 81; and *Eng. Bull.* 1, 3d edition, Carborundum Co., p. 1.
[37] See also "Air Diffusion in Sewage Works," *Tentative Manual of Practice,* 5, Federation of Sewage Works Associations, 1952.
[38] H. R. King, *S. and I.W.*, July, 1952, p. 826.
[39] H. R. King, *S. and I.W.*, August, 1955, p. 894.

same air valve should have the same permeability and should be placed within 0.02 ft of the same elevation to assure the best air distribution among them. The variation of elevation in the entire tank should not exceed 0.05 ft.

Inspection and cleaning are made easier if the plates are supported in removable holders than if they are fastened to immovable supports on the bottom of the aeration tank. Difficulties with clogging of plates has emphasized the need for installing them so that they can be easily removed, cleaned, and replaced.

A rate of application of air of 1 cfm per sq ft of plate surface is advisable to secure a satisfactory uniformity of distribution.

23–19. Location of diffusers. Air diffusers may be located in a longitudinal row near one side of the aeration tank to produce "spiral flow"; or in transverse rows across the tank, called transverse ridge and furrow. Spiral flow is more economical in installation and operation but may be less effective with strong sewage or industrial waste. It seems desirable to place the diffusers in a narrow band, close to the wall, and as low as possible in the tank.

The aim in spiral flow is to maintain a longer period of contact between sewage and the air bubbles. It is accomplished by inducing a transverse circulatory motion of the sewage, the current rising over the air diffusers and descending on the opposite side with sufficient velocity to drag some small bubbles of air down and around with it. As this motion occurs simultaneously with the forward movement of the mixed liquor the hypothetical path of any particle will be helical, erroneously but commonly called "spiral flow."

The rows of plates should be placed to avoid interference between rising streams of bubbles. Rows of diffuser plates should be at least 2 ft and preferably 3 ft apart between centers, and rows of diffuser tubes should be at least 18 in. apart. Tubes may be installed in units of two tubes fastened end to end, with the opposite ends closed, the unit being supported by a bleeder pipe from the air main on the wall, as shown in Figs. 23–6 and 23–7. A valve on each bleeder pipe permits each unit to be separately disconnected from the main and raised from the tank for cleaning without shutting down the aeration tank. The "swing" diffuser [40] in Figs. 23–6 and 23–7 has the advantage that groups of diffusers can be swung up from the mixed liquor for inspection and cleaning, without shutting down the aeration tank. The area of diffusers [41] should be selected on the basis of air re-

[40] See *Sewage Works Jour.*, September, 1943, p. 994.
[41] See H. R. King, *S. and I.W.*, August, 1955, p. 894.

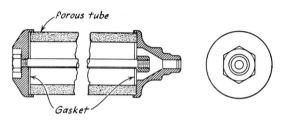

Fig. 23–6. Porous tube holder of Chicago Pump Co., especially adapted for swing diffusers. (From *Manual of Practice* 5, *Air Diffusion for Sewage Works*, Federation of Sewage and Industrial Wastes, 1952.)

quirements of the sewage, the permeability, the rate of flow of air through the plates, and economy in installation, in operation, and in maintenance. Practice shows wide variations in the ratio of diffuser surface area to aeration tank surface area but, in general, it is found to lie between 8 and 18 per cent.

23–20. Air cleaning. Clogging of air diffusers may be caused by rust or dirt coming from the air-distribution pipes, by ferric hydroxide deposited from the reaction of the air with sewage in contact with the diffuser, or by dust and soot from dirty air fed into the system. It is easier to clean the air continuously than the diffusers frequently.

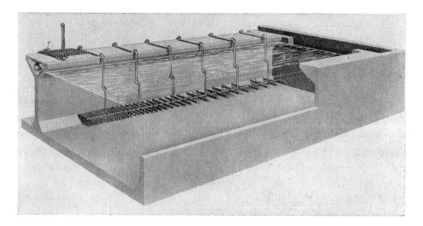

Fig. 23–7. Swing diffusers in tapered aeration tank, showing one set of diffusers swung out of tank for cleaning. (Courtesy Chicago Pump Co.)

Commercially manufactured air filters, particularly air-conditioning equipment, are suitable for protecting air diffusers in the activated-sludge process. The air should be delivered to the diffusers with a dust content of less than 0.5 to 0.6 mg per 1,000 cu ft of air.

Mechanical Aeration

23–21. Place in sewage treatment. An advantage of mechanical agitation over diffused-air aeration lies in the relative simplicity of mechanical equipment. Air compressors, distribution pipes, and diffusers are avoided. Only the mechanical agitator and its driving motor are involved. The work of the operator is simplified. Experience with mechanical agitators has developed such objections as: (1) a relatively large land area is required as compared with air-diffusion aeration, (2) short circuiting, (3) less flexibility, (4) poorer results, particularly in hot weather, (5) not suited to the treatment of many industrial wastes on a large scale, and (6) greater power requirements.

23–22. Methods of mechanical agitation. Any mechanical device that will mix air with the sewage in the tank can be used as a mechanical aerator. Many different devices have been used, such as the Sheffield paddle,[42] the Hartley aerator, the Imhoff submerged paddles combined with diffused air, the brush aerator, and jet aeration. In this last method, also called impingement aeration, a stream of water is directed against a column of air issuing from a relatively large orifice. The air bubbles produced are broken up into finely divided bubbles. The devices now in most common use are the Simplex-type aerator and the aspirator.

Since most mechanical aerators are patented proprietary devices they are commonly specified under performance guarantees, the details of design being in the hands of the manufacturers. Roe [43] presents data showing variations between 0.210 and 0.674 kw-hr per lb BOD removed. This may average about 18 to 20 hp per million gal of normal, domestic sewage treated. Such aerators are designed, as a rule, for installation in 14- to 36-ft square, hexagonal, or round tanks, with flat or hopper bottoms, and depths from 8 to 18 ft.

23–23. Mechanical aerators. Mechanical aerators in common use are proprietary devices with unique, and usually patented, char-

---

[42] See the sixth edition of this book, p. 471.

[43] F. C. Roe, *Sewage Works Jour.*, November, 1938, p. 999.

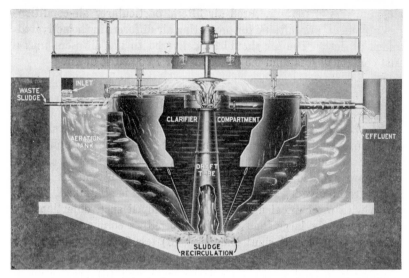

Fig. 23–8. Combination Aero-clarifier. (Courtesy Chicago Pump Co.) Complete activated-sludge process is carried on in this unit. Primary effluent enters at "inlet," mixes with mixed liquor in tank, descends through "aeration tank," rises through "draft tube," is violently agitated on surface, and is continuously circulated by propellor pump shown. Mixed liquor flows continuously into "clarifier compartment," where sludge falls to bottom; some sludge reenters circulating mixed liquor, and excess sludge is drawn off at "waste sludge." Clarified effluent passes out at "effluent."

acteristics. The early mechanical aerators, such as Sheffield paddles,[44] Hartley, brush, and others, are not now widely used. Mechanical aerators used in the United States depend on upward or downward flow in a central, vertical tube in a tank in which the horizontal cross-section, transverse to the direction of flow, is circular, polygonal, or square. The largest horizontal dimension, from wall to wall of the tank, may be up to about 24 ft, with a depth of 15 to 16 ft. In the device shown in Fig. 23–8 liquor enters at the top of the aerator and flows downward around the outside of the central, updraft tube. On reaching the bottom of the tank the direction of flow is reversed and the liquor flows upward through the updraft tube. Motion is caused by a revolving disk at the surface which throws the liquor to the periphery of the aeration chamber, mixing air with the liquor in the process. The unit shown combines aeration with clarification.

[44] See also J. Finch, *Water and Sewage Works,* Vol. 99, 1952, p. 34.

The equipment shown in Fig. 23–9 is a complete treatment plant involving primary and secondary treatment. The aerator, shown in the central unit, functions by causing downward flow in the central tube where aeration is induced by cavitation. In aerators with downward flow in the central tube aeration is accomplished by cavitation or by aspiration.

23–24. Aspiration and cavitation. Air is entrained with water by aspiration because the increasing velocity of liquor falling down the tube creates a partial vacuum which, if open to the atmosphere, entrains air with the falling liquor. In cavitation, air is drawn down

Fig. 23–9. A complete sewage-treatment plant, showing a mechanical aerator. A Cavitator-Spiragester plant. (Courtesy Yeomans Bros. Co.) 1. Spiragester. Primary settling and sludge digestion. 2. Skimming pipe. 3. Supernatant circulation pump. 4. Sludge division box. 5. Sludge withdrawal. 6. Gas vent. 7. Effluent weir trough. 8. Clarifier skirt. 9. Digester hood. 10. Raw sewage inlet. 11. Sludge return pump. 12. Return activated sludge. 13. Pneumatic ejector. 14. Primary effluent to Cavitator. 15. Cavitator. 16. Raw sewage influent. 17. Scum line. 18. Sludge scraper. 19. Spiraflow clarifier. Final settling. 20. Final effluent.

the central tube with the descending liquor. The two are mixed by the high speed of the impeller which creates cavitation [45] and causes the air to be mixed in fine bubbles, with the liquor.

23–25. Aeration-tank design. The principles of design of aeration tanks and of sludge recirculation follow those outlined for air-diffusion aeration except that aeration periods for mechanical aeration should be 40 to 50 per cent greater. Where aeration tanks are placed in series care must be taken to avoid short circuiting of inadequately aerated mixed liquor through the aerator.

Use of Sludge in the Process

23–26. Recirculation of sludge. In the design of an activated-sludge plant, pumps and channels must be provided for the return of a portion of the sludge from the final settling tank to the influent of the aeration tank to form the mixed liquor. This return of sludge is the essence of the activated-sludge process and differentiates it from simple aeration.

The purposes of returning sludge include: the seeding of the influent with active, biological life; the dilution of the influent to the aeration tank; the maintenance of fresh sludge; and the prevention of the loss of sludge during storm-flow periods. The quality and the amount of return sludge are important in the successful operation of the process. These may be measured by such standards as: (1) the ratio, by volume, of return sludge to raw sewage; (2) the ratio of dry solids returned to dry solids in the raw sewage; (3) the maintenance of a standard concentration of total solids in the mixed liquor; and (4) the maintenance of a certain sludge index. So far as the activated-sludge process is concerned the concentration of returned activated particles in the mixed liquor is of importance in successful operation.

23–27. Volume of return sludge. Practice in the United States shows ratios of volume of return sludge to volume of raw sewage between 1:5 and 1:1. This is equivalent to percentages of 16.7 to 50, respectively, of return sludge in the mixed liquor. Percentages found in practice are more commonly within the range of 25 to 35.

Concentrations of solids carried in the mixed liquor seldom exceed 15,000 mg/l, with a normal of about 3,000 mg/l in diffused-air plants, and 1,000 to 2,500 mg/l in mechanical aeration. In high-rate plants,

---

[45] See also a "cavitation system" described by K. L. Schulze and H. S. Foth, *Water and Sewage Works*, February, 1955, p. 74.

discussed in Sect. 23–39, about 600 to 800 mg/l, and sometimes less, may be carried normally. In standard-rate, air-diffusion plants the rate of return solids to incoming solids varies between 10:1 and 40:1, the higher ratio being used where the volatile solids are low.

The ratio to be provided is important in plant design, as the pumps and pipes for a 1:1 ratio must have 5 times the capacity required for a 1:5 ratio for the same quantity of raw sewage treated; and for any given aeration period the smaller ratio of 1:1 will require an aeration tank $1\frac{2}{3}$ times as large as the ratio of 1:5. Kraus [46] has formulated the relationship in which

$$a = \frac{v \times 10^6}{I(1 + v)} \tag{23-6}$$

where a = suspended solids concentration in the aeration tank, mg/l.

v = ratio of returned activated sludge to sewage flow.

I = sludge-volume index (Mohlmann).

Return pumps and channels should be arranged by the designer so that there will be no suction lift and no violent agitation of the sludge, and the breaking of the floc will be avoided. If the time in the aeration channels is more than 5 to 10 minutes, supplementary aeration in the channels may be required.

23–28. Facilities for excess activated sludge. The Joint Committee (see Sect. 5–2) recommends that:

Waste sludge control equipment and piping should have a maximum capacity of not less than 25 per cent of the average rate of sewage flow . . . and function satisfactorily at rates of 0.5 per cent of average sewage flow or a minimum of 10 gal. per min., whichever may be the larger.

23–29. The sludge index. Knowledge of the volume of sludge or of the dry solids in it is insufficient for satisfactory plant operation. Knowledge of their combination is, however, an essential feature in plant operation. Their combination has been expressed as the "sludge index." This index is generally defined as the volume, in milliliters, of one gram of sludge after settling 30 min,[47] sometimes called the Mohlmann index. It can be expressed as

$$\text{Index} = \frac{\text{Volume of sludge settled in 30 min, per cent}}{\text{Suspended solids, per cent}}$$

[46] L. S. Kraus, *Sewage Works Jour.*, July, 1949.
[47] See *Sewage Works Jour.*, January, 1934, p. 121.

Although 30 min has been adopted as a standard time, variations in consolidation taking place in this time have been reported as high as 80 per cent.[48] Finch and Ives [48] have proposed the index:

$$\text{Index} = \frac{\text{Per cent of sludge settled in 6 min}}{\text{Grams of suspended solids per 1,000 ml}}$$

The Mohlmann index continues to be the standard used.

A good settling sludge may have a Mohlmann index well below 100. An index of 200 is indicative of a sludge with poor settling characteristics. A rising index at a treatment plant indicates approaching trouble. Routine observations of the sludge index is practiced in the operation of most sewage-treatment plants.

23–30. Sludge age and suspended-solids concentration. Sludge age is a factor of importance in the design and operation of an activated-sludge plant. Sludge age [49] represents the average time that a particle of suspended solids remains under aeration and is defined as the dry weight, in pounds, of the activated sludge in the aeration tank, divided by the suspended-solids load (pounds per day) in the sewage entering the tank, or

$$S_A = (V \times C_A)/(Q \times C_S) \qquad (23\text{--}7)$$

where S_A = sludge age.

   C_A = average concentration of suspended solids in the aerator, mg/l.

   C_S = average concentration of suspended solids in the sewage, mg./l.

   Q = rate of flow of sewage, mgd.

   V = volume of aerator, mg.

The E_h potential of the activated sludge decreases with sludge age, falling to zero in 15 to 72 hr, and more slowly thereafter.[50]

A normal, desirable sludge age is in the order of $3\frac{1}{2}$ days.

Knowledge of the sludge index and the sludge age is necessary in good operation since there is a critical value of sludge index below which the formation of settled sludge in the final tanks will exceed the return sludge rate. If final tank balance is restored by reducing the suspended-solids concentration in the aerator effluent the sludge volume may be critically lowered.

[48] See J. Finch and H. Ives, *Wastes Eng.*, May, 1954, p. 214.

[49] See also W. N. Torpey and A. H. Chasick, *S. and I.W.*, November, 1955, p. 1218.

[50] See C. E. Keefer and J. T. Meisel, *S. and I.W.*, August, 1953, p. 898.

An aid to the control of suspended solids in the aerator and in the return sludge has been formulated by Torpey and Chasick[51] as follows:

$$C_R = \frac{(Q_S + Q_R)C_A - Q_S C_P}{Q_R} \tag{23-8}$$

$$r = 100 Q_R / Q_S = \frac{(C_A - C_P)100}{C_R - C_A} \tag{23-9}$$

$$C_x = (Q_R C_R + Q_x C_P)/(Q_R + Q_x) \tag{23-10}$$

where C_A = suspended solids in aerator effluent, mg/l.
C_P = suspended solids in primary effluent, mg/l.
C_R = suspended solids in return sludge, mg/l.
C_x = suspended solids in pass,[52] mg/l.
Q_R = return sludge, mgd.
Q_S = primary effluent, mgd.
Q_x = total primary effluent up to and including any point x, mgd.
r = percentage of return sludge.

23–31. Reaeration and reactivation. Activated sludge becomes septic in one to two hours, at normal temperatures, if it is not continuously aerated. It is essential, therefore, to return sludge promptly from the final sedimentation tank to the aeration tank or to reaerate it during storage. Some early activated-sludge plants provided reaeration of return sludge in separate tanks. The principle of reaeration is involved in the more recently introduced biosorption process.[53]

The economy of reaeration or reactivation in a separate tank is questionable since the cost of the additional equipment and its operation may be greater than the cost of applying additional air to the aeration tank. The availability of a reaeration tank, with a reserve of stored activated sludge, serves, however, to give flexibility and control in the operation of a plant subject to rapid changes in the quality of the incoming sewage.

It may be difficult to predict the required size of the reaeration tank that will be advantageous, the best result being secured through a balance of the additional cost of reaeration against the saving in

[51] W. N. Torpey and A. H. Chasick, *S. and I.W.*, November, 1955, p. 1217.
[52] This refers to the section of channel between any two adjacent points of entrance of return sludge.
[53] See T. R. Haseltine, *S. and I.W.*, December, 1952, p. 1533.

operating cost of the aeration tank without reactivation, or by giving a definite value to the additional flexibility attained through re-aeration. Facilities for reaeration are not generally included in plants recently constructed.

Modifications of the Process

23–32. New processes. Modifications of the activated-sludge process have been developed through local experience often found beneficial under diverse conditions. Among such processes may be included: contact aeration, the Hays process, Zigerli process, Kraus process, Okun and Fair process, the Mallory or oxidized-sludge process, the Aero-accelator, the Chicago Pump unit shown in Fig. 23–8, the bisorption process, the dual aeration system, and others. The Zigerli process involves the addition of about 1 mg/l of asbestos to weight the sludge. The Okun and Fair process carries a concentration of 6,000 to 7,000 mg/l of suspended matter in the mixed liquor in the reaction chamber. The liquid is maintained in the presence of commercially pure oxygen.

The oxidized-sludge process comprises a method of control of the activated-sludge process, devised and patented by Mallory,[54] which depends on the maintenance of the "equilibrium index" at a value of 100 or more. The equilibrium index, E_{qx}, can be expressed as

$$E_{qx} = \frac{R^2 D}{BMK} \qquad (23\text{–}11)$$

where A = aeration period, hours.
B = sludge blanket volume, cubic feet or gallons.
C = sedimentation period, hours.
D = clarifier liquid volume, same unit as B.
$K = [(2A/C) - 1]$.
M = mixed-liquor suspended-solids concentration, per cent. To be determined by "standard centrifuge test," described in U. S. patent 2,154,132.
R = return sludge concentration, per cent. To be determined as for M.

The operator uses the index as a guide in controlling plant-operating factors to bring the index to 100. The "oxidation index" is another

[54] E. B. Mallory, *Water Works and Sewerage*, August, 1941, p. 333.

tool devised by Mallory [55] to aid in the control of the activated-sludge process. It is, in effect, the ratio of the observed sludge concentration after settling 60 min to the optimum 60-min concentration. It is to be noted that the Mallory process is a patented, proprietary procedure, upon the value of which all authorities are not agreed. These points should be clearly in mind when its adoption is considered.

The Aero-accelator [56] is a single-unit apparatus treating screened, raw sewage by the activated-sludge process, in which mechanical aeration and all other functions of the process occur within a single tank. It is a proprietary device manufactured by Infilco, Inc. Results of tests on the device, made at the University of Florida, are reported in *Sewage and Industrial Wastes*, February, 1952, p. 149. The device shown in Fig. 23–8, manufactured by the Chicago Pump Company, includes also all functions of the activated-sludge process in a single unit.

The bisorption process [57] is essentially an accelerated activated-sludge process in which sludge from the clarifier is reactivated by aeration so that it can be reused in the mixed liquor, and aerated in the mixed-liquor aeration tank for a period of 15 to 30 min. The aeration time required for reaeration of the concentrated sludge, calculated on the basis of raw sewage flow, is in the range of 90 min. Such short periods of aeration require smaller aeration tanks than are required by the standard activated-sludge process.

23–33. Contact aeration. Contact aeration, or bioflocculation, is a process in which a large surface is exposed to the sewage to induce adsorption at the same time that air is diffused gently through the sewage to induce oxidation. Bioflocculation is the removal of suspended matter from sewage primarily under biological action.[58] Examples of bioflocculators include contact aerators, contact beds, trickling filters, and some forms of mechanical flocculators. A contact aerator is a watertight tank filled with material that will expose a large surface to the sewage in the tank, such as crates filled with wooden laths, broken stone, wicker screens, corrugated metal sheets, or wire netting. Air is distributed beneath the material and diffused through either diffuser plates or swinging, perforated pipe. Bacterial growths form a zoogleal mass on the material submerged in the sewage. Excess growth may be shaken off periodically, or it may be

[55] *Loc. cit.*
[56] See F. A. Eidness, *S. and I.W.*, July, 1951, p. 843; *ibid.*, August, 1957, p. 845.
[57] See A. H. Ullrich and M. W. Smith, *S. and I.W.*, October, 1951, p. 1248.
[58] See also *Sewage Works Jour.*, May, 1941, p. 506.

allowed to slough off naturally. It is collected with the effluent from the aerator in a sedimentation tank. The Clari-Filter is a proprietary device which combines the features of a contact-aerator and a clarifier.[59]

Considerable mechanical equipment is required to compress and to distribute the air and to clean the contact material periodically. The advantage of the process lies in the relatively small amount of air required: 0.2 cu ft of air per gal of sewage, depending on the quality of the influent and of the effluent. The air is applied during a period of 30 to 60 min, and will produce a mediocre effluent. A better effluent can be produced by two-stage or three-stage operation.

23–34. The Hays process.[60] A Hays process plant is a practical application of contact aeration.[61] The plant comprises [62] preliminary sedimentation, first-stage contact aeration, intermediate sedimentation, second-stage contact aeration, and final sedimentation. The aeration tanks are shallower than conventional aeration tanks and contain thin contact plates that extend over the entire area of the tank and for most of its depth. The plates are made of asbestos-cement sheets, $\frac{3}{16}$ in. thick, set vertically about $1\frac{1}{2}$ in. apart. Air is blown into the tank under the plates through orifices in a pipe grid. Utilization of air has ranged between 1.25 and 4.0 cu ft per gal of sewage treated, with an average of about 2.5.[63] Under favorable conditions, particularly in relatively small installations, such as army camps, satisfactory results have been obtained from such plants.

23–35. Dual aeration and the Kraus process.[64] In the dual-aeration process part of the air is admitted through diffusers at the bottom of the aeration tank and part is distributed near the surface to obtain maximum surface turbulence. A part of the activated sludge is continuously aerated in a separate aeration tank. A sufficient portion of the sludge is circulated through this tank to maintain sludge activity and, at the same time, digested sludge is added to this activated sludge to control sludge settleability. The change in sludge volume index (SVI) is proportional to the weighted average of the SVI of the activated sludge and the added digested sludge. The quan-

[59] See also *Sewage Works Jour.*, September, 1945, p. 1099.

[60] See also *Eng. News-Record*, Vol. 130, 1948, p. 138.

[61] See also *Sewage Works Jour.*, November, 1943, p. 1139.

[62] See *ibid.*, November, 1943, p. 1064.

[63] See *ibid.*, November, 1943, p. 1068.

[64] L. S. Kraus, *S. and I.W.*, 1955, p. 1347.

tity of digested sludge added is ordinarily sufficient only to balance the tendency of the SVI to increase.

Among the advantages claimed for this method of operation are included the ability to: (1) maintain a low SVI; (2) treat industrial wastes shock loads; (3) regain clarifying properties of activated sludge immediately after receipt of shock loads; (5) maintain high suspended solids in aeration tanks; (6) produce higher concentrations of suspended solids in waste activated sludge; (7) maintain a high degree of stability in the activated sludge; (8) use at least two or three times more load than normal of 33 lb BOD per day per 1,000 cu ft of aeration-tank volume; and (9) use an aeration period of one-third of that normally considered to be necessary. Other advantages include: reduction of power costs; filtered air is unnecessary; and increased turbulence increases oxygen absorption.

That portion of the process involving the combination of digester liquors containing organic nitrogen and ammonia nitrogen with the activated sludge, and the mixing and aeration of this combination before it is introduced into the mixed liquor entering the aeration tank, is known as the Kraus process. The process is patented and is under the proprietorship of the Pacific Flush Tank Co.

23–36. Stage aeration. It has been found that the changes in the quality of the mixed liquor in the aeration tank occur in two stages: (1) flocculation and clarification, and (2) nitrification. The former occurs within the first hour of aeration; the latter starts towards the end of that period and tapers off slowly after many hours of aeration, as indicated in Fig. 23–10. To take advantage of this phenomenon attempts have been made to conduct the process in two stages, the first in an aeration tank and the second on a trickling filter. The process has sometimes been known as partial purification. It would probably not be economical to design a new plant in this manner, but an existing plant in which the trickling filter is over-loaded might be economically redesigned to provide for a short period of aeration, either with or without activated sludge preliminary to filtration. The process is discussed also in Sect. 21–8.

Two-stage aeration in the activated-sludge process has been practiced in two aeration tanks, in series, separated by an intermediate settling tank. The two aeration tanks are designed with the same aeration periods. Sludge from the intermediate settling tank is returned to the primary aeration tank, which acts as a biological shock absorber to protect the secondary aeration tank and settling basin.[65]

[65] See *Sewage Works Jour.*, September, 1942, p. 1163.

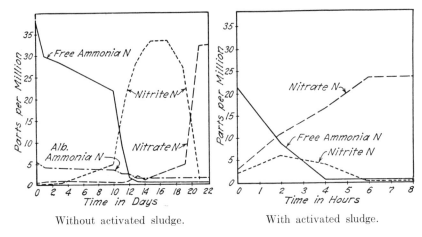

Without activated sludge.   With activated sludge.

Fig. 23–10. The effect of aeration with and without activated sludge. (F. W. Mohlmann, *Modern Sewage Disposal,* p. 68.)

Tests at Calumet Works, Chicago Sanitary District,[66] on a weak sewage, were successful with an aeration period of 2.1 hr and 0.5 cu ft of air per gal of sewage. The process was reported as complicated to operate, biologically sensitive, and requiring careful control.

23–37. Step aeration.[67] In step aeration return sludge or settled sewage may be added to the mixed liquor at various points along its flow through the aeration tank. A flowing-through diagram of such a process is shown in Fig. 23–11. Such a procedure makes possible the provision of adequate sludge age while maintaining low suspended solids entering the final settling tanks. In other words it is possible to control the concentration of suspended solids entering the final sedimentation tank by controlling the rates and points of application of return sludge and settled sewage to the aeration tank, and the concentration of solids in the return sludge.

Example. Let it be assumed that an aerator is equipped to permit the addition of mixed liquor at the upper end *A* and at any of 3 points *B, C,* and *D* equally spaced along the tank. The treated sewage from the primary tank contains 90 mg/l of suspended solids; the mixed liquor contains 20 per cent of return sludge by volume; the aeration period is 3 hr; and the average sludge age is 3.5 days. What will be the concentration of solids in

---

[66] See *Proc. Am. Soc. Civil Engrs.,* April, 1944, pp. 457 and 465.

[67] See W. N. Torpey and A. H. Chasick, *S. and I.W.,* November, 1955, p. 1217.

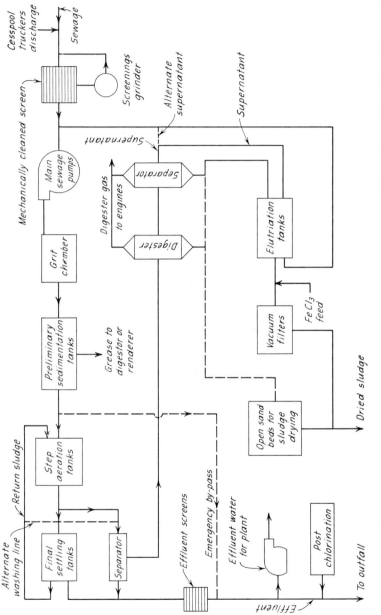

Fig. 23–11. Flowing-through diagram of step-aeration sewage-treatment process. (From *Wastes Eng.*, November, 1955, p. 618.)

the aerator effluent, if all of the return sludge enters at point A? If 50 per cent of the return sludge enters at C and 50 per cent enters at D?

Solution. (a) Sludge age = (solids in tank)/(suspended solids entering the system). Therefore

$$3.5 = \frac{(\text{S.S.})(1.25)(3)}{(90)(24)}$$

and the suspended solids = 2,000 mg/l.

(b) Let C_s = concentration of suspended solids in sludge, and C_A, C_B, C_C, and C_D = concentration of suspended solids in the effluent in or from each one-fourth of the aeration tank.

Then

$$\frac{C_A + C_B + C_C + C_D}{4} = 2,000 \text{ mg/l}$$

$C_A = C_s$ because only sludge enters the compartment and $C_B = C_s$ for the same reason.

The full flow of sludge and one-half the flow of sewage enter compartment C; hence

$$C_C = \frac{0.025C_B + (0.5)(90)}{0.25 + 0.50} = \frac{C_s}{3} + 60$$

$$C_D = \frac{0.75C_C + (0.5)(90)}{0.75 + 0.50} = \frac{C_s}{5} + 72$$

Then

$$C_s + C_s + \frac{C_s}{3} + 60 + \frac{C_s}{5} + 72 = 8,000$$

and

$$C_s = 3,110 \text{ mg/l}$$

Step aeration is used: [68]

1. When there is persistent increase in the volatile content of the activated sludge.

2. When dissolved oxygen is dropping steadily, and

3. In case of high *Sphaerotilus* growths, which are taken as an index of overloading or of poor sludge condition.

Conventional aeration is used:

1. When the primary effluent solids are low or the flow is low, thus requiring less solids in the aerator, but with the same end concentration, avoiding undernourished activated sludge.

2. When there is overaeration, as indicated by high dissolved oxygen and pin-point floc in the final effluent which does not settle readily.

[68] See *Proc. Am. Soc. Civil Engrs.*, April, 1944, p. 474.

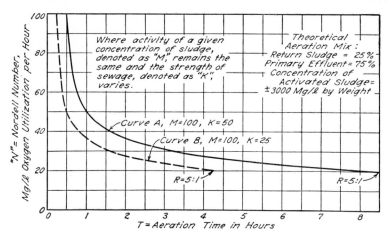

Fig. 23–12. Theoretical curve showing oxygen utilization in activated-sludge mixtures. (From *Water Works and Sewerage*, May, 1937, p. 167.)

Step aeration [69] has the advantage, when compared with conventional aeration, of requiring as little as one-half of the aerator volume, smaller site area, and better control under shock load. Aerator loadings up to 50 lb of BOD per day per 1,000 cu ft of aerator capacity have been reported. Gould [70] reported results from five plants in New York City as follows: BOD removals from 87 to 97 per cent with air consumption from 0.49 to 1.05 cu ft per gal, an aeration period of 2.4 to 4.7 hr, a sludge age of 3.4 to 5.7 days, and suspended solids in the effluent of 900 to 1,100 mg/l.

23–38. Tapered aeration. Tapered aeration consists in the application of air to the aeration tank at a higher rate near the influent end of the tank. Experimental values indicate that from 40 to 50 per cent of the air is required in the first 2 hr; 28 to 31 per cent in the second 2 hr; and 20 to 29 per cent in the third 2 hr, for a 6-hr period, using non-nitrifying sludge.[71] The tapering rate of oxygen demand is indicated in Fig. 23–12, in which M is a measure of the activity of the sludge; K is an index of sewage strength, and is equal to $M \times T_m$; T is the time of aeration; T_m is the time that any particular value of

[69] See *Proc. Am. Soc. Civil Engrs.*, April, 1944, p. 474.

[70] R. H. Gould, *Proc. Am. Soc. Civil Engrs.*, *Separate* 307, October, 1953, and 481, May, 1954.

[71] See *Sewage Works Jour.*, January, 1942, p. 17.

M persists; and R is the ratio of the original value of M to the Nordell number at any time.

A better understanding of the meaning of the preceding terms may be gained from the following definitions:

Sludge activity is measured by its rate of oxygen utilization in terms of the Nordell number.

Nordell number is the milligrams per liter of oxygen utilized per hour by a sludge or sewage.

Sludge activity and the Nordell number are measured by means of the Odeeometer. This is an apparatus for determining the oxygen demand of liquids by direct observation. In its operation a 4-liter sample of the sewage is collected and placed in a container with an air-tight connection to a chamber in the apparatus holding approximately 500 cc of air. The liquid in the sample is gently agitated, consuming the oxygen from the air and creating a partial vacuum that is measured on a manometer tube. The machine can be calibrated to measure oxygen consumption in milligrams per liter per hour.

The varying oxygen-demand:oxygen-supply ratio has led to controlled aeration. It may be controlled by changing the rate of air supply, by slowing down bacterial activity by the addition of chemicals, or by limiting the amount of oxidizable materials by applying return sludge at different points along the aeration tank. The first method of control is tapered aeration. It can be provided for in design by gradually decreasing the area of diffuser surface from influent to effluent, by manipulating valves on the air distribution pipes to provide the concentration of air at various parts of the tank, or by providing a row of swinging tube distributors so unevenly spaced as to give the desired tapered aeration.

Advantages claimed for tapered aeration include a better control of the process, a plant better able to withstand shocks of changes in the quality of the influent, and a marked reduction in the cost of operation. The process has not yet been adopted in large operating plants.

23–39. Modified or high-rate treatment. Modified sewage aeration [72] and high-rate activated-sludge treatment [73] are synonymous terms referring to aeration for shorter than standard periods of time,

[72] See also *Sewage Works Jour.*, July, 1943, p. 629, and March, 1944, p. 278; and W. N. Torpey and A. H. Chasick, *S. and I.W.*, November, 1955, p. 1225.
[73] See *Sewage Works Jour.*, September, 1944, p. 878.

with the return of a smaller than standard percentage of sludge from the settling tank. "Any period of treatment between sedimentation and activated sludge appears possible by controlling the air supply, the aeration period, and the amount of return solids." [74] In modified aeration the sludge formed more nearly resembles primary-sedimentation sludge than activated sludge. Chase [75] recommends the use of spiral-circulation aeration tanks with 2- or 3-hr retention period, 10 to 25 per cent of the sewage as return sludge, and an air supply of 0.5 cu ft per gal of sewage. Sludge age may lie between 0.2 and 0.5 day and final settling tanks may operate at about 1,000 gal per sq ft per day.

Torpey and Chasick [76] point out, concerning modified aeration as compared to conventional activated sludge, that: (1) only two-thirds as much total tank volume, (2) lower sludge volume, (3) lower air ratios, (4) higher digester gas yield, and (5) smaller total area are required.[77] An essential difference between high-rate treatment and standard activated-sludge operation is that the solids in the aeration tank are maintained at an unusually low level, with a sludge age of 0.2 to 0.5 day compared with 3.5 days in conventional systems.

23–40. Activated aeration. An activated-aeration plant consists of two conventional or tapered, activated-sludge plants operating in parallel, each using the same settled sewage as the influent. Excess activated sludge is circulated from the final settling tank of one plant into the aeration tank of the parallel plant, this aerator being called the activated-aerator. Excess sludge from the settling tank following the activated-aeration aerator is run to final disposal or to preparation therefor. It is stated that the process has provided an effluent of intermediate quality at savings in power costs as compared to the conventional activated-sludge process.

In parallel operation at the same plant [78] step aeration, modified aeration, and activated aeration gave the following results:

BOD removal, per cent	95 : 68 : 76
Air, cu ft per gal	0.61:0.29:0.19
Aeration period, hr	2.7 :2.7 :2.7

[74] See *Sewage Works Jour.*, Part II, September, 1941, p. 905.

[75] See *ibid.*, September, 1944, p. 883.

[76] W. N. Torpey and A. H. Chasick, *S. and I.W.*, November, 1955, pp. 1217 and 1229.

[77] See also K. Wuhrmann, *S. and I.W.*, January, 1954, p. 1.

[78] See R. H. Gould, *Proc. Am. Soc. Civil Engrs., Separate* 307, October, 1953; and A. H. Chasick, *S. and I.W.*, September, 1954, p. 1059.

23–41. Final sedimentation. Final sedimentation tanks used in the activated-sludge process are similar to those described in Sects. 18–15 and 21–39. Almost all final sedimentation tanks used in the activated-sludge process are mechanically cleaned because equal results can be obtained, in a shorter time, in such tanks, with a fresher effluent and a better quality of return sludge, than could be obtained in a manually cleaned tank.

Controlling principles in the design of final sedimentation tanks in the activated-sludge process differ somewhat from the principles applicable in the design of preliminary sedimentation tanks because of the nature of activated sludge. It has been pointed out by Anderson [79] that activated sludge, having a slightly greater density than that of the tank contents, produces a "density current," which causes the influent liquor to flow along the bottom of the tank until deflected upward by an obstruction, inducing counter current at the upper levels back toward the tank influent. Some important effects of this upon activated-sludge settling tank design include the following:

1. Details of influent arrangements do not greatly affect the quality of the effluent, provided that the influent is admitted at as slow a velocity as possible without dependence on baffles.

2. Effluent weirs will be located away from upturn of density current. This may bring them anywhere between half and two-thirds of the distance from the influent to the end wall of the tank.

3. The sludge drawoff should be near the tank inlet.

4. There is an optimum tank depth to maintain an effective sludge blanket. The maximum ratios of length of flow to depth of tank recommended by Anderson [80] are: for circular tanks, 5; for rectangular tanks, 7. Minimum depth below effluent weirs is 10 ft, unless at upturn of density current, where minimum depth should be 12 ft.

Some typical arrangements of effluent weirs are shown in Figs. 18–11 and 23–13.

The design dimensions of the settling tank are controlled, in part, by the permissible retention period, and by the relation between the rate of flow through the tank and the surface area. Retention periods vary, in practice. Rates of flow are 600 to 1,200 gal per day per sq ft of tank surface. Other controlling factors are a minimum depth of 8 ft, and an outlet weir such that the discharge rate will not exceed

[79] N. E. Anderson, *Sewage Works Jour.*, January, 1945, p. 50.
[80] *Ibid.*

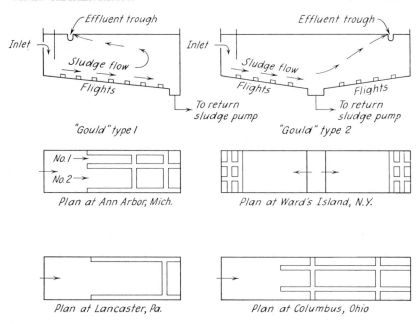

Fig. 23–13. Location of outlet troughs for sedimentation basins. Applicable particularly to flocculent materials. (The "Gould" types in the figure are from W. N. Torpey and A. H. Chasick, *S. and I.W.*, November, 1955, p. 1217.)

5,000 gal per day per ft length of weir. The standard retention period fixed by the New York State Health Department was 2 hours.[81] Anderson [82] allows 20,000 gal per day per ft length of weir when it is located away from upturn of density current, and 15,000 when it is not. Rice,[83] as a result of a study of state health department requirements, concludes that the overflow rates on average flows should not be over 5,000 gal per day per ft length of weir, or over three times this for peak flows. More than one final settling tank should be used when total settling-tank capacity exceeds about 20,000 gal.

Sludge-scraping mechanisms similar to those described in Sect. 18–2 are satisfactory in activated-sludge settling tanks. A sludge thickener, as a separate tank, may be desirable to minimize the volume of the excess solids removed. Circular tanks with sludge-scraping mechanisms have operated successfully at rates of 500 gal of

[81] See *Sewage Works Jour.*, March, 1944, p. 324.

[82] N. E. Anderson, *Sewage Works Jour.*, January, 1945, p. 50.

[83] L. G. Rice, *Water and Sewage Works*, December, 1950, p. 519.

Table 23-7

CONSTRUCTION, OPERATION, AND MAINTENANCE COSTS OF
ACTIVATED-SLUDGE PLANTS OF VARIOUS CAPACITIES

(See *Proc. Am. Soc. Civil Engrs.*, April, 1938, p. 737.)

Costs in Thousands of Dollars

Sewage Treated or Plant Capacity, mgd	Construction Cost				Operation and Maintenance Cost			
	Usual Lower Limit	Average for Aeration		Usual Higher Limit	Usual Lower Limit	Average for Air		Usual Higher Limit
		5 hr	6 hr			0.6 cu ft per gal	1.0 cu ft per gal	
10	560	700	800	940	75	90	110	125
25	1,280	1,600	1,800	2,120	150	185	220	255
50	2,500	3,200	3,500	4,200	250	310	370	430
75	3,700	4,750	5,200	6,200	340	420	495	570
100	5,000	6,300	6,900	8,200	430	520	615	710

aerator effluent per day and 4 lb of activated-sludge solids per day per sq ft of thickener surface. Of two mechanisms primarily for use in activated-sludge tanks, one has uprights resembling a picket fence with the pickets made of 2-in. pipe on 6- to 9-in. centers, erected on the revolving arms to act as chimneys to release entrained gases and water in the sludge; the other mechanism picks up the sludge from the bottom of the tank through a series of nozzles similar to a vacuum cleaner.

Some features to be considered in the design of the sedimentation tank and piping include the following: (1) walkways, beams, launder troughs, or channels that are partly submerged in the tank should be sloped on the underside to prevent the accumulation of septic solids beneath them; (2) a sludge-division box should be provided, to which the sludge collected in the clarifier is sent for measurement, inspection, sampling, and apportionment to waste and to return; and (3)

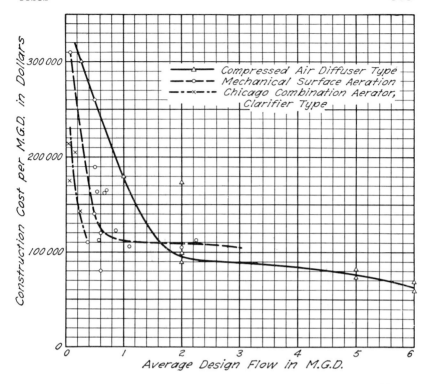

Fig. 23–14. Construction costs of small activated-sludge plants. (S. E. Kappe, *Sewage Works Jour.*, November, 1938, p. 1007.)

if separate sludge-digestion tanks are to be used, provision should be made for concentration of waste sludge before discharging it into the digestion tank. Excess activated sludge is commonly disposed of by separate digestion.

23–42. Costs.[84] Schroepfer[85] has compiled the costs of activated-sludge plants as summarized in Table 23–7, and further information on costs is given in Chapter 28. Information on construction costs, from Kappe,[86] is shown in Fig. 23–14.

[84] A discussion of cost indexes is presented in Sect. 28–7.

[85] See *Proc. Am. Soc. Civil Engrs.*, April, 1938, p. 737.

[86] S. E. Kapp, *Sewage Works Jour.*, November, 1938, p. 1007.

Chapter 24

Sludge handling
and disposal

24–1. The problem. In most sewage-treatment processes the liquid and solid portions of the sewage are separated. The liquid, forming the effluent from the sewage-treatment plant, is disposed of by dilution or on land, and the solids, which form sludge or scum, are disposed of by various means. Sludge is the "accumulated suspended solids of sewage deposited in tanks or basins, mixed with more or less water to form a semi-liquid mass. . . . Scum is a mass of sewage solids buoyed up by entrained gas, grease, or other substance, which floats on the surface of the sewage." [1] Sludge and scum represent the solids that have been removed from the sewage together with such water as may be entrained with them. They create the most difficult problem in disposal because their polluting potentialities, per unit of weight, are greater than those of the liquid effluent from the treatment process that produced them. For example, the median amount of sludge produced in eleven sewage treatment plants [2] is 35 lb [3] per capita annually, with variations from 12 to 169.

Some basic data useful in the selection and design of methods and equipment for the treatment of sewage are compiled in Table 24–1, and some sludge analyses are shown in Table 24–2.

24–2. The disposal of sludge. The disposal of sludge is a problem common to all methods of sewage treatment involving sedimentation in tanks. Sludge may be disposed of by various procedures, including lagooning, burning, land filling, using as a fertilizer or a fertilizer base, and dumping into the sea. Under unusual conditions

[1] See *Proc. Am. Soc. Civil Engrs.*, January, 1937, p. 45.
[2] See J. M. Morgan, Jr., and J. F. Thomson, *Water and Sewage Works*, December, 1955, p. 532, and April, 1955, p. 135.
[3] Dry weight.

Table 24-1

TYPICAL DESIGN DATA FOR SLUDGE-TREATMENT METHODS

(From A. J. Fischer, Sewage Works Jour., March, 1936, p. 248.)

	Primary Treatment	Trickling-Filter Treatment	Chemical Treatment	Activated-Sludge Treatment
Overall suspended solids removed, per cent	60	85	80	95
Raw sludge, dry solids per mgd, pounds	1,020	1,310	1,525 *	1,615
Raw sludge, per cent moisture	94	95	95	96
Raw sludge, thickener, final per cent moisture	90	92	92	93
Raw sludge, thickener, average per cent moisture	92	93.5	93.5	94.7
Thickener sludge detention	2 days	2 days	2 days	2 days
Digested sludge, dry solids per mgd, pounds	555	710	905	1,035
Digested sludge, per cent moisture	91.2	93.1	93.1	94.5
Digester, per cent sludge reduction	45.5	45.5	41	36
Digester, per cent volatile reduction	65	65	58.5	51.5
Digester gas, cubic feet per million gallons	7,900	10,200	10,650	9,850
Digestion period, days:				
Primary	20	20	20	20
Secondary: Filtration, days	30	30	30	30
Sand beds, days	60	60	60	60
1	2	3	4	5
Total digester capacity:				
Cubic feet per capita:				
30-day secondary	0.98	1.53	2.02	2.28
60-day secondary	1.23	1.87	2.15	2.78
Cubic feet per pound volatile matter added:				
30-day secondary	13.7	16.7	21.2	20.1
60-day secondary	17.2	20.4	22.6	24.6
Drying-bed loadings, pounds:				
Dry solids per square foot per year:				
Open beds	35	30	30	25
Covered beds	70	60	60	50
Incinerator,† average tons water evaporated per 24 hr per million gallons sewage:				
Raw sludge	1.30	2.08	2.48	2.97
Digested sludge	0.70	1.02	1.18	1.93
6	7	8	9	10

* Including chemical.   † Incineration is preceded by some form of preliminary drying, such as vacuum filtration.

Table 24–2

ANALYSES OF VARIOUS TYPES OF SLUDGE
Per cent dry basis

(From J. M. Morgan and J. F. Thomson, *Water and Sewage Works*, June 1, 1955, p. R-293; and from *Manual of Practice 2*, Federation of Sewage and Industrial Wastes Associations.)

Constituent	Raw Sludge	Digested Sludge	Activated Sludge	Filter Cake * Raw	Filter Cake * Digested
Volatile matter	60–80	45–60	62–75	55–75	40–60
Ash	20–40	40–55	25–38	25–45	40–60
Insoluble ash	17–35	35–50	22–30	15–30	30–45
Grease and fats	7–35	3–17	5–12	5–30	2–15
Protein	22–28	16–21	32–41	20–25	14–30
Ammonium nitrate	1–3.5	1–4	4–7	1–3	1.3–1.6
Phosphorus, P_2O_5	1–1.5	0.5–3.7	3–4	1.4	0.5–3.5
K_2O	. . .	0–4	0.86		
Cellulose, etc.	10–13	10–13	7.8	8–10	8–12
SiO	. . .	15–16	8.5		
Iron		5.4	7.1		

* The median-average annual rate of dry sludge produced in 7 cities from 1949 to 1953 was 32 lb per capita.

it is sometimes disposed of by dumping into natural bodies of fresh water.

In some methods of disposal the volume and polluting strength of the sludge can be reduced by digestion before disposal. Where sludge is to be used as a fertilizer or as a fuel it may be dried before disposal. The production, digestion, and drying of sludge may involve considerable mechanical equipment, as indicated in Fig. 24–1. In all disposal procedures problems of handling the sludge are involved, and in some disposal procedures savings may be made by recovering values inherent in the sludge.

24–3. Values in sludge. Values in sludge do not ordinarily return the cost of their recovery. The problem in most sewage-treatment plants is to get rid of the sludge as quickly as possible without causing a nuisance. This cannot always be accomplished without subjecting the sludge to some form of treatment. Where the sludge must be treated before disposal it is possible that some value may

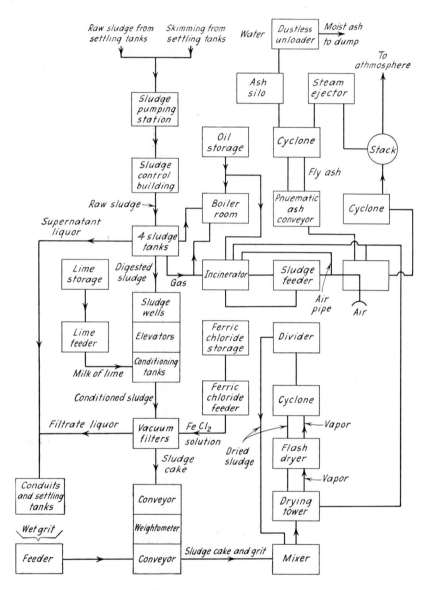

Fig. 24–1. Flow diagram of a sludge-drying system showing extent of mechanization involved. (From *Water and Sewage Works,* May, 1955, p. R-281.)

be recovered to repay in part the cost of treatment. Selling prices of vacuum-filtered sludge are reported[4] for 1953 as varying from $13.95 per ton at Toledo, Ohio, to $33.64 at Milwaukee, Wis.

The principal values inherent in sludges from domestic sewage that can be recovered practically include fertilizer, grease, combustible gas, heat units, and vitamin B_{12}.

24–4. Fertilizing values. The fertilizing value of sewage sludge has been demonstrated by experience and by test.[5] Lunt[6] cautiously concludes, on the basis of experiments, that: ". . . it would appear that immediate increase in crop yields from the use of sludge can hardly be expected under all conditions and with all crops." The use of the term "fertilizing value" in connection with sewage sludge may, however, be misleading to the agriculturist who looks on fertilizer as a material of general plant-food value. The fertilizing value of sludge lies in its quality as a filler for true fertilizers and as a compost and soil conditioner.[7] The fertilizing value of sewage and of sewage sludge cannot be accounted for by the mineral constituents of the material alone. The price of dried activated sludge is often based on its content of ammonia and of phosphoric acid.[8] Fuller and Jourdian[9] conclude that the use of dried sludge "may even add some nitrate to the soil," and helps in the production of humus.[10]

The most convincing method of measuring the fertilizing value of sludge is by the plant growth induced as compared to plant growth in the same soil that contains no sludge. Such a comparison is given for activated sludge in Table 23–1. Normally, however, the value of sludge as a fertilizer is measured in terms of its nitrogen content alone, although potash and phosphorus are sometimes considered.[11] Sludge from all treatment processes is not of equal value in these respects, as indicated by the data in Table 23–2. A characteristic

[4] J. M. Morgan, Jr., and J. F. Thomson, *Water and Sewage Works,* December, 1955, p. 532, and April, 1955, p. 135.

[5] See also "Utilization of Sewage Sludge as a Fertilizer," *Manual of Practice 2,* Federation of Sewage Works Associations, 1946; J. E. Fuller and G. W. Jourdian, *S. and I.W.,* February, 1955, p. 161; and B. P. Skulte, *Wastes Eng.,* May, 1954, p. 222.

[6] See also *Sewage Works Jour.,* November, 1937, p. 861, and January, 1946, p. 46.

[7] See *Mun. San.,* April, 1934, p. 125.

[8] See also *Proc. Am. Soc. Civil Engrs.,* Vol. 81, No. 594, January, 1955, p. 29.

[9] *Op. cit.*

[10] See also L. L. Langford, *Water and Sewage Works,* March, 1955, p. 125.

[11] See also B. A. Schepman, *Public Works,* December, 1955, p. 74.

of digested sludge that adds to its value as a fertilizer is its aerating property which increases the porosity of the top soil to the benefit of plant growth. An undesirable characteristic is the seed content, particularly of tomato seeds, which pass unharmed through digestion tanks and drying beds.

When sludge is applied as a fertilizer to the land, rates of application recommended [12] vary between 10 tons of wet sludge per acre for orchards, to 60 tons for flowers and vegetables. An excess will rarely do harm unless the plants are smothered. Some sludge may delay germination. Applications of more than 50 cu yd per acre have been found, in some cases, to be deleterious, and 150 to 250 cu yd may be disastrous unless the soil is well limed.[13]

As removed from digestion tanks or drying beds, sludge is too moist for economical, long-distance transportation so that its use, without further treatment, is confined to the immediate locality of the treatment plant, and some health hazard is involved in its improper use.

24–5. Hygienic aspects of digested-sludge disposal. The fact that plant seeds will pass through sewage-treatment processes and survive in air-dried sludge leads to the fear that possibly pathogenic organisms may do likewise and that the use of sludge as a fertilizer is not hygienic.[14] (See Sect. 16–26.) The Committee of the American Public Health Association has concluded: [1]

From the hygienic standpoint, heat-dried activated sludge and heat-dried digested sludge appear safe for any reasonable use in agriculture or horticulture. Digested sludge, air-dried, appears safe for such purposes if used like manure and plowed in, when preparing for a crop, and if care is taken not to apply such sludge thereafter on root crops or low-lying leafy vegetables which are eaten uncooked. Thorough digestion and air-drying, as well as storage of the air-dried sludge, afford a sufficient protection. The Committee knows of no case of sickness traceable to the use of digested sludge or activated sludge. Fresh sludge should be regarded as only one degree removed from night soil and treated as such, being used only on forage crops and then applied and plowed in promptly thereafter.

As a result of studies of the longevity of *B. typhosus* in sewage sludge, Ruchhoft [15] concluded that "wet activated sludge can not be

---

[12] See L. W. Van Kleeck, *Trans. Am. Soc. Civil Engrs.,* Vol. 72, 1945, p. 208.
[13] See H. A. Lunt, *Water and Sewage Works,* August, 1953, p. 295.
[14] See Abstract, *Sewage Works Jour.,* November, 1936, p. 1027.
[15] C. C. Ruchhoft, *Sewage Works Jour.,* November, 1934, p. 1054.

Table 24–3

LIPIDS IN DRIED SEWAGE SLUDGE

(Knechtges, Peterson, and Strong, *Sewage Works Jour.*,
November, 1934, p. 1083.)

	Domestic Sewage, Madison, Wis.		Packing House		Milorganite, Dried Activated-Sludge Fertilizer,	Milwaukee Activated Sludge,
Solvent	Sample 1, %	Sample 2, %	Sample 1, %	Sample 2, %	%	%
Petroleum ether	24.7	26.0	18.4	27.8	5.6	6.5
Ethyl ether	23.6	. . .	21.3	. . .	. . .	. . .
Isopropyl ether	31.1	. . .	30.3	. . .	. . .	. . .
Chloroform	42.5	40.5	38.8	46.0	9.6	10.3

considered innocuous. At times it may be quite infectious. Caution should be used when it is used as a fertilizer for truck gardens." In a few states restrictions are placed about the use of sludge as a fertilizer but, in general, no state supervision or legal restrictions exist. In some states wet, digested sludge is disposed of on the land.[16] The use of heat-dried sludge as a fertilizer is generally permitted by health authorities.[17]

24–6. Grease in sludge. Material that can be extracted from sludge by substances that will dissolve fats is known as grease or lipids. The amount extracted depends on the amount present in the sludge and on the solvent used. Some quantities extracted from different sludges are shown in Table 24–3.

24–7. Quantities of sludge produced. The quantity of sludge produced depends on the nature of the sewage and the method of sludge collection, as indicated by the information in Table 24–4. About 32 lb of dry solids may be removed from sewage per capita annually, by plain sedimentation. After the digestion of sludge from plain sedimentation the quantity of solids may be about 12 lb, and from digested activated sludge about 22 lb annually, per capita. If the quantity and quality of suspended matter in crude sewage and in the sludge are known the quantities of sludge produced at various

[16] See H. Hayob, *S. and I.W.*, January, 1954, p. 93.

[17] See also L. W. Van Kleeck, *Water and Sewage Works*, November, 1952, p. 463.

Table 24-4

APPROXIMATE QUALITIES AND QUANTITIES OF SLUDGES
PRODUCED BY DIFFERENT TREATMENT PROCESSES

Process	Per Cent Moisture	Cubic Feet per Million Gallons	Specific Gravity	Per Cent Dry Basis				Dry Solids, Average *	
				Volatile Solids	Total Nitrogen	Phosphates, P₂O₅	Fats, Ether-Soluble	Pounds per Capita per Day	Per Cent Organic Matter
Plain sedimentation with frequent subsurface removal of sludge	97.5	650	1,015	65	2.0	1.67	10.0	0.14	70.5
Plain sedimentation in a mechanical clarifier	95	325	1,02	65	2.0	1.67	10.0		
Imhoff tank, well digested	90	120	1.04	50	2.5	1.75	8.0		
Trickling filter, humus	93	100	1.02	45	2.0	1.2	6.0		
Chemical precipitation	93	700	1.03	60	1.75	1.5	9.0	0.60	46.0
Activated sludge	98–99	2,500	1.005	65	5.75	2.75	7.5	0.22	64.5
Septic tank	93	250	1.03	45	1.5	1.0	9.0		

* From S. I. Zack, S. and I.W., August, 1950, p. 975.

stages of treatment can be predicted. The procedure is shown by the following example: [18]

1. Assume 10,000 population and 1 million gal of sewage flow daily with 78 gm of suspended matter per capita daily. This is equivalent to about 200 mg/l.

2. Assume that the combined sludge from primary and secondary tanks amounts to 90 per cent of the original quantity. This is equivalent to 180 mg/l of suspended matter.

3. Then the pounds of dry sludge produced daily are $180 \times 8.3 = 1,500$. The pounds of wet sludge (95 per cent moisture) produced daily in the tank are approximately 30,000.

At 63 lb per cu ft the volume of wet sludge produced daily is 476 cu ft. Assuming an average digestion of 25 per cent, the daily net accumulation of sludge is 357 cu ft.

4. Assuming 60 days for controlled digestion-tank capacity the required tank capacity is 21,420 cu ft or 2.14 cu ft per capita.

24–8. Quality of sludge. The quality of sludge may be expressed either physically or chemically. Physical characteristics include moisture, density, color, odor, texture, fluidity, and plasticity. Chemically it is customary to express total and volatile solids, total

[18] From S. A. Greeley, Notes on *Gas Produced in the Digestion of Sewage Sludge,* a monograph.

nitrogen, phosphates as P_2O_5, potash as K_2O, and fats as ether soluble. Representative chemical characteristics of sludges from different treatment processes are given in Table 24–4. Undigested sludge from plain sedimentation is gray, offensive in odor, and slimy in texture. Good activated sludge is brown, flocculent, and odorless. Septic sludge is black, typically putrid in odor, and slightly less slimy than sludge from plain sedimentation. Well-digested Imhoff sludge is black, thick and granular, with a tarry odor. Trickling-filter humus is grayish-brown, flocculent, and inoffensive in odor when fresh. Sludge from chemical precipitation is slimy, gray to brown or red, dependent on the presence of iron, and offensive in odor.

Fluidity and plasticity vary with water content and nature of solids. The most fluid is activated sludge, with a water content of 98 to 99 per cent. As the moisture of a sludge is reduced to about 85 per cent a definite thickening can be noted. At 70 to 80 per cent the sludge will no longer flow and is known as sludge cake. It can be handled with a spade or a manure fork. At a moisture content of 10 per cent it is as dry as dust.

24–9. Changes in volume and weight. As sludge is digested its percentage of moisture is reduced and its volume is changed *approximately* according to the relation

$$V_1 = \frac{V(1 - P)}{1 - P_1} \tag{24-1}$$

in which V_1 is the new volume, P_1 is the new percentage of moisture, and V and P are the old volume and the old percentage of moisture, respectively, P and P_1 being expressed as a ratio. A more exact determination of the change in volume can be made from the expression

$$V_1 = \frac{V[1 + P_1(G - 1)](1 - P)}{[1 + P(G - 1)](1 - P_1)} \tag{24-2}$$

in which G is the specific gravity of the solids present in the sludge. This figure is usually about 1.3. The specific gravity, S, of the sludge can be computed from the expression

$$S = \frac{G}{1 - P(1 - G)} \tag{24-3}$$

Example. If 10,000 cu ft of sludge containing 2 per cent solids are produced at a plant, how many cu ft would be pumped into the digester if the sludge were concentrated to 4 per cent solids before pumping? Neglect effect of change in specific gravity.

Solution. From formula 24–1:

$$V_1 = \frac{(10,000)(1 - 0.98)}{(1 - 0.96)} = 5,000 \text{ cu ft} \qquad Answer.$$

24–10. Measuring and metering sludge. The measurement of the volume of sludge in a tank containing both sludge and supernatant liquor is a procedure frequently necessary in the control of plant operation. Accuracy in making the measurement is difficult because the specific gravity of the sludge is usually so nearly the same as that of the supernatant liquor that the insertion of a measuring device may disturb the level of the surface of the sludge or mix it with the supernatant liquor.

In the activated-sludge process of sewage treatment the volume of the sludge may be measured by mixing the sludge and supernatant liquid and allowing a sample of the mixture to settle in a graduated glass container. The volume of the sludge is read from the graduations on the container. This method is possible with activated sludge because of the rapidity with which it will settle.

Sludge is difficult to measure volumetrically because of its heterogeneous nature. When it can be made to flow through a pipe it can be measured through a venturi meter or flume, in a tipping-bucket gage of the type designed by Sperry,[19] over a weir, or by other methods.

Methods by which the operator of a plant can locate the sludge and scum lines are discussed in Sect. 29–19.

24–11. Sludge pipes. Sewage sludge flows like a thin, plastic material, to which the formulas for the flow of water are not applicable, as stated in Sect. 24–12. In practice, where thin sludges are to flow by gravity for short distances in pipes or channels about the treatment plant, a slope of 3 per cent or greater has been found to be satisfactory.

Some principles involved in the design of sludge pipes are discussed in Sects. 12–17 and 18–14. Pipes less than 6 in. in diameter should not be used, in order to avoid clogging and to facilitate cleaning. For the same reason bends are to be avoided where possible. All bends in closed sludge pipes should be provided with cleanouts and 2-in. threaded nipples to which a high-pressure hose can be attached. Ordinarily, cast iron and concrete have been used for sludge pipes and channels.

[19] W. A. Sperry, *Sewage Works Jour.*, July, 1934, p. **799.**

24–12. Flow of sludge.[20]   Sewage sludge is a plastic solid with densities and fluidities so different from those of water that normal hydraulic formulas for the flow of water are not applicable to the flow of sludge unless the velocity of flow is turbulent. In studying the flow of sludge, as met in many sewerage problems, it will be found that the flow may be either laminar or turbulent.

In laminar flow the head-loss-velocity relations can be expressed as [21]

$$\frac{H}{L} = \frac{16S_y}{3\rho D} + \frac{\eta V}{\rho D^2} \quad \text{and} \quad \frac{H_w}{L} = \frac{16S_y}{3WD} + \frac{\eta V}{WD^2} \quad (24\text{–}4)$$

where D = diameter of pipe, in feet.

S_y = shearing stress at the yield point of a plastic material, called yield value, in pounds per square foot. Values are given in Table 24–5.

η = coefficient of rigidity, in pounds per foot per second. Values are given in Table 24–5.

H = the pressure or head causing flow. It is measured in feet of height of the sludge.

H_w = the pressure or head causing flow. It is measured in feet of height of water.

L = length of pipe, in feet.

ρ = density of the flowing substance, pounds per cubic foot.

V = average velocity of flow in the pipe, feet per second.

W = weight of water, pounds per cubic foot.

The upper limit of velocity for laminar flow may be called the *lower critical velocity*, V_{lc}, which can be expressed as

$$V_{lc} = \frac{1{,}000\eta + 103\sqrt{(94\eta^2 + D^2 S_y \rho)}}{D\rho} \quad (24\text{–}5)$$

Between the velocity below which laminar flow always occurs and the velocity above which turbulent flow always occurs there are velocities at which the flow may be either laminar or turbulent, or a combination of both. The velocity above which turbulent flow will always occur may be called the *upper critical velocity*, V_{uc}, which can be expressed as

$$V_{uc} = \frac{1{,}500\eta + 127\sqrt{140\eta^2 + D^2 S_y \rho}}{D\rho} \quad (24\text{–}6)$$

[20] See also *Sewage and Ind. Wastes*, January, 1950, p. 1.

[21] See *Bulls.* 319 and 323, Engineering Experiment Station, University of Illinois, 1939 and 1940, respectively.

Table 24–5

VALUES OF S_y AND η FOR VARIOUS SLUDGES

(From *Bull*. 319, Illinois Engineering Experiment Station, 1939.)

Source	Temperature, °F	Moisture, %	Volatile Solids, %	Specific Gravity	S_y	η
Activated sludge, Indianapolis	36	98.6	66.6	1.008	0	0.001
Digested sludge, Indianapolis	42	92	53.4	1.032	0.405	0.032
Imhoff sludge, Decatur	60	86	40	1.06	0.065	0.0165
Imhoff sludge, Calumet	54–67	93	. . .	. . .	0.0026	0.025
Digested sludge, Stuttgart, Germany	57–68	90	. . .	. . .	0.100	0.077
Clay slurry	89	70.9	. . .	1.225	0.117	0.005
Digested sludge, Kankakee	46	92.7	50.8	1.034	0.026	0.017
Digested sludge, Danville	122	93	48.5	1.008	0.072	0.014
Illinois yellow clay	76	48	0	1.49	0.720	0.028
Tennessee ball clay	82	84.9	. . .	1.110	0.059	0.011
Tennessee ball clay	82	75.2	. . .	1.145	0.532	0.019
Tennessee ball clay *	82	85.2	. . .	1.092	0.081	0.0119

* Glycerin as dispersion medium.

It is to be noted that formulas 24–4 are applicable only where the velocity is below V_{lc}.

Where the velocity of flow is greater than V_{uc} the familiar exponential formulas, such as Hazen and Williams, can be used. In order that such formulas may be applied the sludge must consist of finely divided particles dispersed in water, as in typical sewage sludge, and the velocity of flow must be above critical.

Sludges concentrated to 8 to 12 per cent solids can be pumped successfully through properly designed pipes.[22] Empirical methods are depended on in design, using velocities above critical. If the Hazen and Williams formula is used values of C should be 60 to 80 per cent of those for water, when the sludge contains up to 4 to 6 per cent of solids. With sludges containing up to 8 to 10 per cent of solids the

[22] See also S. G. Brisbin, *Proc. San. Eng. Div.*, American Society of Civil Engineers, *Paper* 1274, June, 1957.

values of C should be 25 to 40 per cent of those used for water.[23] Sludges with solids up to 16 per cent concentration have been pumped successfully.

24–13. Return of sludge to primary tank. In such treatment processes as activated sludge, trickling filtration, and sometimes chemical precipitation, sludge is produced in both primary and secondary tanks. The return of sludge from the latter to mix with sludge in the primary tank has been found advantageous at some plants. The return of chemical sludge will reduce suspended solids and BOD in the primary settling tank, but continued recirculation may give trouble because of ferric iron.

Waste activated sludge can be disposed of by pumping into the primary tanks or by pumping it back into the sewage entering the plant. The waste activated sludge mixes with the plain sedimentation sludge in the primary tank, the drying qualities of the mixed sludges being better than those of either of the sludges alone. The procedure is giving satisfaction although there are times when activated sludge rises in a septic condition to be discarded with the tank effluent, to the detriment of the quality of the effluent, and increasing the load on the aeration tank.

24–14. Disposal into water. In the disposal of sludge into bodies of water, as in the disposal of sewage by dilution, there must be sufficient oxygen available in the water receiving the sludge to prevent putrefaction, and a swift current to prevent sedimentation. Such conditions frequently exist in the sea and may be found sometimes in rivers when they are in flood. Deep discharge of sludge is advantageous as it improves mixing of sludge and the diluting water. A deep discharge is especially important where the specific gravity of the sludge is less than that of water, as in disposal into salt water or into water colder than the sludge. At some seacoast plants plans have been made to mix sludge with sea water before discharging into the sea. In some seacoast cities [24] sludge is taken out to sea in barges and dumped. Since it is not necessary to discharge sludge continuously, it can be stored until the conditions in the body of water are suitable to receive it or until a shipload has been accumulated. Biologic action in sludge-digestion tanks changes the sewage solids into homogeneous materials, with diminished BOD and bacterial con-

[23] C. V. Davis, *Handbook of Hydraulics*, McGraw-Hill Book Co., 1942, p. 943.
[24] See *Water Works and Sewerage*, September, 1941, pp. 385, 391, and 395; and W. F. Welsch, *S. and I.W.*, September, 1955, p. 1065.

tent. The material is more easily dispersed when mixed with a large body of water.[25]

The amount of diluting water required to receive sludge has not been sufficiently well determined to draw reliable general conclusions. A dilution of 1,500 to 2,000 volumes may be considered sufficiently safe to avoid a nuisance provided that there is sufficient velocity to prevent sedimentation. The character of the sludge has a marked effect on the proper dilution, the sludge from septic and sedimentation tanks requiring more dilution than well-digested sludge.

24–15. Lagooning of sludge.[26] Sludge lagoons differ in purpose and type from sewage lagoons, discussed in Sect. 16–27. Three forms of sludge lagoons are: [27] (1) digesting, thickening, and storage lagoons, (2) drying lagoons from which sludge is removed periodically, and (3) permanent lagoons in which the sludge is stored indefinitely. The first type may be constructed as a separate-digestion tank, either open or covered. The period of detention depends on the method of operation. It may, sometimes, be as long as one to two years. The second type may be constructed as a watertight container, not more than about 6 ft deep and in some plants as shallow as 12 to 18 in. Overflow or supernatant liquor may be drawn from the drying lagoon and digested in a separate digester. The period of retention may be as much as 2 yr. Sludge dried in such lagoons may contain about 30 per cent solids. Successful disposal by lagooning has been reported by Bloodgood.[28]

During the period of standing in the lagoon some of the moisture drains out or evaporates, and the organic matter digests, sometimes giving off foul odors. Digestion can be hastened in some plants by seeding the sludge as it is run onto the lagoon. In the course of time biological action ceases and the sludge has become humified and reduced to about 70 per cent moisture.

Sludge lagooning is looked on by some authorities as an inadequate, incomplete, and unsatisfactory method of sludge disposal. It has been objected to also because of offensive odors, so that it should not be used in built-up regions, and the land used should be of little or

[25] See also A. M. Rawn and F. R. Bowerman, *S. and I.W.*, November, 1954, p. 1309.

[26] See also committee reports on sludge lagoons, *Sewage Works Jour.*, September, 1948, p. 817.

[27] See also John Finch, *Water and Sewage Works*, April, 1955, p. 180.

[28] D. E. Bloodgood, *Water and Sewage Works*, July, 1947, p. R-231.

no value for other purposes. The Committee [29] concluded: "There is a lack of reliable data on lagoons and their utilization, as well as their location, probably because they are generally regarded as a temporary measure."

24–16. Burial. Sludge can be disposed of by burial in trenches about 24 in. deep with at least 12 in. of earth cover, without causing a nuisance. The ground used for this purpose should be well drained. This method of disposal is generally used as a makeshift and has not been practiced extensively because of the large amount of land required. Insufficient information is available to generalize on the amount of land required or the time before the land can be used for further sludge burial, or for other purposes. Indications are that the sludge may remain moist and malodorous for years and that the land may be rendered permanently unfit for further sludge burial. Under some conditions the land may be used again for the same or other purposes. For example Kinnicutt, Winslow and Pratt [30] state that 500 tons of wet sludge can be applied per acre and:

The same land, it is claimed, can be used again after a period of a year and a half to two years, if in two months or so after covering the sludge with earth, the ground is broken up, planted, and, when the crop is removed, again plowed and allowed to remain fallow for about a year.

[29] *Sewage Works Jour.*, September, 1948, p. 817.
[30] *Sewage Disposal*, 1913.

Chapter **25**

Sludge digestion

25–1. The process of sludge digestion. The digestion of sewage sludge is accomplished by biological action in which the solid organic matter deposited by sedimentation is liquefied and gasified and the condition of the sludge is so changed that its volume is reduced, the fertilizing qualities are changed, valuable gas is produced, and the drying of the sludge by subsequent processes may be facilitated. The following explanation of the process has been abstracted from an article by Sawyer and others.[1] Satisfactory digestion of organic matter under anaerobic conditions depends on two different groups of bacteria living harmoniously in the same environment. One group, normally present in sewage sludge in great numbers and capable of rapid rates of reproduction, consists of saprophytic organisms which attack the complex organic substances, such as fats, carbohydrates, and proteins, and convert them to simple organic compounds. Among these saprophytic organisms are many acid-forming bacteria which produce low molecular weight fatty acids, such as acetic and propionic, during degradation of the organic material. Such acids are produced in sufficient quantities, in some cases, to lower the pH to a level where all biological activity is arrested. The second group of organisms are the methane-producing bacteria [2] which are capable of utilizing the acid and other end products formed by the first group. It has been demonstrated that the methane-formers are sensitive to pH changes and proliferate within a narrow pH range of about 6.5 to 8.0. Unfortunately these organisms do not occur in great numbers in raw sewage sludge, nor does their reproduction rate compare with many saprophytic organisms; consequently, organic acids may be formed faster than the limited population of methane-formers can assimilate them and, as a result, the accumulated acids reduce

[1] C. N. Sawyer, and others, *S. and I.W.*, August, 1954, p. 935.
[2] T. C. Buck, *S. and I.W.*, September, 1953, p. 993.

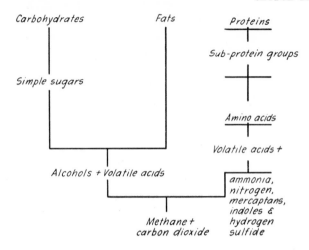

Fig. 25–1. Diagram showing oxidation of organic matter.

the pH to even more unfavorable levels for methane-formers. All organic matter is not oxidized in the same way. The mode of oxidation of three such substances is outlined in Fig. 25–1.

In controlled sludge digestion the environment must be maintained suitable for the continued growth of both saprophytic and methane-producing organisms. The proper environment requires the balance between the population of organisms, food supply, temperature, pH, and food accessibility. Digestion processes are being improved as the conditions which influence organic metabolism are better understood and better equipment and methods are available for controlling these conditions. During the decade preceding 1958 the application of this growing knowledge made possible the reduction of digestion time from the previous standard of 25 to 30 days to between 5 and 7 days.

25–2. Advantages and disadvantages. The digestion of sludge prepares it for subsequent disposal, reduces its volume, makes possible the recovery of valuable gas, and improves, to a slight extent, the availability of the sludge as a fertilizer. It conserves the values that are destroyed by incineration. Among the disadvantages may be included the cost of equipment and the careful operation required to maintain optimum environmental conditions for controlled digestion.

25–3. Conditions affecting digestion.[3] Among the more important conditions affecting sludge digestion may be included: temperature; time; food supply which is influenced by the quality and concentration of solids in the sludge; the manner and degree of mixing; the manner of dosing or feeding the tank; the pH; the volatile acids content of the digesting mixture; and the amount and kind of added chemicals, if any. Conditions of lesser importance include the quality of the public-water supply, copper, fluorides,[4] and the presence of radioactive wastes.[5]

Indexes of digestive action, which may be called measures of digestion, include: (1) gas production in quantity and quality; (2) solids: total, volatile, and fixed; (3) BOD; (4) acidity and pH; (5) volatile acids; (6) grease; (7) sludge characteristics; and (8) odor. The amount of digestion can be expressed as:

$$P = \left[1 - \frac{(100 - R)D}{(100 - D)R} \right] 100 \qquad (25\text{–}1)$$

where P = per cent reduction of volatile matter.
R = per cent volatile matter in raw sludge.
D = per cent of volatile matter in digested sludge.

Conditions in a digestion tank may be considered to be satisfactory when:

1. Methane content of digester gas lies between 55 and 75 per cent, and the sum of methane and carbon dioxide constitute approximately 95 per cent of the gas produced.

2. Solids below about 15 per cent with optimum at about 8 per cent;[6] volatile matter about 50 per cent of solids.

3. pH of digested sludge between 7.0 and 8.0. Below 6.5 to 6.0 digestion is inhibited. Below 4.5 to 4.0, effective digestion ceases.

4. Volatile acids below about 2,000 mg/l. About 300 mg/l may be considered normal.

5. Alkalinity above about 2,500 mg/l, with that in the raw sludge above 1,000 to 2,000 mg/l.

[3] See also *Sewage Works Jour.*, May, 1944, p. 504.

[4] See W. N. Gruene and R. O. Sload, *S. and I.W.*, January, 1955, p. 1.

[5] Studies at the University of Illinois indicated that any effect of normal concentrations of radioactive wastes in sewage had no practical effect on sludge digestion.

[6] See W Rudolfs, *Bull.* 521, New Jersey Agriculture Experiment Station, 1931, p. 36.

Table 25–1

Design Factors for Sludge-Digestion Tanks

(Ten-State Committee *)

Cubic Feet per Capita

Type of Plant	Heated	Unheated
Imhoff tanks		3 to 4
Imhoff tank and filter		4 to 5
Primary	2 to 3	4 to 6
Primary and standard filter	3 to 4	6 to 8
Primary and high rate filter	4 to 5	8 to 10
Activated sludge	4 to 6	8 to 12

* See Sect. 5–2. Volumes to be calculated on basis of bottom having slopes of 30° from horizontal upward from end of sludge withdrawal pipe unless sludge moving equipment is installed. For populations of less than 5,000, and where garbage solids are anticipated, additional capacity should be provided.

6. Grease is practically absent from digested sludge.

7. Digested sludge is black, quickly drainable, noticeably viscous, and inoffensive in odor rather than putrescible.

The nitrogen content of digested sludge will average 1.5 to 2.0 per cent, dependent on its original composition. The phosphoric acid content will vary between 0.3 per cent and 1.5 per cent, averaging nearer the higher figure. No potash will be present.[7] Unsatisfactory digestion is indicated by the presence of hydrogen sulfide, skatol, mercaptans, and other foul-smelling substances, mere traces of which will impart intense, characteristic, and highly offensive odors.

Some basic design factors for sludge-digestion tanks are given in Tables 20–2, 25–1, and 25–2.

25–4. Temperature of digestion. The most practical optimum temperature for sludge digestion, known as the mesophilic range, lies between 90 and slightly under 100° F, preferably about 95° F. Bacterial action diminishes almost directly with temperature below this range until it practically ceases at 50° F. No permanent harm is done, however, to the bacterial life, even at temperatures slightly below freezing as, when the temperature rises, digestion will resume

[7] See *Trans. Am. Soc. Civil Engrs.*, October, 1942, p. 1652.

Table 25–2

PRACTICES IN SLUDGE-DIGESTION TANK DESIGN *

Joint Committee [1]			L. G. Rice [2]			See Reference in Last Column			
Type of Plant	Heated	Tank Cap., cu ft per capita	Type of Plant	Heated	Tank Cap., cu ft per capita	Type of Plant	Heated	Volatile Load, lb per cu ft per day	Source of Infor- mation
I	Yes	...	I	Yes	2–3	II	...	0.28	3
I	No	3–4	I	No	3–5	II	...	0.17	4
II	Yes	2–3	VI	Yes	4	II	...	0.16	5
II	No	4–6	VI	No	6	IX	...	0.21	6
III	Yes	3–4	VII	Yes	3–4	IX	Yes	0.16 [7]	8
III	No	6–8	VII	No	4½–6	II	Yes	0.25	8
IV	Yes	4–5	V	Yes	4–6	III	...	0.098	9
IV	No	8–10	V	No	6–8	II	...	0.197	9
V	Yes	4–6	VIII	Yes	3½–6	II	...	0.22	10
V	No	8–12	VIII	No	5–8				

* Much of the information in this table is from H. E. Schlenz, "Critical Evaluation of Recent Trends and New Developments in Accelerated Sludge Digestion," University of Kansas, *Bull.* 34, *Trans. 5th Annual Conf. on San. Eng.*, 1955.

I. Imhoff tank. II. Primary tank. III. Primary tanks and standard-rate trickling filters. IV. Primary tank and high-rate trickling filters. V. Activated sludge. VI. Primary with flocculation and chemical precipitation. VII. Complete treatment with trickling filters. VIII. Complete treatment with activated sludge. IX. Primary treatment with activated sludge.

[1] See Sect. 5–2. The footnote under Table 20–2 is applicable here.
[2] *Water and Sewage Works*, October, 1950, p. 436.
[3] Iowa City. P. F. Morgan in *S. and I.W.*, November, 1954, p. 1340.
[4] Columbus, Ohio. J. H. Blodgett, *ibid.*, April, 1954, p. 462.
[5] Erie, Pa. T. H. Forrest, at Mo. Sewage Works Assoc., September, 1954.
[6] Bowery Bay Plant, New York City. W. N. Torpey, *S. and I.W.*, February, 1955.
[7] Double loading.
[8] Hyperion Plant, Los Angeles, Calif., *ibid.*, October, 1954, p. 1202.
[9] Cedar Rapids, Iowa. H. E. Schlenz, discussion in *Proc. Am. Soc. Civil Engrs.*, June, 1937, p. 1114.
[10] Cincinnati, Ohio. H. E. Schlenz, *S. and I.W.*, February, 1955, discussion of paper by W. N. Torpey.

normally. Frozen sludge has been found as effective for seeding, as sludge that has not been frozen.

As the temperature rises above 100° F there is a slight diminution in the rate of increase of bacterial activity until, at about 105°, it begins to increase to attain another optimum at about 128° F, known as a thermophilic temperature.

Operation at thermophilic temperatures has not been widely attempted on a plant scale [8] because of the sensitivity of the thermophiles to slight changes in temperature and because of the poor quality of the supernatant liquor.

[8] See also W. F. Garber, *S. and I.W.*, October, 1954, p. 1202.

The Committee on Sludge Digestion of the American Society of Civil Engineers [9] states:

Among the considerations that should be taken into account in selecting an operating temperature, and in designing digestion tanks, are: (*a*) the balance between the cost of providing extra capacity for digestion at the lower temperature and that of extra equipment for heating and insulating at a higher temperature, due consideration being given to the value of the additional gas; (*b*) the capacity of the selected type of tank for being heated and for retaining heat; (*c*) the method of heating and the rate of transmission of heat; (*d*) the effect of higher water temperatures on the rate at which sludge cakes on heating coils; (*e*) the effect on the heat balance of the concentration of solids in the tank sludge and in the fresh sludge; (*f*) the heat lost with the sludge liquor and the possibility of some recovery by heat exchange; (*g*) the effect of more active gas release on the area and depth of the tank and on the formation of scum; (*h*) the need for and the relative cost of winter storage; (*i*) the fact that the total size of sludge digestion and sludge storage tanks is not directly proportional to the time required for digestion; and (*j*) the effect of the duration of low winter temperatures on the relative costs of operation at different temperatures.

25–5. Period of digestion. Periods of digestion used in practice up to about 1942 varied between 30 and 60 days under mesophilic conditions in temperature-controlled tanks. Where the temperature is not controlled, and it may fall into the psychrophilic region in cold weather, as in Imhoff tanks, periods up to 6 months have been used. Tests and limited field experience have demonstrated that with the proper control of environmental conditions, sludge can be digested in 10 days or less.[10] Such a short period of digestion is known as high-rate digestion.[11] It is discussed in Sect. 25–7. Under thermophilic conditions digestion will take place in appreciably less than 10 days. However, partly because of uncertainties in the control of digesters under thermophilic conditions, and because of other factors, and where it is difficult to assure proper operational conditions, conservative designs continue to allow a minimum of 30 days. The trend for large plants is toward the use of periods between 10 and 15 days.

[9] See *Proc. Am. Soc. Civil Engrs.*, January, 1937, p. 45.

[10] See P. F. Morgan and E. N. Sawyer, *S. and I.W.*, April, 1954, p. 462; and E. N. Sawyer and others, *S. and I.W.*, December, 1955.

[11] See also W. E. Copeland, *S. and I.W.*, February, 1955, p. 224; W. N. Torpey, *S. and I.W.*, April, 1954, p. 479, and February, 1955, p. 121; and H. E. Babbitt and H. E. Schlenz, *Bull.* 198, Engineering Experiment Station, University of Illinois, 1929.

25–6. Feeding and mixing. Thorough mixing is essential in sludge digestion to distribute the incoming food, to maintain uniform temperatures, to reduce scum, and to assure utilization of the entire tank contents. Some tanks are equipped with power-driven, mechanical mixing devices. Other methods used include [12] the discharge of digester gases into lower tank levels, recirculation of tank contents by pumping, the admission of sludge at various locations and elevations, and automatic devices suggested by Rawn.[13]

Stirring of sludge in a heat-controlled tank in which heating pipes are provided improves heat transmission from the pipes to the tank contents. Stirring tends to prevent the formation of an insulating layer of sludge around the pipes. Operating experience has demonstrated, however, that under some circumstances as, for example, where supernatant liquor exists, too much stirring can be harmful. In a mechanically stirred tank there is no supernatant liquor. In a small plant without a secondary digester for sludge concentration, the disadvantages of mixing may be serious. In large plants, where secondary digester volume is available, primary digesters are stirred to reduce digestion time. The benefits of high-rate digestion are obtainable only in digestion tanks in which there is mixing of the tank contents. The use of gas recirculation for sludge mixing is being more widely practiced as, for example, in the catalytic reduction process of the Chicago Pump Co., and the Pearth gas recirculation system of the Pacific Flush Tank Co.

25–7. High-rate digestion.[14] Sludge digestion in 10 or less days is now successful [15] in pilot plants. Its success in full-scale plants depends on: (1) continuous mixing, sufficient to seed the incoming sludge and to prevent the formation of scum; (2) feeding a concentrated sludge; (3) feeding as nearly continuously as possible; and (4) a temperature of 90 to 95° F. Recommended loadings are in the order of approximately 0.15 to 0.25 lb of volatile solids per cu ft of tank volume per day with sludge of about 8 per cent solids, on a 10-day digestion period.

In the "Catalytic Reduction Process," a proprietary procedure,

[12] See also *Sewage Works Jour.*, May, 1944, pp. 534 and 538; and Sect. 29–19.

[13] A. M. Rawn, *Sewage Works Jour.*, January, 1931, p. 24.

[14] See also W. N. Torpey, *S. and I.W.*, April, 1954, p. 479. H. E. Schlenz, *Trans. 5th Annual Conf. on San. Eng.*, University of Kansas, 1955, p. 49. P. F. Morgan and C. N. Sawyer, *S. and I.W.*, April, 1954, p. 462.

[15] See also C. N. Sawyer and H. K. Roy, *S. and I.W.*, December, 1953, p. 1356. J. H. Blodgett, *Wastes Eng.*, December, 1953, p. 608; and *S. and I.W.*, July, 1956.

Table 25–3

RESULTS FROM THE CATALYTIC REDUCTION PROCESS
AT COLUMBUS, OHIO

(From J. H. Blodgett, *S. and I.W.*, July, 1956.)

Year	Sludge Solids, per cent	Tank Load, lb per cu ft of capacity per day	Volatile Solids, per cent	Deten- tion Days	Gas, cu ft per lb of volatile added	Volatile Solids Reduction, per cent
1953 *	6.6	0.29	57.7	14	6.2	39.6
1954	6.7	0.28	57.0	15	6.2	37.0
1955 †	6.6	0.23	59.3	17	5.9	41.0

* Started, May, 1953.   † Average for 6 months.

digester gas is diffused through the digestion tank bringing fresh and seed sludge and gas into intimate contact. Blodgett [16] reports results from this process at Columbus, Ohio, as shown in Table 25–3. It is said [17] that when sludge digestion: ". . . is employed in combination with the Dorrco Densludge process of sludge thickening digester capacity requirements are decreased 67 to 78 per cent . . . reductions are due to physical means which increase efficiency by mixing during digestion and by thickening before digestion . . . elimination of supernatant reduces raw sludge heating requirements and digester action becomes more stable." The source from which the sludge is obtained may affect the permissible dosing and feeding rate and period of digestion. Partially dewatered sludges or thickened sludges may be used with satisfaction.[18] One disadvantage of partially dewatering sludges prior to digestion is that non-volatile, biochemical products of decomposition remain in the digested sludge.

A handicap to the adoption of high-rate sludge digestion, in some jurisdictions, is the restriction placed by regulatory authorities on minimum sludge-digestion periods.

25–8. Stage digestion. It is known that in the process of sludge digestion substances are produced in the earlier stages that inhibit

[16] *Loc. cit.*

[17] *Public Works*, April, 1955, p. 175.

[18] See W. N. Torpey, *S. and I.W.*, January, 1955, p. 121; and P. F. Morgan, *S. and I.W.*, April, 1954, p. 462, and November, 1954, p. 1340.

activity in subsequent stages. By separating the digestion into two or more stages, some of these difficulties may be overcome and some of the advantages of gentle stirring secured, through stirring in the primary stage only, with an improved quality of supernatant liquor from the secondary stage and freedom from scum in both stages. The digestive action is most rapid during the first stage, more than half of the total gas being given off during the first 24 hours; the first stage of digestion being complete within a few days.

Periods of 6 to 8 days in the primary stage and 22 to 24 days in the secondary stage have been found to give good results. In some plants it has been found convenient to use the second-stage digester as a storage tank without special heat control. Two-stage digestion has been accomplished by pumping sludge from a primary-stage tank to a secondary-stage, more than two stages rarely being provided. Successful tests have been made in which the first stage was conducted under thermophilic conditions and the second in an unheated tank. In this procedure about two-thirds of all the gas is obtained in about 5 days in the primary stage and the time of digestion is reduced to 12 days.

A vertical, two-stage tank, built like an Imhoff tank, has shown satisfactory results; no pumping is required, as the digested sludge from the first stage drops by gravity into the lower compartment where second-stage digestion takes place. The Multidigester [19] is a proprietary, two-stage digester with both stages combined in one tank.

Among the advantages of two-stage digestion in separate tanks may be included a small cost in tank equipment, since only the primary stage need be equipped for heat control, stirring, and gas collection.

25–9. Quality of sludges as affecting digestion. Data on the digestion of sludge from various treatment processes, and on the design of digestion tanks for each, are given in Tables 20–2 and 25–1 and 25–2. Sludge from chemically precipitated sewage that has been treated with ordinary coagulants and dosages has a slightly higher moisture content and digests somewhat more rapidly and with lower gas yields than sludge from plain sedimentation.

25–10. Gas production and quality. [20] The principal gaseous products of the biolysis of organic matter are methane and carbon

[19] See *Sewage Works Jour.*, September, 1942, pp. 1179 and 1180.

[20] See also A. J. Steffen, *S. and I.W.*, December, 1955, p. 1364; and H. W. Gehm and others, *S. and I.W.*, August, 1950.

Table 25–4

ANALYSES OF SEWAGE GASES AND OTHER GASES

(From W. H. Fulweiler, *Sewage Works Jour.*, July, 1930, p. 424.)

Type or Source of Gas	CO	H₂	CH₄	CO₂	O₂	N₂	O₂+N₂	Illu-mi-nants	Btu per Cubic Foot	Specific Gravity Referred to Air
Decatur, Ill., Imhoff	...	...	69.0	16.8	0.1	14.1	...	...	690	...
Calumet, Chicago, Imhoff	...	...	76.0	14.7	0.5	8.2	...	...	780	...
Stuttgart, Germany, Imhoff	...	4.7	75.5	14.0	...	4.7	...	...	770	...
Separate Digestion										
Milwaukee, Wis.	0.6	...	67.5	30.0	0.2	1.7	...	...	677	...
Halle, Germany	...	...	72.9	24.0	0.6	1.6	...	...	729	...
Birmingham, England	...	...	77.0	18.1	0.4	3.2	...	...	700	...
Baltimore, Md.	...	...	70.5	26.5	0.2	2.8	...	...	707	...
Illuminating Gas										
Coke oven	7.3	50.9	29.2	2.8	...	...	6.9	2.9	541	0.44
Carburetted water gas	29.5	37.6	11.4	5.9	...	...	5.1	9.8	538	0.69
Reformed oil gas	18.2	52.1	16.7	4.0	...	...	5.4	3.6	520	0.47
Sewage gas (average)	...	...	75.0	20.0	...	...	5.0	...	750	0.77
Sewage gas + blue gas	18.2	24.0	39.1	13.0	...	...	5.5	...	530	0.66
Natural gas *	...	...	85.6	2.0	...	2.4	...	12.1 †	1,000	0.63

* W. W. Odell, "Facts Relating to the Production and Substitution of Manufactured Gas for Natural Gas," *Bull.* 301, U. S. Bureau of Mines, 1929.

† Ethane.

dioxide.   These two gases normally form more than 95 per cent of the gas evolved, as indicated in Table 25–4.   The average heat value of the gas [21] is 730 Btu per cu ft.   When the percentage of methane is low the digestion is probably not good, but care must be taken in gas observations that carbon dioxide is not dissolved in the collecting fluid or in the gasometer seal, giving a falsely high percentage of methane in the analysis.   The Btu content of the gas is a function of the percentage of methane, the temperature, the pressure, and the water vapor in the gas.   For example, gas saturated with water vapor at 60° F and 30 in. of mercury pressure has a *net* value, in Btu per cubic foot, of 8.96 times the percentage of methane, expressed as a whole number.   For dry gas the factor is 9.12.   The entire net value is available under a boiler or in an internal-combustion engine.

The maximum volume of gas that can be generated cannot exceed about 8 to 9 cu ft per lb of volatile solids added to the tank, or slightly more than double this volume per pound of volatile solids digested.[22]

[21] See *Proc. Am. Soc. Civil Engrs.*, January, 1937, p. 45.
[22] See *Sewage Works Jour.*, May, 1932, p. 454.

A committee of the American Society of Civil Engineers [23] reported the average gas production in all but a few industrial cities to be about 0.61 cu ft per capita per day from heated digestion tanks, and 0.69 cu ft per capita per day where activated sludge is digested. Van Kleeck [24] reported the average yield of gas from plain sedimentation sludge in the United States to be about 0.8 cu ft per capita daily, with a range from about 0.5 to 1.3, or about 19 cu ft of gas per lb of volatile solids digested; and that when either humus or activated sludge is added to primary sludge the average yield will be increased to about 0.9 cu ft per capita daily.

The quantity and quality of gas produced are probably the best indices of the progress of digestion.

25–11. Effect of grease. Grease digests satisfactorily [25] in digestion tanks, liberating carbon dioxide and methane according to the hypothetical reactions explained by Buswell and Boruff,[26] as follows:

$$C_nH_{2n}O_2 + \frac{(n-2)}{2}\,HO = \frac{(n+2)}{4}\,CO_2 + \frac{(3n-2)}{4}\,CH_4$$

$$(25\text{--}2)$$

in which n is an integer.

It can be seen from this formula that the weight of the products of digestion exceed the weight of the original substance digested, because of the water involved in the reaction.

25–12. Digestion-tank design. Separate sludge-digestion tanks may be of any convenient shape, covered or not covered, heated or not heated, manually or mechanically cleaned. Many tanks are circular, covered, heated, and mechanically cleaned or stirred. Major features to be considered in the design of a separate-digestion tank include: (1) volume of sludge to be digested daily; (2) period of digestion; (3) method of heating; (4) method of stirring; (5) method of adding and removing sludge, and method of removing supernatant; (6) type of cover; and (7) method of gas collection. Much mechanical equipment is required [27] in the tank.

The capacity of the digestion tank may be formulated approximately as

$$\text{Capacity} = \frac{V_1 + V_2}{2}\,t \qquad (25\text{--}3)$$

[23] See *Proc. Am. Soc. Civil Engrs.*, January, 1937, p. 45.
[24] L. W. Van Kleeck, *S. and I.W.*, December, 1950, p. 641.
[25] See *Sewage Works Jour.*, November, 1944, p. 1125.
[26] See *ibid.*, May, 1932, p. 454.
[27] See also F. L. Flood, *Water and Sewage Works*, May, 1954, p. R-219.

where V_1 is the volume of the daily dose, V_2 is the volume of that dose after the period of digestion allowed in the tank, and t is the period of digestion, in days. The approximation is based on the assumption that the rate of reduction of volume varies directly with time of digestion. Tests show that the rate is more rapid in the early periods of the digestion so that the capacity of the tank given by the formula is larger than necessary. Mau [28] calls attention to an effective design which utilizes the tank volume to better advantage and permits the use of smaller tanks than those listed in Table 20–2, which are the volumes recommended by controlling authorities.

The period of digestion, t, is fixed by the time necessary to produce a satisfactory digested sludge, as indicated by the seven conditions listed in Sect. 25–3. V_2 is equal to the volume of sludge removed from the tank, divided by the number of days between removals. Since values of V_2 and t cannot be anticipated correctly, experience is commonly depended on in the determination of tank capacity. Some design data of existing tanks are given in Tables 20–2, 24–1, 25–1, 25–2, and 25–5. If high-rate digestion processes are used these volumes may be reduced to one-fourth or one-third of those listed.

Shapes of digestion tanks found in practice are diverse, and no particular shape seems to possess advantages over all others, although most recently constructed tanks are circular. Sections through two tanks are shown in Figs. 25–2 and 25–3. The Dorrco Clarigester is a two-story, separate sludge-digestion tank equipped with a clarifier mechanism in the upper compartment and digester mechanism in the lower or digestion compartment.

The side depth of the wall in most tanks is about 20 ft. The principal objection to relatively deep tanks is the cost. Otherwise they are desirable. With mechanisms for removing sludge the bottoms of the tanks should be flat; otherwise hopper bottoms with steep slopes of 3 to 4 ft horizontal to 1 ft vertical, or steeper, are desirable so long as structural conditions will permit.

Mau [29] states that the conventional design of separate sludge digesters is uneconomical because not all of the tank volume is available for supernatant and for digestion. A difficulty to be overcome in the introduction of innovations in the design of digesters is the restrictions placed on design by various administrative authorities. Some

[28] G. E. Mau, *S. and I.W.*, October, 1956, p. 1199.
[29] *Ibid.*

Table 25–5

DESIGN FIGURES FOR TANKS FOR THE SEPARATE DIGESTION OF SLUDGE FROM
NORMAL MUNICIPAL SEWAGE WITHOUT AN EXCESS OF INDUSTRIAL WASTES

(Compiled, in part, from H. J. N. Hodgson, *Sewage and Trades Wastes
Treatment*, Adelaide, Australia, 1938, p. 293.)

Type of Sludge	Design * Figure, cu ft per capita	Authority	Type of Sludge	Design * Figure, cu ft per capita	Authority
P.	1⅓–1½	Donaldson	P. + A.S.	5½ †	Stanley
P. + A.S.	3	Donaldson	P. + A.S.	6	Frugate
P. + A.S.	3	Fischer	P. + A.S.	3–4	Travaini
Chemical	2¼	Fischer	P. + A.S.	5½–6½	Ridenour
P. + Humus	2	Fischer	P. + A.S.	‡	Eddy
P.	1¼	Fischer	P.	§	Eddy
P.	1	I. & F.	P. + A.S.	2.5–3.0	I. & F.
P. + Humus	1.3–1.5	I. & F.	Chemical	2.0	I. & F.
			P.	3 ‖	Sperry ‖

P. = primary. A.S. = waste activated sludge. I. & F. = Imhoff and Fair,
Sewage Treatment, John Wiley & Sons, 1940.

* Design figure for thickened sludge. Additional volume allowed for supernatant liquid.

† 40 cu ft per lb of volatile matter added daily.

‡ 25 cu ft per lb of dry suspended solids; 36 cu ft per lb of volatile suspended solids daily.

§ 15 cu ft per lb of dry suspended solids; 21½ cu ft per lb of volatile suspended solids daily.

‖ W. A. Sperry in *S. and I.W.*, June, 1953, p. 741, suggests 3 lb total solids per month per cu ft of digestion capacity.

of these restrictions are listed in Tables 20–2, 24–1, 25–1, 25–2, and 25–5.

It is desirable to have a number of digestion units at a plant rather than to rely on one or two large units, because when something goes wrong with the digestion process in one tank a simple expedient is to give it a period of rest while other tanks carry the load. A number of withdrawal points should be provided at different elevations in the tank to permit the removal of supernatant liquor at the optimum level.

Entrance to the control chamber of the digestion tank should be designed with the safety of the operator and the equipment foremost.

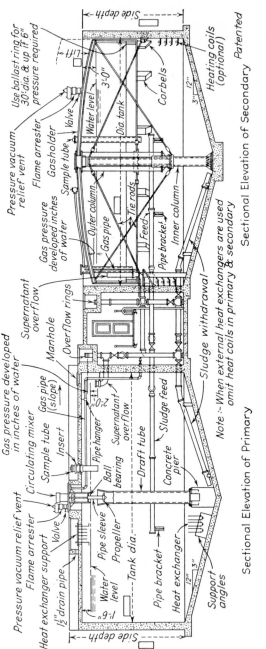

Fig. 25-2. Separate digestion tanks. (Courtesy Dorr-Oliver Co.)

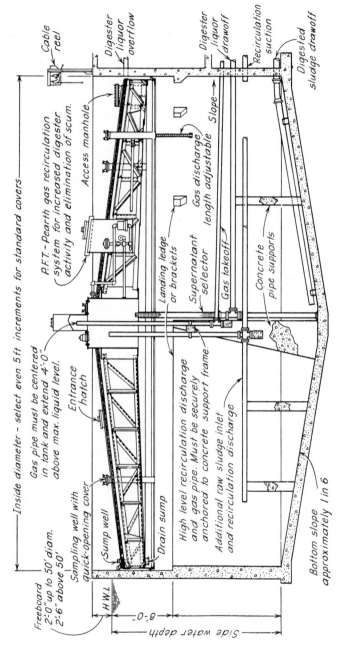

Fig. 25–3. Floating-cover digestion tank. (Courtesy Pacific Flush Tank Co.)

Entrance to the chamber is preferably made by a side entrance at grade rather than by means of a manhole and ladder. The control chamber should be well lighted, ventilated, and equipped with a water service and drain.

25–13. Covers. Two types of covers are used extensively for separate digestion tanks, fixed and floating.[30] A tank with a floating cover is shown in Fig. 25–3. Among the advantages of floating over fixed covers may be included: (1) less scum troubles because solids are constantly submerged; (2) when fresh sludge is added to the tank, or digested sludge or supernatant is withdrawn, it is unnecessary to remove or to add an equal volume of supernatant liquor or sludge, as must be done in a tank with a fixed cover; (3) danger of mixing oxygen with the gas to form an explosive mixture is minimized; (4) it is not always necessary to provide a gas holder unless a large reserve supply of gas is needed.

A fixed-cover tank is illustrated in Fig. 25–2. The fixed cover is low in cost, and has been found to function satisfactorily. The danger of drawing air into the tank has been partly overcome by an automatic device that will cause gas to flow from a gas holder into the digestion tank at any time that the pressure tends to become less than atmospheric. Manholes with airtight covers should be placed in the tank covers to provide access for breaking up, hosing, or removing scum. Special precautions are necessary to avoid fire or explosion when such covers are opened.

The control of scum may be difficult in a covered tank, particularly under a fixed cover where the surface of the scum may have an opportunity to dry. Such formation has been prevented or dispersed by recirculation of the supernatant liquor in the tank, the heated, recirculated liquor being sprayed or distributed over the scum surface under the cover.[31]

25–14. Heating.[32] Methods for the heating of sludge-digestion tanks include: (1) circulation of heated water through pipes hung on the walls on the inside of the tank; (2) circulation of the contents of the tank through a heat exchanger, as shown in Fig. 25–4; (3) injection of live steam into the contents of the tank; (4) injecting hot water into the suction or discharge of the pump putting sludge into

[30] See also F. L. Flood, *Water and Sewage Works,* May, 1954, p. R-219.

[31] See *Civil Eng.,* January, 1947, p. 35.

[32] See *Sewage Works Jour.,* May, 1944, pp. 534 and 538; and *Sewage Works Eng.,* January, 1945, p. 27.

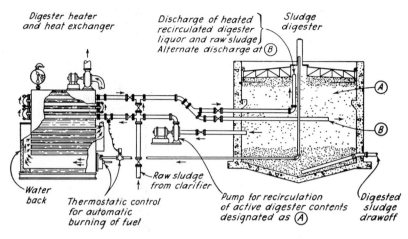

Fig. 25–4. Diagrammatic arrangement of digester heating system using heater and heat exchanger unit and recirculation. (Courtesy Pacific Flush Tank Co.)

the digestion tank; (5) direct heating by submerged combustion;[33] (6) diffusion of heated combustion products through the primary sludge in a small heating tank before the sludge enters the digester;[34] and (7) the use of a heat pump.[35] Methods (1) and (2) are most commonly used, with the trend being towards (2). Because external heat exchangers[36] avoid the objections to internal heating coils, the heat exchangers require continual circulation and mixing of the sludge and the temperature of the tank contents is more easily controlled.

Where circulation coils are used the water normally enters the coils at 120° to 130° F and leaves at about 100° F. Where higher temperatures are used, sludge may become encrusted on the pipe, acting as an insulator against transmission of heat. The coils, made of 2- or $2\frac{1}{2}$-in. pipe, should be placed in the region of most active digestion, with the bottom coil about 3 or 4 ft above the bottom of the tank, and with the top coil at about mid-depth. The high point of the coils should be vented to avoid air lock. Corrosion-resistant materials should be used for pipes and supports in the digestion tank.[37]

[33] See *Water and Sewage Works*, May, 1948, p. 172.
[34] See A. A. Furczyk, *Public Works*, July, 1955, p. 67.
[35] See *S. and I.W.*, December, 1953, p. 1369, and August, 1954, p. 961.
[36] See *Water and Sewage Works*, May, 1950, p. R-173.
[37] See also *Water Works and Sewerage*, May, 1944, p. 185.

A common figure for computing heat transfer through galvanized-iron pipe coils is 10 Btu per sq ft of pipe surface per degree F difference in temperature, per hour. The actual rate is higher in water than in sludge. To conserve heat in a cold climate the tank should be well insulated. One method is to surround the tank with a mound of earth, and to insulate the top with cork or other insulating material, or to cover the tank with a double roof. Another form of insulation of the sides of the tank, and one which improves the appearance of the tank, is to surround it with a brick or tile facing, leaving a dead-air space of about 2 in. between the tank and the tile.

Temperatures maintained in heated digestion tanks are in the mesophilic range between 90 and 100° F.

25–15. Heat balance.[38] The design of the heating compartment to maintain a desired temperature in the digestion tank requires a study of the heat balance in the tank. Where heating is costly it may be economical to insulate the tank against heat losses.[39] Heat is required to: (1) raise the incoming sludge to the required temperature, (2) supply the loss of heat from the surrounding ground or air, and (3) to compensate for the radiation losses from the hot-water pipes outside of the tank. The heat lost from the digestion tank can be expressed as

$$H_2 = A_t(T_t - T_e)(C_1) \qquad (25\text{–}4)$$

where H_2 = Btu lost from the tank, per hour.

A_t = surface area of the tank; top, bottom, and sides, square feet.

T_t = temperature, degrees Fahrenheit, inside the tank.

T_e = temperature, degrees Fahrenheit, outside the tank.

C_1 = coefficient of thermal conductivity in Btu per hour per square foot of tank surface per degree (Fahrenheit) difference of temperature.

Values of C_1 found as a result of tests by various investigators and reported by Moore [40] are given in Table 25–6.

The heat required to raise the temperature of the incoming sludge can be expressed as

$$H_1 = W(T_t' - T_s)(S) \qquad (25\text{–}5)$$

[38] See also "Symposium on Heat Exchange," *Sewage Works Jour.*, January, 1933; *Water Works and Sewerage*, June, 1945, p. R-215; and *Water and Sewage Works*, August, 1947, pp. 287 and 292.

[39] See also *Water Works and Sewerage*, January, 1943, p. 25.

[40] E. W. Moore, *Sewage Works Jour.*, July, 1935, p. 618.

where H_1 = Btu per hour.

W = pounds of sludge entering the tank, per hour.

T_t' = temperature of sludge in tank, degrees Fahrenheit.

T_s = temperature of sludge entering tank, degrees Fahrenheit.

S = specific heat of sludge, taken as that of water = 1.0; actually it may be slightly less than this.

Table 25–6

COEFFICIENT OF HEAT TRANSFER, SLUDGE-DIGESTION TANKS.
AVERAGE OVERALL VALUE OF HEAT-TRANSFER COEFFICIENT

(From E. W. Moore, *Sewage Works Jour.*, July, 1935, p. 618.)

Concrete entirely covered with dry earth. (Rudolfs and Miles)	0.07
Concrete, top exposed to air, surrounded by dry earth. (Haseltine)	0.10
Concrete, top exposed to air, sides in moist earth, bottom in ground water. (Young and Phillips)	0.20–0.25

Heat losses from hot-water pipes can be expressed by equation 25–4, using the appropriate value for the coefficient of heat transfer.

The heat balance in the tank can be expressed as

$$H = A_p(T_W - T_t)C_2$$

$$= W(T_t - T_s)S + A_t(T_t - T_e)C_1 + A_p'(T_W - T_A)C_2' + L$$

$$(25\text{–}6)$$

where the new nomenclature is:

A_p = area of hot-water pipe heating surface in the digestion tank, square feet.

A_p' = area of hot-water pipe heating surface not in the digestion tank, square feet.

L = other losses, Btu.

H = total heat involved, Btu.

T_W = mean temperature of hot water, degrees Fahrenheit.

C_2 = coefficient of heat transfer through bare pipe.

C_2' = coefficient of heat transfer of insulated pipe.

T_A = temperature of the surrounding air.

The solution of the following illustrative problem, based on data given by Moore,[40] will show the method of applying the preceding information:

Let it be required to compute the following: (a) the heat units required daily to heat a digestion tank; and (b) the number of square feet of heating pipe surface required in the digestion tank, under the following conditions and assumptions:

Number of persons served	20,000
Tank diameter	35 ft
Tank depth	20 ft
Tank temperature (T_t)	85° F
Air temperature (T_A)	20° F
Ground temperature outside tank (T_G)	40° F
Effective outside temperature (T_e)	35° F
Entering sludge temperature (T_s)	50° F
Daily sludge addition (W)	40,000 lb
95 per cent water	
Daily gas produced, 70% methane	20,000 cu ft
Efficiency of heating boiler	80%
Coefficient of heat losses from tank (C_1)	0.20
Coefficient of heat transfer through bare pipe (C_2)	10
Recoverable heat yielded by gas engine	60%
Other heat losses	zero
Incoming water temperature (T_1)	133° F
Outgoing water temperature (T_o)	119° F
Mean water temperature (T_W)	126° F

Solution. Substituting in formula 25–6:

(a) $24H = 40{,}000(85 - 50)1.0 + 24 \times 4{,}128(85{-}35)(0.20) = 2{,}400{,}000.$
Therefore $H = 100{,}000$ *Answer.*

(b) From formula 25–6:

$$A_p = \frac{H}{(T_w - T_t)C_2} = \frac{100{,}000}{(126 - 85)10} = 244 \text{ sq ft} \qquad Answer.$$

25–16. Use of activated carbon. Among the advantages claimed for the use of activated carbon in sludge digestion may be included: (a) increase in pH of the digestion tanks; (b) increase in rate of digestion and absence of foaming; (c) increase in the quantity and in percentage of methane in the gas produced; (d) absence of odor in the digested sludge; (e) reduction in the quantity of conditioning chemicals required; and (f) improvement in the drainability of the sludge. These results have not always been obtained in all plants and the evidence is conflicting but it leans toward establishing the fact that activated carbon is beneficial in sludge digestion. The dose has been between 2 and 10 per cent of the dry, raw volatile solids present in the sludge, applied to the sludge in the digestion tank. The dose is equivalent to about 15 lb of activated carbon per million gal of sewage containing 120 mg/l of suspended solids when it is desired to apply 2 per cent carbon. There is an optimum dosage above and below which less satisfactory results seem to be obtained.

25–17. Use of lime.[41] Sometimes lime is added to digesting sludge to correct an acid condition and to prevent foaming, but if it is not properly proportioned and applied the net result may be a worse condition than would prevail without lime. The desirability of its use is controversial. The amount of lime may be estimated or a dose of 5 to 10 lb of hydrated lime per 1,000 persons tributary may be added daily. It is better to add frequently in small doses, mixing well, than to add a large dose unmixed, with a resultant *increase* in foaming. In some plants the lime is mixed only with the supernatant liquor in the digestion tank. In others the sludge is pumped from one tank to another and the lime is thoroughly mixed with the sludge during the process. In the operation of an Imhoff tank, milk of lime may be added through a hose to the active sludge-digestion level to raise the *p*H to about 6.7.

25–18. Gas collection. Attempts to collect gas from sludge-digestion tanks have resulted in the design of various types of gas collectors.

The most common form of gas collector on separate digestion tanks is a dome in the top of the cover, as illustrated in Fig. 25–3. The top of the gas dome must be 4 ft or more above the highest liquid level in the tank, and the gas take-off pipe must extend nearly to the top of the dome to prevent foam, liquid, or solids from entering the pipe. One type of gas dome has a removable cover with a liquid seal, necessitating an anti-freeze mixture in cold weather. The dome may be rigidly attached to the roof, with a pressure-relief device to avoid too great a pressure on the roof.

In the collection of gas and the control of digestion certain control instruments are essential and others desirable. They include: (1) a meter to measure the flow of liquid into the tank; (2) a meter to measure the volume of sludge withdrawn; (3) a meter to measure the volume of heating water circulated; (4) a meter to measure the volume of gas produced; (5) recording thermometers to register the temperature of the tank contents and of the circulating hot water; and (6) a recording calorimeter to register the calorific value of the gas, or, more simply, a methane and carbon dioxide recorder.

25–19. Gas storage. Because of the irregular rate at which gas is given off, some form of storage tank is necessary that will act as an

[41] See also C. N. Sawyer and others, *S. and I.W.*, August, 1954, p. 935.

equalizing reservoir between supply and demand. The required capacity of the holder can be determined by a method similar to that used for a suction or wet well, but, in general, where the rate of demand is constant and all the gas is used, a tank with a capacity of about 110 to 115 per cent of the daily gas yield should be installed. If, however, as much as 10 per cent of the gas can be wasted, the holder in a large plant need have a capacity of only about 40 per cent of the daily gas generation. In smaller plants the gas holder must be relatively larger.

Three forms of storage tanks are in use: floating gasometers, dry-seal gasometers, and pressure holders. Usually these tanks are made of mild steel and are protected against corrosion by paint. Pressure storage in spherical tanks up to 30 to 45 psi has been found to be economical in some plants, the gas being pumped into the tank by a compressor. The adjustment of the rate of gas generation, the operation of the gas compressor, and the storage pressure require careful design and sensitive automatic controls. A combination of gasometers and pressure storage tanks may be desirable.

25–20. Gas piping.[42] Gas piping for both collection and for distribution should be of generous size, at least $2\frac{1}{2}$ in. in diameter, insulated against low temperatures, and laid on a substantial foundation to prevent settling subsequent to construction. The total pressure loss through the appurtenances and the gas lines between the digester and the point of use should be about $1\frac{1}{2}$ in. of water at a maximum gas flow. Since pressures at digesters may not exceed 5 to 6 in. of water, fan-type pressure boosters may be required. Pipe lines should be sloped about $\frac{1}{4}$ in. to the foot or more to condensate traps at all low points. Drains from float-controlled condensate traps should be carried outside of the buildings. Bypasses should be provided at all major items of equipment except flame traps. Pressure-relief and pressure-regulating devices [43] are required to prevent hazardous leakage and to afford proper utilization of gas. Suitable flame traps should be provided on gas lines to boilers, engines, or other utilization devices. The use of explosion-proof electric fixtures where gas may escape is recommended.

25–21. Gas hazards and control.[44] The gas collected during sludge digestion is combustible, explosive, and asphyxiating. Violent

[42] See *Sewage Works Jour.,* September, 1941, p. 1082.

[43] See *Water Works and Sewerage,* September, 1941, p. 423, October, 1941, p. 463, and June, 1943, p. 256.

[44] See *Water Works and Sewerage,* October, 1941, p. 463; and *Sewage Works Jour.,* January, 1945, p. 66.

explosions have occurred at sewage-treatment plants [45] because of inadequate precautions against the escape of gas and its accumulation in confined spaces. Automatic devices are available [46] that will give an alarm upon the approach of dangerous conditions. Gas explosions can be prevented *by keeping gas and air from mixing*. Gas lines should be protected against leakage and, if they are carried in pipe galleries or buildings, adequate ventilation must be provided. Gas pipe lines and gas holders should always be under positive pressure to avoid air being sucked into them and to make the detection of leaks possible.[47] Causes of escaping gas include too low a depth of seal in traps, gas pipes too small, freezing of moisture in gas pipe lines, and accumulation of moisture at low points. Gas pipes should slope to a low point equipped with a drain trap unless there is good reason to do otherwise. Liquid in gas seals should not exceed about 10 in. of equivalent water depth since normal operating pressure on gas systems does not exceed about 7 in. In cold climates water seals should be protected against freezing by the use of anti-freeze mixtures. The tops of liquid-sealed pressure gages should be conveyed to outside vents to prevent the escape of gas into an enclosed space in the event that the seal is broken. Pipe lines and gas equipment should be of sufficient capacity to handle two to three times the normal flow of gas.

25–22. Flame arresters and safety devices. Flame arresters are used to prevent the passage of a flame along the inside of a gas pipe. They are applicable only in relatively small gas lines where the rate of flow of gas is less than about 100 cu ft per hr. They operate on a principle similar to that of a miner's lamp [48] to cool the flame below the ignition point. One type of flame trap is shown in Fig. 25–5. The flame-arresting elements of the trap should be corrosion resistant and should have sufficient area and depth to stop the flame without producing too much resistance to the flow of gas. No flame or relief trap should depend on a water seal for its operation. Water seals are likely to become weakened through evaporation and neglect. It has been found that the velocity of the flame increases as it travels through a pipe and with sufficient velocity the flame may pass the seal. Hence, the trap must be located near the point of combustion. The usual

[45] See *Water Works and Sewerage,* September, 1941, p. 423, October, 1941, p. 463, and June, 1943, p. 256.

[46] *Public Works,* April, 1955, p. 77.

[47] See *Sewage Works Jour.,* January, 1940, p. 128.

[48] See *Water Works and Sewerage,* September, 1941, p. 423, October, 1941, p. 463, and June, 1943, p. 256.

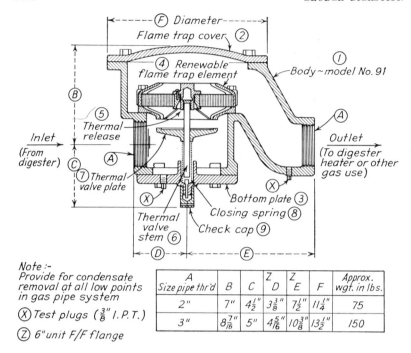

Note :-
Provide for condensate
removal at all low points
in gas pipe system

Ⓧ Test plugs (⅜" I.P.T.)

Ⓩ 6" unit F/F flange

A Size pipe thr'd	B	C	Z D	Z E	F	Approx. wgt. in lbs.
2"	7"	$4\frac{1}{2}$"	$3\frac{3}{8}$"	$7\frac{1}{2}$"	$11\frac{1}{4}$"	75
3"	$8\frac{7}{16}$"	5"	$4\frac{5}{16}$"	$10\frac{3}{8}$"	$13\frac{1}{2}$"	150

Fig. 25–5. Flame trap. (Courtesy Pacific Flush Tank Co.) Flame flashing
back from any source cannot pass the porous element. If it continues to burn
over the element the thermal plug is melted, closing the valve to prevent the
flow of gas from the digester or the passage of flame to the digester.

maximum allowable safe limit is 30 ft from the point of gas combustion. Relief traps are used to relieve excess pressure, other than pressure due to explosions. They should be located close to the source of gas production. Flame traps or arresters should be inspected regularly and frequently because, unless clean, they form a resistance to the passage of gas and, if not properly sealed, they may permit the escape of gas to cause explosions.

When it is not possible to carry a vent to the outside air the condensate trap should be equipped to shut off automatically if the liquid lowers sufficiently to permit the escape of gas. Automatic alarms are available to warn of the presence of explosive gas-mixtures by blowing a whistle, ringing a bell, lighting a red light, or otherwise.

Special precautions should be taken to protect gas equipment from lightning.

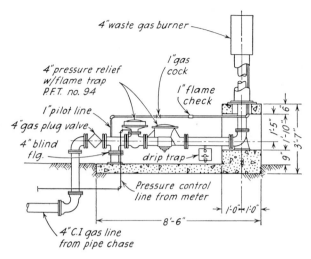

Fig. 25–6. Waste gas burner at Sunnyvale, Calif. (Courtesy Brown and Caldwell, Engineers.)

25–23. Waste-gas disposal. Provision should be made for the burning of waste gas as it is usually impracticable to expect to utilize all of the gas generated. A waste-gas burner is shown in Fig. 25–6. Waste gas should be released at no other place than the waste-gas burner. This should be located more than 25 ft away from the gasometers or other structure containing gas or offering a hazard, and the burner must be protected with a flame trap placed near it. Automatic gas burners are set to open at about 2 in. of water pressure higher than the normal operating pressure, the flame being ignited by a pilot light. It may be desirable to install a pressure-relief valve on the same line, to open at a pressure of about 2 in. of water higher than the waste-gas burner. Since the flame at the burner is usually invisible it should be placed where it is accessible to the operators only, and not to the public.

25–24. Gas utilization.[49] Provision for the utilization of gas from sludge digestion has become almost universal practice in sewage-treatment plant design. The gas is used primarily for heating and for the generation of power at the treatment plant where the gas is produced. In heat value 1,000 cu ft of sludge-digestion gas is equivalent to about 600 cu ft of natural gas, 6.4 gal of butane, 5.2 gal of

[49] See also *Sewage Works Jour.*, July, 1940, p. 807, and January, 1946, p. 17.

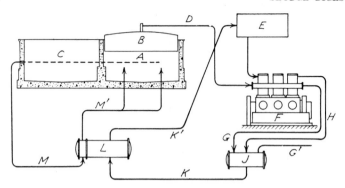

Fig. 25–7. Diagram of gas-engine power system with heat utilization. *Water Works and Sewerage,* November, 1937.) *A,* primary digesting tank; *B,* collector; *C,* secondary digesting tank; *D,* sludge gas; *E,* cooling-water tank; *F,* engine; *G,* exhaust gas to cooler; *H,* cooling water; *K,* heated-water flow; *K',* heated return; *L,* water heater; *M,* water flow; *M',* hot alkaline water.

gasoline, or 4.6 gal of diesel oil. In view of the characteristics of sludge gas, the engine in which it is used must be especially adapted to it.[50] Sludge gas is used in the operation of pumps, blowers, and generators. The most common value of the guaranteed fuel consumption at full load is 10,000 Btu per brake-hp-hr, based on gas with a heat content of 600 Btu per cu ft. Power generation at less than 0.5¢ per kwh has been reported at sewage-treatment works.

A schematic diagram of a gas-engine power system with heat utilization is shown in Fig. 25–7.

Where the gas contains more than 0.25 to 1.0 per cent of hydrogen sulfide it should be passed through a chamber filled with ferric oxide sponge to remove the hydrogen sulfide and to protect the cylinders of the gas engine against corrosion.[51]

25–25. Supernatant liquor. Supernatant liquor in a digestion tank is usually considered to be that part of the tank contents lying between the scum and the sludge. Its withdrawal requires special mechanical equipment.[52] In some tanks it may be difficult to locate the "supernatant" because the scum and the sludge may merge into each other. Openings for supernatant withdrawal may be provided

[50] See *ibid.,* September, 1943, p. 996; and *Water Works and Sewerage,* June, 1945, p. R-225.
[51] See *Sewage Works Eng.,* July, 1942, p. 343; and *Water Works and Sewerage,* February, 1943, p. 61.
[52] See also F. L. Flood, *Water and Sewage Works,* May, 1954, p. R-219.

at a number of different elevations, each opening being separately valved. A positive, unvalved overflow should be provided. Supernatant piping should not be less than 6 in. in diameter, but $1\frac{1}{4}$-in. pipes may be provided for sampling. A good supernatant liquor should not contain more than about 5,000 mg/l of solids. The handling of supernatant liquor is often a problem for which it is difficult to find a satisfactory solution because the liquor is usually septic, high in suspended solids, and high in BOD. Methods of handling it include: draining it on sand beds without other treatment; mixing it with the incoming raw sewage to go through the treatment process again; mixing it with the primary effluent where there is secondary treatment; giving it chemical treatment;[53] oxidizing it; and eliminating it from the effluent by discharging digested sludge from the tank at the same time and rate as the input of raw sludge.

Proprietary devices for the treatment of supernatant liquor are available; examples include the high-rate filter of the American Well Works,[54] and the vacuum aerator of the Pacific Flush Tank Company.[55]

25–26. Garbage digestion or dual disposal. The disposal of garbage or waste food into sewers or sewage-treatment plants, either as a municipal or an individual domestic enterprise is being widely practiced.[56] The practice is known as *dual disposal.*

It can be considered, in general, that the principal effect on a sewage-treatment plant is quantitative, the garbage solids, so far as the treatment processes are concerned, not differing materially from sewage solids. Estimates of garbage quantity and quality indicate that if all the garbage from a community were thrown into the sewer, the organic load on the sewage-treatment plant would be about doubled. No significant effect has been noted on the volume of sewage reaching the plant. Five years of practical experience at Jasper, Ind., with a high percentage of home garbage grinders has corroborated these findings and the report[57] closes with the conclusion: "the disposal of garbage by this means has been successful in Jasper."

The increased load on a sewage-treatment plant may be estimated

[53] See also *Sewage Works Jour.,* July, 1940, p. 738.

[54] See *ibid.,* September, 1943, p. 988.

[55] See *ibid.,* September, 1943, p. 1018, and May, 1944, p. 507.

[56] See also *Water and Sewage Works,* April, 1951, p. R-151; and E. R. Baumann and others, *S. and I.W.,* November, 1955, p. 1245.

[57] F. D. Wraight, *S. and I.W.,* January, 1956, p. 44.

somewhat as follows: [58] (1) primary sludge, 75 per cent; (2) BOD and suspended solids, 10 to 20 per cent; (3) gas generated 100 per cent, and generated more rapidly; (4) heavier supernatant, and (5) fuel value of sludge, 20 per cent. Authorities are not in agreement concerning increased allowances that should be made for sludge digestion, but a safe estimate seems to be to allow double the normal per capita sludge-digestion and sludge-drying capacities for each person using a garbage grinder.

As a result of experience at Lansing, Mich., Wyllie [59] reports:

1. Sewage and garbage solids digest readily and thoroughly.

2. Gas production has increased 230 per cent.

3. Some provision must be made to remove bones, eggshells, and fruit pits from the garbage solids before they are added to the digesters.

4. Account must be taken of the increased gas production in the design of digesters and sufficient capacity provided to handle the increased amount of volatile solids.

5. Stage digestion is indicated as necessary to obtain a supernatant low enough in solids to permit return to the treatment plant.

[58] See also *Sewage and Ind. Wastes Eng.,* January, 1950, p. 15; and S. L. Tolman, *Public Works,* March, 1955, p. 75.

[59] See *Sewage Works Jour.,* July, 1940, p. 760.

Chapter **26**

Sludge drying
and incineration

26–1. Methods of drying.[1] Before sludge can be incinerated or disposed of as fill or as fertilizer it must be suitably dried. The removal of moisture from sludge decreases its volume and changes its characteristics so that sludge containing 75 per cent moisture can be moved with a shovel or garden fork, and can be transported in non-watertight containers.

Methods for drying sludge include sand beds, presses, vacuum filters, centrifuges, and heat dryers. Drying on sand beds is common in small sewage-treatment plants. In large plants extensive mechanical equipment is used. The trend is toward the use of vacuum filters in plants serving 30,000 population or more, and to sand filters in smaller communities. A flowing-through diagram of a sludge-production, gas-utilization, and sludge-drying plant is shown in Fig. 24–1. The amount of mechanization involved becomes evident from a study of this figure. Although sludges can be dried by mechanical equipment, the economy of the process should be demonstrated before it is adopted.

Fluctuation of load is an important consideration in the economy and the selection of the type of sludge drying. In larger plants a two-day sludge-storage capacity and a filter and incinerator capacity to handle three to four times the daily average dry solids should be provided in order that peak loads can be carried. For smaller towns two-weeks storage may be necessary to permit operation of mechanical equipment efficiently on one day a week rather than more frequent and inefficient operations.

Fischer [2] states:

[1] See *S. and I.W.*, August, 1950, p. 975.
[2] A. J. Fischer, *Sewage Works Jour.*, March, 1936, p. 248.

609

For all plant sizes, raw sludge incineration first costs using only 125 per cent peak loads are higher than those for digested sludge filtration without incineration. They are slightly lower, however, in the case of plants of over 15 m.g.d. capacity, than where digested sludge is filtered and incinerated or where mixed digested primary and undigested activated sludge is filtered and incinerated.

Installation costs are lowest where all of the sludge is digested prior to dewatering on vacuum filters. An exception is the case of activated-sludge treatment where filtration of the combined digested primary and thickened undigested activated sludges gives the lowest first cost.

Operating costs of raw-sludge incinerating plants are highest even where only 125 per cent peak loads are assumed.

Operating costs are lowest for plants of less than 10 m.g.d. capacity where open sand drying beds are used. In general, for plants of over 25 m.g.d. capacity the costs of digested sludge filtration or filtration with incineration are lowest.

In the case of activated sludge treatment the desirable procedure from an operating cost standpoint is to combine the digested primary and the thickened undigested activated sludges prior to filtration and incineration.

Operating costs may be reduced considerably in the case of digested sludge handling by resorting to shorter digestion periods (20 days) and by using the elutriation or sludge washing process as developed by Genter.

26–2. Sand beds. The dewatering of digested sludge on sand beds has proved satisfactory at most small and moderate-size sewage-treatment plants. The method can be carried out without odor or fly nuisance. The dried cake remains innocuous, with a characteristic "fertilizer" odor, even when wet again. The drying of sludge on coarse-sand filters is particularly suited to well-digested sludge. This sludge does not decompose during drying, and it is sufficiently light and porous in texture to permit of thorough draining. The sludge from plain sedimentation, chemical precipitation, or the activated-sludge process is high in moisture and is putrescible. When placed on a sand filter bed it settles into a heavy, compact, impervious mass that dries slowly. Lime, or alum, which aid drying by maintaining the porosity of the sludge, may be added to the sludge as it is placed on the beds. The alum is added at a rate of about 1 lb of alum per 100 gal of sludge. Lime is advantageous also in keeping down odors and insects.

Sludge-bed area requirements depend, in part, on the quality of the sludge and in part on the authority fixing the requirement.

Some basic design factors for sludge dewatering beds are given in Table 26–1.

Table 26–1

BASIC DESIGN FACTORS FOR SLUDGE DEWATERING BEDS

(Ten-States Committee *)

	Area in Square Feet per Capita †	
Type of Treatment	Open Beds	Covered Beds
Primary	1.00	0.75
Intermittent sand filter	1.00	0.75
Standard-rate filter	1.25	1.00
High-rate filter	1.50	1.25
Activated sludge	1.75	1.35
Chemical precipitation	2.00	1.50

* See Sect. 5–2.

† For beds located between 40° and 45° North latitude. South of this areas may be reduced 25 per cent. Bed areas should be increased in districts of high rainfall.

In operation, sludge is run onto the bed, at one or more points, to a depth of 12 to 18 in., and allowed to stand until it has dried sufficiently to be removed by a spade or fork. Sludge pipes or channels should be self-draining and should discharge onto splash plates to avoid displacement of the sand. In favorable weather good sludge will dry in two weeks or less to approximately 60 to 70 per cent moisture. It is then suitable for use as filling material on waste land, for composting with garden soil, for incineration, or for further drying by heat. It should be stable, dark, brownish-gray in color, a light, coarse material, granular in texture, with an odor similar to that of well-fertilized garden soil.

Sludge filter beds are made up of 12 to 24 in. of coarse sand, well-screened cinders, washed grit from the grit chamber, or other gritty material, underlaid by about 12 in. of coarse gravel covering 6- or 8-in. open-joint tile underdrains to a depth of at least 6 in. At least the upper 3 in. of gravel should consist of $\frac{1}{8}$- to $\frac{1}{4}$-in. size particles. The underdrain tiles may be laid 4 to 20 ft apart on centers, depending on the porosity of the subsoil. The drainage from the underdrains should be returned to the primary tank. The side walls of the filters are made of concrete planks or of low earth embankments. The type of construction is illustrated in Fig. 26–1. In general, it is desirable

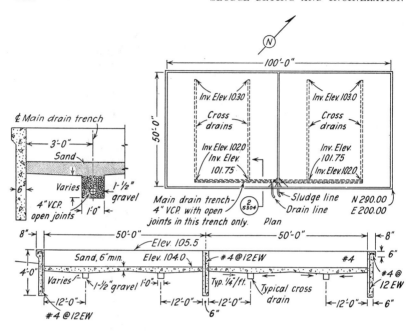

Fig. 26–1. Sludge-drying beds at Vallejo, Calif. (Courtesy Brown and Caldwell, Engineers.)

to construct a number of small units rather than a few large beds, because of the greater flexibility secured in operation.

The moistening and freezing of sludge on exposed beds and the odors emanating therefrom have resulted in the construction, at some plants, of glass covers for the drying beds. The results have not always proved satisfactory, and there is doubt as to the efficacy and economy in such installations. In general, the area of glass-covered beds is made about one-half that for open beds. The use of ⅛-in. plexiglas has minimized breakage. An outstanding defect in the construction of some covers has been the lack of sufficient ventilation to permit the dissipation of the moisture-laden atmosphere above the beds. On the other hand, ventilation permits the escape of odors. In the construction of covers the foundation walls should not extend more than a foot above the sand surface, the sides of the structure should be removable to permit air movements across the surface of the bed, and adequate head room should be provided for men and machinery in removing the sludge from the beds.

Dried sludge may be removed from the beds by hand scraping, care being taken not to remove sand with the sludge. The material removed may be thrown into cars run on tracks laid in the beds. In some plants mechanical scrapers are used. In others tractors carry the sludge in "saddle bags" on the sides of the tractors.[3]

The freezing of sludge, and its occasional moistening by rain on uncovered beds, may not be detrimental to drying. Thawed sludge releases its moisture more rapidly than that which has not been frozen, and the sludge is left in a light, fluffy condition.[4] Operators object to this condition because of the greater difficulty in removing the sludge from the bed. Sludge that is slightly moistened during its drying will dry as rapidly as unmoistened sludge; i.e., some rain may not delay the drying of the sludge on the bed. Too much rain will delay drying.

26–3. Presses. In the plate-and-frame press or the leaf sludge filter, water is removed from sludge by the hydrostatic pressure of the sludge against a filter cloth supported on a corrugated plate or leaf. The sludge press is made up of a number of corrugated metal pieces or plates about 30 in. in diameter with a hole in the center about 8 in. in diameter. The corrugations run vertically except for a distance about 3 in. wide around the outer rim. The face of this rim is smooth and upset so that when two plates are pressed together only the outer rims are in contact. To this smooth portion is fastened, on each side of the plate, an annular ring about an inch thick and 2 to 3 in. wide, of the same outside diameter as the plate. A circular piece of burlap, canvas, or other heavy cloth is fastened to this ring, covering the plate completely. A hole is cut in the center of the cloth slightly smaller in diameter than the center hole in the plate, and the edges of the cloth on opposite sides of the plate are sewed together. The plates are then pressed tightly together by means of the screw motion at the end of the machine, thus making a watertight fit of the joint around the outer rim. Sludge is then forced under pressure into the space between the plates, passing through the machine by means of the central hole. The pressure on the sludge may be from 50 to 120 psi. This pressure forces the water out of the sludge through the porous cloth from which it escapes to the bottom of the press along the corrugations of the separating plate. After a period of 10 to 30 min the pressure is released, the cells are opened, and

[3] See also *Water Works and Sewerage*, June, 1944, p. R-247.

[4] The alternate freezing and thawing of sludge for the purpose of drying is patented under U. S. Patent No. 2,703,782, March 8, 1955.

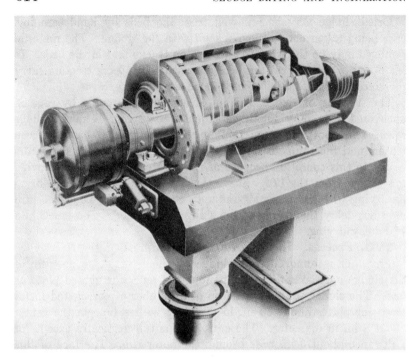

Fig. 26–2. Centrifuge suitable for sludge drying. (Courtesy Sharples Corp.)

the moist sludge cake is removed. The liquid pressed from the sludge is highly putrescible and should be returned to the influent of the treatment plant. The pressing of wet, greasy sludges is facilitated by the addition of 8 to 10 lb of lime per cu yd of sludge. The cake thus formed is more cohesive and easier to handle. The output of the press depends so much on the quality of the sludge that a definite guarantee of capacity is seldom given by a manufacturer. The performance of conventional sludge presses has been formulated empirically by Jones.[5]

In one form of sludge concentrator,[6] dewatering occurs at pressures well below the critical pressure at which sludge particles are crushed. The dewatering is carried out in successive stages with increasing pressures. Results have been no need for conditioning chemicals,

---

[5] B. R. S. Jones, *S. and I.W.*, September, 1956, p. 1103.
[6] See E. G. Smith, *S. and I.W.*, May, 1957, p. 601.

Table 26–2

CENTRIFUGE PERFORMANCE
DRYING OF WASTE ACTIVATED SLUDGE

(From L. S. Kraus and J. R. Longley, *Sewage Works Jour.*, January, 1939, p. 9.)

Material	Rate of Flow, gal per hr	Solids, in Material, per cent	Dry Solids, pounds per Hour	Dry Solids, pounds per Day
Waste activated sludge to the screen	1,824	1.02	156	3,020
From the screen	1,824	15.4	5	90
Waste activated sludge feed to centrifuge	1,820	0.99	151	2,930
Liquor from the centrifuge	1,526	0.25	32	620
Concentrated sludge from centrifuge	294	4.77 *	110	2,310

* The reduction in volume effected by the centrifuge was 83.7 per cent.

reduced power consumption, low space requirements, and a uniform and continuous production rate.

26–4. Centrifuges.[7] Centrifuges used for the dewatering of sludge function continuously, discharging sludge cake and liquor separately. Such a machine is shown in Fig. 26–2. Some data on centrifuge performance are shown in Table 26–2. A machine capable of dewatering 2,000 gal per hr from 98 per cent to 86 per cent moisture will require about 7 or 8 hp. Some difficulty has been found in disposing of the separated liquor which is relatively high in non-settling solids. Centrifuges are not widely used for dewatering sewage sludges, primarily because of the relatively high amount of suspended solids in the liquor and the relatively low sludge-cake capacity of the machines. In their conclusions on centrifuge performance Kraus and Longley [8] point out that the centrifuge cannot handle primary-tank sludge or digested primary and activated sludge because of gritty material present. Bradley and Bragstadt [9] report the successful concentration of activated sludge to 5 per cent solids, the effluent containing about 250 mg/l of suspended solids.

[7] See also *Sewage Works Jour.*, November, 1936, p. 991; and *Wastes Eng.*, January, 1954, p. 22.

[8] L. S. Kraus and J. R. Longley, *Sewage Works Jour.*, January, 1939, p. 9.

[9] L. Bradley and R. E. Bragstadt, *S. and I.W.*, April, 1955, p. 404.

26–5. Vacuum filters.[10] Vacuum filters are probably the most widely used type of mechanical sludge-dewatering equipment, the trend being toward their use in all but the smallest sewage-treatment plants. In some plants the filters are used for dewatering undigested, raw sludge as a preliminary to final disposal.

A vacuum filter, as illustrated in Fig. 26–3, consists of a hollow cylinder covered with filtering cloth supported on a wire netting or, as in the Coilfilter,[11] of two layers of steel coil springs placed in corduroy fashion around the filter drum. The filtering medium forms one side of a series of hollow cells in which various degrees of vacuums or plenums (pressures) can be produced.

As the cylinder revolves about its axis with a peripheral speed of somewhat less than 1 fpm, its lower portion passes through a trough containing the sludge to be dried. A vacuum picks up a layer of sludge as the filter surface passes through the trough. The vacuum is then, customarily, increased. At approximately three-fourths of the revolution a slight plenum is produced on the cells that aids the scraper, or the strings, to remove the sludge in a thin layer. The pick-up vacuum may be between 11 and 26 in. of water, depending on the make of the filter, and the filtering vacuum about 24 to 26 in. for almost all makes. Vacuum filters are available in diameters up to about 19 ft and in many different lengths.

The quality of the filter cloth is important in the performance and life of the filter. Desirable characteristics include: [12] (1) pliability, toughness, snag and abrasion resistance, and low stretch; (2) nap ½ in. or more, in length; (3) a minimum of head loss through the cloth; and (4) resistance to chemicals. Materials that have been used and studied include: cotton, untreated wool, treated wool, vinyon, nylon, saran, dynel, orlon, dacron, and various combinations of the preceding. The weight of blanket materials has varied from 12 to 16 oz. per sq yd. The cloths have been placed in the following order of economic rating: [12] dacron, 100 per cent; dynel, 100 per cent; treated wool, 14 to 15 oz; and wool, 14 to 15 oz.

Woven, stainless steel fabric or coil springs are being used successfully as a filtering medium in such proprietary equipment as

[10] See also A. H. Halff, *S. and I.W.*, August, 1952, p. 962; A. J. Bach and others, *S. and I.W.*, June, 1955, p. 689; P. Coackley and B. R. S. Jones, *S. and I.W.*, August, 1956, p. 963; and B. A. Schepman and C. F. Cornell, *S. and I.W.*, December, 1956, p. 1443.

[11] Manufactured by the Komline-Sanderson Engineering Co.

[12] See W. L. Shedden, *Water and Sewage Works*, May, 1955, p. 216.

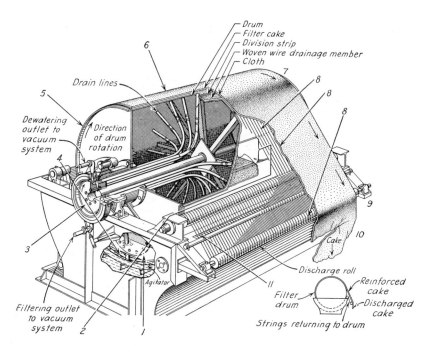

Fig. 26–3. Cutaway view of a vacuum filter. (Published by permission of Filtration Engineers, Inc.) 1. Filter consists of cloth-covered drum revolving in tank filled with sludge to be filtered. Oscillating agitator under drum keeps solids in suspension. 2. Surface of drum is divided into shallow compartments connected by pipes to automatic valve so vacuum can be put on each individually. Spirally woven wire mesh separates cloth from drum so there is space for mother liquor to drain from all parts of compartment into suction line. 3. As drum rotates, each compartment goes through same cycle of operation—filtering, dewatering, and discharging cake—controlled in repeating sequence by automatic valve. 4. Vacuum is applied to submerged segments. This causes mother liquor to flow through filter cloth, internal piping, and valve, while solids are stopped on outside of cloth to form cake. 5. As sections emerge from tank, vacuum dewaters cake as drum carries around to point of discharge. 6. Also along this top portion of drum, any washing or special dewatering operations take place. 7. When all mother liquor that particular filter cake will give up has been removed, automatic valve cuts off vacuum, and cake is discharged from drum by string discharge. 8. String discharge: Endless strings spaced about ½ in. apart around drum. Cake is built up over these strings so that, as they leave drum, cake is lifted away from cloth by strings. Strings then pass around discharge roll. At this point cake is freed from strings. Strings are then fed back over another roll to underside of drum. 9. Motor drives located at this end of filter. 10. Time necessary for filtering and dewatering varies with slurry. In designing filter these needs are filled by proper balance between: degree of submergence of drum; speed of rotation of drum; vacuum; and selection of filter medium. 11. Strings returning to underside of drum through aligning comb.

Table 26–3

Results of Vacuum Filtration of Sludge

Characteristic	San Diego,* Calif.	Cleve- land,* Ohio	Minne- apolis,† St. Paul, Minn.	Buf- falo,† N. Y.	Mil- waukee,† Wis.	Constituent	Filter Cake, † Dry Basis, % ‡ Raw §	Digested §
Type of sludge	DE	AS	RP	DP	RA	Volatile matter	55–75	40–60
Average solids uncon- ditioned, %	4.8	7.0	9.63	9.11	2.33	Ash	25–45	40–60
Ferric chloride, FeCl₃, % dry	5.8	5.8	1.2	2.93	5.58	Insoluble ash	15–30	30–45
Lime, CaO, % dry	. . .	10.5	3.44	11.21	none	Grease and fats	5–30	2–15
Moisture in cake, %	72.3	71.2	66.3	63.1	83.1	Protein	20–25	14–30
Average filter rate, lb of dry solids per sq ft per hr	1.8	3.1	3.40	6.77	1.84	Ammonia ni- trate	1–3	1.3–1.6
						Phosphorus, P₂O₅	1.4	0.5–3.5
						Cellulose, etc.	8–10	8–12

* From S. I. Zack, *S. and I.W.*, August, 1950, p. 975.

† From *Proc. Am. Soc. Civil Engrs.*, April, 1944, p. 487.

‡ The median average annual rate of dry sludge produced from 1949 to 1953 in 7 cities was 32 lb per capita.

§ From J. M. Morgan and J. F. Thomson, *Water and Sewage Works*, June 1, 1955, p. R-293. See also *ibid.*, April, 1955, for other data.

DE = Digested, elutriated. AS = Activated. RP = Raw. DP = Digested, primary. RA = Raw activated.

the Coilfilter [13] and the Rotofelt filter.[14] In the Coilfilter the fabric is separated from the drum as it reaches the end of a revolution, it is washed, and returned to position during each revolution. The use of metallic fabrics permits more rapid rotation of the drums, a thinner cake can be handled, and the life of the fabric is longer. Such filters are satisfactory for sewage sludges but may not be suitable for some industrial wastes with very fine particles of suspended matter.

Some data on the performance of vacuum filters are given in Table 26–3. Their performance has been formulated empirically by Jones.[15]

Costs of operating vacuum filters, exclusive of fixed charges are shown [16] to vary from $15.17 per ton to a profit of $9.01 per ton, with a normal range of cost between $7 and $13 per ton of dry solids; filter periods between 900 and 2,100 hr; and average life of filter

[13] See D. M. Martin and E. Mayo, *S. and I.W.*, May, 1957, p. 594.

[14] See C. F. Cornell and others, *Proc. 11th Ind. Waste Conf.*, Purdue University, 1956, p. 406.

[15] See B. R. S. Jones, *S. and I.W.*, September, 1956, p. 1103.

[16] See also J. F. Thomson and J. M. Morgan, Jr., *Water and Sewage Works*, December, 1955, p. 532, and April, 1955, p. 135.

cloth of 400 to 600 hr. Other information on filter operation is given in Sect. 29–25.

26–6. Sludge conditioning. By the conditioning of sludge is meant preliminary treatment by the addition of substances to the sludge preparatory to its further drying. All sludges cannot be filtered satisfactorily on a vacuum filter without conditioning. Desirable characteristics of sludge to be filtered are: (1) filtrability, that is, the ability of suspended solids to be separated from the liquid; (2) the solids, when removed, must form a mat or "cake," sufficiently thick and tenacious to be easily and completely removable from the filter cloth; (3) the liquid must drain well from the solids through the filter cloth under the action of a partial vacuum; and (4) the sludge cake must be porous to permit drying. Most sludges not amenable to vacuum filtration are conditioned to make them so, where vacuum filtration is to be used.

Methods of treatment to condition sludge include digestion, concentration, elutriation, and mixing.[17] Substances that have been added to sludge to condition it include sulfuric acid, sulfur dioxide, alum,[18] bone ash, peat, ground garbage, paper pulp, ashes, and clay. Some of these substances are still used in a few plants. The most commonly used material is ferric chloride, either with or without lime.

26–7. Elutriation.[19] Elutriation is defined by Genter [20] as the reduction of the alkalinity of a biochemically fouled water by dilution, sedimentation, and decantation in water of lower alkalinity. Elutriation consists in the washing of sludge by decantation to remove soluble materials that act as inhibitors of coagulation, and it may, therefore, be helpful in sludge conditioning. It is a valuable aid in the preparation of sludge for vacuum filtration [21] and it has been used for the thickening of raw sludge for final disposal.[21] Elutriation is accomplished by mixing water or plant effluent with sludge for about 10 minutes, either mechanically or with diffused air, and then allowing the mixture to settle, after which the supernatant liquor is drawn off. This is run to waste. Sludge to water ratios reported [22] in elutriation lie between 1:1.5 and 1:4.5.

[17] See also *Sewage Works Jour.*, November, 1940, p. 1106, and January, 1941, p. 101.

[18] See *ibid.*, September, 1941, p. 855.

[19] See also G. H. Cramer, *Sewage Works Jour.*, May, 1942, p. 621.

[20] A. L. Genter, *S. and I.W.*, July, 1956, p. 829.

[21] See also A. E. Sparr, *S. and I.W.*, December, 1954, p. 1443.

[22] See J. M. Morgan and J. F. Thomson, *Water and Sewage Works*, June 1, 1955, p. R-293.

Advantages claimed for the process [23] include: (1) the reduction of solids content between about 2 and 4 per cent in single-stage elutriation, (2) reduction by 65 to 80 per cent of the amount of conditioning chemical required, (3) lower ash content in the filter cake, and (4) lime not required. Genter [25] stated in 1937:

When a sludge is elutriated but a single time in one settling tank the process is termed single-stage elutriation. If the elutriating water is divided into two or more fractions and the same sludge is successively elutriated with each water fraction, the procedure is fractional elutriation. If the weaker elutriate from a sludge that has been elutriated with fresh water is used for washing a new charge of unelutriated sludge, the process is termed counter-current elutriation. The last process offers such obvious advantages that it should be used wherever practical.

26–8. Flotation. Flotation involves the removal of suspended or precipitated solids from a liquid through the effect of differential specific gravities or by the buoyancy produced by the evolution of gas created by chemicals or by heat. In the treatment of sewage or of industrial wastes the solids are commonly caused to rise to the surface. Where the specific gravities of the suspended particles are near to unity they may be separated from the liquid more economically by flotation than by sedimentation.

Some sludges may be dewatered by flotation through the addition of acid, usually sulfuric, or alum, preferably at a temperature of 100° F to 120° F, and allowing it to stand quiescent for 3 to 4 hours. Carbon dioxide is generated in the process. It brings the sludge to the surface with a moisture content of 88 to 90 per cent. The subnatant liquor is drawn off and, if not of sufficiently good quality, it is returned to the plant influent. The procedure is particularly successful with sludges high in grease. The costs of chemical, fuel, and labor in tests of the process have prevented its adoption on a working scale except on certain industrial wastes from which the value of the recovered substances has been sufficient to repay the cost.

In the Laboon process [26] freshly settled, primary-tank sludge is transferred to a sludge-concentrating tank about 13 ft deep where

[23] See *Public Works,* April, 1937, p. 11; and *Sewage Works Jour.,* January, 1946, p. 26.
[24] See W. N. Torpey and M. Lang, *Sewage Works Jour.,* July, 1952, p. 813.
[25] See *Public Works,* April, 1937, p. 11; and *Sewage Works Jour.,* January, 1946, p. 26.
[26] See *Eng. News-Record,* Oct. 11, 1951, p. 30; and *S. and I.W.,* April, 1952, p. 423.

it is held for about 5 days at a temperature of about 95° F. After this period the concentrating sludge rises to the surface. The subnatant liquor is then drawn off, leaving a sludge with 76 to 84 per cent moisture. Although this sludge is thick and cohesive it can be forced through pipes by such a pump as the Moyno progressing cavity pump, a non-reciprocating, displacement pump designed for moving soft plastics such as wet plaster, glue, and food products. Since the concentrated sewage sludge may be classed as a soft plastic, as stated in Sect. 24–12, with thixotropic properties, the action of the pump increases the fluidity of the sludge so that if pumped at a turbulent velocity it moves through the pipe as a liquid.

Typical of the flotation processes are the Miles acid process [27] and the MacLachlan process.[28] The former depends on acidulation with sulfuric or sulfurous acid, and the use of rising gas bubbles released from aqueous solution, as in the Gibbs flotation unit.[29] In the MacLachlan process the sludge is treated with sulfur dioxide gas.

The Dorrco Vacuator is a device for effecting flotation.[30] It consists of a dome-covered, cylindrical tank to hold the sewage at a depth of about 10 ft. Tanks vary in diameter between 12 and 60 ft. A vacuum of about 9 in. of mercury is maintained in the Vacuator. Sewage, after preliminary aeration, enters the Vacuator. The air which has been dissolved comes out of solution in fine bubbles. Rising through the sewage it entrains suspended matter and rises with them to the surface. The scum thus formed is skimmed off continuously and the clarified effluent passes off through a submerged effluent pipe. Detention periods are in the order of 10 to 20 min; overflow rates between 5,000 and 10,000 gal per sq ft per day; and air requirements from 0.025 to 0.050 cu ft per gal of sewage treated.

26–9. The McDonald process.[31] The McDonald process is basically a solvent-extraction process wherein extraction and drying are accomplished in a closed system into which raw sludge is put and from which dried sludge is taken. The sludge is first centrifuged and then treated with a chlorinated hydrocarbon solvent, followed by heat treatment. The process is rapid, involving small space compared with other complete drying processes, it is free from odor, and its by-products of grease and dried solids have market value. Much

[27] See fourth edition of this book, p. 507.
[28] See also *Eng. News-Record,* Vol. 89, 1922, p. 132.
[29] Manufactured by F. S. Gibbs, Inc.
[30] See also *Am. City,* June, 1953, p. 86.
[31] See R. H. Stolley and E. H. Fauth, *Public Works,* March, 1957, p. 111.

622

mechanical equipment is involved and trained operators are required. The process is said to be technically successful but not yet economically developed.

26–10. Heating and vacuum drying. In the Porteous process [32] the wet sludge is heated for a short period to 360° F. Afterward the bulk of the water can be removed by decantation. The residue is ready for further dewatering by filter press. It is said [33] that heat treatment of primary sludge speeds filtration by a factor of 200 and of secondary sludge by 1,000.

A study of the effect of suddenly releasing the pressure on sludge that had been heated under pressure was made at the University of Illinois.[34] The results indicated no beneficial drying effect. The sludge so treated was pasty and gelatinous and more difficult to dry than before heating.

Although some solids are dried successfully under a vacuum, the drying of sewage sludge in this manner is impractical and uneconomical as compared with other means of drying. Drawbacks to vacuum drying include the cost of heat required to vaporize the liquid, even at a high vacuum; the relatively large capacity required in the vacuum pump because of dissolved nitrogen and other gases in the sludge; and the volume of cooling water required.

26–11. Heat dryers. The moisture content of sludge to be transported or to be used in the manufacture of fertilizer must be reduced to 10 per cent or less. None of the methods of drying so far described can produce such a low degree of moisture and it becomes necessary to use other mechanical equipment such as preheaters, mixers, cage mills, induced-draft fans, ducts, purging systems, cyclone separators, stacks, fly-ash removers, direct or indirect heat dryers, and spray dryers.[35] Sludge-drying and combustion plants may involve considerable mechanical equipment.

Various types of heat dryers are available. The details of a Buckeye dryer are shown in Fig. 26–4. In the operation of this machine moist sludge is fed in at the left at the point marked "feed." The hot gases pass from the firebox up and around the cylinder, which revolves at about 8 rpm. The gases are drawn into the inner cylinder through the openings marked A, which revolve with the two

[32] See *Water and Sewage,* February, 1944, p. 17.

[33] See C. Lumb, *Jour. and Proc. Inst. Sewage Purif.* (Br.), Part I, 1951, abstracted in *S. and I.W.,* September, 1953, p. 1126.

[34] H. E. Babbitt, *The Drying of Sewage Sludge Under Pressure,* Sanitary Eng. Series No. 4, University of Illinois, 1952.

[35] See F. L. Flood, *Water and Sewage Works,* May, 1953, p. R-144.

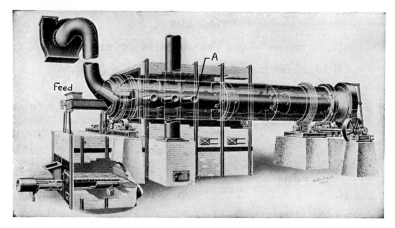

Fig. 26–4. Direct-indirect-heat sludge dryer. (Courtesy Buckeye Dryer Co.)

cylinders. The gases escape from the inner cylinder through the openings to the right and flow towards the left in the outer cylinder. They come into contact with the sludge at this point. The gases then pass off through the fan at the left. The sludge is lifted by the small longitudinal baffles fastened to the outer cylinder, as the drying cylinders revolve. The right end of the cylinder is placed lower than the left so that the drying sludge is lifted and dropped through the cylinder at the same time that it moves slowly toward the right-hand end of the cylinder. These dryers require about 1 lb of fuel for 10 lb of water evaporated. A direct-indirect dryer about 60 ft long and 78 in. in diameter can remove 6,000 lb of water per hr. The temperature around the cake should not exceed about 700° F. Odors from the dryer can be reduced by passing the gases through a dust chamber and washer. Odors from the drying sludge can be avoided by raising the gases to a temperature above 1,200° F. Serious odor nuisance may result if this is not done.

26–12. Spray drying. In spray drying, wet sludge is sprayed into a "hot tower" down which a current of hot gases is passing. Water evaporated from the atomized particles passes off with the hot gases. The dried solids settle to the bottom of the tower. Dust carried with the hot gases is subsequently settled from them in a cyclone dust catcher before cooling. The plant at Plainfield, N. J.,[36] was among the earliest of this type to be put into operation on a large scale.

[36] See J. R. Downs, *Water Works and Sewerage*, September, 1935.

Table 26–4

QUANTITIES OF WATER EVAPORATED IN AN INCINERATOR

(H. J. N. Hodgson, *Sewage and Trade Wastes Treatment,*
Adelaide, Australia, 1938, p. 375.)

	Primary Treatment, %	Trickling-Filter Treatment, %	Chemical Treatment, %	Activated-Sludge Treatment, %
Overall suspended solids removed	60	85	80	95
Raw sludge, thickened, final per cent moisture	90	92	92	93
Incinerator, average tons water evaporated per 24 hr per million gallons				
Raw sludge	1.30	2.08	2.48	2.97
Digested sludge	0.70	1.02	1.18	1.93

26–13. Incineration.[37] Liquid sludge is burned successfully on multiple-hearth incinerators, sometimes with preheaters [38] and sometimes with auxiliary fuel. Drying temperatures are about 700° F and incineration occurs at about 1,000° to 1,200°.

The amount of water to be evaporated from sludge cake normally fed into an incinerator is indicated in Table 26–4. The heat content of fresh, plain-sedimentation sludge, containing about 70 per cent volatile solids, is about 7,600 Btu per lb of dry solids. The fuel value varies approximately with the volatile content. Digested sludge with about 40 per cent volatile matter contains only about 3,900 Btu per lb of dry solids. Filter cake with a moisture content of 60 to 70 per cent can be burned with no, or very little, auxiliary fuel, once combustion has been started.

Formulas for the heat content of sludge, devised by Fair and Moore,[39] are:

Plain sedimentation sludge

$$Q = 85P^{1.085} - 700 \qquad (26\text{–}1)$$

[37] See J. R. Downs, *Water Works and Sewerage,* September, 1935; and M. B. Owen, *Proc. Am. Soc. Civil Engrs.,* Vol. 83, Paper 1172, February, 1957.

[38] See *S. and I.W.,* August, 1950, p. 975.

[39] G. M. Fair and E. W. Moore, *Eng. News-Record,* May 9, 1935, p. 681. See also *Water Works and Sewerage,* January, 1937, p. 132.

Activated sludge

$$Q = 69.2P^{1.085} \tag{26-2}$$

Plain sedimentation sludge with chemicals

$$Q = \frac{85\left[P_c\left(1 + \dfrac{p}{100}\right)\right]^{1.085} - 700}{1 + (p/100)} \tag{26-3}$$

Activated sludge with chemicals

$$Q = \frac{69.2\left[P_c\left(1 + \dfrac{p}{100}\right)\right]^{1.085}}{1 + (p/100)} \tag{26-4}$$

where Q = Btu per pound of dry solids.

P = percentage of volatile matter in dry solids.

P_c = percentage of volatile matter in sludge.

p = percentage of chemical, based on dry solids remaining in precipitated sludge.

Not all of the heat from sludge incineration is available for useful purposes. A hypothetical heat balance resulting from the burning of sludge cake, without additional fuel, is shown in Table 26–5.

Table 26–5

HEAT BALANCE IN SLUDGE INCINERATION

(From A. R. Smith, *Sewage Works Jour.*, January, 1939, p. 35.)

Activated-sludge cake burned per hour, pounds	1,000
Percentage moisture	75
Percentage volatile	60
Btu per hour from sludge	6,000,000
Inherent loss: Btu per hour	
Latent heat vaporization, sludge moisture	3,366,000
Radiation	300,000
Sensible heat of ash	120,000
Hydrogen loss	419,000
Preventable loss	
Sensible heat of stack gases	1,645,000
Unburned combustibles	150,000
Total loss	6,000,000

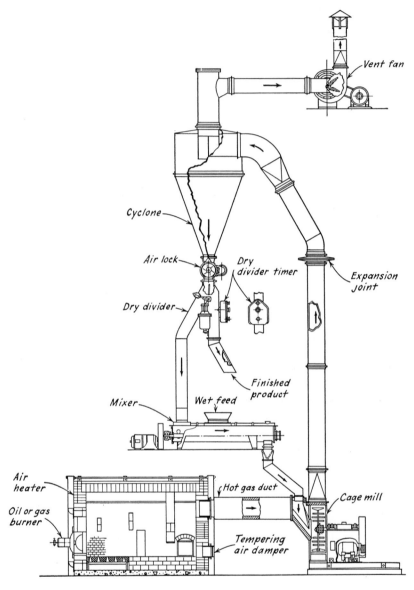

Fig. 26–5. Flash dryer suitable for sewage sludge. (Courtesy Combustion Engineering, Inc., Raymond Division.)

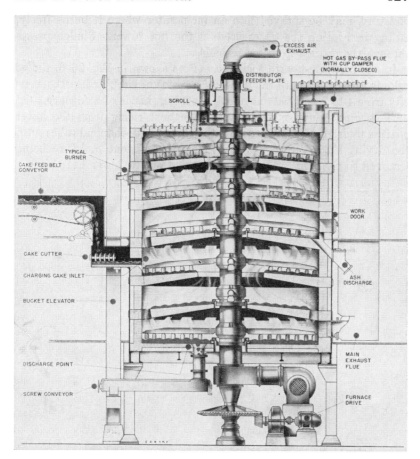

Fig. 26–6. Zone-controlled sludge dryer—incinerator. (Courtesy Morse-Boulger Destructor Co.)

26–14. Types of sludge incinerators.[40] There are two general types of sludge incinerators, the flash and the multiple-hearth. In the flash incinerator, as shown in Fig. 26–5, sludge cake is mixed with dried sludge and is discharged into a vertical "hot tower," the material mixing with rising, superheated gases. Water vapor from the sludge passes off with the hot gases, the dried material being removed and, if desired, ground in a squirrel-cage mill and separated in a cyclone or centrifugal separator. The "dust," containing about 10 per cent

[40] See F. L. Flood, *Water and Sewage Works,* May, 1954, p. R-219.

moisture, may be sprayed into an incinerator where it burns freely, aiding in heating the gases used in the hot tower. Sludge passes through the process in a few seconds.

In the multiple-hearth incinerator,[41] as shown in Fig. 26–6, sludge cake is discharged onto the upper of a series of circular hearths, usually from 4 to 8, located one above the other, inside of a furnace. Oil burners on the upper stages assist the heat rising from the lower hearths to drive off moisture from the sludge. Mechanical rakes push the drying sludge from hearth to hearth, sufficient moisture being removed so that the sludge burns unaided on the lower hearths.

[41] See *ibid.*, June 30, 1957, p. R-317.

Chapter 27

Industrial wastes

27–1. The problem.[1] Problems in the disposal of industrial wastes or in connection with public sewage are increasing to such an extent that special knowledge of industrial processes is necessary for their solution. Since many processes of waste treatment depend on the details of the manufacturing process, only general principles and some details of their application to larger industries can be covered in a limited space. The disposal of industrial wastes involves problems of economics, sociology, and other human relations. Where an industry and its products are of value and its wastes are a liability to a community, values and liabilities must be balanced before a satisfactory solution can be reached.

The problem of industrial-waste disposal may be considered from the viewpoint of the manufacturer, from that of the public, and from that of the engineer. To the manufacturer the waste is a liability to be disposed of with the least possible cost and the greatest expedition. Sometimes value may be found in the waste which will pay for its recovery. When this condition develops no problem of disposal will be passed on to the public. The possibility of the recovery of value from industrial wastes is emphasized by Mohlmann [2] who points to phenomenal recoveries of food substances from distillery wastes. It is shown further by him that corn-products wastes, due to recovery processes, have dropped from a population equivalent of about 5.6 persons per bushel of corn to about 0.6 to 0.8 person.

From the viewpoint of the public, industrial waste may cause deterioration of sewers and treatment-plant structures, increased difficulties and cost in sewage-treatment-plant operation, and stream

---

[1] See also H. H. Black, *Civil Eng.*, October, 1955, p. 96; E. R. Besselievre, *Air Conditioning, Heating, and Ventil.*, April, 1955, p. 99; and *Industrial Wastes Treatment*, McGraw-Hill Book Co., 1952.

[2] F. W. Mohlmann, *Proc. Am. Soc. Civil Engrs.*, September, 1938, p. 1052.

629

pollution of such magnitude as to render streams unfit for domestic, commercial, or recreational purposes.

From the viewpoint of the engineer the problem commences in the industrial plant where knowledge of chemistry and of chemical engineering is applied to reduce the volume and the polluting strength of the wastes. The work of the sanitary engineer commences when it becomes necessary to treat and to dispose of the irreducible minimum of wastes discharged by industry. The tremendous diversity of industries and industrial processes necessitates their classification to simplify the understanding of waste-treatment methods.

Experience has shown that legal restrictions, the threat of police power, or other manifestations of coercion may be less effective than cooperation between industry and public officials. Where treatment of a city's sewage is started for the first time, cooperation is sometimes more easily effected than where operation of an existing plant is injured by industrial development. The question of the justice of requiring public expenditure of funds to care for the disposal of wastes from a private industry is one requiring legal decision. It is frequently less costly to solve the problem through sewage treatment than to attempt to solve it through litigation.

Industries whose wastes cause difficulties are numerous and are increasing in number and in size. In many communities the industrial wastes, both in volume and in population equivalent, exceed the municipal wastes. The population equivalents of various industrial wastes have been reported by Calvert and Parks [3] and by Barnes,[4] and the average amount of polluting materials produced by typical industries by Rudolfs and Setter.[5] Some combined figures from these sources are shown in Table 27–1.

The attitude of most industrialists towards the protection of the purity of streams is that of helpful cooperation. An example of this is shown in the pulp, paper, and paperboard industry, which, through the National Council for Stream Improvement, is operating eight pilot plants in typical locations.[6]

Before attempting to solve the problem by mechanical, chemical, or

[3] See C. K. Calvert and E. H. Parks, *Sewage Works Jour.*, November, 1934, p. 1159.

[4] G. E. Barnes, *Mechanical Engineering*, 1947, p. 465.

[5] W. Rudolfs and L. R. Setter, *Bull.* 610, New Jersey Agriculture Experiment Station, November, 1936.

[6] See *Sewage and Ind. Wastes Eng.*, April, 1950, p. 202.

Table 27-1

INDUSTRIAL-WASTE LOADS

Waste	Unit of Measure	Per Unit	Waste [3]	Avg Pounds of Waste Daily per Employee-Day			Waste per Employee on Basis Domestic Sewage = 1.0	
				Suspended Solids	Settleable Solids	Oxygen Consumed	BOD	Suspended Solids
Laundry [1,2]	lb clothing	0.238 *	Tanning	1.92	0.51	1.73	25.3	12.0
Creamery [1,2]	lb butter	0.092 *	Chem. mfg.	1.18	0.33	1.53	22.5	7.4
Dairy [1,2]	lb raw milk	0.076 *	Organic	0.39	0.10	0.20	2.9	2.4
Canning [1,2]	lb pork & beans	0.027 *	Steel pickling	0.62	0.15	0.25	3.6	3.8
Starch [1,2]	bu corn	0.75 *	Dye	0.87	0.05	3.00	44.2	5.4
Meat packing [1,2]	1 hog	13.2 *	Distillery	29.16	4.32	31.89	22.8	22.2
Paper board [1,2]	ton produced	58.5 *	Dairy	0.92	0.03	3.03	470.0	181.0
Garbage [1,2]	lb garbage	0.84 *	Laundry	3.61	0.05	1.55	44.6	5.7
Starch [10]	ton	0.233 ‡						
Alcohol [10]	ton of grain	20 †						
Canning [10]	100 cases [9]	0.2–25 ‡					Population Equivalent	
Meat [10]	live units	16–55 ‡				Volume of		
Milk products [10]	100 lb	0.2–0.25 ‡				Waste,		
Cotton [10]	100 lb	1–3 ‡	Industry Waste [5]	Unit of Daily Production		1,000 gal per unit	Basis of BOD	Basis of Suspended Solids
Rayon [10]	100 lb	8–10 ‡						
Oil refining [10]	100 lb crude	17 ‡						
Corn refining [4]	ton of corn	0.333 †						
Gun powder [4]	ton powder	200 †						
Industrial alcohol[4]	ton of grain	20 †						
Cotton dyeing [4]	100 lb goods	1–2 †						
Steel plant [4]	ton steel	20–35 †	Brewing	1 bbl [8]	0.470	12–19	6–9	
Strawboard [4]	ton paper	38 †	Canning	100 cases [9]	2.5–16	35–800	9–440	
Tanning [4]	ton hides	16 †	Coke	100 tons coal	360	1,500	. . .	
Canning	100 cases		Distilling	1,000 bu grain	600	3,500	2,300	
lima beans	No. 2 cans	25 †	Poultry	1,000 lb live wt.	2.2	300	160	
peas	No. 2 cans	3 †	Oil refg.	100 bbl crude	7.7	60	120	
Milk bottling [4]	100 gal milk	0.45 †	Paper pulp	1 ton dry pulp	5–85	16–1,330	0–6,100	
Butter [4]	100 lb butter	0.25 †	Tanning	100 lb raw hides	to 0.8	24–48	40–80	
			Textile [6]	1,000 lb goods	to 30	2–108		
			Textile [7]	1,000 lb goods	4.8–19	41–369		
			Rayon goods	1,000 lb goods	13.7	1,180		
			Woolen mill	1,000 lb goods	70–240	400–1,500		

[1] *Sewage Works Jour.*, November, 1934, p. 1159.

[2] *Modern Sewage Disposal*, Federation of Sewage Works Association, 1938, p. 351.

[3] *Bull.* 610, New Jersey Agriculture Experiment Station, November, 1936.

[4] *Sewage Works Jour.*, May, 1945, p. 558.

[5] *Mechanical Engineering*, 1947, p. 465.

[6] Cotton sizing, desizing, bleaching, scouring, mercerizing.

[7] Dyeing.

[8] 31 gal.

[9] No. 2 cans.

[10] From *Water and Sewage Works*, June 1, 1955, p. R-314.

* Population equivalent computed from data in footnote 2.

† Thousands of gallons of waste.

‡ Thousands of gallons per unit.

biological means the industrial problem must be examined to determine whether materials have been used to the best advantage, whether yields are in accordance with theory, and whether all by-products that are usable have been recovered. The next step should be a study of the polluting strength, the characteristics, and the quantity of the waste produced by the industry; fluctuations in rates of discharge, the assimilating capacity of the stream for waste, untreated and treated to various degrees; practicable processes of treatment; and the cost of construction and of operation.

27–2. Legal status. Relief from the nuisance of a polluted stream may be obtained through suit for abatement or for damages under the common law. A comprehensive body of such law has been slowly built up by court decisions and precedents covering a multitude of principles and problems.[7] Unfortunately, relief through recourse to the common law may be expensive and slow, and the outcome is usually uncertain. The uncertainty is due partly to the apparently conflicting court rulings on similar cases which, upon closer study, are found to vary from the conditions of a subsequent case.

Municipal ordinances affecting the disposal of industrial wastes are commonly designed to protect the safety of the sewer structure and the operation and performance of the municipal sewage-treatment plant. In general, municipal ordinances permit the discharge of any non-injurious material into a sewer that will flow to the outlet. The public must turn to state and to federal legislation for the prevention of stream pollution by industrial wastes.

Early state statutes tended to prohibit the discharge of specific polluting substances or wastes into natural waters. These were found to be limited in application and enforceable only by local authorities responsible also for the enforcement of criminal laws. Unless public opinion or political pressure was brought to bear no action was taken.

Threats to the public health by stream pollution from municipal and industrial wastes, unprotected by the nature of the laws against specific forms of pollution and unprotected by laxity in local enforcement, led to the adoption of legislation for the protection of public health, on a state level, and to the administration and enforcement of such legislation by state authorities. Further development of legislation to protect recreation, power, navigation, and other interests, and

[7] See C. M. Henderson, *Proc. 6th Ind. Wastes Conf.*, Purdue University, 1951, p. 43.

Table 27-2

COMPARISON OF INDUSTRIAL LOADS WITH DOMESTIC SEWAGE

(From J. M. Symons, *Water and Sewage Works*, December, 1954, p. 540.)

Source of Waste	Unit of Daily Production	Gal	Pop. Equiv.[1] Volu-metric	BOD mg/	BOD Pop.[2] Equiv.	Suspended Solids mg/l	Suspended Solids Pop.[3] Equiv.
Domestic sewage	per capita	127	1.0	160	1.0	187	1.0
Oil refining [4]	100 bbl crude oil	77,000	600	12.5 to 20	75 to 120	30 to 50	150 to 250
Canning tomatoes [5]	100 cases, No. 2 cans	750	5.9	4,000	150	2,000	75
Wool scouring [5]	100 lb goods	125	1.0	9,300	340	7,300	175
Paper mill	1 ton of paper	39,000	306	19	106	452	2,260

[1] Average per capita flow is 126 gpd.
[2] Average per capita BOD is 0.17 lb per day.
[3] Average per capita suspended solids is 0.2 lb per day.
[4] Minimum figures in this line are not from original reference.
[5] Figures in this line are not from original reference.

the assignment of the administration to other bureaus of the state government, have created further chaos and confusion so that the trend, which may be said to have started about 1920, has been toward the creation of a single administrative body, such as a commission, representing various interests in stream-pollution prevention, including the industrialist. A survey of all state laws made in 1950 [8] showed that only 3 states had no law for regulating stream pollution, but that these states had programs for such legislation. The survey showed also that, of the 42 states requiring approval of plans for new treatment plants before construction, 4 states exercised control over the entire industrial layout, while nearly as many others required nothing more than board permission to discharge wastes into a stream.

The federal government has been influential in the control of stream pollution especially since June, 1948, when Public Law 845 became effective. Even this law, however, does not remove the power of control from the states involved if they care to exercise such power.

27-3. The discharge of industrial wastes into public sewers.[9] The discharge of industrial wastes into public sewers creates economic problems, deteriorates sewer structures, increases maintenance costs, adds problems in sewage treatment, and may increase stream pollu-

[8] See G. Feller and J. Newman, *Industry and Power*, June, 1951.
[9] See also J. F. Byrd and V. E. Tex, *S. and I.W.*, April, 1957, p. 414.

tion.[10]   A comparison of polluting loads of some industrial wastes and domestic sewages is shown in Table 27–2.

Where the discharge of an industrial waste into a public sewer creates an appreciable financial burden for its treatment the industry may be required to pay a part or all of the increased costs. Many schemes for the computation of such charges have been devised.[11]

The *flat rate formula* is

$$D = RN \qquad (27\text{--}1)$$

where D is the charge in dollars, R is the rate charged per industrial-waste unit, and N is the number of units.

The *quantity-quality formula* is

$$D = VR \qquad (27\text{--}2)$$

where D is as before, V is the volume of waste, and R is the rate in dollars per unit of volume, based on concentration of constituents. The value of R can be expressed as

$$R = f[aP_1(s_1 - s_a) + bP_2(O_1 - O_s) + cP_3(c_1 - c_s) + xP_4(y_1 - y_s)] \qquad (27\text{--}3)$$

in which S_1 = suspended solids in wastes, mg/l.

   O_1 = 5-day BOD, mg/l.

   c_1 = chlorine demand, mg/l.

   y_1 = other constituents, mg/l.

   f = factor to convert mg/l to lb per unit volume.

a, b, c, x = factors ranging from 0 to 1.0, depending on local conditions and the per cent of constituent above standard for which charge is made.

s_1, O_s, c_s, y_s = standard or maximum values, respectively, of suspended solids, BOD, chlorine required, and other constituents, for which no charge is to be made above a flat rate.

P_1, P_2, P_3, P_4 = operating costs in cents per lb for handling, treating or disposal.

The *Joint Committee formula* [12] is

$$D = (FO)(A) + (fo)V_1 \qquad (27\text{--}4)$$

[10] See also S. E. Coburn, *Jour. Boston Soc. Civil Engrs.*, January, 1949, p. 64. A. A. Estrada, *S. and I.W.*, January, 1955, p. 40. H. Heukelekian and H. E. Orford, *ibid.*, p. 49. J. M. Symons, *Water and Sewage Works*, December, 1954, p. 540.

[11] See also *ibid.*, April, 1951, p. R-116; and G. W. Schroepfer, *S. and I.W.*, December, 1951, p. 1493.

[12] See *Sewage Works Jour.*, May, 1946; and *S. and I.W.*, April, 1951.

where D = charge, dollars.

A = assessed value of the industry.

F = total fixed cost of sewage works chargeable to the property, divided by total assessed value of the municipality.

O = total operation, maintenance, and replacement cost of sewage works chargeable to the property, divided by the total assessed valuation of the municipality.

f = total fixed cost of sewage works chargeable to users.

o = total operation, maintenance, and replacement cost of sewage works, per unit volume, chargeable to users.

V_1 = volume of waste produced by the industry.

It is to be emphasized that any formula must be used with judgment and that no formula can be depended on to give equitable results under all conditions.

27–4. Standards of quality. The setting of standards of quality for the natural waters of a state is one method attempted in some jurisdictions to control stream pollution. Standards are, in general, physical, chemical, biological, or other means of setting stream quality. Some states establish standards on the basis of the effect on fish or lower forms of life in the stream.[13] An outstanding example of the setting of standards occurs in New York where the fresh surface waters were divided, in 1949, into seven classes, salt surface waters into four classes, and ground waters into two classes. For example, Class AA must be usable as a source of potable supply and any other usage and must meet U. S. Public Health Service Drinking Water Standards. The classes pass through various stages of decreasing requirements down to Class F, the waters of which are "usable for the disposal of sewage or industrial wastes."

The setting of standards of quality of the water into which an industrial waste is to be discharged fixes the amount and degree of treatment which must be given to the industrial waste before discharge into the classified water.

27–5. Methods of treatment. Mechanical, chemical, and biological methods, similar to those used for the treatment of municipal sewages, are used in the treatment of industrial wastes. Such wastes are, however, more individual in their characteristics, and each industrial plant or group of industries will require study to point out the best method of treatment for the disposal of its waste.

Industrial wastes can be divided into two classes for the purpose

13 See H. G. Hess, *S. and I.W.*, January, 1954, p. 83.

Table 27-3

ANAEROBIC DIGESTER LOADINGS

(A. M. Buswell, *Proc. Purdue Ind. Wastes Conf.*, 1950, p. 168.)

	Pekin, Ill. Yeast Molasses	Peoria, Ill. Butanol Grain	Crystal Lake, Ill. Yeast Molasses	Jefferson Junction, Wis. Trickling-Filter Sludge	Carthage, Ohio Distillery Grain
Volume of waste flow, gal/day	223,000	300,000	160,000	2,000	500
Tank solids	2.2 mg	3 mg	0.623 mg	40,000 gal	7,200 gal
volatile, %	1.05	3.0	0.7	3.5	3.0
BOD raw, mg/l	10,000	17,000	5,000	...	16,000
effluent	2,000	2,420	1,500	...	1,600
removal, %	80	69.8	70	...	90
Loadings, lb/cu ft/day	0.108	0.114	0.104	0.10	0.143
Gas, cu ft/lb	5.0	9.3	4.25	9.2	11.0
Volume per tank volume [*sic*]	0.525	1.06	0.43	1.0	1.5

of treatment: those that are treated to minimize putrefactive processes in the stream, and those that are treated for other reasons. In determining the proper loads to be placed on treatment devices for the first class, particularly those involving biological methods of treatment, the load placed on the device by the biochemical oxygen demand of the waste may be converted into population equivalent and the plant may be designed to care for this load in accordance with the principles of sewage treatment described in earlier chapters.

Chemical treatment is practiced more extensively for industrial wastes than for municipal sewages, possibly because of the relatively smaller space requirements, the attractive appearance of the effluent, and the value of the by-products. The use of ionic–exchange materials is seldom economical unless a valuable by-product is recovered. Screening is usually the first step in the treatment of industrial wastes, regardless of what is done later.

Anaerobic fermentation [14] is successful in the disposal of some organic wastes. Some design and loading factors recommended by Buswell [15] are given in Table 27–3.

Warrick [16] has summarized the combinations of treatment processes common for dealing with industrial wastes, as follows:

(1) Remove sizable suspended solids by screening or settling; (2) remove fats, oils, and greasy solids by flotation and skimming procedures, aided in

[14] See also H. W. Gehm and V. C. Behn, *S. and I.W.*, August, 1950, p. 1034.

[15] A. M. Buswell, *Proc. 5th Ind. Wastes Conf.*, Purdue University, 1950, p. 168.

[16] L. F. Warrick, *Modern Sewage Treatment*, Federation of Sewage Works Associations, 1938, p. 340.

some cases by chemical treatment; (3) remove colloidal solids by flocculation with chemical coagulants and electrolytes, followed by settling and possibly filtration; (4) neutralize excessive acidity or alkalinity by addition of chemicals; (5) remove or stabilize dissolved solids by chemical precipitation, or biological processes, or combination of both; (6) decolorize by chemical treatment, with settling or filtration, singly or in combination; and (7) reoxygenate the wastes by suitable aeration methods.

Much if not all of the industrial waste load can be reduced at many plants by modifications of the manufacturing process in such a manner as to recover by-products: recirculate and reuse water and other liquids otherwise run to waste; or treat the wastes during the manufacturing process to reduce its bulk and pollutional potentialities. Methods and equipment to be selected require knowledge of the chemical, biological, mechanical, economic, and other features of the manufacturing process, and of the type and possibilities of available equipment.[17]

Some chemical processes and equipment used in industrial-wastes recovery and treatment include: absorption, boiling, chemical combination, cooking, crushing, crystallization, dilution, dissolving, distillation, drying, emulsification, evaporation, extraction, flotation, filtration, grinding, humidification, incineration, mixing, precipitation, pressing, separation, sifting, and sublimation. These processes and the equipment used with them should be understood by the engineer involved in the disposal of industrial wastes.

27–6. Treatment with municipal sewage. Industrial wastes containing large concentrations of acids, alkalies, toxic substances, grit, clay, and abrasive particles from metallurgical processes, tanning, and canning, and wastes from coal, glass, and ceramic industries, are usually detrimental to biological processes on which most municipal sewage-treatment works depend. Other industrial wastes that might be detrimental when mixed with municipal sewage are those high in total solids and in suspended solids, containing excessive quantities of grease, or burdened with appreciable quantities of floating materials such as hair, hides, feathers, and entrails. Wastes high in total nitrogen may cause downstream troubles from algae.

Under favorable conditions undesirable wastes may be treated by the industry before discharge into a sewer, in order to avoid difficulties that would otherwise be created. Pretreatment by the industry may consist of: (1) equalization of rate of flow and of quality by holding in an equalizing reservoir; (2) sedimentation or fine

[17] See also C. F. Gurnham, *S. and I.W.*, January, 1951, p. 82.

screening to diminish excessive solids; (3) primary treatment for reducing excessive BOD, toxic substances, acidity or alkalinity; and (4) reduction of scum-forming constituents.

Any successful attempt to combine industrial wastes and municipal sewage for treatment must take into consideration the usually greater variations in rate of flow and in strength of the sewage or liquid wastes from an industrial plant, and provision must be made to control rate of flow and strength by means of holding, dilution, and reaction tanks which serve to prevent shock loads. Such loads are detrimental to sewage-treatment processes in approximately the following order: (1) activated sludge, (2) chemical precipitation, (3) trickling filters, and (4) plain sedimentation.

Wastes that are sometimes treated successfully with municipal sewage include those from laundries, meat-packing and slaughter houses, dairies, and food processing.

27–7. Holding ponds or lagoons. Industrial wastes are discharged into holding ponds: (1) for storage until such time as conditions are suitable for discharge into the receiving waters, (2) as oxidizing and sedimentation basins to improve the quality of the waste, (3) to aid disposal of the waste by evaporation or by percolation, and (4) to minimize cost of disposal. Some principles concerning the lagooning of sewage and industrial wastes are discussed in Sect. 16–27. No general rules can be successfully given for the design of a lagoon for all industrial wastes. The use of lagoons is not always either satisfactory or economical because of odors, flying insects, pollution of water sources, ruined land, unhealthful conditions, and unsatisfactory results. The use of lagoons is sometimes attractive when the land required is available, topography is suitable, and a minimum first cost of plant and equipment is desired.

Selected Industries [18]

27–8. Acid wastes.[19] Inorganic acid wastes result from many industrial processes such as steel pickling and from metallurgical plating and other metallurgical processes. The most common methods of treatment are dilution and neutralization. Limestone beds are used for neutralization, high-calcium limestone acting more quickly than dolomitic stone.

[18] The wastes are listed alphabetically in subsequent sections.
[19] See also S. D. Faust and others, *S. and I.W.*, July, 1956, p. 872.

27–9. Acid mine wastes.[20] Drainage water from coal mines may be highly impregnated with iron and sulfides, so that it renders the waters of the streams into which it is discharged corrosive, unpalatable, unsightly, and unsuitable for domestic, commercial, or recreational purposes. Natural mine waters are acid and extremely hard because the acid combines with calcium and magnesium to form sulfates. Ordinarily the natural alkalinity of the stream is sufficient to neutralize the acidity when the dilution ratio is greater than 80 or 100 to 1. Upon exposure to the atmosphere the compounds of iron are oxidized and precipitated to form the familiar, ochre-colored precipitate of ferric hydroxide. When it is mixed with river water aquatic life is killed and the river is discolored. The quantity of drainage water to be cared for from any particular mine is too uncertain to be predicted. The problem of the disposal of acid mine waters is most acute in western Pennsylvania and West Virginia.

Acid mine waters may be disposed of by sealing abandoned mines, by diverting the drainage from active mines to other streams or watersheds, by returning the waters to the subsoil, or by coagulation and sedimentation. In the last method, lime and soda ash are used, but it is necessary that the sulfates be relatively low in order that this method may not be prohibitively costly. Under any circumstances the sludge produced is likely to be voluminous and difficult to dispose of. No satisfactory method of treating acid mine waters is widely applicable.

27–10. Airplane parts. The use of aluminum and magnesium for airplane motors introduced new types of pickling wastes—a chromic acid bath for pickling and anodyzing aluminum, and a hydrofluoric acid bath for magnesium. A waste solution of caustic soda for cleaning aluminum castings may be used for neutralizing the acid wastes, possibly with the addition of solid caustic soda.

27–11. Beet-sugar wastes. The production of sugar from beets is an extensive and important industry, particularly in the western portion of the United States. It is seasonal, producing large quantities of putrescible wastes, the season lasting between 70 and 100 days from January to October. The principal polluting waste, constituting approximately three-fourths of the volume of discharge, is known as the wheel waste. It consists of water used in fluming and washing the beets and contains silt and tailings, but it is low in BOD until the latter part of the season. The pulp water, coming from the dif-

[20] See also *Sewage Works Jour.*, March, 1942, p. 404; E. M. Jones, *S. and I.W.*, February, 1950, p. 224; and J. E. Cooper, *Chem. Industries*, May, 1950, p. 684.

Table 27–4

CHARACTER OF BEET-SUGAR WASTES

Determination	Flume Water Reference *	Flume Water Reference †	Lime Cake *	Process Waste †	Steffen's Waste *
Volume, gal/ton of beets	2,200	2,000–3,000	75	325	98
Suspended solids, mg/l	800	400	450	1,300	750
Volatile solids, %	. . .	35	. . .	75	. . .
Total solids, mg/l	1,580	. . .	3,310	. . .	43,00
BOD, mg/l	200	200	1,420	1,600	54,000
Oxygen consumed or chemical oxygen demand, mg/l	110	175	500	1,500	10,560
Sucrose, mg/l	. . .	100	. . .	1,500	. . .

* See H. J. N. Hodgson, *Sewage and Trade Wastes Treatment*, Adelaide, Australia, 1938, p. 490.

† From E. A. Pearson, *Proc. Purdue Ind. Wastes Conf.*, 1951.

fusion cells and pulp presses, constitutes approximately 15 per cent of the waste volume. It is high in BOD and fine suspended matter.

The process in most plants is completed in the "straight-house," in which the finished product is a heavy molasses. In a few factories the process known as Steffen's process is extended to the extraction of sugar from this molasses. The relative quantities and polluting strengths of the wastes from the various stages in the process are summarized [21] in Table 27–4.

Liquid wastes may be disposed of by broad irrigation,[22] lagooning, or chemical precipitation. Biological treatment by trickling filters has been used on the effluent from chemical precipitation and on the process waters. Provision should be made, however, to assure having a mature filter at the commencement of the beet-sugar season. This will probably be found possible only at small factories. Lagooning of flume waters, possibly with treatment with lime or other chemicals, is not always successful due to silting and to septic action due to high BOD.

[21] See E. F. Eldredge and F. R. Theroux, *Bull.* 51, Michigan Engineering Experiment Station, 1933.

[22] See R. Porges and G. J. Hopkins, *S. and I.W.*, October, 1955, p. 1160.

Lime cake may best be handled separately, while the Steffen's waste may be spray dried. Sludge can be readily dewatered on vacuum filters. Lime cake may be press filtered and removed almost dry from the filter presses. Otherwise the slurry may be vacuum filtered, the cake being disposed of by burial or otherwise, and the filtrate discharged.

27–12. Cane-sugar wastes. The wastes from cane-sugar production consist principally of the crushed cane, known as bagasse, and a mixture of waste juices and wash waters from the refinement processes and from the plant. Bagasse may be burned as a fuel, or it may be used as an animal feed. The liquid wastes are frequently disposed of on the land, either for irrigation or in oxidation ponds, or they may be treated biologically in septic tanks or on trickling filters, or both.

27–13. Canning and other food processing. Food processing wastes include wastes from the handling and canning of vegetables and fruits, and the preparation and freezing of foods, other than fish, meats, and beverages. The liquid wastes from canneries are putrefactive,[23] high in total solids, and high in BOD. Information on the volume and character of various cannery wastes is given in Table 27–5. They may be classified as: [24] (1) water derived from the heat sterilization and cooling of sealed containers; (2) factory process waters from the washing of products, blanching, spillage, and cleaning of equipment and floors; (3) solid wastes; and (4) special wastes from special products or canning methods.

Methods of treatment include screening, sedimentation with or without coagulants, biological filtration, especially high-rate filters,[25] lagoons, land irrigation by spray irrigation or otherwise,[26] and absorption fields. Wastes from preliminary processes may be treated in lagoons [27] and by either spray or ridge-and-furrow irrigation. Spray irrigation [25] involves the availability of wooded land or other cover crop, and the preliminary screening of the waste. The waste may be applied at the rate of 0.4 to 0.6 in. per hr during 10 to 12 hr. A total of 1,200 in. has been absorbed [28] in a year.

[23] See also J. T. Norgaard, *S. and I.W.*, August, 1950, p. 1024; and L. V. Lunsford, *S. and I.W.*, April, 1957, p. 428.

[24] See N. H. Sanborn, *Sewage Works Eng.*, April, 1949, p. 199.

[25] See N. H. Sanborn, *Canning Trade*, 1952; *S. and I.W.*, September, 1953, p. 1034; L. E. Nelson, *Wastes Eng.*, 1952, p. 398; and *Purdue Ind. Wastes Conf.*, 1952, pp. 130 and 181.

[26] See also H. H. Black, *S. and I.W.*, March, 1954, p. 300.

[27] See F. K. Bieri, *Purdue Ind. Wastes Conf.*, 1951, p. 70.

[28] See also A. H. Dunstan and J. V. Lunsford, *S. and I.W.*, July, 1955, p. 827.

Table 27-5

CHARACTERISTICS OF CANNERY WASTES *

(See N. H. Sanborn, *Sewage Works Eng.*, April, 1949, p. 199.)

Product	Volume per Case, gal	BOD, mg/l	Suspended Solids, mg/l
Apricots	57–80	200–1,020	260
Asparagus	70	100	30
Beans, green or wax	26–44	160–600	60–85
lima	50–257	189–450	422
Beets	27–65	1,580–5,480	740–2,188
Carrots	23	520–3,030	1,830
Corn, cream style	24	623	302
whole kernel	25–70	1,123–6,025	300–4,000
Cherries, sour	12–40	700–2,100	20–605
Grapefruit	5–56	310–2,000	170–287
Mushrooms	6,600 †	76–390	50–242
Peaches	2,600 †	1,350	600
Peas	14–56	380–4,700	272–400
Pumpkin	20–42	2,850–6,875	785–2,500
Sauerkraut	20–43	6,300	630
Spinach	160	280–730	90–580
Tomatoes, whole	3–15	570–4,000	190–2,000
juice or products	38–100	178–3,880	170–1,168

* Reported minimum or maximum values. Single values are for one de termination only.
† Per ton.

Lagoons are used in many plants to permit the accumulation of wastes during the canning season and to allow their slow discharge into the receiving waters over a longer period of time and when a greater rate of flow of diluting water is available. Templeton[29] describes desirable features of anaerobic digestion in an open pond where aerobic oxidation in a lagoon, possibly with the aid of sodium nitrate, is too costly.

Fine screening removes coarser solids and may suffice for wastes such as those from pea canneries, where the bulk of the solids is of a coarse nature. It is not economical to employ a screen of less than 16 mesh, and it is better to have one less than 8 mesh. Plain sedimen-

[29] C. W. Templeton, *S. and I.W.*, December, 1951, p. 1540.

tation will remove more of the solids than fine screening. Plain sedimentation should be used where clarification without color removal is satisfactory. If color removal is necessary the sedimentation should be accelerated by chemical precipitation with alum, or lime and sulfate of iron. In such a process the sludge, being putrefactive, should be removed continuously or at frequent intervals. As much as possible of the solids should be removed before the effluent is sent to a treatment plant, in order to reduce the organic load on the plant. The effluent from plain- or chemical-sedimentation tanks is unfit for disposal without high dilution. The large volume of sludge resulting from chemical precipitation discourages the adoption of the process. The required dilution can be reduced by the use of trickling or percolating filters, followed by sand filtration if required.

Deep-type, high-rate biofilters with loadings up to 12,000 to 17,000 lb BOD per acre-ft per day [30] have been used. Settling tanks, following such filtration, may have a retention period of about 75 min and an overflow rate of about 1,500 to 1,600 gal per sq ft of tank-surface area.

The activated-sludge process is not usually suitable in the treatment of cannery wastes because of the sudden variations in the character of the load and the seasonal nature of the industry.

27–14. Chromium wastes. Chromium wastes are produced in metallurgical processes, especially in electroplating. The chemistry of chromium compounds is complex, some 2,000 compounds being known.[31] Some permissible limits of concentration [32] of chromium and other metallurgical wastes are shown in Table 27–6. Wastes containing more than 5 mg/l of hexavalent chromium should not be discharged into a city sewer and not more than 0.5 mg/l when discharged into a stream.[33]

The principal methods for the treatment of chromium wastes are: (1) reduction and precipitation, and (2) precipitation and partial recovery of desirable constituents by electrolysis. Tyler,[34] Black,[35] and others [36] report on the possibilities of treatment by ion exchange.

[30] See R. A. Webster, *S. and I.W.,* December, 1953, p. 1432.

[31] See D. E. Bloodgood and A. Strickland, *Purdue Ind. Wastes Conf.,* 1950, p. 232.

[32] See S. E. Coburn, *Water and Sewage Works,* June 1, 1955, p. R-335.

[33] See K. S. Watson, *S. and I.W.,* August, 1953, p. 921.

[34] R. G. Tyler and others, *S. and I.W.,* August, 1951, p. 1032.

[35] H. H. Black, *Civil Eng.,* October, 1955, p. 96.

[36] See also R. J. Brink, *S. and I.W.,* February, 1954, p. 197. L. M. Corcoran, *S. and I.W.,* November, 1955, p. 1259.

Table 27–6

LIMITS OF CONCENTRATION OF TOXIC AND DELETERIOUS WASTES

(From *Sewage Works Jour.*, Vol. 21, 1949, p. 522.)

Primary Treatment

Items	No Sludge Digestion	Sludge Digestion	Secondary Treatment
pH	5.0	6.5	6.5
Total iron, mg/l	5.0	5.0	5.0
Total copper, mg/l	3.0	1.0	1.0
Total chromium, mg/l	5.0	5.0	3.0
Total cyanide, mg/l	2.0	2.0	2.0
Oils	none	none	none

The removal of hexavalent chromium, and possibly of other toxic metals, may be accomplished by reduction with ferrous sulphate and precipitation as the hydroxide at a pH of 8.5 to 9.0, using lime.

27–15. Citrus fruit wastes. The activated-sludge process [37] has been used satisfactorily in the treatment of wastes from the citrus fruit industry. Other biological processes have also been used, but in any case adequate preliminary treatment is required to avoid too strong an influent.[38]

27–16. Corn-products wastes. The disposal of corn-products wastes presents a problem that is most acute in the Middle West. The wastes are usually warm, acid, and almost sterile, but they decompose rapidly when discharged into sewers or natural streams and greatly increase the BOD, as shown by the analysis in Table 27–7. In some corn-products plants the shelled corn is first steeped in a 0.4 per cent solution of sulfur dioxide, after which it is ground and passed through the various processes for separating hulls, germ, gluten, and starch. The most important wastes are the overflow from the gluten and starch settlers, losses from vacuum pans in which steep water or glucose is evaporated, bone-filter wash water, filtrate and wash water from gluten or starch filters, and soap wastes. Gluten and starch overflows comprise more than three-fourths of the polluting material.

[37] See J. B. Lackey and others, *S. and I.W.*, April, 1956, p. 538; and M. H. Dougherty and others, *S. and I.W.*, July, 1955, p. 821.

[38] See R. R. McNary and others, *S. and I.W.*, July, 1956, p. 894.

Table 27-7

RESULTS OF TREATMENT OF CORN-PRODUCTS WASTES AT ARGO, ILLINOIS

(See *Jour. Ind. and Eng. Chem.*, Vol. 18, October, 1926, p. 1076.)

Treatment	Aeration Period, hours	Cubic Feet of Air per Gallon	Gallons per Acre per Day on Trickling Filters	Temp. of Influent, °F	Temp. of Effluent, °F	Influent, mg/l				Effluent, mg/l			
						Nitrogen	Suspended Solids	Total Solids	5-Day BOD	Nitrogen	Suspended Solids	Total Solids	5-Day BOD
Activated-sludge treatment:													
winter	13.5	4.3	...	90	74	50.3	183	980	490	14.7	86	694	98
summer	9.2	2.9	...	105	98	31.9	136	737	325	5.7	24	528	15
Trickling-filter treatment:													
winter	..	...	657,000	...	...	51.6	197	...	490	11.7	33	...	33.5
summer	...	...	762,000	...	...	32.9	145	...	325	2.3	20	...	7.5

The wastes, after screening and sedimentation, can be treated successfully by biological methods comprising either the activated-sludge process or trickling filters. Sedimentation alone is of little value, and the activated-sludge method may not be continuously successful; it is expensive, and the problem of sludge disposal has not been solved.[39] Treatment on trickling filters has been found to be successful at all seasons.

The American Maize Company [40] has successfully solved much of its waste-disposal problems through by-products recovery accomplished by modifications of processes within the plant. Among these modifications are those listed in Table 27-8.

Cooperation between sanitary authorities and industrial management has been significant in solving the problem of disposal of corn-products wastes. So successful were the results of studies at Argo and Decatur, Ill., and at Roby, Ind., that the profit to the industry was appreciable and the problem of the disposal of the wastes was greatly reduced.

27-17. Cyanide wastes. Cyanide wastes are produced in metallurgical processes, especially in electroplating. Recovery [41] of cyanide within the process has been found desirable. The wastes are deleterious because of their high toxicity to fish life and the dangers resulting

[39] See also *Proc. Lake Mich. San. Congress,* July, 1927, p. 33.

[40] E. M. Van Patten and G. H. McIntosh, *Water and Sewage Works,* December, 1951, p. 516.

[41] See also L. Weisberg and E. J. Quinlan, *S. and I.W.,* August, 1956, p. 998.

Table 27–8

CORRECTIVE MEASURES MADE BY AMERICAN MAIZE PRODUCTS COMPANY IN
THE RECOVERY OF BY-PRODUCTS AND IN THE CONTROL OF ITS WASTES

(Data from E. M. Van Patten and G. H. McIntosh,
Water and Sewage Works, December, 1951, p. 516.)

1. Reduce solids entrainment losses in refining evaporation to minimum by installation of new concentrating equipment or rebuilding of existing facilities.

2. Install equipment to eliminate excess amounts of starch wash and filtrate waters that were unbalancing reuse of process water.

3. Devise means for limiting amount of bone wash sewered daily.

4. Eliminate the sewering of all process, filtrate, and manufacturing water.

5. Isolate all condensates from cooling waters in the steep water and manufacturing water concentration operations.

6. Discard feed-house concentrating equipment and install new equipment allowing for additional capacity to concentrate filtrate and wash waters that normally would be sewered.

7. Eliminate sewering of evaporator pan boil-out water and devise other means of separately disposing of this material.

8. Completely revamp concentrating equipment and methods in the lactic acid department to eliminate losses.

from their presence in a public water supply. Some permissible limits of their concentration are shown in Table 27–6. Care must be taken in the treatment of such wastes not to release hydrocyanic acid gas into the atmosphere.

Methods in use for the treatment of cyanide wastes [42] are acidification, chemical precipitation, and chlorination. Chemical methods predominate according to Black.[43, 44] These methods include: (1) control of pH to (a) break oil emulsions, (b) increase reaction rates, (c) prevent evolution of dangerous gases, and (d) precipitate metallic constitutents; (2) neutralization; (3) oxidation of cyanides, possibly with chlorine; and (4) reduction of hexavalent chromium. Alkaline chlorination is a common form of oxidation. The first application of about 3 lb of chlorine per lb of cyanide converts cyanide to cyanate. Then about 5 lb completes the cyanide destruction. About 1.25 lb of caustic are needed per lb of chlorine. The pH is controlled in the range of 8.5 to 10.0, with 8.6 optimum for the precipitation of metal.

[42] See J. W. Townsend, *Wastes Eng.*, December, 1953, p. 615.
[43] See H. H. Black, *Civil Eng.*, October, 1955, p. 96.
[44] See also R. W. Simpson and J. L. Samsel, *Wastes Eng.*, April, 1954, p. 169.

Sulfites are commonly used to reduce hexavalent to trivalent chromium. Sulfuric acid is added to assure rapid reduction at pH 2.5 to 3.0. An alkali, usually lime, is used to adjust pH to 8.5 to precipitate trivalent chromium. The chemical dosages are approximately: sulfur dioxide, 2 lb per lb of chromium; sulfuric acid, 1.5 to 2.0 lb per 1,000 gal of waste; lime, 1.5 to 2.0 lb per 1,000 gal of wastes plus 2.5 lb per lb of chromium.

It has been shown that cyanide wastes can be treated with ozone [45] and that hexavalent chromium can be reduced more effectively at pH of 3 to 5.5 with sulfur dioxide than with either ferrous sulfate or sodium bisulfite.[46]

27–18. Dairies.[47] The dairy industry, although not the most valuable economically, is probably the most widely scattered industry creating waste-disposal problems. Its products are highly concentrated, perishable,[48] and are so strongly polluting that they cannot be disposed of indiscriminately into natural water courses. Their discharge into municipal sewers for treatment with domestic sewage is the preferable method of disposal, where it is feasible.

Wastes produced in the handling of milk and the manufacture of dairy products can be classified as domestic wastes; cooling waters; spoiled products or excess supply of skim milk, whey, or buttermilk; drips, leaks, and first rinses; and alkaline wash waters. Such wastes should be separated before treatment to minimize the treatment problem. Analyses of some of these wastes are given in Table 27–9.[49] These wastes in a stream vary in effect all the way from beneficial to plant and animal life to injurious to fish life, rendering the water unfit as a source of public water supply, or to developing odors so offensive as to constitute a public nuisance. Dairy wastes can be disposed of by dilution in the same manner as other organic refuse. They require treatment only where the capacity of the stream is insufficient to receive them. The capacity is measured in the same manner as in the disposal of sewage by dilution. They can be combined with municipal sewage when the load on the plant does not become too great and some form of secondary treatment is provided.

[45] See R. G. Tyler, *Purdue Ind. Wastes Conf.*, 1951, p. 64.

[46] See H. B. Channon, *S. and I.W.*, August, 1953, p. 921.

[47] See also abstract in *Sewage Works Jour.*, July, 1942, p. 917; S. I. Zack, *S. and I.W.*, August, 1956, p. 1009; and F. J. McKee, *S. and I.W.*, February, 1957, p. 157.

[48] See also H. A. Trebler and H. G. Harding, *S. and I.W.*, December, 1955, p. 1369.

[49] From E. F. Eldridge, *Bulls.* 24 and 28, Michigan Engineering Experiment Station, 1930; and C. W. Watson, *S. and I.W.*, January, 1955.

Table 27–9

ANALYSES OF WHOLE MILK AND OF BY-PRODUCTS

(From E. F. Eldridge, *Bulls.* 24 and 28, Michigan Engineering
Experiment Station, 1930.)

Substance	Total Solids, %	Organic Solids, %	Ash, %	Fat, %	Sugar, %	Protein, %	BOD 5-Day, mg/l	Oxygen Consumed, mg/l
Whole milk	12.5	11.7	0.80	3.6	4.5	3.8	102,500	36,750
Skim milk	8.23	7.45	0.78	0.10	4.6	3.9	73,000	32,200
Buttermilk	7.75	6.88	0.87	0.50	4.3	3.6	64,000	28,600
Whey	7.20	6.40	0.80	0.40	4.4	0.8	32,000	25,900

Plain sedimentation is ineffective, and septicization is usually unsatisfactory.

The Pennsylvania State Sanitary Water Board has set limits on the maximum BOD content of various forms of dairy wastes, as indicated in Table 27–10.

In the treatment of dairy wastes alone, the first step is to pass the waste through a grit chamber and screen to intercept dirt, sawdust, glass, and other large materials. Primary plain sedimentation is valueless, as most of the polluting material is soluble or colloidal. Black [50] states that the high oxygen demand and ready availability of the lactose and protein of milk waste require aerobic treatment to prevent the development of detrimental acidities.

Satisfactory methods of final treatment and disposal include: irrigation and disposal on land; high-rate trickling filters; and aeration or activated sludge.[51] Some desirable conditions of treatment by aeration include the maintenance of temperatures between 80° and 90° F, and good agitation without foaming.

Weak wastes may be treated in septic tanks [52] with detention periods between 24 and 72 hr. Periods of less than 24 hr are undesirable because the intermittent nature of the discharge may result in too short a period in the tank. The use of Imhoff tanks is im-

---

[50] H. H. Black, *Civil Eng.,* October, 1955, p. 98; and *S. and I.W.,* March, 1954, p. 300. G. E. Haver, *S. and I.W.,* October, 1953, p. 1271.

[51] See S. D. Montagna, *S. and I.W.,* January, 1940, p. 108; P. M. Thayer, *S. and I.W.,* December, 1951, p. 1537; and *Water and Sewage Works,* January, 1953, p. 34.

[52] See also *Sewage Works Jour.,* September, 1938, p. 868.

Table 27–10

Pennsylvania Limitations of Maximum BOD Content of Dairy Wastes

(From *Sewage and Industrial Wastes Engineering*, February, 1950, p. 73.)

Process	BOD,* pounds — For Each 10,000 lb of Milk or Milk Equivalent for 1st 50,000 lb of Milk	For Each 10,000 lb over 50,000	Process	BOD,* pounds — For Each 10,000 lb of Milk or Milk Equivalent for 1st 50,000 lb of Milk	For Each 10,000 lb over 50,000
Receiving and cooling milk	7	6	Skim condensing, super-heated	12	12
Tank truck delivery, to and from plant	1	6	Skim drying:		
Storing in tanks	1	1	roll	20	10
Evaporating whole milk:			spray	4	2
floor waste	4	3	Whey condensing, sweet:		
entrainment loss	2	2	floor waste	16	8
Canning and sterilizing evaporated milk	4	3	entrainment loss	4	4
Spray drying	4	2	Whey condensing, acid:		
Cream separating	4	4	floor waste	12	8
Cream pasteurizing.			entrainment loss	3	3
Cooling and can filling	4	4	Whey drying	10	6
Cottage-cheese making, also casein	16	16	Buttermilk condensing	12	8
American cheese making:			Milk pasteurizing, cooling, bottling	10	8
unwashed curd	10	8	Ice cream mix making:		
washed curd	16	4	pan	8	6
Skim condensing, plain:			vat	8	6
floor waste	6	6	Ice cream freezing	2	2
entrainment loss	3	3	Cultured buttermilk making	10	10
Skim condensing, sweetened:			Butter churning and washing	6	6
floor waste	8	8			
entrainment loss	3	3			

* Where primary treatment only is required, use 65 per cent of these figures. Where complete treatment is required use 15 per cent of these figures. Untreated wastes may not exceed the figures shown in these columns.

practicable because the less expensive septic tank, under proper conditions, will produce satisfactory results.

Chemical precipitation may be effective but it calls for too much supervision and is more expensive than biological methods. If it is used, sufficient lime should be added to precipitate and to neutralize the caseins and lactic acid, to prevent septicity in the settling basin.

Whey and concentrated dairy wastes are best treated by adding approximately 35 per cent excess lime to neutralize the acidity, which may run as high as 6,500 mg/l; by heating to the boiling point to form a curd that will settle readily; and by treating the cooled effluent from the settling tank in a septic tank with subsequent filtration. The settled curd, when dried, may have some value as stock feed.

The trend in treatment is toward a modified activated-sludge process wherein the sludge is recirculated until stabilized. Minimum design requirements appear to be 1 cfm per lb of BOD using jet-type aeration, 30-hr retention in a combined equalization tank, 2-hr final settling, and provision for continuously returning all sludge to the aeration tank with the raw waste. The use of aeration alone, followed by sedimentation [53] and the complete activated-sludge process have been found practical. In straight aeration an air supply as low as 0.5 cfm per lb of BOD per day has been used.

It has been concluded also, on good authority [54] that "results have proven beyond any doubt that a trickling filter plant . . . can do an excellent job of milk waste treatment."

It would seem, therefore, that under favorable conditions almost any type of biological treatment in a well-designed plant can treat dairy waste successfully.

27–19. Explosives. *Powder plants.* Dickerson [55] points out that aeration followed by high-rate filtration will remove 85 per cent of BOD and that the activated-sludge process should provide good efficiency in treatment of the waste. Coagulation and sedimentation are not effective methods of treatment.

Phosphorus. This can be precipitated and settled in an hour by adding lime to effect a pH of about 11.0.[56]

Picrates. The problem of the disposal of picrate wastes is similar to that of TNT wastes. The wastes are bright yellow, and the color persists in high dilution.

Smokeless powder. These wastes are more acid than from TNT or picrates, and have a low BOD. The acidity of the waste is neutralized with lime or limestone.

Shell casings. These are mainly ferrous sulfate pickling wastes plus a small amount of copper. Copper-bearing wastes are biologically toxic, precluding biological methods of treatment.

Trinitrotoluene.[57] This is made from a mixture of nitric and sulfuric acids.

[53] See J. P. Horton and H. A. Trebler, *S. and I.W.*, August, 1953, p. 941.

[54] See J. W. Rugaber, *S. and I.W.*, November, 1951, p. 1425.

[55] B. W. Dickerson, *Purdue Ind. Wastes Conf.*, 1951, p. 30.

[56] See R. Owen, *S. and I.W.*, May, 1953, p. 548.

[57] See *Ind. and Eng. Chem.*, October, 1943, p. 1122.

The wastes are produced in the wash house wherein the "tri-oil" is purified and TNT is crystallized. The volume of water used in these washes averages 35 gal per 100 lb of TNT. The wastes are quite acid, with an acidity of about 25,000 ppm in the first wash and 7,000 in the second. They are bright yellow and odorless. After the acid has been removed by the washes the TNT is crystallized and washed with a solution of about 5 per cent of sodium sulfite ("sellite"). The waste sulfite solution is usually run to waste, separate from the acid wastes. It is deep red in color and is alkaline to methyl orange with a pH of 9.2 and an alkalinity of approximately 900 ppm. The volume averages 38 gal per 100 lb of TNT.

The wastes have no odor and no appreciable BOD. In a sewage-TNT-waste mixture containing 5 per cent or more of TNT waste there is interference with the efficiency of the activated-sludge process; and if the TNT waste is 25 per cent, or more, it interferes with the efficiency of trickling-filter operation.[57] The wastes are stable and resistant to biological oxidation. All the available methods of sewage treatment are ineffective for removal of organic matter and color except the use of chlorine for decolorization. For several TNT works, dilution alone, with provision for storage of concentrated wastes, was adopted. Where the water was used for water supply, an increase of color of 15 to 20 in the filtered water was accepted. Where the water was not mixed with the water supply increase of color in the river water up to 85 was approved by at least one state board of health. The alternative to this scheme comprises an expensive and elaborate system of neutralization of wastes, evaporation to a sirup in multi-effect evaporators, incineration of the sirup to an ash or thick sirup in rotary kilns, and flushing of the ash or liquid to the nearest watercourse.

This use of stream flow in wartime appears justifiable where the only effect on the stream is a slight increase in color, no appreciable reduction in alkalinity, no odor, no killing of fish, and no toxic effect on those who drink the filtered water.

27–20. Gas manufacturing wastes.[58] The most common product manufactured from ammonia liquor at gas works is sulfate of ammonia. The ammonia liquor is fed to the top of a vertical still, flows down, and meets an upward current of steam liberating the "free" ammonia. The "fixed" ammonia is liberated by the addition of lime in the lower section of the still. The liberated ammonia, sulfuretted

[58] See also J. J. Priestly, *Gas World*, London, April 15, 1950, p. 408.

hydrogen, hydrocyanic acid, and some of the phenol pass into a saturator containing sulfuric acid. Ammonium sulfate separates out, is removed, and dried. The accompanying gases pass through coolers and then to purifiers containing oxide of iron. The liquor condensed in the coolers is known as *devil liquor*. The liquor, leaving the bottom of the still free from ammonia, is run to settling pits for the separation of the lime and cooling of the liquor. There are thus two effluents from the manufacture of sulfate of ammonia: the spent liquor from the still, and the devil liquor. The noxious constituents in the wastes are phenols, higher tar acids, thiocyanate, and thiosulfate. The 4-hr, 27° C BOD in the combined waste varies between 4,000 and 8,000 mg/l.

Spent gas liquor can be mixed with normal sewage in a ratio of 1 part of waste to 150 up to 1,200 parts of sewage, and the mixture can be treated biologically, the activated-sludge process being more sensitive than the trickling filter to a heavy load of gas liquor. It may be desirable to remove tar from the liquor before mixing it with sewage. This can be removed by straining the liquor through a wood-wool filter on which the tar collects. The filtering material requires frequent removal and renewal. Devil liquors can be treated biologically when mixed with normal sewage, but they are sometimes evaporated, by spraying into producer furnaces or otherwise, in order to reduce the load on the treatment plant. The devil liquor is the stronger waste, but it constitutes only 10 to 15 per cent of the total volume to be cared for. Higher tar acids, thiocyanate, and thiosulfate are best removed during the manufacturing process for the purpose of recovering valuable by-products. The treatment of phenol wastes before disposal is important.

27–21. Gasoline wastes.[59]   The production of high-octane gas introduced more complex operations in oil refineries, including catalytic crackers of various types. The clarification of refinery wastes has been given considerable attention by the American Petroleum Institute, which issued a manual [60] giving basic design data for the design of the so-called "A.P.I. separator." The average oil content of the effluent from the separator is approximately 35 mg/l. Detention periods of an hour or more are recommended, and baled straw is

[59] See *Manual on Disposal of Refinery Wastes,* 5th edition, American Petroleum Institute, 1953.

[60] American Petroleum Institute, *Disposal of Refinery Wastes,* Sect. I, *Waste Water Containing Oil,* 1941.

Table 27–11

LAUNDRY WASTES

(F. W. Mohlmann, *Proc. Am. Soc. Civil Engrs.*, September, 1948, p. 1052.)

Ratio	Tons Dirty Clothes Daily	Wastes in 1,000 Gal per Ton	BOD	Pounds per Ton		
				Suspended Solids	Total Nitrogen	Grease
Average	9.3	16	100	53	1.7	34
Maximum	22	24	168	91	2.4	42
Minimum	3.2	12	56	26	0.7	28

used in the second tank of the separator for final, rough, and rapid straining of the effluent.

27–22. Laundries.[61] Laundry wastes do not ordinarily cause great trouble in their disposal because they are usually sufficiently diluted to have no marked effect on treatment processes. Mohlmann[62] reports pollution losses to streams from 13 laundries in the Sanitary District of Chicago as shown in Table 27–11. The undiluted waste is turbid, soapy, and alkaline, containing dyes, grease, and dirt washed from the clothes. "Laundry wastes alone or combined with sewage can be readily and economically treated to any desired degree by existing physical, chemical, or biological methods or by combinations and improvements of such methods."[63] Radioactivity in laundry wastes has no practical effect on the method to be used for their treatment.[64] Tests reported by the Atomic Energy Commission[65] indicate that no adverse effect will result from the release of normal, radioactive laundry wastes to the public sewers.

When treatment is necessary the pH should first be adjusted by means of sulfuric acid and the waste then precipitated with lime or alum. The pH should be adjusted to 2.6 if lime is to be used and to 7.0 if alum is to be used. Laundry wastes have been treated by the flotation of flocculated coagulants "which adsorb and entrain the

[61] See also R. Eliassen and H. B. Schuloff, *Water Works and Sewerage*, November, 1943, p. 418.
[62] F. W. Mohlmann, *Proc. Am. Soc. Civil Engrs.*, September, 1948, p. 1052.
[63] See *Sewage Works Jour.*, May, 1944, p. 571.
[64] See L. M. Reading and others, *S. and I.W.*, December, 1953, p. 1414.
[65] See Abel Wolman and A. E. Gorman, *Wastes Eng.*, June, 1955.

Table 27-12

STRENGTHS OF PACKINGHOUSE WASTES

(F. W. Mohlmann, *Proc. Am. Soc. Civil Engrs.*, September, 1948, p. 1052.)

Animal	Liquid, gal per ton	Pounds per Ton			
		BOD	Suspended Solids	Nitrogen	Grease
Cattle	3,225	28.5	25.3	3.17	2.01
Hogs	4,300	31.4	20.9	3.15	3.29

suspended or colloidal soils" [66] in such a manner that 87 per cent of the water has been recovered for reuse in the laundry.

27-23. Meat products.[67] The slaughter of animals and the preparation and packing of meat products result in the production of wastes with high polluting characteristics, from 10 to 15 times stronger than normal domestic sewage, as measured by the total solids and the BOD. Mohlmann [68] reports average pollutional wastes from slaughterhouses to be as shown in Table 27-12. The sewage contains straw, paunch manure, blood, grease, offal, and other organic refuse. The strength of the wastes varies widely throughout the day and between various days in the same industrial plant, depending on its activities. The wide variations in quantity and quality may materially affect the method and the results of treatment.

A review of the methods in use for the treatment of meat-industry wastes shows a wide variety in successful use. Biological methods are generally satisfactory [69] and chemical methods, using chlorinated lime and alum, have been found satisfactory in small abbatoirs.[70]

Anaerobic treatment has removed 95 per cent of the BOD and 90 per cent of the suspended solids at loadings up to 0.2 lb BOD per cu ft of digester volume per day. At one plant [71] design criteria are:

[66] See H. J. Wollner and others, *S. and I.W.*, April, 1954, p. 509.

[67] See also E. F. Eldridge, *Bull.* 96, Michigan Engineering Experiment Station, 1942.

[68] F. W. Mohlmann, *Proc. Am. Soc. Civil Engrs.*, September, 1948, p. 1052.

[69] See *Jour. Ind. and Eng. Chem.*, October, 1926, pp. 239 and 1076. *Sewage Works Jour.*, July, 1930, p. 435, and March, 1945, pp. 292 and 301.

[70] See H. H. Black, *Civil Eng.*, October, 1955, p. 98.

[71] Wilson and Co. at Albert Lea, Minn. From H. H. Black, *Civil Eng.*, October, 1955, p. 98; and *S. and I.W.*, March, 1954, p. 300. W. J. Fuller, *S. and I.W.*, May, 1953, p. 576.

Volume of equalizing tank is 27 per cent of total flow.

Rate of discharge is constant at average rate of flow.

Heaters (two) maintain digesters at 95° F.

Digesters (two) have capacity of 0.15 lb of BOD per cu ft per day and 0.15 lb volatile solids per cu ft per day.

Degasifiers (two) remove all the methane and most of the carbon dioxide. Design is for 20-in. vacuum.

Separators (two) provide 1:1 to 3:1 return sludge at 600 gpd per sq ft of surface loading.

Trickling-filter rate of application is 23 mgad, and BOD loading is 2,600 lb per acre-ft per day.

Final clarifiers (two) have surface loading of 800 gpd per sq ft.

Trickling filters are dependable for medium size and large plants with BOD loadings up to 6,000 to 8,000 lb per acre-ft per day on roughing filters, frequently followed by conventional filters.

The activated-sludge process may be successful when treating diluted packinghouse wastes.

Packinghouse wastes may be treated by the same processes as are used in the treatment of domestic sewage, although some modifications of the processes may be necessary.[72] The wastes should first be passed through a grit chamber, and grease removed by skimming. The collected grease is usually valueless as it is gummy and polluted with grass seed and other putrefactive material so that its recovery is too difficult and expensive to repay the cost. The sewage or waste should next be passed through a screen with about 8 meshes per inch to remove suspended matter, which might otherwise cause difficulty in subsequent stages of treatment. Finer screens give trouble from clogging. The screened sewage is passed into a sedimentation chamber or chambers, in series, with a retention period of 2 to 4 hr, from which the deposited sludge is preferably removed continuously by some mechanical device. It is desirable, where possible, to dilute the effluent from the tank treatment with screened and settled sewage, after which the mixture may be treated by the activated-sludge process or on trickling filters. Both diffused air and mechanical aeration have been successful. At Chicago [73] a 9-hr period of aeration with $3\frac{1}{2}$ to 5 cu ft of diffused air per gal of waste was used in the activated-sludge process, and a rate of 600,000 to 1,000,000 gal per acre per day was used on the trickling filter. The period and amount of

[72] See L. Bradney and others, *S. and I.W.*, June, 1950, p. 807.

[73] See *Jour. Ind. and Eng. Chem.*, October, 1926, p. 1076.

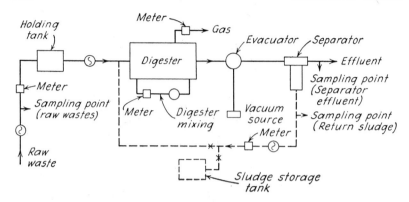

Fig. 27-1. Flow diagram of anaerobic contact process as applied to packing-house waste. (From G. J. Schroepfer and others, *S and I.W.*, April, 1955, p. 460.)

aeration or rate of filtration should be computed, so that the load for the removal of BOD may approximate the standard loads adopted for the treatment of domestic sewage.

An anaerobic contact process has been developed [74] which, it is claimed, will remove up to 98 per cent of the BOD and 90 per cent suspended solids at loadings up to 0.2 lb BOD per cu ft of digester volume per day. It is stated [75] that "with retention periods of 48 hr and a loading of 0.114 lb per cu ft of digester capacity, over 90 per cent of BOD reduction can be obtained." A schematic flow diagram [76] for this process is shown in Fig. 27-1.

If the packinghouse wastes are very strong and cannot be mixed with domestic sewage, chemical precipitation may be desirable. The recovered proteins may be sufficiently valuable to repay some of the cost of treatment. The proteins may be precipitated by sulfuric acid, by iron or aluminum compounds, by oxidizing agents, or by other organic coagulants. Liquid chlorine may be used successfully as a precipitant. About 1 to 1½ parts of chlorine are required for each part of total nitrogen when the pH is adjusted to about 4.0. Since the waste may contain 150 mg/l or more of total nitrogen the amount of chlorine required is high when compared with that used in sterilization. Much of the chlorine is used, however, in oxidation of the

[74] See G. J. Schroepfer and others, *S. and I.W.*, April, 1955; and W. Rudolfs and V. Del Quercio, *Water and Sewage Works*, February, 1953, p. 60.

[75] W. Rudolfs and V. Del Quercio, *op. cit.*

[76] See G. J. Schroepfer and others, *S. and I.W.*, April, 1955, p. 460.

organic matter, so that the BOD of the effluent is less than that obtained by a mere removal of the nitrogenous compounds.

27-24. Metallurgical wastes. Industrial processes producing metallurgical wastes, in addition to the metal-treating industries listed alphabetically herein, include such related process wastes as emulsified cleaners, coolants, organic and inorganic acids, fermentation wastes, solvents, organic chemicals,[77] machine oils, spent soluble oil, and wastes containing high suspended solids combined with some of the above. It is desirable, where possible, to combine the treatment of such wastes with the industrial process producing it.[78]

27-25. Oily wastes.[79] Among the principal sources of oil pollution are oil-burning and oil-cargo vessels, ship-repair yards, oil terminals, oil refineries, gas manufacture, and some metallurgical processes. In some cases the volume of waste produced may be high. For example, the refining of 100 barrels of crude oil may produce about 77,000 gal of waste, with a population-equivalent, on the basis of BOD, of about 76 persons, and on a suspended-solids basis, of about 160 persons. Oily wastes are so difficult to treat that every effort should be made to cut them off at their sources before the problem of treatment presents itself. Inadequately treated wastes cause difficulties in water-treatment works on account of tastes and odors, on bathing-beach and waterfront property because of the slimy scum deposited, and in sewage-treatment plants because of the thick and unsightly scum on the surface of tanks and the clogging of filters. Where oil has collected on the surface of settling basins or in quiescent pools it may be skimmed off and burned.[80]

Chemical flocculation of oily waste waters, gravity separators, centrifugation of oil sludges, and the burning of oil sludges are practiced in the disposal of oily wastes. Soluble oil wastes are treated by flotation by air, the skimmings being treated in a plate- or pressure-filter.[81] At the Atlantic Refining Company,[82] aluminum chloride is used as a coagulant with alum as an alternate, with the occasional use of activated silica, clay, and lime slurry. The sludge is dewatered

---

[77] See also J. A. Liontas, *S. and I.W.*, March, 1954, p. 310.

[78] See also L. E. Lancy, *S. and I.W.*, September, 1954, p. 1117.

[79] See also *Sewage Works Jour.*, January, 1935, p. 104. R. F. Weston, *Chem. Eng. Prog.*, Vol. 48, 1952, p. 459. *Manual on the Disposal of Refinery Wastes*, 5th edition, American Petroleum Institute, 1953. *S. and I.W.*, July, 1954, p. 855; and H. E. Elkin and others, *S. and I.W.*, December, 1956, p. 1475.

[80] See also *Proc. Am. Soc. Civil Engrs.*, Vol. 53, 1927, p. 1653.

[81] See also A. H. Beebe, *S. and I.W.*, December, 1953, p. 1314.

[82] See also H. H. Black, *Civil Eng.*, October, 1955, p. 96.

on vacuum filters, with sufficient oil usually in the filter cake to support combustion.

Oily wastes produced in metallurgical processes may often be separated in gravity, oil-water separators. Emulsified oils may be treated in lagoons. They have also been treated with alum and sulfuric acid to lower the pH in mixing and flocculation, followed by 4-hr sedimentation, the addition of caustic to raise the pH, and finally separated by pressure flotation.[83]

In oil-producing fields a brine is sometimes obtained from the oil wells. This is highly injurious to water supplies, rendering the water non-potable because of the increased mineral content and the taste. Attempts have been made to evaporate the brines to recover the valuable salts, but with little or no economic success. The return of brine to underground strata is often unsuccessful and is generally undesirable as a hazard to underground water, except near the seacoast and under other special, local conditions.[84] Where brine is returned through a well the well casing should be kept tight and, when the well is abandoned, it should be sealed off. The problem of the disposal of oil-field brines has not been successfully solved.

Where oily waste waters are involved in oil production or refining, the gravity-type, oil-water separator designed in accordance with American Petroleum Institute recommendations [85] are standard equipment in petroleum refineries and are capable of highly effective operation.[86]

27–26. The paper industry. The paper industry is probably the most economically valuable industry that produces large quantities of troublesome wastes. The relative pollution load from various wastes of mills in Wisconsin is indicated by the figures in Table 27–13.

Paper products are made from different pulps in various proportions. Wood pulp accounts for 90 per cent of the products. The remainder is made from rags, straw, jute, hemp, reclaimed paper stock, and other fiber-producing materials. In the manufacturing process the raw materials are first reduced to pulp by grinding or cutting. The pulp is then cooked to aid in the removal of intercellular matter,

[83] Cited by H. H. Black from C. W. Hathaway and R. E. Harvie, *S. and I.W.*, November, 1954, p. 1363.

[84] See also C. B. Johnston, *Public Works*, April, 1954, p. 93.

[85] See *Manual on the Disposal of Refinery Wastes*, 5th edition, American Petroleum Institute, 1953.

[86] See R. N. Giles, *Purdue Ind. Wastes Conf.*, 1951, p. 1; *S. and I.W.*, March, 1951, p. 281; and H. F. Elkin and W. E. Soden, *S. and I.W.*, July, 1954, p. 854.

Table 27–13

PAPER MILL WASTES, QUANTITY AND POLLUTION LOAD

(From L. F. Warrick and K. M. Watson, *Paper Trade Jour.*, June, 1930.)

Waste	Number of Mills	Quantity of Wastes					Pollutional Values
		Gallons of Water per Ton	Pounds per Ton of Product				Population Equivalent per Ton per Day
			Fixed Suspended Solids	Volatile Suspended Solids	Soluble Solids	5-Day BOD	
Paper mills	24						
Average		31,100	8.0	43.6	84.5	3.7	22.2
Maximum		100,000	30.7	143.7	890.0	9.0	54.0
Sulfite pulp and paper mills	5						
Average		89,050	13.8	123.0	1,831.0	154.0	834.0
Maximum		160,000	44.0	192.0	3,840.0	250.0	1,500.0
Groundwood pulp and paper mills	3						
Average		18,400	7.2	53.0	35.3	2.5	15.7
Maximum		30,300	11.7	73.1	41.6	3.6	21.6
Kraft pulp and paper mills	6						
Average		77,350	31.2	73.0	395.0	119.0	717.0
Maximum		141,000	65.0	183.0	879.0	438.0	2,628.0
Rag pulp and paper mills	2						
Average		86,500	104.0	206.0	569.0	46.0	276.0
Maximum		106,000	162.0	331.0	1,111.0	64.0	384.0
Board mills	3						
Average		26,500	5.0	41.1	61.3	11.1	66.6
Maximum		40,700	10.0	64.0	129.0	14.0	84.0
Sulfite pulp mills	9						
Average		66,883	11.0	72.0	3,104.0	185.0	1,108.0
Maximum		213,000	30.0	224.0	6,405.0	440.0	2,640.0
Groundwood pulp mills	4						
Average		35,125	7.7	69.6	62.0	7.8	46.8
Maximum		102,000	27.0	116.0	91.0	15.4	92.4

which is undesirable in the production of fiber. The process of manufacture frequently takes its name from the quality of the cooking liquor used.

The three principal processes are: the *sulfite,* the *sulfate,* and the *soda* processes. In the first the cooling liquor is prepared by burning sulfur and absorbing sulfurous acid gas either in milk of lime or in towers filled with limestone over which the water is sprayed. The cooking liquor forms soluble calcium salts of lignosulfonic acid, and the lignin and other matter are removed by washing and bleaching.

In the sulfate process or Kraft mills, the cooking liquor consists of caustic soda and sodium sulfate. In the soda process the cooling liquor is a solution of caustic soda.

Waste products from paper manufacture include bark and sawdust from the preparation of the wood, or dust from the rag stock; washings from the cookers and thickeners; black-carbon residue from the black ash in soda pulp mills; lime sludge, principally from the alkali room of soda and sulfate pulp mills; wash water from the heaters, containing finely divided fibers; wash water from the paper machines containing fibers, pigments, and clay; and wash water from reclaimed paper stock containing fiber, clay, and carbon from removed ink.

The effect of these wastes on a stream is to reduce its dissolved oxygen by the presence of sulfur dioxide; to increase its BOD by the fibrous organic matter introduced; to inhibit fish life; to increase the alkalinity of the stream by spent liquor from soda and sulfate mills; to disfigure its appearance by discoloration and the production of a frothy scum; and to increase its turbidity and hardness by the discharge of clay and of lime sludge.

The wastes from the various stages of the processes should be treated separately, as valuable by-products can be recovered from them. Bark and sawdust are recovered from the pulp-preparation processes by screening and flotation or sedimentation. The dried product is available as fuel. Dust from the rag department is precipitated and is available in the manufacture of roofing paper and other products. Waste water from the thickeners is passed to detention tanks or save-alls where 98 per cent of the suspended fiber is removed for reuse before the water is run to waste or reused in the process. The lime sludge from soda and sulfate mills can be dried, first by filtration and then by heat dryers, after which it is prepared for market as agricultural lime and whiting, or is reburned to be reused to causticize more soda. Wash water from the beaters and excess white water from the paper machines are passed through sedimentation tanks, where 98 per cent of the suspended fibers and more than 90 per cent of the clay can be removed before the water is run to waste or reused. Waste sulfite liquor is the most difficult to treat. Methods [87] used principally for the treatment of white waters and waste waters include: (1) screening; (2) settling in detention basins with or without chemical pretreatment; (3) pretreatment with chemicals and pressure aeration followed by flocculation and skimming;

---

[87] See V. J. Calise, *Water and Sewage Works,* November, 1950, p. 480.

(4) coagulation with chemicals and clarification in a "solids contact" reclaimer; (5) anaerobic digestion; and (6) the activated-sludge process where the waste has been concentrated to a BOD of 4,300 mg/l. Anaerobic digestion for 4 or 5 days at 30° to 35° C, with added nitrogen has removed 70 to 80 per cent of applied BOD.[88] Lagooning has given satisfaction in Wisconsin.[89]

Every method of sewage treatment used in municipal practice has been attempted on sulfite waste liquor, but none has proved satisfactory. Processes reported by Gleeson[90] include fermentation with yeast, with alcohol as a by-product; evaporation either with or without burning; aeration of the natural stream receiving the sulfite waste, by means of compressed air diffused in the stream; lagooning; the Howard processes consisting of multiple lime coagulation; heating under high pressure; and base exchange to substitute such bases as ammonia, magnesia, and soda for calcium. Gleeson concludes that "there is not as yet any universally simple and economic means of disposal of sulfite waste liquor."

The sulfite waste liquor, if sufficiently concentrated, can be used as a road binder, as a tan extract, as linoleum cement, and for other miscellaneous purposes furnishing a limited outlet. The material, after evaporation, contains about 8,000 Btu per lb and has been used by some coal companies as a binder in the manufacture of hard-coal briquettes.

27–27. Pharmaceutical wastes. The production of penicillin, streptomycin, and other pharmaceuticals produce wastes containing high, soluble organic content with high BOD. Combined treatment with domestic sewage is satisfactory, but, where this is not possible, the wastes may be treated by aeration followed by biological filtration. Conditioned trickling filters have proved to be satisfactory.[91] At the Willow Island plant of the American Cyanamid Company, aerators and primary clarifiers remove about 60 per cent of the BOD. The BOD loading on the primary filter averages 2,000 lb, and on the secondary filter 1,300 lb, per acre-ft per day with 1,000 lb a good operating figure for the secondary filter.

27–28. Phenol wastes. Phenol wastes are produced as a result of processes of manufacture involving coal, tar, and gas as raw

[88] See W. Rudolfs and H. R. Amberg, *S. and I.W.*, September, 1952, p. 1108, and December, 1952, p. 1509.

[89] O. E. Muegge, *S. and I.W.*, June, 1953, p. 721.

[90] G. W. Gleeson, *Wastes Eng.*, August, 1951, p. 415.

[91] See K. H. Edmondson, *Wastes Eng.*, January, 1954, p. 30.

materials. The nuisance created is mainly tastes produced in water supplies, particularly after chlorination. The taste of phenols is noticeable in dilutions as high as 1 part of phenol in 750,000,000 parts of water, by weight.

Several methods are available for the disposal of phenol wastes, none of which is completely satisfactory. A relatively inexpensive method involves the evaporation of phenol-bearing liquid by using it to quench coke. It is possible to treat the waste by either activated sludge or trickling filters provided that it is diluted with sewage in a ratio of about 2 parts of waste in 98 of sewage. Centrifugal extractors have been reported as able to remove phenols from waste ammoniacal liquors.[92] Phenols have been oxidized by chlorine with color and odor removal.[93]

Valuable phenols may be reclaimed by passing the liquor through benzol scrubbers, where the phenol is removed by the benzol. The benzol is then scrubbed to remove the carbon dioxide and is next treated with caustic soda to form sodium phenolate. The dephenolated benzol is reused in the process and the sodium phenolate is treated with sulfuric acid to form sodium sulfate and phenol.

27–29. Radioactive wastes.[94] The increasing use of radioactive substances is focusing attention on the problem of the disposal of these indestructible substances.[95] Fortunately many of the substances are of such a nature that their nuclear disintegrations are sufficiently rapid as to render them harmless in a short time. On the other hand some materials may need storage for many years before becoming harmless. Hence, holding or storage until harmless is one method of handling some wastes.

Methods for the disposal of radioactive wastes include: (1) storage long enough to permit disintegration; (2) dilution in natural water courses, with inert substances, or by combining the radioactive isotope with the stable isotope of the same element; (3) burial in the ground; or (4) burial at sea.[96]

Disposal by dilution in natural bodies of water is not completely satisfactory. It has been estimated that if the world's consumption

[92] See H. R. Kaiser, *S. and I.W.*, March, 1955.

[93] See N. S. Chamberlin and A. E. Griffin, *S. and I.W.*, June, 1952, p. 750; and C. P. Straub, *Proc. Am. Soc. Civil Engrs.*, Vol. 83, Paper 1275, 1957.

[94] See also *S. and I.W.*, August, 1950, p. 1073, and March, 1956, pp. 280 and 286; and Abel Wolman and A. E. Gorman, *Wastes Eng.*, June, 1955.

[95] See also W. L. Wilson, *Proc. Inst. Civil Engrs.*, (Br.) Part III, April, 1955.

[96] See *S. and I.W.*, March, 1953, p. 313, and J. A. Liebermann, *Am. Jour. Public Health*, March, 1957, p. 345.

Table 27–14

SOME CHARACTERISTICS OF RADIOISOTOPES

Isotope	Half-life *	Grams Curies	Body Tissues Affected	Max Permissible Concentration	
				Microcuries per cc	mg/l
Uranium, U^{238}	4.5×10^9 yr	2.9×10^6	Bone	8×10^{-5}	
Radium, Ra^{226}	1.6×10^3 yr	1	Bone	4×10^{-8}	4×10^{-8}
Cesium, Cs^{137}	33 yr	3.8×10^{-2}	Muscle	1.5×10^{-3}	5.7×10^{-5}
Strontium, Sr^{90}	25 yr	6.1×10^{-3}	Bone	8×10^{-7}	4.9×10^{-9}
Strontium, Sr^{89}	53 d	3.6×10^{-5}	Bone	7×10^{-5}	2.5×10^{-9}
Phosphorus, P^{32}	14 d	3.4×10^{-6}	Bone	2×10^{-4}	6.8×10^{-10}
Iodine, I^{131}	8 d	7.8×10^{-6}	Thyroid	3×10^{-5}	2.3×10^{-10}
Sodium, Na^{24}	15 h	1.1×10^{-7}	Total body	8×10^{-3}	8.8×10^{-10}

* yr = years, d = days, h = hours.

of power generated by radioactivity continues at a normal rate the volume of water required for dilution, by the year A.D. 2000 would be greater than an appreciable percentage of the volume of the world's oceans.[97]

Some values of permissible concentrations, and other information concerning radioactive substances, are given in Table 27–14. Allowable limits for the discharge of radioactive wastes into sewers [98] are well below the limits [99] shown in the table. In general, a discharge of more than 100 microcuries per liter is not permissible. This might result in concentrations in sewage in the order of 0.25 to 0.6×10^{-4} microcurie per liter, which is less than standards for drinking water set by the Atomic Energy Commission.[100] However, reconcentration by biological activity, sedimentation, and other conditions may be possible.[101] The Atomic Energy Commission has approved [102] a regulation which permits discharge into sewers of radioactive wastes when: (1) the material is readily soluble in water, and (2) for each milligram of sewage the radioactive material shall not exceed one millicurie [103] of Strontium [90] or Polonium [210]; 100 mc of Iodine [131] or

[97] See also J. A. Liebermann, *Civil Eng.*, July, 1955, p. 44; and C. E. Renn, *Jour. Am. Water Works Assoc.*, May, 1956, p. 535.

[98] *Handbook* 49, U. S. Department of Commerce, National Bureau of Standards, 1951.

[99] See F. W. Kittrell, *S. and I.W.*, August, 1952, p. 985.

[100] See C. C. Ruchhoft and L. R. Setter, *S. and I.W.*, January, 1953, p. 48.

[101] See J. F. Newell and C. W. Christenson, *S. and I.W.*, July, 1951, p. 861.

[102] See *ibid.*, March, 1956, p. 322.

[103] Equal to 37×10^{-6} atomic disintegrations per second.

Phosphorus[32]; or any radioactive material having a half-life less than 30 days; or 10 mc of other radioactive material.

Radioactivity is destroyed only by radioactive disintegrations which are affected only by time. The treatment of radioactive wastes involves the removal of the radioactive particles from the waste; or the dilution of the waste to permissible limits of radioactive concentration. If the time required for radioactive disintegration in the retained portion of the waste is too long to permit storage then the waste must be buried in the earth or at sea.

If the waste is to be buried in the earth the selection of burial grounds is important. Consideration must be given to topographical, geological, economic, and other factors. These include soil stability both chemical and physical, ground-water movement, and other possibilities for the dissemination of the wastes either immediate or in the remote future. Burial grounds are forever withdrawn from any other use.[104] They must be fenced, posted, guarded, and monitored.

Burial at sea is considered even more expensive and dangerous than in the earth.[104] It is costly because of the special form of transportation required, the difficulty of finding proper areas for disposal into the ocean, and the cost of containers strong enough to resist disintegration, both chemical and physical, in the sea water at the great depths called for.

Where storage is required the wastes can be concentrated to reduce the required volume of storage containers.[105] Methods for the concentration of radioactive wastes, or their removal from solution,[106] include: (1) evaporation, (2) precipitation, (3) trickling or sand filtration,[107] (4) ion exchange, (5) electrodialysis, (6) metallic displacement or scrubbing, (7) differential volatility, (8) electrolytic separation, (9) solvent extraction, (10) biological processes, (11) crystallization, and (12) isotopic dilution. High-level fission products may be prepared in ceramic pellets from which the radioactive material cannot be leached and the pellets will not be crushed by ocean pressures. Isotopic dilution is effected by the addition of the stable isotope of the radioactive element.

27–30. Spirituous liquors. Distilleries,[108] breweries, malt houses, wineries, etc., produce wastes that may be classified as wastes from

[104] See A. B. Joseph, *Jour. Am. Water Works Assoc.*, May, 1956, p. 538.

[105] See Abel Wolman and A. E. Gorman, *Wastes Eng.*, June, 1955.

[106] See A. P. Straub, *S. and I.W.*, February, 1951, p. 188; and C. C. Ruchhoft and L. R. Setter, *S. and I.W.*, January, 1953, p. 48.

[107] See M. W. Carter, *S. and I.W.*, May, 1953, p. 560.

[108] See *Sewage Works Jour.*, March, 1942, p. 38.

Table 27–15

CHARACTERISTICS OF DISTILLERY WASTES

Typical 3,000-bu. distillery with dryhouse

(From A. B. Davidson, *Sewage and Ind. Wastes*, May, 1950, p. 654.)

Type of Waste	Amount, 1,000 gpd	Solids mg/l Total	Solids mg/l Sus-pended	BOD mg/l	BOD lb	pH	Temp, ° F
Evaporator condensate	45	130	12	600	225	3.9	125
Washes	21	1,050	400	1,000	176	6.0	70
Cooling tower overflow	24	1,100	200	550	110	8.0	115
Doubler *	3	240	40	1,000	26	5.0	170
Domestic sewage	7	830	300	200	14	6.8	70
Total or average	100	610	160	670	551	5.0	110

* Steam-heated kettle in which beer is redistilled or doubled to remove various impurities.

the production of spirituous liquors. In general each plant offers a special problem. Most of these industries produce wastes from three different sources that may be classed as process water, wash water, and cooling or condensing water. Some data on volumes and characteristics of distillery wastes are given in Table 27–15. The process water is usually the important waste. It may contain from 10,000 to 70,000 mg/l total solids, of which the major portion is dissolved organic matter.

Methods of treatment giving satisfactory results include activated sludge with high aeration, trickling filters at a relatively low rate of application of waste to filter surface, and chemical precipitation. Anaerobic digestion is not usually successful because of the acidity of the wastes, which makes the acid phase of digestion difficult to overcome, the volatile acid content of the digester rising above the critical 2,000 mg/l. Preliminary treatment of the wastes, to be successful must, therefore, be aerobic and rapid, like vacuum filtering, pressing, centrifuging, or fine screening. The solids removed from these processes usually contain valuable recoverable substances; the liquids are sent to the biological treatment devices in preparation for final disposal. For example, the dilution load from grain distillery has been reduced from 50 to 3 equivalent population per bushel of grain reclaimed for animal feed.[109]

[109] See C. S. Boruff and R. K. Blaine, *S. and I.W.*, October, 1953, p. 1179.

27–31. Steel industry. Wastes from the steel industry include those from coke wastes, blast furnaces, and rolling mills. The last may contain acids, alkalies, soluble and insoluble oils, and mill scale. The first stage in the treatment of such wastes is often their neutralization by controlled mixing. The most objectionable part of coke wastes are phenols and cyanogen compounds. The treatment of these wastes is discussed in Sects. 27–20 and 27–28. The cyanide problem has frequently been handled within the process. Coke quenching with recirculation of the quenching water eliminates phenols in wastes except for a residual trace in blast-furnace gas wash water. Suspended solids removed by plain sedimentation or with coagulation from blast-furnace, flue-gas wash water may be used for part of the blast-furnace charge. In some plants wastes, with the exception of flue-dust-laden waters, are combined and treated as follows: [110] primary thickener, 80 min; flash mixer, 1 min; flocculator, 25 min; final clarifier, 2 hr. Lime added maintains the pH between 8.0 and 8.2.

Neutralization with lime and the production of ferrous sulfate are two processes in use for the treatment of large quantities of steel manufacturing wastes. Wastes from the lime bath can be disposed of by mixing with normal sewage. The recovery of ferrous sulfate promises some value but it may not be commercially profitable.

27–32. Tanneries.[111] The process of tanning involves the washing, soaking, rinsing, and scrubbing of hides under various conditions and with different chemicals, many of the steps in process producing quantities of highly offensive, discolored, putrefactive, and odoriferous wastes.

The wastes from the processes generally include: (1) wash water from green hides, (2) wastes from the liming tanks and unhairing machines, (3) wash water from the fleshing and draining floors, (4) exhaust or spent tan-liquors and rinse water from vats in the layaway yard, (5) excess tan liquor carried by the heads and bellies when removed from the tanning vats, (6) leakage from the leaching vats and small amount of wash water, and (7) spent alkali and acids from bleaching vats. Some characteristics of tannery wastes are shown in Table 27–16.

All the wastes are alkaline except the acid bleach, the acid-water bleach, and the spent tan liquor. The intermittent wastes are the most difficult to treat; they furnish about three-fourths of the total BOD, whereas the continuous wastes furnish two-thirds of the volume

110 See H. H. Black and G. A. Howell, *S. and I.W.*, March, 1954, p. 286.
111 See J. W. Harnly, *Ind. Eng. Chem.*, Vol. 44, 1952, p. 520.

Table 27–16

CHARACTERISTICS OF TANNERY WASTES

(From R. Sutherland, *Ind. and Eng. Chem.*, Vol. 39, 1947, p. 628.)

Solids in 1,000 mg/l

Source of Waste	Total	Soluble	Sus-pended	Volatile, %	Ash, %	BOD, mg/l	pH
Soak	15	13.5	1.5	1.23	0.27	1,200	6.6
Lime	26	18.8	7.2	1.2	1.4	2,770	11.6
Wash, all types							
bate	4.4	4.3	0.11	0.32	0.12	410	8.2
pickle	61.2	60	1.24	0.59	5.53	790	2.4
Vegetable tan	18.4	17.1	1.29	1.50	0.34	5,500	5.0
Chrome tan	76.8	74.8	1.99	1.58	6.10	618	3.2
Color and fat liquor	2.46	2.01	0.45	0.06	0.18	472	3.9

and only one-fourth of the BOD. The spent tan-liquor and the three bleach liquors contain most of the coloring matter.

Most, but not all, authorities have reached the conclusion that the proper method of treating tannery wastes is to combine them and treat them by chemical precipitation, subsequently running them through trickling filters, humus tanks, and sand filters. According to Reuning,[112] coagulation and sedimentation of the combined wastes, with uniform discharge of clarified effluent, provides adequate treatment in many cases. Black [113] states that combined treatment with domestic sewage is common practice. Separation of the spent-vegetable tanning liquors and disposal by evaporation or lagooning is effective where a high degree of color removal is desired. Chemical treatment and filtration can be applied as a final step. Sludge can be dewatered on sand beds or by vacuum filters or centrifuges. Sludge lagooning has been found to be satisfactory. Under certain circumstances it may be more economical to separate the wastes so that those portions suitable for biological treatment may bypass the chemical precipitation process, being mixed with the effluent therefrom to form the influent to a trickling filter.

27–33. Textile wastes.[114] The wastes produced in the textile industry are of great variety in characteristics, quantity, and polluting

[112] H. T. Reuning, *Sewage Works Eng.*, March, 1949, p. 133.

[113] H. H. Black, *Civil Eng.*, October, 1955, p. 96.

[114] See E. F. Eldridge, *Bull.* 96, Michigan Engineering Experiment Station, 1942; and W. Rudolfs and N. L. Nemeron, *S. and I.W.*, Vol. 24, 1952, pp. 400, 661, and 882.

power. The principal processes of manufacture producing wastes to be cared for are: the bleaching of cotton; the bleaching and retting of flax, hemp, and jute; and silk boiling. The finishing processes include: dyeing and printing, stiffening and loading, carbonizing and stripping, and yarn washing and piece scouring. The wastes from the manufacturing processes are amenable to treatment by biological methods, whereas the finishing processes produce wastes best treated by chemical precipitation.

The processes of bleaching cotton, flax, hemp, and jute are essentially the same, so far as the quality of the wastes produced is concerned. The stage of the process that produces the most obnoxious waste consists of boiling the goods, under pressure, in the presence of milk of lime or soda. The waste is highly alkaline and contains fatty and oily matters that adhere to the fibers washed from the goods. The wastes from this stage should be treated separately from other wastes by neutralization and precipitation with sulfuric acid. The supernatant liquid can be mixed with the other wastes from the factory and the whole treated by biological means, preferably after being mixed with sewage.

The retting of flax, hemp, and jute consists in separating the crude fibers from the plant. The plants are steeped in water for a week or two until the fibers are softened by fermentation. The liquid waste has an offensive odor and is high in organic matter and in BOD. Since retting is usually accomplished in rural districts the liquid can be disposed of by broad irrigation or dilution. Otherwise the wastes may be neutralized with lime and precipitated with alum, the effluent from the sedimentation tank being treated by trickling filtration or the activated-sludge process.

Raw silk is boiled in successive vats of soap solution containing some sodium carbonate, to remove dirt and other foreign matters such as cocoons and dead worms adhering to the fibers. The waste from the boiling vats is a highly putrescible, thick, brown liquid of a jelly-like consistency. It contains soap, sericine, coloring matter, cocoons, chrysalids, and other organic matter. It has an offensive odor and putrefies rapidly. In quantity it can be estimated that about 275 gal of water and 25 to 35 lb of soap are used per 100 lb of silk washed.

In spite of its undesirable appearance the waste can be treated successfully by precipitation with aluminoferric or ferric chloride, and the effluent from the precipitation tank can be further treated by biological methods. The resulting sludge is difficult to treat, however, if it is desired to recover valuable products. It can be dried successfully on drying beds and disposed of for fertilizer, or buried.

In many processes of dyeing and printing textiles, the goods, which have been thoroughly washed, are soaked or boiled in the dye vats, either before or after passing through mordants to fix the color. They are then thoroughly washed again, either with clean water or with soap, soap bark, or fuller's earth. The waste is not highly polluting and can be cared for by screening and sedimentation, with or without chemical precipitation, followed by biological treatment if necessary. The screening is necessary to remove the relatively large amounts of loose fiber present, and chemical precipitation, followed even by sand filtration, may be necessary to remove color. Some special dyeing processes, such as indigo dyeing, involve intermediate treatment of the wastes to recover valuable products, the final wastes being amenable to methods of treatment similar to those available for the wastes from the majority of dyeing processes. Processes of dyeing involving the use of certain coal-tar derivatives dissolved in sodium sulfide produce wastes of a highly polluting character because of the high BOD. The volume of these wastes can be minimized by proper management of the process and recovery of by-products, the final waste being treated by chemical precipitation, the sludge dried on drying beds, and the supernatant liquid aerated and filtered biologically after mixing with sewage.

Wastes from stiffening and loading are small in amount and can be diluted with other textile wastes before final disposal or treatment by biological means. Carbonizing and stripping, processes in the manufacture of shoddy, a mixture of cotton and wool, produce acid wastes, alkaline wastes, and wash waters containing large quantities of solids, none of which is highly putrefying. The wastes can be mixed, neutralized, and settled without chemical precipitation, the effluent not requiring further treatment before disposal. Piece and yarn scouring are necessary since, in the process of manufacture of goods, grease and oil are added to the raw materials to make them workable. In the removal of these and other added substances, much wash water, soap, and some chemicals are used, producing soapy, turbid, putrid wastes, with a frothy scum. In treatment the grease may be recovered by acid cracking, as in the Miles acid process or wool-scouring processes, and the effluent may be neutralized with lime or other alkali, and treated biologically.

Methods for the treatment of textile wastes may be summarized as follows: (1) separation of wastes; (2) equalizing, also called composting or averaging; (3) screening, aeration, or other preliminary treatment; (4) mixing to cause self-precipitation, also called co-precipitation; (5) chemical precipitation; (6) mechanical filtration; (7) biological treatment, such as high-rate filtration [115] or the activated-sludge process; and (8) miscellaneous methods. Black [116] states that there appears to be a definite trend toward combined treatment of certain textile wastes with domestic sewage and that chemical treatment is frequently employed to augment plain sedimentation.

27–34. Wool washing. Wool washings constitute a highly polluting waste consisting of an emulsion of dirt and bacteria in water, with soap and complex proteins as emulsifying agents.[117] The washing of 100 lb of goods may be expected to produce 125 gal of waste with a BOD population equivalent of 57 and a suspended-solids population equivalent of 38. Considerable amounts of dissolved organic and nitrogenous compounds are present, and valuable lanoline may be recovered by proper treatment.

Methods of treatment of these wastes include coagulation and sedimentation, and acid cracking. Many coagulants have been tested, but those in most common use include calcium chloride, calcium chloride with carbon dioxide, and calcium hypochlorite.[118] Acid cracking with sulfuric acid breaks the emulsion and precipitates the grease, after which it is drawn off to be discharged onto drying beds. After drying, the greasy sludge is filter-pressed under heat and may be further refined. The effluent from the acid-cracking tank is highly acid but of good appearance. It may require further treatment before final disposal. It is best neutralized with lime and allowed to settle, after which it can usually be disposed of without further treatment. Other methods for the recovery of lanoline may be adopted, such as centrifuging, or diffusing air through a shallow tank containing the waste and skimming off the greasy froth that is formed. Neither of these methods is so effective in recovering a grease or in producing a good effluent as the method of acid cracking, but under some conditions they may be more economical. Black [119] reports that calcium chloride treatment has given BOD reductions of 70 per cent and grease removals of more than 90 per cent.

[115] See R. H. Souther and T. A. Alspaugh, *Am. Dyestuff Reporter*, June 6, 1955; and abstract in *Public Works*, August, 1955, p. 122.

[116] H. H. Black, *Civil Eng.*, October, 1955, p. 96.

[117] See J. A. McCarthy, *Sewage Works Jour.*, January, 1949, p. 75.

[118] H. H. Black, *loc. cit.*

[119] H. H. Black, *loc. cit.*

Attempts to recover grease by soaking the unwashed wool in solvents is usually objected to because of the undesirable condition in which the wool is left for further manufacturing processes. Wool-washing plants can, in general, be so controlled that there need be very little discharge of liquid refuse, and that little should be of a nature that renders it easy to treat for disposal.

Chapter 28

Summary of
sewage-treatment processes

28–1. Combinations of processes. In combining various sewage-treatment devices a logical procedure must be followed. Biological processes may be arranged to follow the "cycle of life and death" described in Sect. 15–28 in such a manner that anaerobic action will precede oxidation, sedimentation will precede filtration, and so forth. For example, an intermittent sand filter would be illogically followed by a septic tank.

Flowing-through diagrams of typical sewage-treatment processes illustrating some combinations used are shown in Fig. 28–1.

28–2. Bases of selection. The selection of any particular process of sewage treatment must be based on the study of a number of conditions such as:

The quality of the sewage to be treated.

The conditions downstream after treatment.

The efficiency and characteristics of the treatment process.

The quality and amount of diluting water available.

The conditions for the disposal of sludge.

The availability of materials, and the life of structures and equipment.

The availability and experience of operating personnel.

The facilities for maintenance and repair.

The area, the topography, and the subsurface conditions at the site.

The available fall (hydraulic head) needed for operation.

Construction and operation costs, and the amount of money available.

These conditions cannot be set apart independently, and rules cannot be fixed for the adoption of a particular type of treatment for

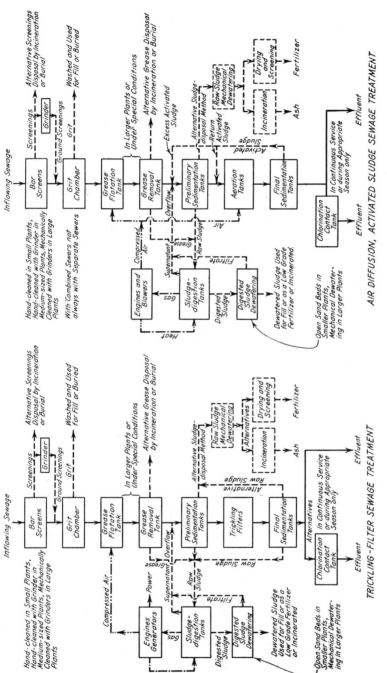

Fig. 28–1. Flowing-through diagrams of typical sewage-treatment processes. (By permission of Samuel A. Greeley and Wm. E. Stanley, from *Davis Handbook of Applied Hydraulics*, McGraw-Hill Book Co.)

each condition, because the type of treatment process to be selected is dependent on all the conditions and the manner of their combination. For example, if a strong, stale sewage is flowing into the dry bed of a stream it would need extensive treatment to prevent odors, yet if the same strong sewage were to discharge into a large stream it might not require any treatment. It would not be correct to conclude that all strong sewages must be extensively treated.

In considering the efficiency and characteristics of any treatment process neither the total nor the per cent reduction of any characteristic is an adequate measure of the plant performance. The criterion must be the quality of the effluent produced.

In comparing the processes of sewage treatment it must be borne in mind that operation may be of more importance than design and that by proper operation the nature of the effluent can be altered so that some processes of sewage treatment may give desirable results under unfavorable conditions.

28–3. Dilution requirement. The dilution requirement has been the most important and often the only consideration in the determination of the treatment process to be adopted. If the quantity of diluting water available is low, the treatment must be more complete than if plenty of good water is available for dilution. An arrangement of the various sewage-treatment processes in the approximate order of the magnitude from the greatest to the least dilution requirements of their effluents would place them somewhat as follows:

Dilution	Chemical precipitation
Grit chambers	Contact beds
Coarse screens	High-rate filters
Fine screens	Contact aerators
Septic tanks	Trickling filters
Sedimentation	Activated sludge
Imhoff tanks	Intermittent sand filters
Chlorination	Broad irrigation

The above order is not exact, and not all the processes have been included in the list. It may be possible by the careful operation of a trickling filter to produce an effluent requiring less dilution than is required by the effluent from an activated-sludge unit operating with a small amount of air, or for a sedimentation-tank effluent to require less dilution than a septic-tank effluent, and so forth. The above order presupposes equally careful operation and that all conditions with regard to the quality of the sewage to be treated are the same.

The dilution demand by the processes listed will vary from the greatest demand by crude sewage to no dilution required by the effluent from an intermittent sand filter.

Combinations of the processes are common and sometimes necessary. Grit chambers, coarse screens, Imhoff tanks, and trickling filters are frequently combined, the sewage running through them in the order stated. Certain other combinations would be unnecessary and inefficient. There would be no purpose in running the effluent from a septic tank through an Imhoff tank.

28–4. Plant performance. The principal measures of the performance of a sewage-treatment process are its efficiency in the reduction of BOD and of suspended solids, and in the quantity of these in the effluent. Limitations of performance which may be expected are listed in Table 28–1. Among the important physical characteristics to be considered in the effluent are appearance of the effluent, appearance of the body of diluting water after receiving the effluent, and sludge-bank forming potentialities. Some improvements effected by several sewage-treatment processes are listed in Table 28–2.

Table 28–1

LIMITATIONS OF OVERALL REMOVALS TO BE EXPECTED FROM VARIOUS
STAGES OF SEWAGE-TREATMENT PROCESSES *

Percentages of Removal

Method of Treatment	BOD	Suspended Solids
Primary	25–40	40–70
Chemical precipitation	50–75	70–90
Trickling filtration, conventional	80–95	80–90
High-rate trickling filter, single stage	60–85 †	. . .
High-rate trickling filter, two stage	80–95	. . .
Activated sludge	85–95	85–95
Sand filtration (intermittent)	90–95	85–95
Rapid sand filtration ‡	60–85	80–95

* From "Sewage Works Design Standards," published by Pollution Control Commission, Pacific Northwest Basin, 1951. These agree with information published by L. G. Rice in *Water and Sewage Works*, October, 1950, p. 436, except as noted.

† L. G. Rice gives single-stage limits as 60–80, and two-stage as 60–95.

‡ These figures are given by L. G. Rice only.

Table 28–2

IMPROVEMENT IN SEWAGE EFFECTED BY SEVERAL TREATMENT PROCESSES *

Type of Plant	Location	Year	Popu- lation, 1,000's	Flow, mgd	Suspended Solids mg/l Infl.	Suspended Solids % Red'n	BOD mg/l Infl.	BOD % Red'n	Source of Informa- tion from S. and I.W.
P	Detroit, Mich.	1949	2,500	394.3	228	53	140	44	July, 1950, p. 944
P	Kenosha, Wis.	1949	...	11.4	150	53	101	40	June, 1950, p. 841
P	Rochester, Mich.	1948	4.2	0.5	251	72	197	47	Jan., 1950, p. 115
P	Danville, Ill.	1950	35	4.7	183	61	211	61	Aug., 1951, p. 1050
P	Dist. of Columbia	1953	1,038	163.8	207	81	139	32	July, 1955, p. 861
P	Dist. of Columbia	1954	1,031	159.4	178	56	142	31	July, 1955, p. 861
I	Dallas, Texas	'49 '50	484	38.2	347	78	316	38	Aug., 1951, p. 1048
I	Worcester, Mass.	1949	187	21.8	205	67	220	80	Jan., 1952, p. 100
IRT	Worcester, Mass.	1953	190	32.1	158	88	139	84	July, 1956, p. 936
IRT	Worcester, Mass.	1954	200	29.1	103	74	121	83	July, 1956, p. 936
ITF	Dallas, Texas	'49 '50	484	38.2	347	90	316	72	Aug., 1951, p. 1048
ITF	Worcester, Mass.	1949	187	21.8	205	86	220	79	Jan., 1952, p. 100
ITF	Worcester, Mass.	1948	187	26.1	147	63	208	62	July, 1950, p. 948
ITF	Fond du Lac, Wis.	1955	31.5	4.0	595	94	205	84	Feb., 1957, p. 228
ITF	Toledo, Ohio	1953	...	41.1	214	94	209	23	June, 1955, p. 749
TFT	Dallas, Texas	'49 '50	484	38.2	78	56	196	85	Aug., 1951, p. 1048
TFT	Worcester, Mass.	1949	187	21.8	68	57	145	68	Jan., 1952, p. 100
TFT	Worcester, Mass.	1948	187	26.1	49	8	126	37	July, 1950, p. 948
AS	New Britain, Conn.	'49 '50	80	11.3	209	80	187	71	Nov., 1950, p. 1489
AS	Airport, Miami, Fla.	1950	2.8	0.09	320	97	192	99	Aug., 1951, p. 1046
AS	Muskegon Hts., Mich.	1950	20	1.75	238	83	247	90	Jan., 1952, p. 102
AS	Jackson, Mich.	1955	50	10	184	93	143	96	Feb., 1957, p. 229
AS	Cranston, R. I.	1954	35.6	3.8	192	83	266	89	April, 1957, p. 489
AS	Easterly, Cleveland, Ohio	1954	...	103.9	198	94	147	93	April, 1957, p. 489

* All information from *S. and I.W.*, as indicated in last column of the table.
P = primary treatment, usually involving sedimentation and separate sludge digestion.
I = Imhoff tank. See Table 20–3 for other results.
ITF = Imhoff tank, trickling filter, and final sedimentation.
TFT = trickling filter and final sedimentation.
AS = activated sludge and final sedimentation.

28–5. Area requirements. Sewage-treatment processes are listed in Table 28–3 in the relative order of the area required per unit rate of flow through them. This order is based on the rates of flow for each process stated.

28–6. Sludge production. The production of sludge may prevent the adoption of a process of sewage treatment otherwise desirable. The bulk of sludge, the difficulties of its disposal, and the cost of preparation therefor are all-important considerations in the choice of a process of sewage treatment. The activated-sludge process re-

Table 28–3

RELATIVE AREA REQUIREMENTS BY SEWAGE-TREATMENT PROCESSES

Process	Number of Persons Cared for per Acre	Process	Number of Persons Cared for per Acre
Sewage farming in the United States		Activated sludge	120,000
in Europe		Trickling filter,	
Lagooning	300	high capacity	200,000
Intermittent sand		Bisorption	480,000 *
filtration	1,500	Plain sedimentation	
Contact beds		Chemical treatment	
Trickling filter		Fine screening and	
conventional	37,500	comminution	

* From G. W. Reid, *Public Works*, July, 1955, p. 89.

Note: The process with the largest requirements is listed first.

quires less dilution than most other sewage-treatment processes and yet, the volume of sludge produced is greater than in any other process. Under conditions where the disposal of sludge is difficult the activated-sludge process would be less desirable than some other process producing less sludge. The quantities of sludge produced in different sewage-treatment processes are indicated in Table 24–4.

28–7. Cost. (See also Sect. 2–4.) A comparison of the costs of various sewage-treatment processes should include the first cost, the cost of operation, and the cost of amortization. The last item is difficult to estimate, particularly as most plants become obsolete before they are worn out. One result is that cost comparisons are sometimes made by considering only the first cost and the cost of operation.

Valuable and comprehensive data on the costs of sewage-treatment plants are contained in a report made in 1927 by Alvord, Burdick, and Howson [1] to the United States District Engineer in Chicago. Valuable data were published more recently by Schroepfer,[2] many of which are reproduced in tables in this text applicable to different processes of sewage treatment. Other information by Schroepfer is given in Tables 23–7 and 28–4, and some operating costs are given in Tables 28–5 and 28–6. The information is of value for comparative pur-

[1] See *Bull.* 23, Illinois State Water Survey, 1927.

[2] See *Proc. Am. Soc. Civil Engrs.*, April, 1938, p. 737.

Table 28–4

Costs of Trickling Filter Plants

(From G. P. Schroepfer, *Proc. Am. Soc. Civil Engrs.*, April, 1938, p. 737.)

Costs in Thousands of Dollars

Plant Capacity or Sewage Treated, mgd	Construction Cost			Operation and Maintenance Cost		
	Usual Lower Limit	Estimated in This Analysis	Usual Higher Limit	Usual Lower Cost	Estimated in This Analysis	Usual Higher Cost
10	900	1,200	1,500	22	30	38
25	2,130	2,850	3,550	47	62	78
50	4,130	5,500	6,850	83	110	138
75	6,000	8,000	10,000	115	155	195
100	7,900	10,500	13,200	145	195	245

Table 28–5

Sewage-Treatment-Plant Operating Costs Related to BOD and Suspended Solids

(From Edmund B. Besselievre, *Eng. News-Record*, June 14, 1945, p. 91.)

Plant Location	Type of Plant	Cost of Operation, dollars per million gallons	BOD, ppm		Cost in Dollars per 100 pounds BOD Removed	Suspended Solids, ppm		Cost in Dollars per 100 pounds Suspended Solids Removed
			Raw Sewage	Per Cent Removal		Raw Sewage	Per Cent Removal	
Rockville Centre, N. Y.	AS	59.68	288	86.3	2.90	234	89.3	3.42
Hartford, Conn.	SD	14.90	137	13.0	9.92	117	78.6	1.94
Anderson, Ind.	Gug.	17.73	157	91.7	1.47	233	88.9	1.02
Gary, Ind.	AS	8.79	133	94.5	0.84	229	97.4	0.47
Galesburg, Ill.	TF	15.94	165	81.9	1.42	193	83.4	1.18
Pasadena, Calif.	AS	10.86	149	91.1	1.75	303	91.1	0.86
Elgin, Ill.	SDTF	13.79	123	72.4	1.86	196	81.2	0.98
Danville, Ill.	CP	15.73	185	53.0	1.92	148	60.8	2.07
Waukegan, Ill.	CP	19.22	195	51.3	2.31	201	75.0	1.53
Washington, D. C.	SD	4.39	171	31.6	0.97	180	50.6	0.58
Ft. Dodge, Ia.	SDTF	27.94	825	91.0	0.44	616	90.4	0.60
Urbana-Champaign, Ill.	ITF	16.11	314	91.0	0.67	211	84.3	0.82
1	2	3	4	5	6	7	8	9

AS = activated sludge; SD = sedimentation and separate sludge digestion; Gug. = Guggenheim process; TF = trickling filters; CP = chemical precipitation; SDTF = sedimentation and separate sludge digestion with trickling filters; and ITF = Imhoff tank and trickling filter.

Table 28-6

COSTS OF SMALL SEWAGE-TREATMENT PLANTS IN ILLINOIS AND IOWA

Illinois *					Op'n Costs, dollars			Iowa †			
City	Type	Year Built	Design Pop. in 1,000's	Const'n Costs, dollars per cap.	Per Cap. Equiv.	Per 1,000 lb BOD Removed	Per Cap. Con-nected	City	Design Pop. Equiv. 1,000's	Year	Const'n Costs, dollars per cap. pop. equiv.
Activated Sludge								Alta	2.1	1951	48.50
Belvidere	SS, Am	1937	10	15.00	0.80	13.52	0.81	Clear Lake	16	1954	36.40
Chicago Hts.	SS, Ad	1936	30	8.37	0.51	8.80	0.49	Griswold	1.4	1952	65.30
Kewanee	SS, Am	1937	20	7.30	0.24	4.11	0.51	Grundy Center	2.5	1954	52.00
Springfield	SS, Ad	1929	90	8.24	0.69	11.99	0.54	Laurens	2.7	1953	46.20
Trickling Filters								Manchester	5.4	1951	36.30
Aurora	SS, Fn	1929	67	10.90	0.60	12.16	0.51	Maxwell	1.2	1953	48.20
Bloomington-Normal	I, Fn	1928	55	12.06	0.88	15.55	0.71	New Sharon	1.3	1953	47.00
Clinton	I, Fr	1935	12	7.67	. . .	. . .	0.65	North English	2.0	1953	57.20
Decatur	Ad, I, Fn ‡	1924	60	17.13	0.27	4.75	0.53	Onawa	5.8	1950	32.70
Dekalb	SS, Fn	1930	16	10.46	0.38	6.89	0.63	Reinbeck	1.9	1953	51.60
Elgin	SS, I, Fn	1926	40	13.09	0.84	18.82	0.67	Rock Rapids	4.4	1953	45.30
Galesburg	SS, I, Fn	1932	24	14.36	1.05	23.67	1.02	Indianola	7.1	1953	32.60
Hinsdale	I, Fn	1930	18	18.47	0.70	12.45	0.89	Jefferson	6.2	1950	27.00
Chemical Precipitation								Knoxville	9.2	1949	22.50
Danville	M, SS	1937	40	5.39	0.63	19.06	0.72	Williamsburg	2.0	1953	41.40
Waukegan	M, I	1937	50	12.00	0.78	23.91	0.83				

* From H. E. Babbitt and G. L. Farnsworth, "Operation Costs in 15 Illinois Sewage Treatment Plants," *Sewage Works Jour.*, January, 1942, p. 97.

† From P. E. Morgan and E. R. Baumann, *S. and I.W.*, March, 1955, p. 257.

‡ Preaeration plant operated only for short time each year.

Ad = activated sludge, diffused air; Am = activated sludge, mechanical aeration; Fn = trickling filters, nozzle distribution; Fr = trickling filters, rotary distributors; I = Imhoff tanks; M = chemical precipitation; SS = separate sedimentation.

poses only; if used for present-day conditions the appropriate cost indices must be applied.

Costs of construction and operation of sewage-treatment plants and of pumping stations were estimated for 1960 by Brown and Caldwell [3] in their 1958 report on the sewerage and drainage of Seattle, Wash. These costs are limited to plants larger than 5 mgd and are based on an *Engineering News-Record* index of 800. The costs are:

Construction.

Primary plants	$C_1 = 210Q_1^{0.8}$	(28–1)
Secondary plants	$C_1 = 380Q_1^{0.8}$	(28–2)

Operation.

Pumping stations,		
single stage	$C_2 = HQ_2^{0.9}/62$	(28–3)
Primary plants	$C_2 = 20Q^{0.63}$	(28–4)
	$C_3 = 52/Q^{0.37}$	(28–5)
Secondary plants	$C_2 = 24Q^{0.64}$	(28–6)
	$C_3 = 62/Q^{0.37}$	(28–7)

where C_1 = costs, thousands of dollars.

C_2 = annual operating costs, thousands of dollars.

C_3 = costs per million gallons treated.

H = lift, feet.

Q_1 = design capacity, mgd, limited to a minimum of 5.

Q_2 = peak, wet-weather flow, mgd.

The *Engineering News-Record* cost index was 700 in 1957, and 100 in 1913. It has risen in a straight line, since 1947, according to the expression

$$I = 400 + 30y \qquad (28\text{–}8)$$

where I is the cost index and y is the number of years after 1947.

Morgan and Baumann,[4] in 1955, gave costs of construction of sewage-treatment plants for Iowa communities, on a basis of dollars per capita of design population, as follows: (1) complete treatment, including trickling filters, for 17 cities between 5,000 and 117,000 population, maximum $50, average $36, and minimum $26; (2) primary treatment in 12 cities between 6,000 and 113,000 population, maximum $48, average $26, and minimum $11; (3) primary treatment for 13 villages with population between 700 and 2,000, maximum $39, average $29, and minimum $22; and (4) complete treatment for vil-

---

[3] Consulting engineers of San Francisco.

[4] P. E. Morgan and E. R. Baumann, *S. and I.W.*, March, 1955, p. 257.

Table 28–7

STATUS OF SEWAGE TREATMENT *

Source of Sewage	Number of Plants	Persons Served, millions	Method of Treatment	Number of Plants	Persons Served, millions
Connected to sewers		74.7	Sand filters	448	0.98
Discharging raw sewage		27.9	Applied to land	422	1.30
Discharging treated sewage		46.8	Oxidizing ponds	45	0.16
Method of Treatment			Contact beds	67	0.21
Septic tanks	1,291	1.32	Dunbar filters	59	0.16
Imhoff tanks	1,073	4.86	Contact aeration	17	0.64
Separate tanks	465	10.98	Magnetite filters	19	1.68
Chemical treatment	197	5.25	Miscellaneous	30	0.26
Activated sludge	324	11.56			
Trickling filter:			Total	5,786	46.8 †
standard rate	1,459	8.76			
high rate	122	0.71			

* From J. R. Thoman, *Supplement 213, Public Health Reports,* 1950.
† Discrepancies in total are caused, in part, by duplications in the list.

lages with populations between 700 and 4,000, maximum $88, average $53, and minimum $33.

Cost data published in previous years may be compared with up-to-date conditions by the application of the cost index, published periodically in *Engineering News-Record.*

28–8. Trickling filters and activated sludge. Two methods of secondary treatment that are frequently competitive are trickling filters and activated sludge. For example, the trickling filter is considered to be more "rugged," that is, capable of functioning satisfactorily under sudden changes of quality or rate of flow of influent. On the other hand the physical appearance, and often the quality of the effluent, from the activated-sludge process is superior and the nitrates in the effluent are more easily controlled. The utilization of oxygen in the reduction of BOD by the two processes has been shown to be in the order of 1 cu ft of oxygen per gal of sewage treated. This similarity is despite the fact that the reduction of BOD depends on the condition of the organic matter in the sewage and on the manner of its exposure to oxidation. For example, a raw sewage and a settled sewage, each with a BOD of 100 mg/l cannot be expected to utilize equal unit weights of oxygen, nor can the conditions of oxygen utilization in a trickling filter be expected to match those in an activated-sludge tank, since one contains mostly bacteria and the other protozoa.[5]

[5] See A. Rumpf, *S. and I.W.,* March, 1956, p. 260.

On the basis of dollars per pound of 5-day BOD removed, total annual costs are usually unfavorable to the trickling filter for large installations but are in its favor for small plants. The advent of the high-rate filter may change this situation, but, in turn, the low cost of power from sludge gas is a factor in favor of the activated-sludge process.

28–9. Sewage-treatment plant installations. The relative importance of various sewage-treatment processes, based on the number of installations in the United States, is indicated by the information in Table 28–7.

Chapter 29

Plant operation
and maintenance

29–1. Principles.[1] Maintenance involves the work devoted to keeping a plant running. It can be classified as preventive maintenance,[2] which constitutes work and precautions taken to prevent breakdown, and corrective maintenance which involves the making of repairs after breakdown. Preventive maintenance is more economical and provides reliability in operation. Operation involves the maintenance and running of the plant. The operator receives the devices and instruments prepared for him by the designer and has the responsibilities of making them work. Fortunate is the operator whose designer has had the experience with, and retains active understanding of, problems of the operator. An operator must expect trouble. The facilities of the plant are at his service to overcome them.

Some features of design that the operator feels should be considered before the plant is built include: [3] (1) Machinery should be indoors, under cover. (2) Outside valves should be eliminated and quarter-turn valves save time. (3) Motors should not be on the floor. (4) Pumps should be connected direct to sludge lines rather than to wells. (5) Proper capacity at lift stations is important. (6) If a pipe discharges into a wet well or similar container, the end of the pipe should be such that a connection can be made to it. (7) Automatic switches should be provided on pumps handling drainage or overflows. (8) Piping should be short. (9) Sludge pipes should

---

[1] See W. H. Wisely and L. W. Van Kleeck, *Mun. San.*, 1937.

[2] See F. A. Sanders, *S. and I.W.*, March, 1954, p. 329.

[3] See also A. F. Lehmann, *Am. City*, May, 1942; and recommendations by operators, *S. and I.W.*, May, 1957, p. 601; and R. O. Sylvester, *S. and I.W.*, July, 1955, p. 757.

be of generous size. (10) It should be possible to operate groups of tanks as a unit. (11) Tanks should not float or crack when emptied. (12) Provisions should be made for recirculating sludge in digesters, and for returning unfilterable sludge. (13) Provision should be made for sludge withdrawal from settling tanks. (14) Provision should be made for shelter for the operator in wet weather. (15) An adequate system of walks, with railings in hazardous places, should be provided. (16) Maintenance problems resulting from steep embankments should be avoided. (17) Good ventilation should be provided where needed. (18) A fence should be provided around the plant, and around open tanks. (19) A workshop, wash room, and locker room should be provided. (20) Stairways should be used instead of ladders. (21) Windows that are easily broken in outlying structures should be avoided.

29–2. Personnel. Various authorities have set standards of qualifications for operators of sewage-treatment plants, and in some states certificates of competency are either granted by a state authority or are required by law.[4]

Qualifications proposed by a committee of the American Society of Civil Engineers [5] are:

A *Grade A* Superintendent should be a graduate of an engineering technical school of recognized standing, and should have had experience for not less than five years in problems relating to sewage treatment. He should also be able to supervise and direct the work of others.

A *Grade B* Superintendent should be at least a high school graduate with additional training in chemistry and engineering, and should have had experience for not less than five years in problems relating to sewage treatment. He should be able to supervise and direct the work of others.

A *Grade C* Superintendent should have at least an elementary school education with the training equivalent to that of a skilled mechanic or skilled laborer. He should be able to supervise and direct the work of others.

Grades of Superintendent Required. All sewage-treatment plants should be operated under technical control and supervision.

In the case of large plants, serving approximately 100,000 or more people and involving such treatment as Imhoff tanks, sedimentation and separate sludge digestion, trickling filters, or the activated sludge process, *Grade A* Superintendents should be employed.

For moderate-size plants, serving approximately 50,000 to 100,000 people, *Grade B* Superintendents may be satisfactory; but for more complicated

[4] See also *Sewage Works Jour.*, January, 1948, p. 137.
[5] See *Trans. Am. Soc. Civil Engrs.*, Vol. 95, 1931, p. 1273.

plants it is desirable to have the operation supervised by a sanitary engineer or chemist who has the qualifications of a *Grade A* Superintendent.

In the case of less complicated plants, such as fine screening, serving less than about 50,000 persons, *Grade C* Superintendents may be satisfactory, provided there is adequate supervision by a sanitary engineer or chemist with the qualifications of a *Grade B* or a *Grade A* Superintendent. For small plants of a complicated type, or for dealing with difficult conditions, a *Grade B* or a *Grade A* Superintendent may be required.

Qualifications proposed by a committee of the Federation of Sewage Works Associations [6] are similar to the preceding but more detailed.

The morale of the personnel of a plant will be helped if: (1) job classification, duties, and titles are specified; (2) incentives are established for performance of duties; (3) operational cost records are made available to the operators; (4) the state is called on when assistance is needed; and (5) time is allowed for the work required to make the plant attractive to visitors.

The number of employees required at a plant will depend on the size and type of the plant, with an average of about 80 employees per million population served by secondary treatment, and a proportionally larger number per unit of population for smaller plants. Primary plants may require only about 75 per cent of the number of employees required in secondary treatment.[7]

Costs of operation lie between about $24 per million gal for primary plants smaller than one mgd, down to $13 for plants above about 6 mgd capacity. The cost of operation of secondary plants may be between 12 and 25 per cent more than for primary plants.

29–3. Duties. The principal duty of the operator is to run his plant so that it will fulfill its purpose, but to do only this is insufficient. The operator must maintain the plant and equipment to protect the capital investment; expend the funds allotted to him with the best combination of effectiveness and economy; maintain records and make reports to prove the efficacy of his plant; and maintain cordial relations with the public so that his plant and its accomplishments may receive public support.

The accomplishment of any one of these duties may aid in the accomplishment of others. For example, keeping the buildings and grounds attractive will preserve the investment, please the public, support the morale of the personnel, and be conducive to satisfactory operation. The principles of good housekeeping should control in this

[6] See *Sewage Works Jour.,* November, 1943, p. 1235.
[7] See also *Wastes Eng.,* March, 1955, p. 134.

maintenance. Dust is an abomination; cobwebs should be unknown; a routine weekly schedule of sweeping, dusting, lawncutting, leaf-raking, and so forth, should be followed. There is no excuse for un-cleanliness in an adequately manned plant.

The operator should have control over the sewer system so that he can prevent its unauthorized use either through improper connec-tions or through dumping improper materials into it. The existence of such connections can sometimes be detected through too large a flow during storms and an unusual night flow when the rate of flow of sewage should drop with the rate of water consumption. The appearance of such matter as industrial wastes, oil, or brewers' mash can frequently be traced to the industry creating it, and cooperation can be effected to minimize or adjust the load on the plant.

29–4. Hazards.[8] The work of an operator of a sewage-treatment plant presents many hazards that must be guarded against. Prob-ably the most spectacular are the hazards of poisonous, asphyxiating, or explosive gases. Accidents from these are rare in comparison with injuries from falls, deaths from drowning, and strains from overexertion in closing or opening valves, moving weights, and other tasks. Icy, narrow walks over tanks to be traversed in dark, rain, fog, and wind; ladders and spiral staircases; all offer an ever-present danger against which the operator must always be alert. Gas masks should be available in a location that cannot become contaminated by gas. First aid should be applied quickly to cuts and bruises, which must be kept uncontaminated by the environment. Food must not be eaten from dirty hands.

29–5. Maintenance of buildings and other structures. Some items to be considered in the maintenance of buildings and other structures are:

1. Avoid corrosion by hydrogen sulfide that will attack lead paint, certain metals, and concrete. To do this: ventilate, operate to avoid unenclosed putrefaction, burn gases, use corrosion-resistant metal, and use bituminous or zinc paints. Conditions conducive to the pro-duction of hydrogen sulfide in sewers include [9] the temperature, the strength, and the turbulence of the flow of sewage. The control of sulfates is reported as valueless in affecting the production of hydro-gen sulfide in sewers.

[8] See also Sect. 13–4 and *Sewage Works Jour.*, July, 1938, p. 731.
[9] See R. Pomeroy and F. D. Bowlus, *Sewage Works Jour.*, July, 1946, p. 597.

2. Avoid and reduce dampness and condensation. Do this through: good ventilation, the insulation of cold-water pipes, and by warming the atmosphere.

3. Use good paint plentifully. (See also Sect. 7–32.) Cheap paint wastes labor. Apply paint only to a *clean* surface, free from grease, oil or rust. Use a standard color scheme such as that of the American Standards Association, or a modification thereof.[10]

4. Weather-proof concrete to avoid spalling. This can be done by applying high-penetration asphalt at a high temperature in warm weather to dry concrete previously cleaned and washed with a dilute acid solution.

5. Plug all leaks in concrete tanks.

6. Keep the interior of buildings and enclosures clean, ventilated, and illuminated when in use.

7. Avoid freezing temperatures where pipes containing standing water or sewage may be exposed to them. Otherwise, drain the pipes.

8. Avoid accumulations of quiescent pools of surface water that may serve as breeding places for mosquitoes and other insects. Where pools cannot be filled in or drained they should be coated with oil in the event that mosquito larvae (wigwags) are observed.

29–6. Care of grounds. A sewage-treatment plant need not be a public garden, but those that approach this ideal are high in public favor. Ordinarily the maintenance of grounds requires no more than reasonable skill and attention in keeping the roads and walks in good condition, controlling weeds, cutting the lawn, trimming the shrubbery and the trees, raking the leaves, shoveling the snow, and keeping the grounds "policed." Attractive results can be obtained by means of shrubbery and trees not requiring unusual care. Elaborateness and ornateness should be avoided unless adopted as a policy to attract public attention.

Many interested operators become active in landscaping the grounds, with the advice of garden enthusiasts and other public-spirited citizens who can be and should be interested. Through co-operation with a park board it may be possible to attain the same end, i.e., a well-landscaped site.

29–7. Care of equipment.[11] Some helpful hints in the maintenance of equipment are included in the following list of suggestions:

---

[10] See Chas. Saunders, *S. and I.W.*, August, 1955, p. 967.
[11] See *Sewage Works Jour.*, May, 1941, p. 603, and January, 1942, p. 185.

1. Maintain a file of all instruction sheets and other printed or written material concerning each piece of equipment, and post important operating instructions in a readable and protected position near each piece of equipment.

2. Lubricate according to directions with the lubricant that is recommended or that experience has proved to be satisfactory.

3. Clean, wipe, paint, or otherwise protect equipment from grease, grit, and corrosion.

4. Periodically check for leaks, squeaks, and wear in machinery, and test for efficiency. Equipment will last longer and the demand for power will be lessened.

5. Periodically test safety devices on electrical equipment. Both the equipment and the operator may last longer.

6. Periodically examine equipment for clean contacts, armatures smooth and free from grooving, arcing brushes, corroded or worn insulation, cleanliness and lubrication of spindles on magnetic switches, clogging of dash pots, and labels on switchboards, cabinets, and other equipment. Carbon tetrachloride is a good cleaner for electrical equipment.

7. Avoid the use of aluminum paint on switchboards; use asphaltic enamels.

8. Maintain a record of inspections, observations, and repairs. More efficient maintenance will result, and things are less likely to be overlooked.

Ice formation is a common difficulty in winter operation of exposed equipment in cold climates. It is fought by the use of sodium or calcium chloride, or by spraying relatively warm sewage continuously on the rails or other parts of the equipment subjected to ice formation.

29–8. Odor control.[12] Odors from sewage-treatment plants are the most common cause of complaint. The most common sources of odor are points of contact between sewage and the atmosphere as in grit and screen chambers, tank surfaces, dosing chambers, trickling filters, sludge movements, sludge-drying beds, and sludge-drying equipment. Odors may be avoided by making changes in the sewer system to assure fresher sewage reaching the treatment plant; diluting stale sewage with water or plant effluent during periods of low sewage flow; reducing periods of detention in tanks holding septic material; maintaining immaculate cleanliness about the plant; enclosing odor-

[12] See *ibid.*, September, 1941, p. 956, and November, 1941, p. 1230; and *Water Works and Sewerage*, June, 1945, p. R-237.

producing devices and ventilating them into ducts leading to gas incinerators with a temperature above 2,100° F; using activated carbon; and using chlorine.[13]

Odors are being controlled at some plants by spraying vapor-counteractants into the air at the source of odor production and where conditions are favorable to the production and dissemination of odors.[14]

29-9. Operation records.[15] A thorough set of records should be maintained, but this need not be either exhausting or discouraging. Satisfactory records may include a daily log and a daily weather record, together with a set of maintenance cards. The daily log should cover all non-routine events,[16] and the maintenance cards should contain a complete record of each item of equipment, structure, or other feature requiring preventive maintenance.[17] Each card should contain the history of the item it represents, with the manufacturer's directions for operation, maintenance, and replacement of parts; the number and the location of the place where spare parts are procurable; the probable time required to obtain spare parts; dates of the last and the next inspection; and other pertinent items. Through the use of punched cards it is possible to select quickly, items requiring special attention, the routine of inspections for any day, or other grouping of information.

29-10. Reports.[18] Operating reports are maintained as an aid to better operation, as an inspiration to the operator to excel previous performance, as proof of the efficacy of the plant's operation, for future reference, and sometimes to comply with the law. Items entered in the report should represent complete records and should be a guide to an operator, or his successor, in the operation of his plant. The reports may serve as valuable material in the event of legal suit resulting from nuisances claimed to come from the plant or from improper downstream conditions.

Annual, monthly, and daily reports should be kept, each summarizing and commenting on the data in the preceding and current reports. In the daily report there should be a statement concerning the

[13] See *Sewage Works Eng.*, January, 1948, p. 29.

[14] See N. Post, *S. and I.W.*, February, 1956, p. 225.

[15] See F. H. Lind, *S. and I.W.*, April, 1954, p. 550.

[16] See *ibid.*, June, 1954, p. 796.

[17] See J. T. Norgaard, *S. and I.W.*, November, 1954, p. 1399; and W. M. Colony, *Water and Sewage Works*, June, 1954, p. R-191.

[18] See *Sewage Works Jour.*, May, 1942, pp. 589 and 593.

weather—temperature, rainfall, wind, and sunshine—and the results of periodic measurements of quantity and quality of the raw sewage and the influent to and the effluent from the various treatment devices. Where possible there should be maintained a continuous record of the rate of flow of sewage, summarized daily. Records should also be kept of the analyses of daily composite samples of the raw sewage and of the effluent from the various important treatment devices, of which chemical and physical analyses should be made, as recommended herein under the discussion of the particular method of treatment.

In addition to such routine material the daily report should contain a record of any unusual happenings about the plant, e.g., construction work, a flood, complaints, or visitors.

The monthly report summarizes the daily records and includes such additional information as downstream conditions, special analyses made, equipment repaired or renewed, and changes in personnel. In some states a standard form of monthly report has been prepared for submission to supervising authorities. Such a form is shown in Fig. 29–1.

The annual report is an accounting, by the superintendent to his board and to the public, of the performance, the economy, and the needs of the plant as shown by the year's experience. It contains a summary of the information in the daily and monthly reports, a record of the major changes in plant equipment, methods of operation, and personnel, together with comments, comparisons, and recommendations for the future.

29–11. Operators' tools and equipment. An important item of equipment is a well-indexed and complete set of plans and specifications for the construction of the plant. They should be carefully preserved, as they are invaluable when making repairs and adjustments. Tools should include the ordinary hand tools, wood tools, grinding tools, wrecking tools, pipe-fitting tools, and such machine tools as may economically be used by the plant personnel. The careful operator marks a place for each tool, indicating the place by a full-size outline drawing of each tool as it hangs or rests in its place. A missing tool is instantly indicated by a glance at the tool board. In addition to tools for the maintenance of equipment there should be provided the ordinary janitor supplies; also picks, shovels, rakes, shears, and wheelbarrows, for grounds maintenance; and garden hose and fire hose for sprinkling lawns and flushing tanks, walks, and other equipment. Attention to the care of tools, replacing them where they belong when

To: STATE SANITARY WATER BOARD
IN COOPERATION WITH
DIVISION OF SANITARY ENGINEERING
STATE DEPARTMENT OF PUBLIC HEALTH
SPRINGFIELD, ILLINOIS

SEWAGE TREATMENT WORKS
OPERATION REPORT

____
(PLACE AND PLANT)
MONTH OF ____________ 19 __

Date	Weather			Stream Flow	Sewage Temperature and Flow							Aeration									Sludge and Gas							Electric Current-K.W.H.				Analyses															
					Temperature, deg.F.		Flow-m.g.d.					Air, 1000 cu.ft.	Aerators		Solids			Return Sludge			Gal. Prim. Pumped	Dry Solids Added, lbs.		Waste Activated, gal.	Digester or Sludge		Gas cu. ft.					B.O.D.-p.p.m. 5 Day			Suspended Solids			Settleable Solids			pH			Stability Final Eff.	Dissolved Oxygen		
	Rainfall	Wind	Temperature		Raw	Final	Rate: Max.	Rate: Min.	Total to Plant	By-passed: Raw	By-passed: Settled		Units Used	Total Hours	Susp., p.p.m.	Sett. %: 15 min.	Sett. %: 60 min.	1000 gal.	Susp. Solids, p.p.m.	Sett. Solids, 1 hr.		Total	Volatile		Temp.	pH		Aerators	Sewage Pumps	Other Purposes	Total	Raw	Prim. Eff.	Final Eff.	Raw	Prim. Eff.	Final Eff.	Raw	Prim. Eff.	Final Eff.	Raw	Prim. Eff.	Final Eff.		Final Eff.	Stream: Above	Stream: Below
1	2	3	4	5	6	7	8	9	10	11	12	13	14	15	16	17	18	19	20	21	22	23	24	25	26	27	28	29	30	31	32	33	34	35	36	37	38	39	40	41	42	43	44	45	46	47	48
1																																															
2																																															
3																																															
4																																															
5																																															
6																																															
7																																															
28																																															
29																																															
30																																															
31																																															
Total																																															
Ave.																																															
Max.																																															
Min.																																															

	% Purification		
	B.O.D.	Susp. Solids	Sett. Solids
R/S			
S/F			
R/F			

Date	Sludge			
	Drawn to Bed No.	Depth on Bed Inches	Removed from Bed No.	Cubic Yards Removed

REMARKS: (Include unusual sewage or stream flows, operating troubles, lime to sewage or digestor, chlorination, complaints, etc., giving dates)

Fig. 29–1. Type of operation report form used at Springfield, Ill.

they are not in use, and supplying missing items are essential to good operation.

Equipment should include fuses, light bulbs, thermal elements, and other minor electrical equipment, and spare parts for machines that may be required in an emergency and cannot otherwise be obtained without delay. Judgment and the advice of the manufacturer must be followed in the selection of these items to avoid an accumulation of unnecessary, obsolete, and forgotten items.

A card index inventory of all items of equipment and tools should be maintained and checked annually, a notation being made on the card, annually, of the condition of the equipment. Each item of equipment, special tool, and so forth, should be marked indelibly with an identifying number corresponding to the index card.

29–12. Use of bypass. A bypass should be used only when equipment to be bypassed, or the entire plant, cannot discharge a satisfactory effluent. If the rate of flow through a plant becomes too great, or other danger impends, the bypass may properly be opened. Conditions permitting the opening of a bypass under normal operation may be based on previous tests and experience.

29–13. Public relations.[19] Objectives in sewage treatment include the promotion of the health and comfort of the public. Success in these objectives requires public understanding and sympathy. Good public relations are necessary, therefore, and are important in accomplishing the objectives in sewage treatment. Factors to be considered in good public relations include: appearance; operator appearance, attitude, and courtesy; the conduct of interesting and informative plant tours to which visitors are invited and made welcome; and public explanations before schools, service clubs, and other gatherings, concerning the work and objectives of the plant.

Operation in Different Methods of Treatment

29–14. Screens. *Screens must be kept clean* to prevent too great a loss of head through them. Frequency of cleaning depends on the kind of sewage and on the size of screen openings. Only experience can dictate the required frequency of cleaning. Automatic, mechanically cleaned screens remove this chore from the operator's immediate attention, but periodic inspection is desirable to see that the equipment is functioning properly.

[19] See G. T. Lohmeyer, *S. and I.W.*, June, 1956, p. 810.

Infrequent cleaning may cause upsewer overflows to go into operation; derangement of plant functioning when screens are cleaned and a large flow of sewage is suddenly released into the plant; septic condition of sewage; and deposition of solids in the approach sewer.

Hand-removed screenings should be placed on a drainage platform when they are taken from the screen and they should be immediately flushed with a hose to wash back into the sewer small particles of organic matter. The screenings should then be allowed to drain for a short time, after which they should be placed in a covered can and disposed of daily or more frequently.

The daily record of operation should show frequency of cleaning, volume (cubic feet) of wet screenings removed, and daily power consumption for mechanically operated screens. The average dry-solids content of the screenings should be reported at least monthly.

29–15. Grit chambers. In the maintenance of a mechanically cleaned grit chamber, routine inspection and lubrication of the mechanical equipment should be followed. Tools used for hand-cleaned grit chambers include a long-handled shovel, a wheelbarrow, a hose with water under pressure, and possibly two 5-gallon buckets with ropes. The grit is removed frequently enough to prevent the filling of the storage compartment more than about one-half full, special attention being needed after a storm. When the chamber is to be cleaned by hand, the flow is cut off and the chamber is emptied by gravity or by pumping. Then the operator, with boots on, descends into the chamber and shovels the grit out or loads it into buckets to be hauled out. The exact method of removing the grit depends on the construction of the chamber. No man should work alone at this task.

The routine observations made on the grit chamber in its operation should include measurement of the depth of grit at least three times monthly and after every large storm.

The record of operation should show the dates of cleaning, the amount (cubic feet) of grit removed, the total flow through the chamber, and the method of disposal of the grit.

29–16. Primary sedimentation tanks. Cleanliness is essential in the operation of these normally unsightly devices. Oil, grease, algae, and fungi may gather on walls, weirs, and walks. All exposed parts of the tank and channel should be washed frequently, daily if necessary, and scraped or squeegeed to prevent the accumulation of exposed deposits. Skimmings may be dumped directly into a wheelbarrow and carried to the incinerator, dumped into the screenings barrel, or otherwise disposed of promptly. If the flow in the tank becomes so slow as to permit the approach of septic conditions, the flow may be increased by throwing other tanks out of service or by diluting the incoming sewage with creek water or plant effluent pumped into the tank influent. Operating tools include a rubber-edged squeegee, a scum shovel made of a coal shovel bent at right angles with the handle, and a ¼-inch-mesh wire skimmer.

In primary sedimentation tanks the sludge must be removed with sufficient frequency to avoid the development of septic conditions. The approach of these conditions may be recognized by the rising of bubbles or clumps of sludge, or by a decrease in the pH of the sludge. When sludge is withdrawn it must be moved so slowly and steadily that water will not be mixed with it. When the sludge is being pumped, samples should be withdrawn frequently from the pump and examined for the presence of additional water. When a sample shows a thin sludge it is time to stop pumping. If the sludge is withdrawn with mechanical devices the equipment may be operated continuously or on a predetermined, mechanically controlled period of intermittent stopping and starting. The operator should occasionally check the operation of the mechanism and the quality of the sludge removed. Mechanical equipment can be protected against interference by ice by painting vulnerable parts with heavy tractor oil, or by the use of salt and sand where traction is desirable.

Operation reports should show frequency of cleaning, method of cleaning, flow through the tank, volume of sludge and scum removed (cubic feet), and percentage of moisture in sludge and scum. Less frequently than daily the reports may include volatile matter, BOD, and other measures of sludge characteristics.

29–17. Chemical precipitation. Some important points in the operation of chemical dosage include:

1. Unless automatic, proportional-feed devices are used, readjust the rate of feed manually at frequent intervals to follow changes in rate of flow of sewage. Three or four changes daily are usually sufficient.

2. Test the dosing machine to assure the correct calibration of the machine.

3. Inspect feeding and dosing devices frequently to make sure that the apparatus is functioning and that it is not clogged, and that the chemicals are not "arched."

4. Select, by experimentation, the most desirable point to apply the chemical to the sewage. Where two chemicals are used it is usually better to apply them at different places. For example, lime is usually thoroughly mixed with the sewage before ferric chloride is added, when the two are used in the same plant.

5. Mix rapidly and with turbulence. Flocculate gently, adjusting speed of flocculator arms so that sedimentation of the floc will just be prevented.

6. Keep the flocculator tanks well skimmed and free from grease.

7. Operate sludge-collecting mechanisms or methods as in plain sedimentation tanks to avoid septicity, and also to avoid too great an accumulation of sludge.

Chemical-treatment processes require numerous and frequent observations for their proper control. Records of the observations may be entered into the daily record and may include temperature of the influent, amount (pounds) of each chemical used, the volume (gallons) of sewage treated, frequent pH observations during the day, solids (milligrams per liter) removed, volume (cubic feet) of sludge removed, sludge moisture content, and, less frequently, 5-day BOD reduction, volatile solids, and such other information as may be desirable.

29–18. Imhoff tanks. The principles of operation applicable to a plain sedimentation tank are applicable to the operation of the flowing-through channel of an Imhoff tank. It is essential to keep sludge from accumulating on the sloping bottom of the flowing-through trough, and to keep the sludge in the digestion chamber 18 in. or more below the bottom of the slot. The gas vents offer a convenient place for the disposal of skimmings from the flowing-through channel. When placed in the vents the skimmings should be well worked down into the scum. The slot may be cleaned by dragging a short piece of chain through it with a swaying motion as frequently as necessary and at least once a week. Where possible the flow through the tank should be reversed when it is necessary to maintain a level sludge line in the digestion compartment.

Additional principles applicable to the operation of Imhoff tanks include:

1. Break up the scum in gas vents by soaking it semi-weekly, or more frequently, with water or supernatant liquor from a fire hose applied under pressure to break up the scum; punch 3-in. holes through the scum at 2-ft intervals, with a pole 8 to 10 ft long; add 10 lb of hydrated lime per 1,000 population, daily. If these expedients are

not effective, remove the scum and place it on sludge beds to drain and dry.

2. Make monthly, or more frequent, observations of sludge level at three or more points in the digestion compartment. Test the sludge for ripeness by withdrawing a little. If it is odorless, black, granular, and well-humidified it is ripe and ready for withdrawal.

3. Withdraw sludge in warm weather frequently (bi-weekly or monthly) in small quantities, rather than at longer intervals in large quantities. Manipulate sludge withdrawal so that the digestion compartment contains only a small amount of sludge at the onset of cold weather. Avoid drawing sludge in cold weather unless the digestion-compartment capacity is overtaxed. When withdrawing sludge do so slowly to avoid breaking through the sludge blanket (layer of sludge) with resulting mixing of water with the sludge. When the sludge becomes thin or brown, or gray streaks appear, it is time to stop drawing.

If the sludge is slow in starting it may be agitated with water through pipes usually supplied therefor or through a fire hose, or it may be stirred around the inlet by long rods inserted through the gas vent or sludge riser pipe. After use the sludge pipes should be filled with water or sewage to prevent hardening of sludge in them.

Foaming is one of the principal troubles in the operation of Imhoff tanks and has been one of the chief causes of their unpopularity. Schlenz [20] has summarized the causes of foaming as follows:

(1) Excessive loadings of raw solids in relation to digesting solids in the tank. (2) Increased activity causing rapid formation of gas and "boiling" action. (3) Objectionable organisms in the sewage and in solids settled from the sewage. (4) Character of sewage; predominance of objectionable products such as cannery, laundry, brewery wastes, etc. (5) Departures of the pH from normal. (6) Marked viscosity of the liquid or scum and also the mechanical action of gas attempting to escape through the scum having a high surface tension. (7) Character of the raw solids loading. (8) Restricted area of gas vents.

Schlenz suggests ten possible remedies, none of which is infallible, and some of which may be harmful. They are:

(1) Maintain proper balance of raw and digesting sludge. (2) Draw all sludge from the tank and start again. (3) Add lime to produce a pH of about 6.7. (4) Add about 3 ppm of chlorine to the incoming sewage. (5) Take the tank out of service for a rest period or lighten the load

[20] H. E. Schlenz, *Sewage Works Jour.*, July, 1936, p. 609.

materially. (6) Break up scum in the gas vents by mechanical churning. (7) Remove scum from the gas vents. (8) Saturate the scum with supernatant liquor. (9) Push the scum down into the digestion compartment. (10) Heat the contents of the tank.

In addition to these expedients good may result by drawing some, but not all, sludge from the digestion compartment, or spraying the foam gently with a stream of water; violent disturbance is undesirable. In adding lime care should be taken not to add too much and thus increase the difficulties.

The operating record for an Imhoff tank should include: (a) settleable solids in raw sewage and tank effluent (daily); (b) dates and conditions of skimming and cleaning the flowing-through compartment, removing scum, and cleaning slots; (c) dates of sludge removal, volume (cubic feet) of sludge removed, and total and volatile solids content of the sludge as removed; (d) depth of sludge (at least monthly); (e) pH of sludge (at least monthly); (f) depth of scum in gas vents (monthly); and (g) dates, kinds, and amounts of chemical used.

29–19. Separate sludge-digestion tanks.[21] *Placing in operation.* If the tank is covered it should be filled with water, sludge, or sewage to expel all air. If the tank is to be heated the liquid in the tank should be raised to the desired temperature. If the tank is equipped with a floating cover it should be lowered to the lowest point before the filling of the tank is commenced. Sometimes if ripe sludge and fresh sludge are mixed in a ratio of 1 or 2 to 5 before being run into the digester, active, alkaline digestion may be expected within a few days at a favorable temperature. Otherwise weeks may elapse while the sludge passes through the acid stage of digestion.

If the tank is not covered the sludge mixture may be run directly into the empty tank.

An outline of procedure in starting digestion is given in Table 29–1.

Feeding the tank. (See also Sect. 25–6.) The dose should be proportioned to the assumed period of digestion. It is desirable to apply relatively small doses frequently, rather than large doses intermittently, and the volatile solids in the tank should not exceed 3 per cent to 5 per cent if unheated, up to a maximum of 8 per cent if heated. Charging rates should average 1 to 2 lb of fresh solids for each 40 lb of digesting volatile solids in unheated tanks, and 2 to 4 lb to 40 lb in heated tanks. In feeding a tank with a fixed cover, care must be taken to avoid an excessive pressure in the tank. This may be done

---

[21] See *Sewage Works Jour.,* May, 1944, p. 504.

Table 29-1

OUTLINE OF PROCEDURES FOR STARTING OF DIGESTION

(From H. E. Schlenz, *S. and I.W.*, October, 1957, p. 1190.)

Starting volume	Use least capacity available. In multiple tank installation—start the digestion in one tank only. In Floating Cover installations—fill the tank only sufficiently to float the cover. Use fresh raw sewage or water for filling. *Caution:* If an existing "sour" digester is to be restarted; remove the sour contents completely and have inside walls and bottom thoroughly cleaned.
Temperature control	Initially heat contents to approximately 95° F. Maintain temperature uniform within 3° F ($\pm$).
Seeding culture	Not absolutely necessary, but will hasten start of digestion action. Use sludge and/or digester liquor from a nearby digestion installation showing an active methane digestion. (Normal gas being produced and contents low in volatile acids.) *Desired Quantity:* Approximately 0.5% (dry wt) of weight of liquid in the tank.
Feed of sludge	Add no more than 10% of the anticipated ultimate daily load each day. When the gas produced is 50% of that calculated from the volatile solids added (approx. 5 cu ft/lb of dry volatile solids), and the volatile acids do not rise sharply—increase the feed by 50% to 100% of initial feed daily until the ultimate load is reached.
Recirculation of contents	Recirculate contents daily. At start, overturn the complete tank contents (bottom to top) for a 2-hour period at least once daily. Recirculation for external heating with suction taken from point about one-third of side water depth from bottom to top of liquid.
Volatile acid determination	Make determination daily before adding feed. Continue daily determination until ultimate load is reached. (See "Standard Methods" 9th Edition—or recent revised procedure as described in February, 1956, issue of *Sewage & Industrial Wastes*.) Should not exceed 2,000 mg/l.

Table 29–1 (*Continued*)

	If volatile acid concentration shows continued increase, or digestion does not start—reduce or interrupt feed of raw sludge.
Gas yield	Measure and record gas production daily.
	Check CO_2 content of gas. (Simple rough determinations are sufficient.)
	Should expect approximately 10 cu ft per lb of volatile solids added in raw feed per day.

When the ultimate calculated load for one digester is reached—other digesters in a multiple tank installation will be easily started by transferring a limited amount of best digested sludge and the overflow liquor from the first (initially started) digester to provide an active seeding culture.

by drawing sludge from the tank at the same rate that the dose is being added to the tank. A slight pressure above atmospheric, that is, a plenum, must be maintained in the tank to avoid the drawing in of air and a resulting explosive mixture.

Detecting sludge line. The line of demarcation between the surface of the sludge and the supernatant liquor may sometimes be determined by: (1) slowly and steadily lowering the end of a suction hose attached to a low-capacity, hand-operated, pitcher pump. When sludge appears in the pump discharge the sludge line has been reached; (2) slowly and steadily lowering a thin, flat disc weighing about 2 to 5 lb and about 12 to 18 in. in diameter, in a horizontal plane. When the tension on the supporting cord suddenly decreases the sludge line has been reached; and (3) by lowering into the tank, in a vertical position, a stick along the length of which stoppered, wide-mouth bottles have been placed at convenient intervals. When the stick is in position all the stoppers are pulled out simultaneously by a cord attached to them. The stick is then withdrawn from the tank. The highest container with sludge in it reveals the level of the sludge line. Some devices for locating the sludge line are shown in Fig. 29–2.

Removing sludge. Sludge should be withdrawn only when experience indicates that it is ripe; all of the ripe sludge should not be withdrawn at one time; and it must be allowed to flow at a slow, even rate to avoid sudden changes in pressure. The location of the sludge line in the tank can be determined by sampling at different levels or, if

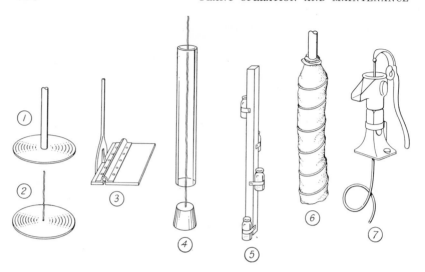

Fig. 29–2. Sludge and scum measuring and sampling devices. 1. Flat disk, about 6 in. in diameter, on a stick. 2. Light, metal disk, about 6 in. in diameter, on a string. 3. Hinged trap. When pulled up beneath scum the bottom of scum can be detected. 4. 2-in. pyrex glass tube with rubber stopper on end of chain. 5. Wide-mouth bottles on a stick. 6. Terry cloth wrapped stick. Portion of cloth is stained by sludge. 7. Hand pump and suction hose.

the tank is not covered, with the aid of such instruments as are shown in Fig. 29–2. The pump at (7) in the figure is useful also in a covered tank, as the appearance of sludge in its discharge shows that the suction pipe has reached the sludge line. Digested sludge, when it appears, should be dark, grayish-brown, or black, without visible raw, sewage solids. If the tank has a floating cover a slight pressure may be maintained during sludge removal by lowering the floating roof. If the tank has a fixed cover gas, not air, may be run into the tank, or in either case raw sludge may be run into the tank at the same or at a faster rate than digested sludge is being withdrawn. If the sludge refuses to flow when the valve is opened, agitation with water jets may get it started. A head of at least 4 ft of water should be available to start and to maintain an adequate rate of flow.

Scum control.[22] It is desirable to keep the scum layer less than 2 ft thick. The removal of scum is seldom necessary, but occasionally

[22] See *Sewage Works Jour.*, July, 1941, p. 788.

leaves, sticks, and so forth, may gather to clog the gas dome or the gas strainers. Under such circumstances the dome must be opened, and the exposed parts of the tank washed with a stream from a fire hose. The danger of explosion is great at this time and special care should be taken to avoid sparks or an open flame in the immediate vicinity of the work.

Entering the tank.[23] If it becomes necessary to enter the tank great care must be taken to avoid explosion or asphyxiation. The gas lines should be shut off; the gas dome and other top openings should be opened; and the tank should be emptied and then refilled with liquid to the overflow level to expel all gas. In some cases an inert gas is used to fill the tank when the water is withdrawn to assure the absence of explosive gas in the tank. All possible openings in the tank should be open to provide ventilation when the tank is entered. Open flames and sparks should be prohibited and rescue equipment should be on hand.

A summary of certain other desirable practices in the operation of a separate sludge-digestion tank follows:

1. Make daily, or more frequent, observations of pH and maintain it in the vicinity of 7.0 to 7.3. This may be done by judicious application of lime to the upper sludge layers, by reducing the rate of feeding, and sometimes by withdrawing sludge.

2. Avoid returning a supernatant liquor from a digestion tank to the incoming sewage if the liquor contains more than about 3,000 mg/l of suspended solids. Under such circumstances place the liquor on sludge beds, either with or without lime, returning the drainage to the incoming sewage. Select by trial the best level from which to withdraw supernatant, and withdraw only small quantities at a time for return to the incoming sewage.

3. Stirring and circulation of sludge in digestion tanks is successful in some plants, unsatisfactory in others. Only experience with a particular sewage can decide the best practice.

4. Break up scum by pumping supernatant liquor on it as required to keep the scum moist.

Use of a biocatalyst. A biocatalyst may be any biological material, commonly referred to as an enzyme, which, when added to digesting sludge, may improve its digestion. Proprietary substances claim-

---

[23] See *Public Works,* January, 1938, p. 16.

ing to be successful biocatalysts are on the market. Because of controversies [24] concerning the claims made by producers of these substances, a study was made by a Committee of the Federation of Sewage and Industrial Waste Associations. The Committee reported [25] that: ". . . the addition of biocatalytic substances in properly designed and operated plants will produce no benefits." Unfortunately this pronouncement has not settled the discussion as contrary experiences continue to be reported.[26]

Operating record. The operating record of the tank should include a report on the average pH of the sludge (monthly), the kind and amounts of chemicals used to aid digestion, the average amount of heating water used daily, a continuous record of the temperature of the heating water or of the circulating sludge entering and leaving the digester, the amount of gas added to and removed from the tank, the volume of sludge in the tank at the end of each month, and the characteristics, quantity, and method of disposal of the sludge and of the supernatant liquor.

Use of lime.[27] The desirability of the use of lime as an aid to digestion or to raise the pH is controversial, but the weight of opinion is opposed to its use except under especially favorable circumstances. However, if used moderately it will do no harm to the digester and it may, in an emergency, avoid other difficulties.[28]

29–20. Gas-collection equipment.[29] In the operation of gas-collection equipment the gas lines may be flushed with water when the pressure loss during flow becomes high, in order to remove accumulations of sediment. Gas pipes should be kept free from sediment also, to minimize the spontaneous combustion of iron sulfide deposits. Gas meters require occasional lubrication, diaphragm replacement, and draining. Flame traps require frequent checking, particularly if the trap contains a fusible plug that may have been fused. The water seal in traps depending thereon must be maintained at a safe level, and replaced with a non-freezing solution in cold

[24] See also A. C. Bryan, *Public Works,* December, 1952, p. 69; and R. R. Robinson, *Public Works,* April, 1954, p. 116.

[25] See *S. and I.W.,* September, 1954, p. 1162, and December, 1954, p. 1425.

[26] See W. A. Corder, *Water and Sewage Works,* January, 1955, p. 42; and W. N. Wells and R. E. McKinney, *Water and Sewage Works,* August, 1955, p. 871.

[27] See *S. and I.W.,* March, 1950, symposium on "To Lime or Not to Lime."

[28] See B. F. Rockecharlie, *S. and I.W.,* May, 1953, p. 613.

[29] See *Sewage Works Jour.,* May, 1944, p. 626.

weather. Cold-weather precautions include: the inspection of safety devices to assure their good order and readiness to function; the draining of drip pots when the gage glass indicates the need therefor; the replacing of the water seals with oil or other non-freezing liquid where traps are exposed to freezing; and the periodic inspection of automatic devices to assure good operation. Before servicing flame traps shut off the gas flow through the line. Do *not* use a bypass.

When inspecting pressure-relief devices the elevation of the water or of the liquid in the seals should be noted, and the seals should be refilled as needed; mechanically operated valves should be tested by inducing a pressure in the lines high enough to force the valves to function.

Routine observations may include: a continuous record of the rate of flow of gas, and of the gas pressure; the volume of gas wasted daily; and the dates of inspection and cleaning of the gas equipment.

29–21. Trickling filters. Difficulties arising in the operation of trickling filters include pooling; clogging, drooling, or refusal of dosing equipment to operate; clogging and freezing of spray nozzles and distributing pipes; clogging of the underdrains; growth of filter flies; and septic action in or overloading of the humus tank. Methods of overcoming these difficulties include the following:

1. To overcome pooling try washing the surface of the filter with a strong stream of water; punch holes through the top layer of filter medium with iron bars to permit the water to get down to the filter; rest the filter for a short time and resume with a lighter dose; fork over the stones at the surface, again washing with the hose if necessary; drag automobile tire chains attached to the revolving distributor arms, over the surface; chlorinate the influent with a dose not to exceed 8 to 10 lb of chlorine per 1,000 sq ft of filter; then try smaller doses of influent.

2. Inspect dosing equipment daily, cleaning off growths and removing possible clogging material. The siphon chamber should be enclosed and, where possible, ventilated to a high stack or to an incinerator because of the intensity of odors that are frequently liberated here.

3. Inspect and clean the spray nozzles and the orifices of moving distributors frequently and as required. Pick out sticks and matches; use a stiff brush to clean off accumulated slime. Raise or lower the outer ends of revolving distributor arms to secure even distribution. Flush distributor arms and piping three or four times a month by

removing the plugs on the end of the pipe, or, if plugs are not provided, remove the last nozzle on the fixed-nozzle distributor arm.

4. Observe the flow from the underdrains daily. If the flow is not even, clean clogged underdrains by "rodding" as in a clogged sewer.

5. Control filter flies [30] (*Psychoda alternata*) by flooding the unit with sewage above the top of the stone. This procedure will drown the flies and wash out eggs and larvae. It may cause trouble in the humus tank or downstream, however, because the filter will unload as a result of the treatment. Other expedients are to maintain a growth of insect enemies, *Achroutes viaticus*, or springtails; to apply chlorine to the influent to obtain a concentration of about 3 mg/l of chlorine; to spread common salt over the beds at the rate of 4,400 lb to the acre; to rest the bed; to apply gammaexane weekly at a rate of about 1 lb per acre, or DDT at 5 to 10 lb per acre; to burn concentrations of adult flies with a gasoline blowtorch or spray them with a mixture of $\frac{1}{2}$ lb of pyrethrum powder to 1 gal of kerosene, or to use both. Since the life cycle of the fly exceeds 7 days, weekly treatment of the filter should control the flies.[31] It has been found that where *Psychoda alternata* predominate, benzene hexachloride (BCH) may be effective. The spraying of filter walls, grass areas, and buildings with a 5 per cent DDT solution and keeping down grass and weeds will aid in the control of the fly nuisance.

6. In winter cover the dosing tanks lightly to avoid freezing of the siphons and particularly to avoid freezing of the small air pipes that control the action of the siphons. These pipes become clogged with hoar frost. If ice tends to form in the distribution pipes open a drain valve at the lower end of the distribution system to maintain a flow, or drain the pipes between doses; revolving distributor arms and nearby walls may be kept free from ice, under favorable conditions, by coating with heavy crank-case oil; by using salt on the wall at points of greatest trouble; and by setting a nozzle on the end of the revolving distributor to spray the wall as the arm revolves. If none of these expedients will prevent the formation of ice, chip the ice off the wall by hand with an axe.

The operating record of a trickling filter should include: the number of units or area (square feet) of filters in service (daily), the number of nozzles cleaned (daily), dates of flushing the distribution system, dates of flushing and cleaning underdrains, dates and method of clean-

---

[30] See D. E. Dreier, *Water and Sewage Works,* May, 1953, p. R-186.

[31] See *Sewage Works Jour.,* March, 1946, pp. 181, 208, and 330; and T. C. Schaetzle, *S. and I.W.,* February, 1952, p. 124.

ing filter surface, putrescibility of filter effluent (semi-weekly), settleable solids in effluent (daily). The monthly report may include such other observations as are needed to indicate the operating conditions of the filter, such as BOD and suspended solids of influent and effluent, difficulties with flies, with odors, with freezing, and such other unexpected difficulties as may have arisen.

29–22. Activated sludge.[32, 33, 34] In an activated-sludge plant variables that influence plant performance and that are partly or entirely under the control of the operator include: [35] (1) concentration of solids in the mixed liquor, (2) volume of air used, (3) aeration period, (4) settling period, (5) dissolved oxygen in aeration and settling tanks, (6) rate of sludge return, and (7) sludge condition or index. Some operating practices involving these variables are:

1. *In the aeration tank.* (*a*) The optimum solids content usually lies between 1,000 and 3,500 mg/l,[32] or more closely 1,500 to 2,500 mg/l [34] for diffused air and 500 to 1,200 in mechanical aeration.[35] (*b*) If the quality of sludge varies widely, maintain a low concentration of solids to be prepared for sudden increase of solids load. Frequent and routine observation of suspended solids content and of sludge index is desirable. (*c*) Determine the dissolved oxygen at various points in the tank, maintaining a minimum of 2 mg/l in the effluent by adjusting the rate of application of air. (*d*) Avoid overaeration to prevent breaking up of the floc. (*e*) Watch the air distribution at the surface. If it becomes uneven add chlorine to the air supply to remove organic matter,[36] or aviation gasoline to remove grease, from the diffusers. If neither expedient will correct the trouble, remove diffuser plates from the tank and clean them. (*f*) Keep mechanical aerators free from fungus or algal growths by cleaning them, and prevent the accumulation of sludge in mechanical-aeration tanks by proper baffling. (*g*) Maintain a continuous air supply. (*h*) Chlorinate the air supply periodically.

Frothing [37, 38] is frequently, and sometimes erroneously, attributed

---

[32] See *Sewage Works Jour.*, September, 1942, p. 909, and January, 1945, p. 101.

[33] See *ibid.*, January, 1942, pp. 3 and 32.

[34] See T. R. Haseltine, *Water and Sewage Works,* May, 1954, p. R-211.

[35] See A. A. Kalinske and H. W. Gillard, *Public Works,* May, 1952, p. 68.

[36] See *Proc. Am. Soc. Civil Engrs.*, April, 1944, p. 479.

[37] The term *frothing* has been used for aeration tanks and foaming for digester tanks.

[38] See E. S. Chase, *Water and Sewage Works,* February, 1953, p. 45; P. N. Degens, Jr., *S. and I.W.*, December, 1954, p. 1494; and A. E. Sparr, *Public Works*, April, 1957, p. 99.

to synthetic detergents. Experience has shown that froth or foam will form under widely divergent conditions with syndets as a major cause. On the other hand froth may form or not form under apparently identical conditions in parallel aeration tanks. Froth persistence has been shown to be closely related to the susceptibility of a synthetic detergent to biological degradation.[39] Methods of foam or froth control include [40] (a) the addition of 1 mg/l of kerosene, gasoline, or crank-case oil to the surface of the liquid in the aerator, (b) the maintenance of solids in the aerator above the concentration of 3,000 to 5,000 mg/l, (c) the decrease of the volume of air supplied, (d) the addition of defrothing agents such as "Depuma" [41] or "Hodag S-88," [42] and (e) sprinkling the froth with water. Bright sunlight appears to break froth.

2. *Synthetic detergents.*[43] (See also Sect. 18–20.) The diffused-air process is somewhat inhibited by the presence of anionic detergents in concentrations of 50 to 55 mg/l, and higher, active matter until the sludge becomes acclimated to it, after which no influence is observed.[44] However, adverse effects may result from the carry-over of emulsified grease and more air may be needed in the aeration tank. The reaeration constant of the body of diluting water may be diminished for a long distance below the plant outlet.[45]

3. *Rate of sludge return.* The rate of sludge return is related to the condition of the sludge, solids in the mixed liquor, and other conditions of plant operation. (See also Sect. 23–26.) Too low a rate of return may result in the sludge becoming septic and bulking, and too high a rate will result in a light, voluminous sludge, because insufficient time has been given for its concentration in the clarifier.

4. *Cleaning of diffuser plates.*[46] Porous, ceramic diffuser plates become clogged on the air side because particles of dust, oil, or other substances in the air supply have passed through the air filters, have fallen from the air distribution pipes, or have entered with sewage when the air supply has been interrupted. Clogging on the liquid

[39] See R. H. Bogan and C. N. Sawyer, *S. and I.W.*, May, 1956, p. 637.

[40] See *ibid.*, September, 1950, p. 1238.

[41] See E. S. Chase, *Water and Sewage Works*, February, 1953, p. 45.

[42] See Phil Hirsch, *Public Works*, September, 1955, p. 97.

[43] See P. C. G. Isaacs, *Water and San. Eng.*, 1953, Vol. 3, pp. 413 and 453.

[44] See P. N. Degens, Jr., and others, *S. and I.W.*, January, 1955, p. 10.

[45] See W. O. Lynch and C. N. Sawyer, *S. and I.W.*, October, 1954, p. 1193.

[46] See *Sewage Works Jour.*, January, 1942, p. 45, September, 1942, p. 930, January, 1943, p. 81; and *Water and Sewage Works*, April, 1951, p. 184, and June 1, 1955, p. R-26.

side may result from: fine solids entering the diffusers when the air supply is interrupted; the formation of a coating of iron salts and carbonates when the water supply is hard; organic growths; grease; and the precipitation of miscellaneous debris.

Diffuser plates should be cleaned when air distribution is uneven or air pressure rises 1 to 2 psi above normal. If the plates can be removed from the tank: (a) Soak the plates in a 50 per cent nitric acid solution. (b) Boil in a 15 per cent caustic solution. If the plates cannot be removed try any of the following expedients: (c) Draw the water down in the tank until about ½-in. depth of water remains over the plates, and allow the air to pass through them gently; then flush the surface of the plates with a hose stream. Shut off the air and dissolve about 0.1 lb of lye in the water per square foot of diffuser area. Allow to stand for 15 min. Double the amount of clean water and then turn on the air at full rate. (d) Dry the plates and sand-blast the surface. (e) Dry the plates and turn on air at full rate; heat the diffuser surface with a blowtorch until it spalls off; sweep off the particles of sand. (f) Dry the plates and blow them out with a high rate of air; then allow them to rest for several days to a week or more. (g) Blow the plates out with steam under a pressure of about 10 lb per sq in. and scrub with a stiff brush. (h) Blow the plates out with clean water under a pressure of about 15 to 20 psi and scrub with a stiff brush. (i) Scrub the diffusers with 30 per cent hydrochloric acid or with a solution consisting of 1 g of sodium dichromate in 50 ml of concentrated sulfuric acid applied in two doses of about 100 ml on each of two succeeding days. Other expedients are used.

5. *In the secondary settling tank.* (a) Maintain a minimum of 2 mg/l, and preferably more, of dissolved oxygen in the tank. (b) Maintain a sludge blanket (layer of sludge) about 2 ft thick; too thick a layer leads to septicity; too thin a layer is inefficient. (c) Routine microscopical examinations of the sludge may be helpful in detecting changes in sludge quality more quickly than where they are not made.[47] (d) Operate the sludge mechanism continuously and return only fresh sludge to the aeration tank. (e) Study short circuiting, and avoid it by the judicious use of baffles. (f) Waste sludge slowly to the digestion tank to assure settlement before wasting. (g) Operate the tank otherwise as a primary sedimentation tank. If the sludge blanket rises it generally means that gas, usually nitrogen, is bringing it up, because the blanket is being held in the tank

[47] See *Sewage Works Jour.*, January, 1942, p. 28.

too long.[48]   The condition may be corrected by decreasing the rate of application of air in the aeration tank, by increasing the sewage load, by a mechanical shock that will release the entrained gas bubbles, or by earlier removal of the sludge.   Sludge rising is not the same as sludge bulking.[49]

6. *Sludge bulking.*[50, 51]   When sludge bulks it occupies a greater volume than would be occupied by a sludge that is not bulked, but which contains the same weight of suspended solids.   It is thought that bulking is caused principally by an unsatisfied early demand for oxygen.   When sludge bulks corrections may be made in: solids concentration; rate of application of air; aeration period which is possibly too short; inadequate, or inadequately distributed, dissolved oxygen in the aeration tank, or in the final settling tank; aeration tank which is possibly overloaded, probably with carbohydrates; inadequate, or stale, return sludge.   Remedies that may be attempted include: (*a*) Reduce the rate of flow of sewage to the aeration tank, even taking it out of service temporarily.   (*b*) Reduce the ratio of return sludge.   (*c*) Increase the air supply.   Tapered aeration is a method for supplying an increased amount of oxygen for early demand.   (*d*) Dilute the incoming sewage with plant effluent or fresh water.   (*e*) Dump the bulking sludge and build up new activated sludge.   (*f*) Combine any of the preceding expedients.   (*g*) Dose with chlorine between 1 and 7 mg/l.   The chlorine dosage required may be estimated from Grune's [52] expression

$$Cl = 0.0000834 \times SI \times F \times W \qquad (29\text{–}1)$$

where Cl = lb chlorine per day.
   SI = sludge index, Mohlmann.
   F = return sludge, mgd.
   W = suspended solids in return sludge, mg/l.

Apply lime to obtain a pH of 8.6 to 8.8 or apply chlorinated copperas or clay to the mixed liquor, or apply copper ammonium sulfate to the return sludge.   Chemicals must be used with care, starting with small doses, since overdosing may be extremely harmful.

[48] See *Surveyor,* January 19, 1945, p. 37; and January 5, 1945, p. 7.
[49] See *Sewage Works Eng.,* March, 1948, p. 141.
[50] *Ibid.*
[51] See also *Sewage Works Jour.,* July, 1940, pp. 556 and 694, September, 1940, p. 849, and January, 1941, p. 39.
[52] W. N. Grune, *Water and Sewage Works,* August, 1955, p. 350.

Warning of the onset of bulking may be given through a rise in the sludge index, or through the appearance of filamentous organisms (*Sphaerotilus natans*) [53] as detected by the microscope. These organisms are a result, not a cause, of bulking. A diminishing sludge index may not be altogether desirable since this may occur when oxidation fails to keep up with adsorption, with resulting loss in clarification. On the other hand too much oxidation gives a low index but it may produce a "pin point" floc with a turbulent effluent.

7. *Oxidation-reduction potentials.* A correlation between oxidation-reduction potentials and stages in the activated-sludge process is shown in Fig. 29–3. Attempts have been made to show a relation between oxidation-reduction (redox) potentials and the control of the activated-sludge process.[54] No relation has been satisfactorily established for general use.

8. *Shock loads.* Routine tests may be made to warn of shock loads. These tests [55] include pH determinations and analyses for heavy metals, sugar-carbohydrates, chlorine demand, and other suspected deleterious substances.

9. *Chironomus larvae* or *blood worms.* These organisms frequently infest the aeration tank, causing unsightly scum, loss of efficiency, and a partly septic sludge. Remedies include more rapid circulation of sludge, increased aeration, wasting the infested sludge, and preventing oviposition by the use of copper sulfate.

Operating records should include: aeration period in hours (monthly); air in cubic feet per gallon of sewage (monthly); ratio of sludge volume returned to volume of sewage flow, expressed as percentage (monthly); settleable solids in aeration tank, percentage by volume settling in ½ hour (at least daily); suspended solids in aeration tank (at least daily); suspended solids in effluent from the secondary sedimentation tank (daily); volume of waste sludge in cubic feet, and cubic feet per million gallons of sewage (monthly); and sludge index (daily).

29–23. Intermittent sand filtration. Sand filters, when not overloaded, cause little difficulty in operation, but certain routine work must be performed on them. For example, it is necessary to cut each bed out of service periodically, allow it to dry, and rake and scrape the surface clean and level, removing the weeds and grass. To correct

[53] See *Sewage Works Jour.,* November, 1934, p. 1041.
[54] See G. A. Rohlich, *Sewage Works Jour.,* May, 1944, p. 540.
[55] See W. D. Hatfield, *S. and I.W.,* December, 1954, p. 1491.

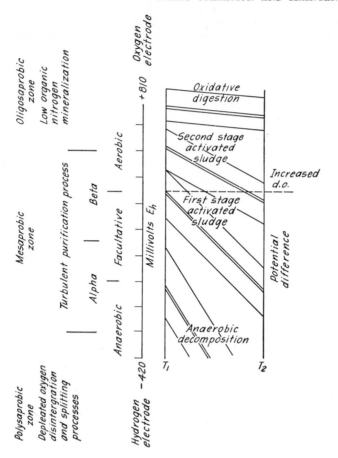

Fig. 29–3. Correlation of ecological classifications with oxidation-reduction potential, showing diagrammatically sludge activity reaction result with respect to time. (From J. W. Hood and G. W. Spohr, *Public Works*, January, 1957, p. 129.)

pooling the bed must be rested and dried, the mat on the surface being removed by scraping, raking, or rolling it up. Punching holes in the bed is *not* good practice. More than about ¼ in. of sand should not be removed; raking deeply drives the clogging material down into the bed. It is necessary to replace sand occasionally because of the inevitable loss when the bed is cleaned. The distribution system should be watched when the siphon discharges to see that the distribution is even; if it is not, the gates should be readjusted. In winter,

where ice may form on the bed, the surface may be plowed into ridges
and furrows, 2 ft apart, about 12 in. deep. The ice then forms a protective sheet over the filter beneath which the sewage will run without
freezing. If severely low temperatures are anticipated, some of the
units may be taken out of service to shorten the rest periods of the
others. Surface solids should be moved before the surface is leveled
in the spring.

The operating record should include: statement of units and area
in use (square feet, daily); date of cleaning each bed and amount
(cubic feet) of material removed and sand added; putrescibility of
final effluent (semi-weekly); dates and duration of rest periods; load
(million gallons) per acre between rest periods; condition of bed
(monthly).

29–24. Sludge-drying beds. Sludge may be run onto the drying
bed to a depth of 12 in. or to such depth as experience shows will dry
in about 2 weeks of good drying weather. Occasionally the grit or
sand on the bed should be replaced; the bed should not become less
than 3 in. thick, 6 in. being the preferred minimum.

Before drawing sludge onto drying beds its suitability for draining
may be tested by allowing a liter sample of the sludge to stand in a
graduated cylinder for 18 to 24 hr. If the sludge solids are mainly
at the top and about 40 per cent volume of clear water is beneath, the
sludge should drain well. Otherwise it will dry slowly, mainly by
evaporation.

Wet sludge must not be discharged on top of old dried sludge because the wet sludge will not drain. Weeds may be pulled, burned,
or poisoned.[56]

Operating records should include: depth of wet sludge, pH, percentage of moisture of sludge, and beds dosed; dates, bed numbers,
depth, cubic feet of dry sludge, time required for drying, and type of
weather during interim; solid and volatile content, pH, and moisture
in dry sludge removed; and method of disposal.

29–25. Vacuum filters.[57] A few important hints are:

In starting the filter soak the cloth with water before running sewage into the trough; do not start the drum until the trough is filled
with sludge, and keep the sludge agitator in motion; use the pick-up
vacuum until the drum is slightly more than half covered, when the

---

[56] See L. A. Conn, *Water and Sewage Works,* June, 1954, p. 284.

[57] See *Sewage Works Jour.,* September, 1941, pp. 868, 874, and 879, and
November, 1941, p. 1164; and B. A. Shepman, *Public Works,* December, 1955,
p. 74.

drying vacuum may be turned on; when the drum is covered with sludge turn on the compressed air and place the scraper; in the event of shutdown wash the filter clean and drain the vat or trough to prevent sludge drying on and sticking to the cloth.

As a result of extended tests Shepman [58] has concluded that:

(1) Rate of cake formation increases about 30 per cent for primary activated sludge, and up to 60 per cent for primary raw sludges when pick-up vacuum is increased from 10 in. to 20–25 in. of mercury. The highest vacuum is the best at which to operate. (2) Filtration rates increase almost directly with solids concentration in the feed. (3) Sludge-cake formation rate decreases sharply after 0.5 to 0.75 min for most sludges. (4) Optimum filtration rates are obtained when (a) drum submergence is 20 to 25 per cent of filter diameter; and (b) drum is operated so that cake no thicker than is required for good discharge is formed. (5) Filtration rates can be increased from 25 to 100 per cent by the use of metal filter media as compared with cloth.

Operating records should include: hours operated each month; chemicals used, expressed in pounds per pound of dry sewage solids (monthly); average thickness of filter cake (monthly); pounds of wet cake produced (monthly); dry-solids content of wet filter cake, pounds, and in pounds per mg of sewage flow (monthly); and method of disposal of sludge cake (monthly).

[58] *Loc. cit.*

Appendix

Problems

Answers are given for some of the problems. The correctness of these answers is neither guaranteed nor implied. Errors may have occurred in computations, in printing, or in basic theory.

2-1. A bond issue of one million dollars is to be paid by annuity bonds maturing semi-annually and bearing 3 per cent annual interest. The issue is to be retired in 20 years (40 payments). All payments, including principal and interest, are to be of the same amount. (*a*) What is the amount of each payment? (*b*) What is the amount of principal included in the first payment? (*c*) What is the amount of principal included in the 40th payment? (*d*) It is desired that all bonds shall have a face (par) value of $1,000, except the last bond to be paid which shall have a value of less than $1,000. How many bonds will be retired at the last, or 40th payment?

Answers. (*a*) $33,430; (*b*) $18,430; (*c*) $32,930.

2-2. The financial scheme in the preceding problem is to be paid off by a sewer service, or rental, charge. If the average, daily dry-weather flow from the sewer, exclusive of infiltration, is one mgd, the annual maintenance charge for the system is $1,500, and all capital charges are to be retired in 20 years, what should be the charge for service per 1,000 gal of sewage contributed to the sewer?

3-1. Estimate the population of Kankakee, Ill., in 1980, using all mathematical methods described in Sect. 3-3, except the theory of Verhulst.

3-2. A sewer district with a density of population of 50 per acre has an area of 300 acres. (*a*) Find the average rate of domestic sewage flow from the district, in gallons per day, on the assumption that the average per capita flow is the same as that shown in Table 3-7 for high-cost dwellings. (*b*) What would the maximum and minimum rates of flow be if the fluctuations were the same as those for the average curve in Fig. 3-3? (*c*) What would the maximum rates of flow be if computed by the formulas in Sect. 3-10?

Answers. (*a*) 225,000; (*b*) Max is 315,000 gpd and min is 146,000 gpd; (*c*) 654,000 and 585,000 gpd.

3-3. If the scale of a map is 400 ft per in., the density of population is 175 persons per acre, with a flow of 125 gcd, what will be the maximum rate of sew-

713

age flow, in cfs, from 10 sq in., 100 sq in., and 1,000 sq in. of map area, respectively, if the ratio of maximum to average flow is taken as $Q = 5q/P^{0.2}$?

3-4. If a contractor presents two alternative bids on a project, one for excellent joints and the other for good joints, both being formed in a wet trench, determine the difference in cost per mile of pipe that is economically justifiable if the cost of building the sewer can be formulated as $C = kQ^n$ where C is the cost in cents per foot, $k = 150$, $n = 0.04$, and Q is the flow in cfs. There will be infiltration of 10,000 gal per mile of pipe per day through excellent joints, and 50,000 gal through good joints. Normal, dry-weather flow, without infiltration, is 100,000 gal per day. *Answer.* $69.

3-5. The Burkli-Ziegler formula, in metric units, is $Q = 0.5RA(S/A)^{0.25}$ using the nomenclature of Sect. 3-23, and using a medium value for the coefficient. Q and R represent liters per second per hectare, S is the general slope of the drainage area per 1,000, and A is the hectares drained. Rewrite the formula in English units of cubic feet and acres, with S representing the slope ratio.

3-6. Plot the Burkli-Ziegler and McMath formulas graphically on a single sheet of logarithmic coordinate paper, using discharge in cfs as ordinates and area in acres as abscissas. Assume slope in all cases to be 30 per 1,000; the areas to vary between 1 and 100 acres; in McMath formula the value of C is to be 0.75 and of R to be 2.75, and in the Burkli-Ziegler formula R is to be 2. All other needed constants are to be selected as described in Sect. 3-23. Tabulate the values of Q for all multiples of 10 acres from 10 to 100.

Answer. Acres	10	20	40	60	80	100
McMath, cfs	25.7	44.6	77.7	107.3	135.0	162.0
B-Z cfs	18.5	30.8	52.1	70.7	87.6	103.7

3-7. A densely populated portion of a city, with completely paved streets, sidewalks, and yards, is rectangular, and contains 20 square blocks, each 350 ft on a side. The area has a continuous slope of 5 in 1,000 from northeast to southwest. Determine the runoff from this area using the four formulas mentioned in Fig. 3-7, and the constants included.

3-8. A watershed of 3,200 acres has a coefficient of $C = 100$ in Fuller's formula No. 3-10. (*a*) What would be the maximum 5-yr flood from this area in cfs? (*b*) If the cost of caring for this runoff varies as the square root of the rate of runoff, what would be the ratio of the cost of caring for the maximum 10-yr flood to the cost for the maximum 5-yr flood? *Answer.* (*a*) 1,260.

3-9. The main sewer of a drainage system was designed to serve an area of 20 sq mi with an average prospective population of 70 per acre; average rate of sewage flow was 85 gal per person per day, the maximum flow is 50 per cent in excess of the average, and there is a rainfall equivalent of $\frac{1}{5}$ in. per day, all of which runs off. What was the assumed flow in cfs? *Answer.* 285.

3-10. An intercepting sewer is to drain an area of 1,600 acres. Determine the maximum rate of flow, in cfs, under the following conditions: rainfall to be cared for is $\frac{3}{4}$ in. per 24 hr; two-thirds of the rainfall flows into the sewer in 24 hr; house sewage is 80 gcd, the maximum discharge corresponding to one-half flowing off in 8 hr; and the population density is 70 per acre.

3-11. Assuming a prospective population of 200 persons per acre, an average sewage flow of 200 gcd, maximum rate in planning sewers is 50 per cent in excess of the average rate, and the scale of the map used in designing is 300 ft to the in. What will be the maximum rate of flow in cfs per unit of area (1 sq. in.) of map surface?　　　　　　　　　　　　　　　　　　　　　　　*Answer.* 0.19.

3–12. Assume a sewer district in St. Louis with an area of 1,500 acres; the average slope of the surface is 5 in 1,000, and the time of concentration is 60 min. Find: (a) the ordinary maximum intensity of rainfall anticipated, using Talbot's ordinary-storm formula shown in Table 3–13; (b) the probable runoff, using McMath's formula with $C = 0.75$, and the rate of rainfall found in the previous step; and (c) the maximum runoff from the area by the rational method, on the assumption that the area is 40 per cent impervious.

3–13. Determine the maximum runoff from the area described in problem 3–7 using the rational method and Talbot's rainfall formula for maximum storms shown in Table 3–13, with a time of concentration of 60 min and an imperviousness of 0.70. State the result in cfs.　　　　　　　　*Answer.* 157.

3–14. Using the rational method and Talbot's rainfall formula for ordinary storms, determine the runoff, in cfs, from an area of 5 acres, if the time of concentration is 20 min, the duration of the storm is 50 min, and the percentage of imperviousness is computed by Gregory's formula in Sect. 3–17 to the effect that $I = 0.175t^{0.33}$.

3–15. Determine the maximum rate of runoff between manholes 2 and 1 in Fig. 3–6 with the data in Table 3–18, except that the inlet time is doubled for each block, and the time between manholes is 7 min. Solve by the rational method using C. D. Hill's rainfall formula in Table 3–13.　　　*Answer.* 64 cfs.

3–16. Determine the required capacity, in cfs, of the storm sewers between each consecutive pair of manholes shown in the accompanying figure. Assume

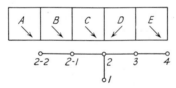

that the time of flow in the sewer from any manhole to the next lower manhole is 5 min, and that other information is as shown in the table. Use $R = 105/(t + 15)$.

Block	Acres	*I*, %	Time, min
A	10	60	10
B	7.5	75	8
C	6.25	50	5
D	15	70	10
E	7.5	80	7

3–17. (a) What proportion of the rate of flow from manhole 3 to manhole 2 in Fig. 3–6 is being contributed by area B 10 min after the start of the storm? (b) Construct a diagram, similar to Fig. 3–5, using a scale of 1 min = ¼ in. and 10 cfs = ½ in. Use data given in Fig. 3–4, except that district A is 15 acres in area, and district C is 5 acres. B remains 10 acres. (c) What is the maximum rate of flow from manhole 2 to manhole 1, and how long after the storm starts does it occur?　　　　　　　*Answers.* (a) 44 per cent; (c) 106 cfs in 16 min.

3–18. A 21,000 gal holding tank is placed at manhole 4 to reduce the peak rate of flow between manhole 4 and manhole 3, in Fig. 3–6. The arrangement is such that water is diverted into the holding tank only when the flow from district A is 25 cfs or greater. Thereafter water enters the holding tank at a rate equal to two-thirds of the difference between the flow from district A and 25 cfs. After the tank is full all flow from district A goes down the sewer. When the rate of flow from district A decreases to 25 cfs and less, a pump starts, at 750 gpm, to empty the tank into the sewer. (*a*) What is the maximum rate of flow from manhole 4 to manhole 3? (*b*) How many minutes after the storm starts does this occur? (*c*) What percentage of the flood peak that would have occurred without the holding tank, does this rate of flow represent? (*d*) How many minutes after the storm started will the tank have been emptied by the pump?

3–19. (*a*) What is the total flow, in gallons, on each of the days shown by the hydrographs in Fig. 3–3, if the ordinates represent rate of flow, and the average flow on the average day is 1,200,000 gal? (*b*) Under such conditions, what is the ratio of maximum to average flow on each day shown?

Answers. (*b*) Max day ratio = 1.54; avg day = 1.50; and min day ratio = 1.43.

4–1. Construct a diagram similar to Fig. 4–5, with n constant, showing the hydraulic elements A, R, Q, and V of a circular section, using Manning's formula. Locate points on each curve that correspond to depths of 0, 0.1, 0.2, 0.3, 0.4, 0.5, 0.6, 0.7, 0.8, 0.9, and 1.0. The height and width of the full section in the diagram are to be 5 in. in length.

4–2. If $n = 0.01525$, $R = 1.2$, and $S = 0.002$, compute the velocity of flow by: (*a*) Kutter's formula; (*b*) Kutter's formula omitting the term $0.0028/S$; and (*c*) Manning's formula. If Kutter's formula is considered to be correct, what are the percentage errors resulting from the use of each of the other formulas and modifications.

4–3. What percentage of error is introduced into the value of V when using Manning's formula, assuming Kutter's value of V to be correct, with the values of n, R, and S given below:

	1	2	3	4	5	6	7	8
n	0.010	0.010	0.010	0.010	0.020	0.020	0.020	0.020
S	0.0001	0.01	0.0001	0.01	0.0001	0.01	0.0001	0.01
R	0.5	0.05	5.0	5.0	0.5	0.5	5.0	5.0

Answer. Number	1	2	3	4	5	6	7	8
Per cent error	4.6	5.6	1.8	3.6	22	9.4	1.5	0.6

4–4. In the table below there are given three of the five factors n, V, Q, S, and D involved in problems in circular pipes running full. Determine the remaining factors by the use of Fig. 4–2, 4–3, and 4–4.

1. $Q = 4$; $D = 21$; $n = 0.015$.
2. $Q = 40$; $S = 0.00055$; $n = 0.015$.
3. $Q = 400$; $V = 5.1$; $n = 0.015$.
4. $D = 66$; $S = 0.0022$; $n = 0.010$.
5. $V = 2$; $D = 15$; $n = 0.020$.
6. $V = 1.48$; $S = 0.0025$; $n = 0.020$.
7. $Q = 1.5$; $D = 10$; $S = 0.0170$.
8. $Q = 50$; $V = 3.9$; $D = 48$.
9. $V = 2.5$; $D = 60$; $S = 0.0002$.
10. $Q = 0.42$; $V = 5.0$; $S = 0.2000$.

Answers. (1) $V = 1.7; S = 0.0009.$ (6) $D = 15$ in.; $Q = 1.75$ cfs.
(2) $V = 2.5; D = 54$ in.   (7) $V = 2.7; n = 0.020.$
(3) $D = 10$ ft; $S = 0.00075.$ (8) Indefinite.
(4) $Q = 215; V = 9.$ (9) $Q = 50; n = 0.010.$
(5) $Q = 2.46; S = 0.005.$ (10) $D = 4$ in.; $n = 0.019.$

4–5. Complete the solution of the following problems in circular pipes running full, using Fig. 4–2, 4–3, and 4–4.

1. $Q = 250; D = 72; n = 0.018.$ 2. $Q = 3; S = 0.0018; n = 0.012.$
3. $Q = 15; V = 3.70; n = 0.016.$ 4. $D = 72; S = 0.00425; n = 0.019.$
5. $V = 4.70; D = 24; n = 0.011.$ 6. $V = 4; S = 0.011; n = 0.020.$
7. $Q = 4; D = 21; S = 0.001.$ 8. $Q = 300; V = 5.88; D = 96.$
9. $V = 10; D = 60; S = 0.0045.$ 10. $Q = 2.0; V = 2.5; S = 0.0035.$

4–6. Solve the following for circular sewers flowing partly full. (*a*) Given $S = 0.0125$, $D = 18$ in., $V = 4$ fps when one-third full. Find n, and Q when one-fourth full. (*b*) Given $n = 0.010$, $S = 5.28$ ft per mile, $D = 120$ in. Find Q when 0.3 full, and V when sewer is carrying 0.3 of its capacity. (*c*) Given $Q = 25$ cfs when flowing ¹⁄₁₆th capacity, $V = 8$ fps when full, and $S = 0.4$ per cent. Find D and n. (*d*) Given $V = 5.5$ fps when sewer is flowing with 0.8 of its capacity, $Q = 35$ cfs when flowing 0.61 full, and $n = 0.010$. Find S, V when one-half full, and Q when 0.2 capacity. Use Fig. 4–5 with n constant.

Answer. (*a*) Q at 0.25 full $= 1.35$; $n = 0.016$; (*b*) Q at 0.3 full $= 138$; V at 0.3 capacity $= 7.6$; (*c*) $D = 96$ in.; $n = 0.019$; (*d*) $S = 0.006$; V at 0.5 full $= 5$; Q at 0.2 capacity $= 10$.

4–7. Solve the following for circular sewers flowing partly full. Use Fig. 4–5, with n constant. (*a*) Given $S = 0.020$, $D = 48$ in., $V = 10.7$ at 0.6 full. Find Q at one-half velocity, Q full, and n. (*b*) Given $n = 0.017$, $D = 42$ in., $S = 0.01$. Find Q at 0.4 full and V when carrying 40 per cent of capacity. (*c*) Given $n = 0.020$, V when carrying 75 per cent capacity is 3.85 fps, and Q when velocity is 60 per cent of full velocity $= 4.5$ cfs. Find S, V at 0.3 full, and Q at 0.5 full.

4–8. Solve the following for circular pipes flowing partly full. Use Fig. 4–5, with n constant. (*a*) Given $S = 0.0225$, $D = 18$ in., and V at two-thirds full $= 6$ fps. Find n, and Q at one-fifth full. (*b*) Given Q at ¹⁄₁₂th capacity $= 30$ cfs, V full $= 11$ fps, and $S = 0.005$. Find D, and n. (*c*) Given $S = 0.0052$, $D = 48$ in., and V at three-eighths capacity $= 5.5$ fps. Find n and Q when three-fourths full.

Answers. (*a*) Q at 0.2 full $= 0.9$; $n = 0.019$; (*b*) $D = 78$ in.; $n = 0.014$;
(*c*) Q at 0.75 full $= 67$; $n = 0.018$.

4–9. Compute the hydraulic radius of the covered, square sewer shown in Fig. 4–8, (*a*) when full and (*b*) when one-fourth full. The diameter of the sewer is 10 ft.

4–10. Compute the hydraulic radius of the egg-shaped sewer shown in Fig. 4–6, (*a*) when full and (*b*) when two-thirds full. The diameter of the sewer is 6 ft.
Answers. R full $= 1.16$; R at 0.67 full $= 1.3$.

4–11. The velocity in a circular sewer is 7.05 fps when it is flowing 68 per cent full, and Q is 136 cfs when carrying 65 per cent capacity. $n = 0.020$. Find D, S, V, and Q when full. Assume that n is constant at all depths of flow.

718

4–12. A 60-in. circular sewer, is on a slope of 0.002. $n = 0.015$ at all depths of flow. Find: (a) Q and V when the sewage is flowing 18 in. deep; (b) Q and V when the sewer is carrying 0.4 of its capacity; and (c) depth of flow and V when Q is 60 cfs.

Answers. (a) $Q = 20$; $V = 3.9$; (b) Q at 0.4 capacity $= 40$; V at 0.4 capacity $= 4.9$; (c) Depth $= 33$ in., V when Q is $60 = 5.3$.

4–13. A 12-in. vitrified clay sewer runs east on a slope of 0.036. At the west end of the line an 8-in. concrete sewer enters from the north. It is on a slope of 0.0365. Another 8-in. sewer of vitrified clay enters from the south. It is on a slope of 0.0074. The two 8-in. sewers are flowing full. Find: (a) the rate of flow in the 12-in. sewer; (b) the depth of flow in the 12-in. sewer. Assume the only flow in the 12-in. sewer comes from the 8-in. sewers.

4–14. Two circular sewers join. One is 84 in. in diameter and at maximum flow it carries 55 cfs on a slope of 0.0002. The branch sewer is 30 in. in diameter and is on a slope of 0.0015. It carries a maximum rate of flow of 9.5 cfs. At what height must the invert of the smaller pipe be above the invert of the larger sewer so that during maximum flow there will be no backing up of sewage in the smaller sewer. Use $n = 0.015$. *Answer.* 38 in.

4–15. A covered, square sewer has a diameter of 9.13 ft. It is on a slope of 0.1 per cent, and it has a coefficient of roughness of $n = 0.010$. What diameter of egg-shaped sewer on a slope of 0.2 per cent and with $n = 0.018$ will have the same velocity of flow when flowing 0.3 full as the velocity in the square sewer when it is carrying 20 per cent of its capacity?

4–16. A covered, square sewer with a diameter of 3 ft is on a slope of 0.002, and has a value of $n = 0.015$. Find the velocity when the sewer is flowing full, and the capacity when full. *Answer.* $V = 3.7$ fps; $Q = 33$ cfs.

4–17. An egg-shaped sewer, of the type shown in Fig. 4–7, has a diameter of 5 ft. The invert elevation at manhole 5 is 120.67, and at manhole 4 it is 119.84. The distance between the manholes is 497 ft. $n = 0.015$. Find Q and V when the sewer is flowing one-half full.

4–18. A 6-ft circular sewer on a slope of 0.0006, with $n = 0.013$, is to be extended by means of an egg-shaped sewer (Fig. 4–7) with a value of $n = 0.020$. The normal, maximum flow of both sewers is to be at 0.8 full, under which conditions the velocities and rates of flow in both sewers will be the same. The junction is to be constructed so that the elevations of the surfaces of the sewage in both sewers are to be the same. Make no allowance for loss of head due to turbulence or friction at the junction. (a) What is the diameter of the egg-shaped sewer? (b) How far below the invert of the circular sewer is the invert of the egg-shaped sewer at the junction? (c) On what slope is the egg-shaped sewer? *Answers.* (a) 7.6 ft; (b) 1.3 ft; (c) 0.0015.

4–19. Draw the hydraulic elements diagram for a 10-ft diameter, barrel-section sewer as dimensioned in Fig. 4–6. The diagram should be similar to that shown in Fig. 4–7, assuming n constant for all depths of flow. Full conditions are to be indicated by coordinates 5 in. long.

4–20. Draw a hydraulic-elements diagram for the open-cut section of the Mill Creek sewer in St. Louis, shown in *Eng. Record*, Vol. 70, page 435. The diagram is to be similar to Fig. 4–7, with coordinates when full a length of 5 in.

4–21. A rectangular sewer with a flat bottom and vertical sides is 3 ft wide and is on a slope of 0.0081. The flow in the sewer is 200 cfs when $n = 0.013$. (a) What is the normal depth of flow? (b) What is critical depth of flow?

Answers. (a) 5.75 ft; (b) 5.14 ft.

4–22. An open sewer of rough brickwork has the shape of an isosceles triangle, apex down, in which the width equals twice the depth. $S = 0.0001$, $Q = 200$ cfs, $n = 0.017$. (a) What is critical depth of flow? (b) What is normal depth of flow? (c) What is the diameter of a circular concrete sewer equivalent to this triangular section when the triangular section is carrying 200 cfs at normal depth of flow?

4–23. A rectangular, concrete culvert, 5 ft x 5 ft, is constructed with an invert slope of 0.0025, with $n = 0.013$. If the culvert is carrying 200 cfs of storm water, what is: (a) normal depth of flow? (b) critical depth of flow? Determine critical depth by three methods: by the method suggested in the text, by the calculus, and graphically. *Answers.* (a) 5 ft; (b) 3.7 ft.

4–24. A covered, square sewer has a capacity of 250 cfs when on a slope of 0.0064, with $n = 0.01486$. The outlet is unobstructed. (a) What is the diameter of the sewer? (b) What will be normal depth of flow? (c) How far above the outlet will the flow reach normal depth? Use vertical increments of 0.1 ft in the solution.

4–25. A rectangular channel with a flat bottom is 10 ft wide, $n = 0.015$, and the slope is 0.0081. The sewer is carrying 220 cfs. The discharge falls free from the mouth of the sewer into a large river. (a) What is critical depth of flow in the sewer? (b) What is the depth of flow at the outlet?

Answers. (a) 2.47 ft; (b) 2.0 ft.

4–26. A trapezoidal channel has a flat bottom 8 ft wide and side slopes 1:1. $n = 0.01486$. The invert is on a slope of 0.001. The flow in the channel is 800 cfs. (a) What is normal depth of flow? (b) What is critical depth? (c) At what distance above the lower end of the channel will the water surface have dropped 0.5 ft below normal depth? Use vertical increments of 0.25 ft in the solution.

4–27. A rectangular channel 4 ft wide, with vertical sides, is on a slope of 0.040 with $n = 0.01486$. At point A the slope changes to 0.0009. The rate of flow is 300 cfs. (a) Does a jump occur? If so, is it free or submerged? (b) If it occurs how far above or below A will it be located? (c) How high would it jump? *Answers.* (a) Submerged jump; (b) 208 ft above A; (c) 4.7 ft.

4–28. A rectangular channel 8 ft wide with vertical sides is on a slope of 0.045, with $n = 0.01486$. At point A the slope changes to 0.00154. When the rate of flow is 235 cfs, find: (a) Is the jump free or submerged? (b) What is the height of the hydraulic jump? (c) What is the energy lost in the jump? Answer in feet of water and in horsepower. (d) At what distance upstream or downstream from A does the jump occur?

4–29. A rectangular conduit 10 ft wide, discharges into a body of water the surface of which is 7.0 ft above the bottom of the conduit. The normal depth of flow in the conduit is 4.5 ft, with $n = 0.015$. The slope of the invert of the conduit is 0.001. Determine the length of the surface curve, using 0.5-ft vertical increments. Is the surface curve a backwater or a dropdown curve? Why?

Answer. Backwater because d_n less than 7.0 ft.

4–30. A rectangular channel 20 ft wide carries a flow of 800 cfs with $n = 0.015$. Plot a curve showing the specific energy (E_s) and pressure plus momentum $(P + M)$ similar to Fig. 4–10. Take points close together near the critical depth to show it more precisely. (a) Solve for critical slope, using Manning's formula. (b) Determine from your diagram: (1) critical depth; (2) minimum specific energy; (3) specific energy when depth is 7.6 ft; (4) depth when specific energy is 8.0 ft; (5) depth after a hydraulic jump has taken off from a depth of 1.7 ft; (6) height of the hydraulic jump; (7) specific energy before and after the jump; (8) loss of energy in the jump; and (9) horsepower lost in the jump.

4–31. The storage yard of a large manufacturing company was drained by a 5-ft square, concrete sewer. The inside top of the sewer was 1 ft below the lowest point in the storage yard. The sewer, on a slope of 0.0005, discharged into a stream 900 ft away. The sewer was designed to carry a 10-yr storm discharge of 62 cfs, with $n = 0.01486$. During a 25-yr storm the surface of the stream arose 3.0 ft above the invert of the sewer at the outlet, and the flow in the sewer reached a rate of 125 cfs. Water backed up into the storage yard and caused damage. The engineer claimed that: (a) The sewer was adequately designed to handle the 10-yr storm. (b) The sewer would have handled the 25-yr storm without backing up into the storage yard if the sewer had not been obstructed by rubbish in the sewer. Prove that the engineer was correct or incorrect in his claim. *Answer.* Claim justified. Dropdown curve is longer than 900 ft.

4–32. An open sewer is triangular in shape with its apex down. The angle at the apex is 90° and the slope of the invert is 0.0016. Find the energy lost in a free hydraulic jump in this channel when the normal depth of flow below the jump is 9 ft. $n = 0.014$.

4–33. An open, rectangular sewer 8 ft wide is carrying 500 cfs. Its invert is on a slope of 0.0625 which changes at point A to 0.00181. The elevation at A is 125.00 ft. The invert continues on the slope below A for 4,000 ft where the channel discharges, unobstructed, into a natural stream. $n = 0.01486$. (a) What is the elevation of the invert at the outlet? (b) What are the normal depths of flow above and below point A? (c) Draw the profile of a transition hump that will suppress the hydraulic jump, assuming that the shape of the rising water surface is a reverse curve. Use a horizontal scale of 50 ft = 1 in. and a vertical scale of 5 ft = 1 in. Use a length of 180 ft for the transition. (d) If the bottom of the channel continues below the hump at a slope of 0.00181, what is the new elevation of the invert at the outlet? (e) What horsepower is exerted by the transition hump and the flowing water to lift the water the height that the invert has been raised?

Answers. (a) 117.76 ft; (b) $d_n = 2.1$ and 7.7 ft, respectively; (d) 125.57; (e) 444.

4–34. A 10-ft square sewer on a slope of 0.00102 is joined at an angle of 45° with its center line by an 8-ft square sewer on a slope of 0.000773. The two sewers discharge into a rectangular sewer 10.25 ft wide and 10 ft in vertical height from invert to roof. Its center line is continuous with the center line of the 10-ft approach sewer. Both of the approach sewers are flowing three-fourths full. The planes of the normal surfaces in the approach sewers when three-fourths full, and the plane of the water surface in the outfall sewer (not the normal surface) all intersect at the junction at elevation 100.0. In answering the following questions use Manning's formula, where necessary, with $C = 100.0$.

(a) What are the elevations of the inverts of each approach sewer at the junction? (b) What are the normal depths of flow in each of the three sewers? (c) What is the elevation of the bottom of the outfall sewer at the junction? (d) What is the head loss due to turbulence at the junction? Answer in feet of water. (e) As an engineer checking the design should you approve it? Why?

5–1. Lay out a sanitary sewer system to serve the area east of State Street on Fig. 5–4. All sewage is to be discharged into Fish Creek at Tennessee Street. (a) Locate all sewer lines and number the contributing areas and manholes according to the system recommended in the text. (b) Determine the maximum flow into each manhole on the main line. Assume an average rate of flow of 140 gal per capita daily, a density of population of 30 per acre, and ground-water infiltration of 35,000 gal per mile of pipe per day. The main line should be the longest line above the outlet.

5–2. Draw the profile of the main-line sewer laid out in the preceding problem. Arrange the computations as in Table 5–2 and draw the profile as in Fig. 5–5. Use a horizontal scale of 1 in. = 100 ft, and a vertical scale of 1 in. = 10 ft. Use $n = 0.015$.

5–3. Determine, by the rational method, the maximum storm-water runoff in cfs from areas 17, 18, and 19 in Fig. 5–4, using Talbot's formula for the maximum storm exceeded two or three times in a century. Imperviousness is 35 per cent, and time of concentration from area 18 is 11 min.　　*Answer.* 9.75.

5–4. If the slopes given in column 16, Table 5–3 were increased by 0.002, what would be the time of concentration in line 21, column 13? Use $n = 0.015$.

5–5. Lay out a storm-sewer system to drain the entire area west of Long Street in Fig. 5–3. The main-line sewer is to be laid in Tennessee Street draining east, and is to be the longest line in the system. (a) Locate and number all manholes. (b) Draw the outlines of areas draining into each manhole and number each drainage area. (c) Determine, by the rational method, the preliminary-design rate of flow from the entire area under the following conditions: (1) Minimum time of concentration for any block is 10 min. (2) The imperviousness of private property is 40 per cent, and of public property (streets and sidewalks) is 60 per cent. (3) Determine rate of rainfall by Kuichling's formula in Table 3–13. (4) Draw the map to a scale of 1 in. = 200 ft. (5) Assume the time in the sewer to be one-half min per 100 ft of sewer, with times used to nearest one-half minute. (d) Set up computations as in Table 5–3, and follow standards of practice and method outlined in the text.

6–1. How many cubic feet of concrete are there above the crown of the sewer, in the manhole shown in Fig. 6–3? The distance from the crown of the sewer to the surface of the ground is 16 ft. How many manhole steps would be required?

6–2. (a) How many type B inlets shown in Table 6–1 will be required in a street gutter on a slope of 1 per cent to carry off a gutter flow of 3.12 cfs? (b) If a type E inlet were used, how many would be required? (c) If two type A inlets of equal length were used, what would be the length of each inlet?

　　　　　　　　　　　　　　　　　　Answers. (a) 4; (b) 3; (c) 6.8 ft.

6–3. (a) What volume of water is discharged at each flush of the automatic flush tank with 6-in. siphon shown in Fig. 6–12, assuming that the tank is circular with a diameter of 5 ft and the vertical distance from A to B is 32 in.? Answer in gallons? (*b*) On what slope would this volume of water be sufficient to cleanse a 10-in. sewer, according to the data in Table 13–2?

6–4. (*a*) How many gallons of water will be required for flushing the sewer between manhole 148.5 and 148.4 in Fig. 5–5, according to the data in Table 13–2? (*b*) How far will the greatest effect of the flush be felt, if $n = 0.015$. See Sect. 4–26. (*c*) At what rate must the flush tank discharge to obtain maximum flushing effect? (*d*) At what depth would this quantity of water stand over the bottom edge of the bell shown in the flush tank in Fig. 6–12, if the diameter of the tank is 4 ft?

Answers. (*a*) 410; (*b*) 100 ft; (*c*) 4.05 cfs; (*d*) 4.4 ft.

6–5. A leaping weir similar to that shown in Fig. 6–16, is set in a 48-in. circular sewer which is on a slope of 0.001. $n = 0.015$. If all flows at a depth 12 in. or less are to fall through the gap into the dry-weather intercepter, and the vertical distance between the lips of the weir is 8 in., what is the required width of the gap, in inches?

6–6. A 15-in. sewer on a slope of 0.013 intercepts the dry-weather flow from a 42-in. combined sewer on a slope of 0.00118. If the maximum vertical drop permitted in the bottom of the 42-in. sewer, for the purpose of constructing a leaping weir, is 9 in., what should be the width of the gap to intercept not more than the full capacity of the intercepting sewer? *Answer.* 28 in.

6–7. A leaping weir is built to intercept the dry-weather flow in a 60-in. combined sewer on a slope of 0.0005, with $n = 0.013$. The lower lip of the weir is 18 in. below the upper lip and 20 in. downstream. (*a*) Above what flow in the sewer will all of the flow continue in the 60-in. sewer? (*b*) What will be the depth of flow in the 60-in. sewer?

6–8. (*a*) What would be the length of weir required in the illustrative problem solved in Sect. 6–15 if the Smith and Coleman formula had been used? (*b*) The Parmley formula? (*c*) The Lea formula? (*d*) The Fruhling formula? Let $y_1 = (h_1 + h_2)^{1/2}$.   *Answers.* (*a*) 13 ft; (*b*) 3 ft; (*c*) 7 ft; (*d*) 4 ft.

6–9. A new, 50-acre subdivision is to drain into a 7-ft circular sewer that is already flowing full. The sewer is on a slope of 0.001 with $n = 0.015$. The time of concentration for the district is 30 min, and its average imperviousness is 0.40. Runoff from the district may be estimated by Talbot's rainfall formula for ordinary storms in eastern United States. What length of an overflow weir, placed 4.48 ft above the invert, will be required to divert sufficient water to a relief sewer upstream from the subdivision to provide capacity in the 7-ft sewer for runoff from the subdivision? Use Fruhling's formula.

6–10. An overflow weir, 20 ft in length, is installed in a 48-in. sewer on a slope of 0.0049, with $n = 0.010$. The weir is 18 in. above the invert. What is the flow over the weir when the 48-in. sewer is flowing three-fourths full and the weir discharges according to the Lea formula? *Answer.* 45 cfs.

6–11. Plot curves showing rates of flow vs. depth in Parshall flumes with widths of 1.0, 2.0, and 4.0 ft. Plot abscissas to a scale of 1 in. = 0.5 ft, and ordinates 1 in. = 5 cfs. Use depths of 0.5, 1.0, 1.5, 2.0, and 3.0 ft.

6–12. An inverted siphon consists of two pipes 15 in. and 30 in. in dia., respectively. They are each 928 ft long, with $n = 0.013$. The invert at the outlet is 3.11 ft lower than at the inlet. What are the rates and velocities of flow in each pipe? Neglect losses due to bends.

Answers. For 15-in. pipe $V = 2.9$ fps, and $Q = 3.6$ cfs. For 30-in. pipe $V = 4.4$ fps, and $Q = 21.4$ cfs.

6-13. Determine the diameters and the elevations of the outlets of a 3-pipe siphon to pass under a river, if the elevation of the inlets of all pipes is 410.60, the minimum permissible velocity in any pipe is 3.0 fps when full, the ratio of the capacities of the three pipes is 1:2:3, and the combined capacities of all pipes is 18 cfs. Each pipe is 1,000 ft long and $n = 0.013$. Neglect head loss in bends. Use only standard-size circular pipes. The loss of head at entrance and at exit are each one velocity head. The outlets are not necessarily to be at different elevations.

6-14. What are the rate and velocity of flow in each pipe in the siphon shown in Fig. 6-24, if the head loss across the siphon is 4.5 ft and the developed length of each pipe is 187 ft. All other required dimensions are to be scaled from the figure. Use Hazen and Williams formula with $C = 100$ for all pipes.

Answers. Q in 14 in. $= 6.0$ cfs, and $V = 5.7$ fps; in 54-in. $Q = 124$ cfs and $V = 7.8$ fps.

7-1. Two types of concrete pipe are being considered as alternatives for an outfall sewer. The pipes are to be laid so that the distance between cracks made by mortar joints, as measured parallel to the length of the line, is 4 ft. Pipes will be in contact at all joints. The nominal internal diameter is 24 in. (*a*) What is the weight, in pounds, of one length or section of each style of pipe made in the molds shown in Fig. 7-3(*b*)? Assume concrete to weigh 150 lb per cu ft. Answer to the nearest 10 lb. *Answer.* Old pipe, 1590 lb.

8-1. A 24-in. standard, vitrified-clay sewer pipe is laid with ordinary bedding in a trench 4 ft wide. The pipe is covered with 20 ft of dry sand. (*a*) Is the design safe? (*b*) If first-class bedding had been used, what would be the factor of safety? (*c*) If the pipe were covered with 16 ft of saturated top soil, what would be the factor of safety if first-class bedding were used? *Suggestion,* see Fig. 8-3. *Answers.* (*a*) No; (*b*) 1.07; (*c*) 1.06.

8-2. A 36-in. diameter, standard, reinforced-concrete sewer pipe is laid in a recommended-width trench under 24 ft of saturated, yellow clay. A concrete-cradle bedding is proposed. (*a*) What is the load per foot of pipe, in pounds? (*b*) What would be the factor of safety with the concrete-cradle bedding? (*c*) If a concentrated load of 15,000 lb is placed on the trench, will the safety of the pipe be threatened? Assume a laying length of 3 ft.

8-3. Identical, concentrated, superimposed loads are placed on two sewers installed in trenches of recommended width. One sewer is a 12-in., vitrified-clay pipe with 2 ft of cover and the other is a 36-in. vitrified-clay pipe with 6 ft of cover. If the weight of the backfill is neglected: (*a*) Which sewer would be subjected to the greater load per linear foot? (*b*) What is the ratio of the load on the more heavily loaded pipe to the load transmitted to the more lightly loaded pipe? *Answers.* (*a*) 12-in.; (*b*) 2.3.

8-4. A 30-in. standard, vitrified-clay pipe is to be laid in a trench of the minimum recommended width, and it is to be covered with 8 ft of partly compacted, damp, yellow clay. A light, street railway passes over the sewer. The sewer passes through a storage yard where bricks are piled to a height of 3 ft over the backfilled trench. (*a*) What is the greatest load on the pipe, in lb per ft of length? (*b*) What type of bedding should be recommended if a factor of safety of 1.5 is required? Allow 75 per cent for impact.

8–5. A 27-in. standard, reinforced-concrete sewer pipe is to be laid in a trench of minimum, recommended width and is to be covered with 10 ft of saturated, top soil. An 8-in. concrete pavement will be laid on top of the backfill and will extend the full length of the pipe. The unit weight of concrete is 150 lb per cu ft. Heavy, city traffic is expected on the street. Allowing 100 per cent for impact and a factor of safety of 1.5, what type of bedding should be recommended?

Answers. Shown in Fig. 8–3*d*.

8–6. A 12-in., vitrified-clay, sewer pipe is laid in a trench of minimum, recommended width and it is covered with 30 in. of dry sand. The pipe passes under a coal storage yard. (*a*) If ordinary bedding is used, to what height can coal be piled over the pipe if a factor of safety of 1.5 is to be maintained? (*b*) How high could the coal be piled if the sewer were of unreinforced concrete with sand bearing?

8–7. The supporting strengths of various sizes of a special pipe, in pounds per linear foot, with sand bearing, are as follows:

Pipe size, in.	8	10	12	15	18	21	24	27	30	36
Regular	1,950	2,100	2,250	2,625	3,000	3,300	3,430	3,930	4,570	5,570
Extra strength	3,000	3,000	3,375	4,125	4,950	5,775	6,600	7,050	7,500	9,000

Compute the factor of safety for each of the sizes of regular and of extra-strength pipe in the table for 3 ft of cover above the crown of the pipe laid with ordinary bedding. Assume backfill to be saturated, top soil. Base surface-load computations on a 10-ton axle load with an impact factor of 1.5.

Tabulate the results under the following headings:

Size	B_d	H/B_d	C_d	$B_d{}^2$	Backfill load	C_t	Surface load	Total load	Allowed load	Safety factor

Answers. Safety factor for 36-in. regular is 1.87; for 36-in. extra is 3.02.

8–8. A concrete pipe with an internal diamater of 8 ft and a wall thickness of 12 in. is subjected to a load of 20,000 lb per ft of length. What is the maximum bending moment on any cross section of the pipe. Answer in foot pounds per foot length of pipe under the following conditions: (1) The load is uniformly distributed across the full diameter of the pipe; (2) The load is uniformly distributed over the central section of the pipe which subtends an angle of 90°; and (3) The load is uniformly distributed over the central section of the pipe which subtends an angle of 60°.

10–1. A sewer is to be laid between manholes *A* and *B* to give the least volume of excavation. The conditions are: distance between manholes, 600 ft; flow in the sewer, 100 cfs; ground surface at *A* is at elevation 114.4 and at *B* it is 118.6; the elevation of the inside of the *crown* of the sewer at manhole *A* is 105.0; trench has vertical sides, it is 2 ft wider than the nominal, inside diameter of the pipe, and the bottom of the trench is 6 in. below the invert (inside) of the pipe. (*a*) What is the diameter of the sewer that will require the least excavation? (*b*) What is the volume of this excavation, in cubic yards?

(c) If the maximum permissible velocity is limited to 10 fps what diameter of pipe would give the least excavation?   *Answers.* (a) 4.0 ft; (b) 2,395.

10–2. If the flow in the sewer described in problem 10–1 is 1.6 cfs and other conditions are the same except that the width of the trench is to be as recommended in Table 8–6: (a) What would be the diameter of the sewer that would give the least volume of excavation? (b) What would be the volume of this excavation, in cu yd?

10–3. What is the shortest length of a trench that is 4 ft wide and 15 ft deep that can be excavated by machine at a cost equal to or less than by hand excavation? The excavating machine costs $35,000; interest on capital is charged at 5 per cent annually; the hourly cost of machine operation, including labor, fuel, overhead, and depreciation, is $13; and the cost of moving the machine to the job and setting it up is $425. The machine will operate about 1,600 hours annually, excavating 125 cu yd per hr. The cost of hand excavation, all items included, is $2.40 per cu yd.   *Answer.* 84 ft.

10–4. (a) Prepare a bill of material required for complete vertical sheeting for 100 ft of the trench in problem 10–3. Use the California specifications described in Sect. 10–18. A sketch should be made to show spacing and dimensions of rangers, cross braces, and sheeting. (b) How many feet, board measure, will be required if the length of sheeting is 16 ft?

10–5. A man can excavate 20 ft of sewer trench to a depth of 8 ft and a width of 27 in. in 8 hr. He costs $2.95 per hour, including overhead and insurance, etc. An excavating machine, costing $21,000, has a life of 6 yr and a salvage value of $5,000. It can be used 8 hr per day for 200 days annually. When operating it costs $12.50 per hour for labor, fuel, and maintenance. It will excavate 1,000 linear ft of 27-in. trench to a depth of 8 ft in 8 hr. Capital is charged at 8 per cent annually. A sinking fund to replace equipment will draw 6 per cent interest. The cost of moving and setting up the machine on a job is $1,200. How many cu yd of excavation are necessary to make the use of the machine less costly than hand excavation?   *Answer.* 770.

10–6. (a) In what stage was the construction of the sewer, shown in Fig. 10–15, when the picture was taken? (b) Why was steel sheeting used under the conditions shown? (c) Is the ground thrust probably greater at the top or the bottom of the trench? Why?

10–7. The specific capacity (discharge in gpm per ft of drawdown) of the well point shown in Fig. 10–18 has been shown by test under local conditions on a job to be 4.0. The test showed also that the radius of the circle of influence was 3.16 ft for a drawdown of 4 ft, and that the radius of the circle of influence varied directly with the drawdown. (a) What is the least distance apart that the wells may be spaced alongside the deepest trench shown in Fig. 10–18 to prevent ground water from entering the trench and, at the same time, avoid interference between the wells? Answer in feet. (b) What will be the discharge from each well under these conditions? Answer in gpm. (c) How deep will the wells be? Answer in feet. (d) If the wells remain at this depth can the space between them be increased without allowing ground water to enter the trench? Why? (e) What will be the static suction lift to the ground surface, in each well?   *Answers.* (a) 15; (b) 38; (c) 20.

11-1. (*a*) What is the maximum possible uplift, in pounds per foot length of form, that might be exerted on the form shown in Fig. 11-12, if the concrete is fluid, weighs 150 lb per cu ft, and is poured and vibrated so rapidly that no set occurs until the form is filled? The form is semi-circular with a diameter of 12 ft 8 in. Other needed dimensions should be scaled or estimated from the illustration. (*b*) At what rate, according to formula 11-1, may the form be filled in order that the uplift will not exceed 50 per cent of the maximum possible? Assume $H = R/2$; $C = 0.25$; $S = 3.33$; and $T = 80$. (*c*) What, if any, provision is made, as shown in Fig. 11-12, to prevent the form from rising when concrete is poured?

11-2. A sewer system comprising about 25 miles of pipe, discharges into a treatment plant whose nominal capacity is 4 mgd. The cost of pumping and treatment has been found to be about $20 per mg of sewage treated, regardless of its strength, within normal limits. If capital costs for money are about 4 per cent, how many dollars can be expended justifiably, per mile of pipe of subsequent sewer construction, to reduce the present rate of infiltration of 50,000 gal per mile of pipe per day to 5,000? *Answer.* $8,225.

12-1. If the electric motors shown in Fig. 12-3 each delivers 1 hp; the ejectors shown have an overall mechanical efficiency of 25 per cent and discharge 500 gal at each discharge; and the total lift, static plus dynamic, is 10 ft: (*a*) What is the shortest possible time between discharges from the pumping station? (*b*) What is the maximum possible discharge from the pumping station, in gallons per day? (*c*) What, if any, provisions have been made to protect the motors against damage by moisture? (*d*) What is the function of the motors in the pumping station?

12-2. Sewage is flowing into a wet well at a rate of 90 gpm. The capacity of the wet well between cut-in and cut-out elevations is 600 gal. If a pump and motor whose characteristics are shown in Fig. 12-5, are used in the wet well: (*a*) What would be the time between cut-in and cut-out if the pumps cut in and operate continuously at a discharge head of 103 ft? (*b*) What would be the time if the cut-in occurred when the head is 103 ft and the cut-out with a head of 113 ft? In this case the pump operates under a varying head while the rate of inflow is constant at 90 gpm. Solve by taking increments of 1 min. *Answers.* (*a*) 10 min; (*b*) between 15 and 16 min.

12-3. A wet well in a pumping station, with a capacity of 12,000 gal, is equipped with three automatically controlled pumps whose capacities, in gpm, are 300, 600, and 1,800. The small pump starts when the well is one-third full, the intermediate pump starts when the well is two-thirds full, and the largest pump starts when the well is full. Once started, each pump continues in operation until the well is empty. The rate of inflow to the well is 2,000 gpm. (*a*) How long will it take to fill and empty the well? (*b*) How long will each pump be in operation during a complete filling and emptying cycle? Answer in minutes.

12-4. If the wet well being used under the conditions shown in Fig. 12-4, together with the same pumps, has a capacity of 5,000 gal: (*a*) How many gallons of water are in the well at 6 A.M.? (*b*) Is the well filling at 12.30 P.M.? Why? (*c*) If power failure were to cause all the pumps to stop at noon, how much time would be available for starting of auxiliary power before the wet well overflows? (*d*) If the pumps were to cut in again just as the well fills after the preceding shutdown, at what minimum rate must they operate to prevent an overflow? (*e*) If the 500-gpm pump is started alone at some moment when the wet well is full, what is the longest time that this pump could operate continuously? (*f*) Would the pump have to be stopped or another pump cut in at the end of this period? (*g*) At about what time would the pump have to start and stop or receive assistance from an additional pump?

Answers. (*a*) Almost 5,000 gal; (*c*) about 15 min; (*e*) about 12 hr; (*g*) start at 8.30 A.M., run until 8.30 P.M. when well will be empty.

12–5. (*a*) Construct a 24-hr mass diagram for the hydrograph of the average day flow of sewage shown in Fig. 3–3. Use as abscissas 1 in. = 4 hr, and as ordinates 1 in. = 200,000 gal. The daily flow of sewage is 1 mg. (*b*) There are three pumps in the pumping station with the following capacities, respectively, in mgd: 0.175, 0.525, and 1.05. What is the smallest capacity of a wet well, in gallons, that will require a minimum of one hour for all pumps working together to empty the well.

12–6. (*a*) What horsepower will have to be developed by an electric motor to drive a centrifugal pump delivering 420 gpm against a head of 55 ft, assuming a pump and power transmission efficiency of 69 per cent? (*b*) If, after installation, it is found that the pump will deliver 490 gpm against a 58-ft head with an overall pump and power transmission efficiency of 64 per cent, by what per cent will the motor be overloaded? *Answers.* (*a*) 8.45; (*b*) 32.5 per cent.

12–7. A pump-and-motor unit, when new, was designed for a discharge head of 110 ft. Age and other conditions increased the discharge head to 119 ft. If the characteristics of the unit are as in Fig. 12–5: (*a*) What was the rate of discharge at the time of installation, in gpm? (*b*) What was the rate of discharge when the head reached 119 ft? (*c*) What was the overall efficiency of pump and motor when the unit was installed? (*d*) What was the overall efficiency when the discharge head reached 119 ft? (*e*) If power costs 2.2 cents per kwh, did the total annual pumping cost increase or decrease, and by how much? (*f*) How much did the unit cost of pumping increase, in cents per 1,000 gal? (*g*) What was the percentage increase in the unit cost of pumping?

Answers. (*a*) 125; (*c*) 64.7 per cent; (*e*) decreased $197; (*g*) 73 per cent.

12–8. (*a*) Does sewage flow through either of the pumps shown in Fig. 12–10 when the pump is not operating? Why? (*b*) How are the "Flushkleen" strainers cleaned in regular operation? (*c*) The inlet pipe to the pumping station is shown entering above the water in the wet well. Is this necessary? Why? (*d*) What, if any other than the normal, path is provided for water in the event of need?

12–9. (*a*) The operator, in Fig. 12–6, is apparently working on a valve. Is it open or closed? Why? (*b*) What kind of a valve is it? Why? (*c*) Was either pump in operation when the picture was taken? Why?

Answers. (*a*) Far open; (*c*) yes, pressure is shown on gage.

12–10. (*a*) How many pumps are shown in the pumping station in Fig. 12–7? (*b*) How many bearings are shown on the vertical shaft between the pump and the motor? (*c*) Where does the sump pump discharge? (*d*) Can air or odors travel through the building from the wet well to the dry well? Why? (*e*) If the inlet sewer into the wet well is never submerged, what are maximum and minimum static lifts of the pumps? Where necessary, scale from the figure using the distance between the centers of pumps as 5 ft.

12–11. If the net internal diameters of the suction and the discharge pipes for each pump shown in Fig. 12–9 is 12 in., and the internal diameter of the discharge manifold is as shown in the figure, and the maximum permissible velocity of flow in any pipe is 10 fps: (*a*) What is the capacity of each pump, and (*b*) of the pumping station? Answer in gpm.

Answers. (*a*) 3,250; (*b*) 11,000.

12–12. The diaphragm pump shown in Fig. 12–17 has a stroke of 4 in.; operates at 45 rpm; the suction and discharge valves are, respectively, 5 in. and 4 in.; the suction lift is 8 ft; and the discharge lift is 2 ft. The diameter of the pump chamber is 18 in., and of the moving part of the pump chamber is 15 in. (*a*) If the displacement efficiency of the pump is 85 per cent, what is its capacity, in gpm? (*b*) If the mechanical efficiency is 75 per cent what horsepower must be delivered to the pump by the motor that drives it?

Answers. (*a*) 31.4; (*b*) 0.105.

12–13. Name those parts of the pump bearing indicated in Fig. 12–16 which revolve when the pump is running.

12–14. (*a*) What is the static lift by the pump shown in Fig. 12–19, if the water surface is at elevation 122.0? (*b*) What is the lowest elevation from which sludge can be lifted? Suggestion, scale the distance on the drawing. (*c*) At what elevation is air admitted to the pump? (*d*) What is the diameter of the air-supply pipe leading into the induction head? (*e*) Is a foot valve needed? Why? (*f*) Must the pump be primed to start? Why?

Answers. (*a*) Zero; (*c*) 113.25; (*e*) no.

14–1. If each chemist working in the laboratory shown in Fig. 14–2 requires a 6-ft length of laboratory bench, in addition to a share of other facilities in the laboratory, how many chemists may work simultaneously in the laboratory?

Answer. Three.

15–1. Sewage flows into a treatment plant at the rate of 2.32 mgd with variations according to the "average day" curve in Fig. 3–3. What is the minimum volume of a composite sample that will be collected on a 24-hr, hourly, proportional sampling schedule? See basic requirements in Sect. 15–3.

15–2. A rural community with a population of 2,250 consumes 62 gal of water per capita daily. (*a*) What is the probable BOD of the domestic sewage? There are no industries in the community. (*b*) Is this a strong, medium, or weak sewage? (*c*) If the water consumption increased to 142 gcd what would be the probable BOD of the sewage?

Answers. (*a*) 340 mg/l; (*b*) strong; (*c*) 148 mg/l.

15–3. An industrial sewage flow of 2.55 mgd has a BOD of 21,000 lb daily. The waste is added to the domestic sewage flow of 7.5 mgd. The BOD of the domestic sewage is 185 mg/l: (*a*) What is the concentration of BOD in the industrial waste? (*b*) What is the concentration of BOD in the combined sewage? (*c*) What are the probable population and the per capita flow of sewage? (*d*) What are the population equivalents based on the BOD load and based on the hydraulic load?

15–4. A state health department has ruled that a stream is being seriously polluted by the discharge of raw, municipal sewage into the stream. You have been employed by the city to study the case and to confirm or contradict the ruling with supporting evidence. The following information has been collected: Population, 1,000; average, per capita, daily sewage flow, 130 gal; minimum stream flow recorded, 8.0 cfs; BOD above sewer outlet, zero; minimum dissolved oxygen in stream 1,000 yards below sewer outlet, 8.0 mg/l; no industrial wastes. Would you confirm the health department's ruling? Why?

Answer. No. BOD is low and DO is high.

15–5. If the minimum concentration of dissolved oxygen required to sustain fish life in a stream is 4.0 mg/l, what is the minimum percentage of dissolved oxygen saturation permissible in the stream if the temperature varies between 35° and 86° F? Use Truesdale figures in Table 15–3.

15–6. The BOD results shown below were determined on a sample of raw sewage at 26° C:

t, days	0	1	2	4	6	8
BOD, mg/l	0	32	57	84	106	111

Determine the value of K and of L_a at 20° C, using the Thomas method described in Sect. 15–10.   *Answers.* $K = 0.096$; $L_a = 127$ mg/l.

15–7. If the 5-day, 20° C BOD of a sample is 800 mg/l, what will be its 3-day, 35° C BOD? Use equation 15–3.

15–8. If the 3-day, 12° C BOD of a sample is 120 mg/l, what will be its 7-day, 25° C BOD? Use equation 15–3.   *Answer.* 358 mg/l.

15–9. The 5-day, 20° C BOD of a sample of sewage is 200 mg/l. (*a*) Determine its 3-day, 20° C BOD by the monomolecular equations, with K at 20° C = 0.13. (*b*) Determine the 3-day, 20° C BOD by the logarithmic method. (*c*) What is the per cent deviation of the logarithmic result from the monomolecular result? (*d*) What is the deviation of the ratio of monomolecular to logarithmic results found from the ratio shown in Fig. 15–3?

15–10. The 7-day, 15° C BOD of a sample of sewage is 325 mg/l and its 3-day, 37° C BOD is 500 mg/l. (*a*) What is the value of K, the deoxygenation coefficient necessary in the monomolecular procedure, to accord with the data? (*b*) What is its 5-day, 20° C BOD as determined logarithmically? (*c*) What is its 5-day, 20° C BOD as determined by the monomolecular method? (*d*) What is the per cent deviation of the logarithmic from the monomolecular values found in (*a*) and (*b*)?   *Answers.* (*a*) 0.2; (*b*) 354 mg/l; (*c*) 354 mg/l.

15–11. (*a*) Plot a graph of the ratio between BOD at 30° C as computed by the monomolecular procedure for a period of 1 to 15 days and as read from Fig. 15–1. Results are to be based on the assumption that readings from Fig. 15–1 are correct. Use time as abscissas with 1 in. = 3 days, and the desired ratio as ordinates with a ratio of 1.0 = 5 in. (*b*) In how many days will the ratio drop to 90 per cent?

15–12. (*a*) If the color of a sample in a relative stability test disappears in 4.5 days at a temperature of 37° C, what is its relative stability? (*b*) In how many days would the color disappear if the sample were stored at 20° C?

Answers. (*a*) 89.5; (*b*) 9.8.

16–1. A town with a population of 8,500 is designing a sewage-treatment plant to handle both its domestic and its industrial wastes. There are three industrial plants: a dairy, a packing plant, and a cannery. A sanitary survey revealed the following: dairy, 0.6 mgd of waste with BOD of 1,200 mg/l; packing plant, 0.75 mgd with BOD of 480 mg/l; and cannery, 1.20 mgd with BOD of 250 mg/l. Domestic sewage is 92 gcd and per capita oxygen demand is 0.18 lb per day. An expansion factor of 15 per cent is to be provided. Find: (a) design population equivalent for the plant; (b) organic loading; and (c) hydraulic loading.

Answers. (a) 83,300; (b) 15,000 lb BOD per day; (c) 3.83 mgd.

16–2. A study of the dissolved-oxygen conditions is being made in connection with the design of a sewage-treatment plant. The following information has been gathered: (1) Population contributing = 10,000. (2) Domestic waste: (*i*) 122 gcd, (*ii*) BOD 0.191 lb/cap/day; (*iii*) temperature 64° F. (3) Ground water infiltration into sewers, 116,000 gal per day with temperature of 51° F. (4) Industrial wastes: (*i*) milk waste is 76,000 gal per day, BOD is 1,700 mg/l, and temperature is 84° F; (*ii*) packing waste is 180,000 gal per day, BOD is 800 mg/l, and temperature is 95° F; (*iii*) stream conditions, dissolved oxygen 8.0 mg/l, and minimum flow is 4! cfs. (a) What is the average BOD in the domestic waste, in mg/l? (b) What are the following characteristics of the total waste as it reaches the stream: (1) BOD in pounds, (2) BOD in mg/l, and (3) temperature, degrees F? (c) What is the ratio of the pounds of oxygen contributed daily by the river to the pounds of BOD per day of the waste? (d) Does the river provide sufficient oxygen to satisfy the BOD?

16–3. The following observations have been made on a river:

	Point A	Point B	Point C
BOD mg/l	7.40	3.37	. . .
DO mg/l	6.10	1.90	4.37
DO deficiency mg/l	2.43	6.63	4.16

The time of flow between stations A and B is 4.3 days and between B and C is 2.0 days. Conditions are uniform between each pair of contiguous stations. K_1, the deoxygenation constant, is 0.12 at 24° C. (a) What is the value of K_2 the reoxygenation constant, at 20° C, between A and B, and between B and C?

Answers. From A to B, $K_2 = 0.068$; from B to C, $K_2 = 0.182$.

16–4. A city discharges 30 mgd of sewage into a stream whose minimum rate of flow is 750 cfs. The velocity of flow in the stream is 3 mph. The temperature of the sewage and of the diluting water is 15° C. The BOD of the sewage is 180 mg/l and of the diluting water is 1.0 mg/l. The sewage contains no dissolved oxygen, but the diluting water is saturated with it. The coefficient of reareation of the stream, at 20° C, is 0.5. (a) What will be the percentage of saturation of the stream with dissolved oxygen 37½ miles downstream? (b) What will be the minimum dissolved oxygen concentration in the stream? (c) How many miles downstream will the minimum dissolved oxygen concentration occur?

16–5. A stream with a normal, summer temperature of 76° F has a minimum, summer flow of 2,100 cfs. It is tributary to a larger stream which it joins after 6 days of flow below a point where an industrial waste is to be discharged into it. The industrial waste has an expected population equivalent of 127,000, a flow of 9 mgd, and a temperature of 95° F. It will contain no dissolved oxygen.

The BOD of the stream at the point of pollution is 10 mg/l with a dissolved oxygen deficiency of 2.0 mg/l. The reaeration constant of the stream is 0.25 at 20° C. What would be the probable percentage saturation with dissolved oxygen at the mouth of the tributary stream 6 days after it has been polluted by the industrial waste, if no additional pollution occurs? *Answer.* 69.4.

16–6. How much dilution is required to maintain a minimum of 40 per cent saturation with dissolved oxygen after 10 days in a stream into which there is being discharged 20 mgd of sewage at 60° F, with a BOD of 300 mg/l? The temperature of the stream is 60° F, its reaeration constant is 0.25 at 20° C, the per cent saturation with dissolved oxygen is 90, and the BOD is 4.0 mg/l. Answer in mgd.

16–7. Plot the oxygen-sag curve for the stream conditions of problem 16–5. Use time, in days, as abscissas, and dissolved oxygen in mg/l as ordinates. Use scales of 1 in. = 1 day, and 1 in. = 2 mg/l.

Answers. Days	0	1	2	3	4	6
Deficit, mg/l	2.01	4.52	5.01	4.66	3.98	2.59

16–8. A city with a population of 100,000 plans to discharge its settled sewage, devoid of oxygen, into a river in which the minimum flow is 119.2 cfs. (*a*) Will the absorption of oxygen through the surface of the river be sufficient to prevent depletion of dissolved oxygen in the stream under the following conditions: (1) The BOD removal from the sewage in the settling tanks is 35 per cent; (2) deoxygenation is caused only by the sewage and reoxygenation results only from atmospheric oxygen; (3) the average rate of sewage flow is 110 gcd; (4) the temperature of the stream is 22° C; (5) velocity of flow in the stream is 0.8 mph; (6) the width of the stream averages 55 ft; (7) the stream, above the point of pollution, is saturated with oxygen; (8) K_1 at 20° C is 0.1, and reaeration is as shown in Fig. 16–2. (*b*) What is the value of K_2, the reaeration coefficient?

16–9. A strong domestic sewage (Table 15–1) is to be treated in an oxidation pond designed under the limitations set in Sect. 16–28, for moderate-weather conditions. The flow of sewage is 96,000 gal per day. State the following relative to the pond: (*a*) Depth, in ft; (*b*) surface area, acres; (*c*) water load, gal per acre per day; and (*d*) detention period, days.

> *Answers.* (*a*) 3 or 4; (*b*) 4.8; (*c*) 20,000; (*d*) 65 for 4-ft depth; 49 for 3-ft depth.

16–10. What is the maximum Kiker coefficient of percolation allowable to satisfy the conditions in the last line of the table in Fig. 16–3, assuming a septic tank capacity of 50 gal per capita and a sewage flow from motels shown in Table 3–7? *Answer.* 1.36.

16–11. An oxidation pond depending on biological activity and photosynthesis is to be designed for the sewage load described in problem 16–9. What should be: (*a*) Depth of pond, in ft? (*b*) Surface area, in acres? (*c*) Water load, in gallons per acre per day? (*d*) Detention period, days? It is known that $I_i = 1,750$ ft candles; $\alpha = 0.001$; Min temp is 68° F; $P = 1.5$; $h = 6$; $S = 200$; $T_c = 1.0$; and $F = 0.1$.

17–1. A screen chamber with flat bottom and vertical sides is to be designed to control an average sewage flow of 8 mgd of grit-free domestic sewage. The maximum rate of flow is 3 times the average, and the minimum rate is 0.7 of the average. The discharge falls over a standard weir ($Q = 3.33\ Lh^{1.5}$) whose length is one-third of the width of the channel or chamber. The maximum velocity of flow through the chamber is 2 fps and the minimum velocity is 1 fps. (a) Determine: (1) width of the screen chamber, ft; (2) height of weir crest above chamber floor, ft; (3) depth of sewage in the chamber at maximum rate of flow, ft; and (4) depth at minimum rate of flow, ft. (b) A bar screen with ½-in. rectangular bars is to be placed in the chamber, sloping at 30° with the horizontal. What will be the spacing between the bars if the maximum velocity normal to the screen is 1.5 fps? Answer in inches. (c) What will be the velocity normal to the screen at minimum rate of flow? Answer in fps. (d) At what angle with the horizontal must the screen be placed so that the average velocity normal to the screen will be 0.5 fps?

17–2. The surface of a drum screen is a perfect cylinder, 8 ft in outside diameter. The screen revolves about a horizontal axis supported on bearings. The length of the effective surface of the screen is 12 ft. The sewage passes into the screen through the cylindrical surface and drains out, horizontally, through one end. When operating, one-half of the exterior surface of the screen is submerged up to the elevation of the horizontal axis. The screen revolves about its horizontal axis at one-fourth revolution per minute. Its surface is cleaned by revolving brushes which travel horizontally along the top of the screen parallel to the axis, brushing the accumulated screenings onto a conveyor at one end of the screen. Each brush covers an effective width of 1 ft on the screen surface. The brushes are 18 in. apart. The screen openings represent 20 per cent of the screen surface and are formed by rectangular slots $\frac{1}{16}$ x ½ in. (a) If the loss of head through the openings is 1 ft what is the approximate magnitude of the flotation force, in pounds? (b) What is the nominal capacity of the screen, in gpd? (c) What should be the linear velocity of travel of the cleaning brushes in the direction parallel to the axis of the screen, in order that all portions of the screen may be brushed twice in each revolution of the screen? Answer in fpm. (d) How many pounds of screenings will be removed by each brush per trip across the screen, when the screen is removing 40 cu yd daily, with screenings weighing 60 lb per cu ft?

Answers. (a) 6,000; (b) 9.75 mgd; (c) 18.8.

18–1. There are three grit chambers in a sewage-treatment plant, arranged as shown in Fig. 17–3. The velocity of flow from each chamber is controlled by a proportional-flow weir whose crest is 3 ft above the bottom of the channel. Each channel is 3 ft wide. The maximum permissible depth of accumulation of grit is 1.5 ft, and the maximum permissible head on an outlet weir is 1.8 ft. The rate of flow over the weir is 11.6 times the head, in feet. The rate of flow of sewage varies between 8 and 40 mgd. During operation, when the level of sewage rises to the limit in one chamber, another chamber is put into service and the depths of flow in all basins that are operating are the same. (a) Plot curves showing the rate of flow as ordinates and velocities of flow in the basins as abscissas for all flows from 8 to 40 mgd with no grit accumulation, and with maximum grit accumulation. (b) When the rate of flow is 36 mgd with maximum grit accumulation, what are the velocities in each chamber, in fps?

Answer. (b) 2.

18-2. State the width and length of a grit chamber, the width of the control flume, and the magnitude of Z, as shown in Fig. 18-7, under the following conditions: The grit chambers will operate in parallel, receiving sewage from a 48-in., circular sewer on a slope of 0.00255; with $n = 0.010$. The minimum rate of flow in the sewer occurs at 0.3 full depth. The maximum rate of flow is divided evenly between the two chambers. Velocities of flow in the grit chambers are to lie between 0.95 and 1.05 fps. Period of retention is 90 sec.

18-3. (a) Determine the dimensions of a proportional-flow weir for a maximum head on the weir of 2.5 ft. Tabulate the width of opening for each 3 in. of head on the weir and for a head of 1 in. Allow no additional area below the "design crest" to compensate for an area cut off by bringing the sides down vertically from a head of 1 in. Refer to Fig. 18-6. (b) What is the length of the crest of the weir, in feet? (c) What is the width of opening at a height of 1.5 ft above the crest, in feet? *Answers.* (b) 2.21; (c) 0.52.

18-4. In problem 18-3: (a) What is the rate of discharge for a head of 1 in. on the design crest? (b) What should be the length of the weir if it is cut down vertically at a depth of 3 in. on the "design crest"? (c) If the length of the weir found in step b is used, how much should the crest be lowered in order that the discharge over it may be the same as in step a with the same depth of water in the approach chamber? Answers are to be in feet and seconds.

18-5. A grit chamber is to be designed on the principles stated in Sect. 18-6, under the following conditions: (1) flows between 6 and 10 mgd; (2) an overflow weir ($Q = 3.33\ Lh^{3/2}$) at the outlet extending across the width of the chamber; (3) detention period is 45 sec at maximum rate of flow; (4) velocity at maximum flow, with maximum permissible grit storage, is 1.3 fps; (5) cross section is similar to Fig. 18-7 with maximum grit storage to depth of 2 ft; fillets slope 2 vertical to 1 horizontal; (6) bottom width is 0.5 ft and width between vertical sides is 2.5 ft; (7) bottom is flat and horizontal. (a) Determine the length, and the depth of flow in the chamber. (b) What are the minimum and maximum velocities of flow when grit storage is empty, and when full? (c) Using Camp's formula, $V = 1.3\sqrt{(S-1)D}$ with the nomenclature of equation 18-2 except that D is in mm, what is the diameter of the smallest particle with a specific gravity of 2.65, that will be removed? Answer in feet and seconds except part c to be in mm.

Answers. (a) Length, 58.5 ft; depth for max flow, 4.77 ft, for min flow, 4.34 ft; (b) grit full $V = 0.86$ and 1.3 respectively, and grit empty, $V = 0.67$ and 1.04, respectively; (c) 0.161 mm.

18-6. (a) Sketch a plan and longitudinal section along the center line of a grit chamber and Parshall-flume control, similar to Fig. 18-7, for the conditions stated below. All cross sections are rectangular, without fillets. Width of grit chamber is 4 ft. Rates of flow lie between 3 and 12 cfs. Detention period is 60 sec. (b) What is the length of the grit chamber, and the depth at maximum velocity? (c) What is the magnitude of Z if the velocities lie between 0.95 and 1.05 fps? (d) Tabulate the velocities of flow in the grit chamber for each increment of 20 per cent of the maximum rate of flow. What is V when $Q = 6$ cfs? (e) What is the width of the transition section of the flume for each 0.1 of its length? Tabulate the preceding information and state the length and the greatest width. Show all controlling dimensions on the sketch required in *a*. Answers in feet and seconds.

18–7. Determine the length and width, in feet, and the overflow in gallons per square feet per day, for a horizontal, continuous-flow, primary sedimentation basin, rectangular in plan and cross section, to remove sewage solids from 4 mgd of sewage. The principles of Sect. 18–11 and of the Joint Committee in Table 18–6 are to be followed.

Answers. Width 30; length 150; depth 10 ft; overflow rate, 900.

18–8. Determine the dimensions of a rectangular sedimentation basin for a flow of 1.5 mgd, if the detention period is 1.5 hr, the ratio of length to width is 4:1, and an overflow rate of 850 gal per day per sq ft is desired.

18–9. (*a*) What is the diameter, in mm, of the smallest particle with a specific gravity of 1.2, that will be removed by sedimentation when the load is 25,000 gal per day per sq ft of surface, according to Tables 18–3 and 18–5? (*b*) What is the settling velocity, in mm per sec? (*c*) If the velocity of flow in the chamber is 1 fps, what is the diameter of the smallest particle that will remain in the chamber? Answer in mm, use formula 18–2.

Answers. (*a*) 1.3; (*b*) 17.2; (*c*) 0.42.

18–10. What should be the length, width, depth, and flowing–through velocity for a rectangular, grease-skimming tank, according to the requirements stated in Sect. 18–19? Answer in feet and seconds.

18–11. (*a*) What would be the lowest reasonable cost, exclusive of baffles, in dollars, of three continuous-flow, rectangular in plan and cross section, sedimentation basins under the following conditions: (1) Basins are of same dimensions, and are contiguous with common dividing wall. (2) Detention period in each basin is 90 min. (3) Rate of flow through the treatment plant is 18 mgd. (4) One basin is held in reserve, each of the other two handling 9 mgd. (5) Cost of floor, all items included, is $1.50 per sq ft; cost of outside walls is $0.4H^2$ in dollars per ft of length of wall where H is depth of water in feet; cost of common dividing walls is $0.3H^2$; and cost of all appurtenances for each basin is $3,500. (6) Volume of basins to be increased 10 per cent above requisite water volume, to provide freeboard. (*b*) What are the length, width, and depth of each basin, in ft? *Answer.* (*a*) $80,000.

18–12. How many cu yd of sludge will be collected by primary sedimentation, per mg of sewage, at Muskegon, Mich., according to Table 18–1, if the sludge contains 95 per cent moisture and has a specific gravity of 1.02?

18–13. In a test of the sedimentation basin shown in Fig. 18–11, 10 lb of sodium chloride were dropped into the influent when the rate of flow was 1.25 mgd. The concentration of chlorides was determined at the effluent, with the following results:

Time after dosing, min	60	70	80	85	90	95	100	105	110	115	120
Concentration Cl_2, mg/l	.02	.03	.60	1.3	2.2	3.7	5.2	7.2	8.3	8.5	8.75

The tank is 75 ft long. Scale other dimensions from the figure. If the volume of the sludge-storage hopper is neglected, what is the retention efficiency of the basin? *Answer.* 83 per cent.

18–14. (*a*) What is the maximum, permissible rate of flow through the basin shown in Fig. 18–10, to meet the limitations stated in Sect. 18–11? Answer in mgd. (b) If the tank is operated at the rate given in the preceding answer, and the elevation of the surface of the water in the tank is 102.92, what is the ratio between the actual load and the load recommended by Imhoff and Fair, as stated in Sect. 18–11?

18–15. One mgd of medium sewage, with characteristics shown in Table 15–1, is chlorinated to prevent septicization and is passed through a sedimentation tank in 6 hr. (a) If the performance of the basin is as shown in Fig. 18–4, what is the concentration of suspended solids in the effluent, in mg/l? (b) If the cost of operation of the basin is $30 per day, regardless of the rate of flow through it, what is the cost, in cents per pound, of solid matter removed during a 6-hr holding period? (c) What holding period, in hours, would be required to attain the minimum cost, and what would be this minimum cost?

Answers. (a) 96; (b) 1.77; (c) 12 to 18 hr at 0.27 cent per lb.

19–1. How much slaked lime is required, in mg/l, to react with 2.5 grains per gal of anhydrous ferric chloride in coagulation? *Answer.* 19.4.

19–2. Assuming that the suspended solids in raw sewage average 180 mg/l: (a) compute the percentage removal of suspended solids by the various methods of sewage treatment listed in Table 19–5 for both quiescent and for continuous settling. Compute also the percentage increase in efficiency over plain settling, accomplished by each method of treatment. Tabulate your results. (b) State the percentage efficiency increase in continuous settling by chemical precipitation.

19–3. How many pounds of lime, as $Ca(OH)_2$, must be added, per million gallons of medium-strength sewage as shown in Table 15–1, to react with a chemical feed of 2,200 lb of chemically pure aluminum sulfate added as a coagulant? The aluminum sulphate will first react with the natural alkalinity in the sewage and will require only enough lime to complete the reaction.

Answer. 1,930.

19–4. If raw sewage is coagulated with 360 lb of copperas, containing 54.7 per cent $FeSO_4$, per million gallons: (a) How many pounds of commercial hydrated lime, of which 85 per cent is available $Ca(OH)_2$, must be added? (b) What will be the amount of dissolved oxygen in the effluent, in mg/l, assuming 4.0 mg/l of dissolved oxygen in the raw sewage and no reaeration in the coagulation process?

19–5. The suspended solids in a raw sewage average 270 mg/l and are 90 per cent removed by sedimentation following precipitation by the addition of 450 lb of commercial alum, containing 17 per cent aluminum sulphate, per million gallons. (a) How many cu ft of 95 per cent moisture sludge, with a specific gravity of 1.05, will be accumulated per million gallons of sewage treated? All insoluble precipitates resulting from the coagulation are included in the sludge. (b) How many cubic feet of sludge are formed by the added chemical alone?

Answers. (a) 628; (b) 10.6 cu ft per mg.

19–6. (a) At what rate of dosing must a chlorinator, reading in pounds of chlorine per day, be set to apply 34 mg/l of chlorine to a flow of 1,450 gpm of sewage? (b) By how much would this dose of chlorine reduce the BOD of the sewage, according to the information in Sect. 19–22?

20–1. What volume of sludge-storage, in cubic feet per capita, is required in an Imhoff tank receiving 3 mgd of "medium" sewage, as shown in Table 15–1?

How does this volume compare with the Joint Committee requirements in Table 20–2? The rate of flow of sewage is 110 gcd; 65 per cent of the total suspended solids are settleable in the tank. The fresh sludge contains 95 per cent moisture and the digested sludge 90 per cent; 30 per cent of the solids in the fresh sludge are subsequently dissipated by gasification and hydrolyzing. The specific gravity of the sludge may be determined by formula 24–3, using the specific gravity of solids in the sludge as 1.3. Storage volume provided is to be 180 days. At the end of that time 70 per cent of the sludge is fresh and 30 per cent is digested.

20–2. If the length of the sedimentation compartment in Fig. 20–3 is 48 ft, and the period of detention is 2½ hr, approximately how many gallons of sewage are passing through the tank daily? Scale needed dimensions from the figure.

Answer. 881,000.

20–3. The bottoms of the sludge-digestion compartments of the Imhoff tank shown in Fig. 20–3 are formed of six inverted pyramids, 11 ft by 14 ft at the upper base. In computing volumes assume the area of the lower base to be zero. The rate of flow of sewage is 1 mgd. The daily, per capita flow of sewage is 70 gal. Average sludge storage allowed is 0.005 cu ft per capita daily. How many days will be required to fill all of the sludge compartments with sludge?

20–4. If 70 per cent of the suspended solids in medium sewage, as shown in Table 15–1, is settled in an Imhoff tank; 50 per cent of the solids is gasified and hydrolyzed, and the digested sludge has a specific gravity of 1.03 and a percentage of moisture of 94, how many cubic feet of sludge should be removed quarterly from an Imhoff tank treating 1 mgd of medium sewage? *Answer.* 20,340.

20–5. The digested sludge from an Imhoff tank contains 94 per cent moisture and a specific gravity of 1.02. If it is dried to 70 per cent moisture, what will be its specific gravity? See Sect. 24–9.

20–6. A hospital for 100 mental patients and staff of 20 is to be served by a 2-compartment septic tank. What should be the three dimensions of each compartment, if the first compartment has twice the volume of the second?

Answers. Width, 8 ft; depth, 5 ft; length 1st compartment, 13 ft 4 in.; of 2nd, 6 ft 8 in.

20–7. The hospital in problem 20–6 is to be served by an underground disposal field. For economic reasons the overall cost of sewage disposal should not exceed $100 per patient or a total of $10,000. It is estimated that the cost of sand in place will be $16.30 per cu yd, and that it will represent 25 per cent of the total cost of sewage disposal. The Kiker percolation coefficient is known to be 0.30. The rate of sewage flow will be 150 per cent of the minimum shown in Table 3–7. (*a*) What will be the cost of sewage disposal for 100 patients? Answer in dollars per patient.

21–1. (*a*) How many square feet should be used in the surface of a contact bed 4.0 ft deep, to care for a flow of sewage of 1 mgd? (*b*) What should be the percentage of voids in the contact material to allow three complete fill-and-draw cycles daily? (*c*) What should be the duration of each portion of the dosing cycle if there are three cycles daily? Answer in min. The rate of rise and fall of sewage is 0.1 fpm, and the time standing empty is equal to the time standing full.

Answers. (*a*) 112,500; (*b*) 9.9; (*c*) 200 full, 200 empty, 40 filling, 40 emptying.

21-2. How should the control pipes be arranged in Fig. 21-8 to cause the siphons to discharge in the reverse order to that shown in the figure?

21-3. A city with a population of 3,050 and a rate of water usage of 90 gcd plans to build a sewage-treatment plant using a standard-rate trickling filter. If 35 per cent of the BOD in the sewage is removed by primary treatment, what diameter of filter with a 7-ft depth of rock, will be required? See Ten-State requirements in Table 12-1.   *Answer.* **65 ft.**

21-4. (*a*) What diameter of circular, high-rate filter will be required, according to Sect. 21-31, if the filter is 6 ft deep and the following control: (1) The hydraulic load is 20 mgad. (2) The organic load is 60 lb BOD per 1,000 cu ft of filter material. (3) Raw sewage flow is 3 mgd from an equivalent population of 31,000. (4) BOD removal in primary tank is 30 per cent. (*b*) What recirculation ratio will be required?

21-5. A type *B* biofilter, shown in Table 21-4, is 4 ft deep and is to treat 4 mgd of strong sewage, as described in Table 15-1. (*a*) What is the minimum allowable acreage for the filter, according to the requirements of Sect. 21-31? The primary tank has removed 32 per cent of the BOD. (*b*) What should be the diameter of the filter, in ft? (*c*) What is the highest recirculation ratio that is to be provided, according to Table 21-5? (*d*) If the higher recirculation ratio were used what would be the hydraulic load on the filter? (*e*) With the higher recirculation ratio, how much larger would the primary clarifier have to be than without recirculation?   *Answers.* (*a*) 0.52; (*c*) 2.25:1; (*e*) 3.25 times.

21-6. If a trickling filter operates successfully in treating a typical weak sewage, as described in Table 15-1, at a rate of 4 mgad, what should be the rate, in mgad, that a typical medium-strength sewage should be treated if the BOD load is not to exceed that on the filter when treating weak sewage?   *Answer.* **2.**

21-7. A city with a population of 25,000 has an average rate of flow of sewage of 122 gcd. If 35 per cent of the BOD is removed in the primary tanks: (*a*) How many filters with the same diameter and 6 ft deep would be required under the following conditions? (1) Loads must not exceed 4 mgad or 500 lb BOD per acre-ft per day. (2) Filter diameter must be less than 140 ft. (*b*) What would be the diameter of the filters? (*c*) If high-rate filtration were used, how many filters would be required if the hydraulic load limits were 10 to 30 mgad and 3,000 lb BOD per acre-ft per day? (*d*) What is the hydraulic load on the standard-rate and on the high-rate filters, in mgad?   *Answer.* (*b*) 132 ft.

21-8. A trickling filter, dosed at a rate of 4 mgad, is underlaid by Type *C* underdrainage blocks shown in Fig. 21-10. The cross section of the stream of flowing sewage in the side channels is 0.11 sq ft, and of the channel above it, through which ventilating air flows into the filter, is 0.10 sq ft. The velocity of flow of sewage is 0.75 fps and of air, in these side channels, is 1,000 fpm. The central collecting gutter is 2 ft wide and flows 9.75 in. deep. It is on a slope of 0.0067, with $n = 0.013$. Sewage from the side channels falls unobstructed, into the central channel. There is a side channel on each side of the central channel. (*a*) How many feet of central channel can be used with these side channels, if velocity head is neglected? (*b*) What is the maximum number of feet of side channel that can supply ventilating air to rise at 1 fpm through the filtering material that has a porosity of 25 per cent?   *Answer.* (*b*) **300.**

21–9. A final clarifier in a standard-rate trickling-filter plant is to carry a load of 1 mgd. According to Table 21–8: (*a*) What is the minimum permissible size of the clarifier, in cubic feet? (*b*) What is the greatest depth of clarifier permissible? Answer in feet. (*c*) What is the shortest overflow trough permitted, in feet? *Answers.* (*a*) 5,570; (*c*) 66.6.

21–10. There are 4 distributor arms on a trickling filter, each arm extending 50 ft from the central column. The filter is 101 ft in inside diameter. There are 50 reaction jets equally spaced on each arm. Jet No. 50 is 50 ft from the center of the bed and jet No. 1 is 18 in. from it. The dosing tank discharges 6,900 gal between elevations of 6 ft and 2 ft above the nozzles in a period of 10 min. Each distributor arm is 4 in. in diameter. The dosing tank is shaped so that the rate of flow from it varies directly as the head on the nozzle. (*a*) At what average rate, in gpm, should the influent to the filter flow from each nozzle if the maximum permissible surface dosing rate stated in Sect. 21–6 controls? (*b*) What is the maximum rate of discharge from each nozzle, in gpm? (*c*) How many times will the dosing tank discharge daily? (*d*) How many minutes will elapse between the stopping of one dose and the beginning of the next? (*e*) Let it be assumed that: (1) the rate of discharge from a nozzle is proportional to the square root of the total head on it; (2) the total head on the nozzles varies as a straight line from H at nozzle 50 to $H/3$ at nozzle 1, where H is the elevation of the water in the dosing tank. What is the coefficient of distribution as defined in Sect. 21–32? *Answers.* (*a*) 1.9; (*c*) 80.

21–11. A type B, high-rate filter, as described in Table 21–4 and in Fig. 21–11, is to be designed to treat 1 mgd of medium-strength sewage, as described in Table 15–1. Primary treatment removes 35 per cent of the BOD. Filter dimensions are to permit the highest dosing loads stated in Sect. 21–31. Recirculation rates, as recommended in Table 21–5, are to be used. The surface area of each filter is to be the smallest permissible. The minimum conditions in Sect. 21–32 are to control. The coefficient of distribution need not be observed. (*a*) What should be the diameter and depth, in feet, of the first-stage filter? (*b*) What are the intensities of load on the first stage in mgad, in pounds per acre-foot per day, and in pounds per cubic feet per day? Which of these loads controlled in determining the diameter of the filter? (*c*) What should be the diameter and depth, in feet, of the second-stage filter? (*d*) What are the intensities of load on the second-stage filter in the same units as above? Indicate which of these loads controls in the design. (*e*) What will be the concentration of BOD in the effluent from the plant, according to the appropriate formula in Sect. 21–32? (*f*) What will be the percentage removal of BOD by the combined filters? (*g*) Answer each of the preceding questions on the assumption that "strong sewage" (Table 15–1) is to be treated with only the lowest permissible intensities of load being used in design.

Answers. (*a*) Dia. 63 ft, depth 7 ft; (*c*) dia. 62 ft, depth 5 ft; (*e*) 50 mg/l.

21–12. A controlled, 3-section trickling filter that is 25 ft in diameter and 18 ft deep is to treat 1 mgd of sewage with a maximum rate of flow of 1.8 mgd, a minimum rate of 0.7 mgd, and an average BOD of 200 mg/l. The primary tank removes 35 per cent of the BOD. The allowable organic load in the effluent is 250 lb per million gal. (*a*) What are the loads on each of the three sections at maximum, average, and minimum rates of flow, and are these loads recommended or permissible according to Sect. 21–35? State hydraulic loads in mgad. State organic loads in pounds per acre per day and in pounds per acre-foot per day for each of the three sections, and for maximum, average, and minimum loads on the first section only. (*b*) What area of filter surface in square feet, and volume of stone in cubic yards would be required by a standard-rate filter for this maximum load under maximum permissible limits stated in Sect. 21–6? (*c*) Answer a similar question for a high-rate filter under the limits stated in Sect. 21–31?

> *Answer.* (*b*) Standard filter 6 ft deep requires 24 times area and 8 times rock volume.

22–1. An intermittent sand-filter plant consists of eight quarter-acre units. The average rate of dosing is 55,000 gal per acre per day. (*a*) What is the nominal, daily capacity of the plant, all filters operating? (*b*) What should be the capacity of the dosing tank, in gallons, to apply a dose to a depth of 3 in. on one unit? (*c*) How many times a month will each unit be dosed, assuming that the beds are dosed in rotation? (*d*) What is the depth of flow, in feet, in the main distribution trough, which is 12 in. wide with flat bottom and vertical sides, and is on a slope of 0.005, with $n = 0.013$. The beds are square and the dosing trough runs diagonally across each bed. *Answers.* (*b*) 20,400; (*d*) 0.56.

23–1. Compute the capacity, in cubic feet, of an aeration tank in an activated-sludge treatment plant under the following conditions: (1) rate of flow of raw sewage is 2.0 mgd; (2) detention period is 6 hr, based on flow of raw sewage; and (3) mixed liquor is composed of 25 per cent, by volume, of return sludge.

23–2. At what concentration of BOD in the influent to an aeration tank receiving 750,000 gal of sewage daily will the operation of the tank be controlled by the BOD load rather than by the nominal aeration period of 8 hr? Answer in mg/l. *Answer.* 178.

23–3. The mixed liquor entering an aeration tank in an activated-sludge plant is to have the same concentration of activated sludge particles as is supplied by 35 per cent return sludge containing 98 per cent moisture, where the volume of the return sludge represents 35 per cent of the volume of the raw sewage. If the moisture in the return sludge is later reduced to 97 per cent, what percentage of the sludge should be returned? Answer in per cent, by volume, of the incoming raw sewage. Assume that the specific gravity of the sludge is 1.01.

23–4. An activated-sludge treatment plant is to handle 2.5 mgd of medium-strength, domestic sewage. The sewage contains 320 mg/l of suspended solids, and 210 mg/l BOD. It is to be treated in a ridge-and-furrow, air-diffusion, aeration tank which is rectangular in cross-section, with a flat bottom, and 12 ft deep. Plate diffusers, with a permeability of 40 are used. The period of aeration, based on flow of raw sewage, is to be 6 hr when the volume of return sludge is 35 per cent of the incoming sewage. The return sludge has 99 per cent moisture. One cu ft of air is to be used per gal of sewage. The air is delivered from a blower to the diffuser plates by a pipe that is 400 ft long. The temperatures of both the air and the sewage are 60° F. The specific gravity of the return activated sludge is 1.01 and all of the solids returned may be considered as suspended. (*a*) What should be the capacity of the aeration tank, in gallons? (*b*) What should be the average rate of flow of mixed liquor into the tank, in cfs? (*c*) If 45 per cent of the suspended solids in the raw sewage is removed by sedimentation before entering the aeration tank, what will be the concentration of suspended solids in the mixed liquor? (*d*) What should be the length of flow of sewage in the channels of the aeration tank? (*e*) What is the area of the surface of the aeration tank, in square feet, for each million gallons of sewage treated daily? (*f*) How many square feet of diffusion plates will be required per mg of sewage treated daily, using a ratio of plate area to tank surface of 1:9? (*g*) What is the rate of flow of air through the diffuser plates in cubic feet per minute per square foot of plate? (*h*) What would be the head loss, in inches of water, due to friction through the porous plates, if the head loss through the plate varies directly as the rate of flow through the plate? (*i*) What should be the rate of flow of air from the blower, expressed in terms of cubic feet of free air per minute? (*j*) What should be the diameter of the air pipe, in inches, assuming the loss of pressure due to friction to be about 1 psi? Use the next largest commercial diameter to that given by the formula in Sect. 23–17. (*k*) What is the aeration period, based on the volume of the aeration tank and the rate of flow of raw sewage? (*l*) How much does the addition of return sludge lower the nominal aeration period computed in part *k*? (*m*) If 35 per cent of the raw-sewage BOD is removed in the primary settling tank, what is the volume of the aeration tank in cubic feet per pound of BOD?

       Answers. (*a*) 843,500; (*c*) 2,750 mg/l; (*e*) 3,750; (*g*) 1.67; (*i*) 1,735; (*k*) 8.1 hr; (*m*) 39.7.

23–5. (*a*) What should be the capacity, in cubic feet, of the final sedimentation tank, following the aeration tank in problem 23–4, to provide a 2.5-hr sedimentation period if sludge is to be removed continuously? (*b*) What should be its surface area, in square feet, if the maximum permissible surface rate stated in Sect. 23–41 for this type of sewage is used? (*c*) If the tank is a circular clarifier, what should be its depth, in feet? (*d*) If the tank is a circular clarifier what is the minimum permissible length of overflow weir? (*e*) What will be the rate of discharge over the effluent weir, in gpm, if sludge is to be removed continuously at the rate of 35 per cent return sludge? Use Joint Committee standards.   *Answers.* (*b*) 4,050; (*e*) 1,735.

23–6. What was the cost of construction of a 5-mgd, air-diffusion, activated-sludge plant the year that Fig. 23–14 was first published? (*b*) What was the cost of a secondary treatment plant in Seattle, Wash., in 1958, according to the formula 28–2? (*c*) What was the *Eng. News-Record* cost index the year that Fig. 23–14 was first published, according to the costs given in the two preceding answers? *Suggestion,* refer to Sect. 28–7.   *Answer.* (*b*) $1,370,000.

23–7. (*a*) What is the rate of change of the Nordell number for each hour shown in Fig. 23–12, according to curve *A* shown in the figure? (*b*) If the cost of aeration remains constant, what is the relative cost of reducing the Nordell number at the second hour of aeration as compared with the cost at the first hour? *Suggestion,* use a graphical solution.   *Answers.* (*a*) −1.2; (*b*) 4.5 times.

23–8. (*a*) List the units named in Fig. 23–11 in the order in which sewage passes through them from plant inlet to plant outlet. (*b*) Name three devices provided for dewatering sludge that are shown in the figure. (*c*) Two "separators" are shown. What are their purposes?

23–9. If it costs $10 per hr to aerate sewage or mixed liquor at a stated rate of aeration, and it is required to produce an effluent with approximately 24 mg/l of nitrate nitrogen, what will be the cost of creating such a concentration by aeration without activated sludge, and by aeration with activated sludge, according to Fig. 23–10?   *Answer.* 20 hr without activated sludge cost $200.

23–10. An operator of a sewage-treatment plant finds, by laboratory tests, that solids are low in the mixed liquor in the aeration compartments of the units shown in Figs. 23–8 and 23–9. Which valve or valves in each figure should be opened or closed to increase the solids in the mixed liquor?

23–11. Let it be assumed that the average rate of application of diffused air to the tapered aeration tank shown in Fig. 23–7 is the same as that shown for Boise, Idaho, in Table 23–3. What is the approximate maximum rate of application? *Suggestion,* count aerators and scale proportionate distances from the figure.   *Answer.* 2.2 cu ft per gal.

23–12. The following information is given concerning air diffusers of the porous-tube type shown in Fig. 23–6: Length between gaskets, 24 in.; internal diameter of tube, 3 in.; thickness, $\frac{5}{8}$ in.; permeability, 60. How many such tubes would be required in the plants at Muskegon Heights, Mich., and Fort Wayne, Ind., according to the information in Table 23–3?
Answer. Fort Wayne, 118.

23–13. If the pipe shown in the lower left corner of Fig. 23–4 is tar-coated steel, and were to carry air to the aerators at Marion, Ind., mentioned in Table 23–3, at the minimum velocity given in Sect. 23–17: (*a*) What should be its internal diameter, to the nearest half inch? (*b*) What is the pressure loss, in inches of water per 100 ft of this pipe, according to formula 23–4?
Answer. (*b*) 0.3.

23–14. The mixed liquor in the aeration tank of an activated-sludge plant treating 10 mgd contains 25 per cent return sludge. The velocity of flow in the return-sludge pipe is 1 fps. (*a*) What should be the diameter of the return-sludge pipe, to the nearest inch? (*b*) What should be the capacity of the sludge pump, in gpm? (*c*) If the head loss due to friction in the sludge line and sludge pump is 0.5 ft, what is the total lift of this pump, in feet?   *Answer.* (*c*) 2.5.

23–15. Sewage is flowing at 17.3 mgd through a sedimentation tank similar to that at Columbus, Ohio, in Fig. 23–13. The tank is 90 ft long, 20 ft wide, 15 ft deep at the inlet or left end in the figure, and 10 ft deep at the opposite end. The side and end walls are vertical. The bottom is a flat, sloping plane. No space is to be allowed for sludge storage. The distance from the inlet to the nearest point in a trough is 30 ft. One transverse outlet trough, or launder, is in the middle of the tank, and the other is 75 ft from the inlet. Effluent flows over all edges and ends of the launders at the same rate per unit of length. (*a*) What are the nominal, horizontal velocities of flow, in fpm, in the tank at the following distances from the inlet: 38 ft, 50 ft, and 80 ft? (*b*) It is desired to localize these velocity variations by relocating the troughs. They are 2 ft wide, 2 ft deep, must be at least 12 in. apart, and not less than 6 in. from a tank wall. In what position and location can the troughs be placed to provide the same effective length of overflow edge and, at the same time, the greatest length of tank in which the horizontal velocity is constant? (*c*) What is this distance, in feet? *Answers.* (*a*) 4.3 fpm at 50 ft; (*c*) 74.8 ft.

24–1. (*a*) How many cubic yards of sludge will be collected, per million gallons of sewage, as a result of treatment by plain sedimentation in a mechanical clarifier, according to the figures in Table 24–4? (*b*) What will be its approximate specific gravity if its percentage of moisture becomes 97? The specific gravity of the sludge may be computed by formula 24–3. *Answer.* (*b*) 1.01.

24–2. (*a*) What is the specific gravity of sludge containing 90 per cent moisture, if the specific gravity of the solids is 1.35? (*b*) If the moisture content of 1,500 cu ft of this sludge is increased to 94 per cent, how much additional storage volume will be required? *Answer.* (*b*) 1,020 cu ft.

24–3. (*a*) Determine the diameter of a cast-iron pipe 3 miles long, required to carry 1 mgd of sludge with a total head loss of 135 ft of water. The sludge constants were determined as follows: $\eta = 0.02$, $\rho = 63.0$; and $S_y = 0.07$. (*b*) What is the velocity of flow in this pipe, in fps? (*c*) What is lower critical velocity, in fps? *Answers.* (*a*) 10 in.; (*c*) 3.8 fps.

25–1. If the flow of medium-strength sewage, as described in Table 15–1, is 90 gcd, and 60 per cent of the volatile solids enter the digester where 48 per cent will be destroyed, what maximum rate of gas production can be expected? Answer in cubic feet per capita per day.

25–2. A city with a population of 50,000 has an average daily sewage flow of 130 gcd. The sewage corresponds to the medium-strength sewage shown in Table 15–1. Laboratory tests indicate that 65 per cent of the suspended solids are removed by sedimentation. (*a*) How many cubic yards of sludge with 94 per cent moisture will be removed daily from the sewage by sedimentation? (*b*) Assuming that the settled sewage, containing 70 per cent volatile matter in the solids, is transferred to digestion tanks in which 70 per cent of the volatile matter is gasified and hydrolized, and the moisture content is reduced to 85 per cent, what should be the capacity of the digestion tank to hold one month's accumulation of sludge? Answer in cubic feet per capita. *Answer.* (*a*) 103.

25–3. Compute the cubic feet of gas, at 60° F and 760 mm of mercury pressure, that should be produced by the digestion of 1 lb of volatile matter under the assumption that 1 lb of volatile matter will produce 1.1 lb of gas. The gas analysis shows 66 per cent methane, 29 per cent carbon dioxide, and 5 per cent nitrogen. Percentages are by volume. *Answer.* 16.9.

25–4. What volume of sludge storage should be allowed in an unheated, sludge-digestion tank, in cubic feet per capita, which is cleaned semi-annually and is to receive sludge accumulated in a sedimentation tank treating 80 gcd, of sewage containing 220 mg/l of suspended solids? The combined primary and secondary sludge amounts to 75 per cent of the original suspended solids. Assume an average digestion of 40 per cent. The sludge in the tank averages 95 per cent moisture.

25–5. What was the flow of sewage, in gcd, for each method of sewage treatment in Table 24–4, for which adequate information is given?

Answer. Activated sludge, 93.

25–6. In a study of the effect of temperature on sludge digestion, test observations were made on three digesters, as follows:

Tank Number	Dry Solids Digested, cu ft per yr	Vol. Used for Digestion, cu ft	Temp ° F
1	1,393	18,100	60
2	2,410	19,200	90
3	2,614	18,850	100

(*a*) If 0.6 cu ft of dry solids are produced per capita per year, what was the sludge digestion capacity, in cubic feet per capita, measured at each temperature? (*b*) Draw the straight line of approximate nearest fit through these plotted points and determine the straight-line relationship between V, the gas produced in cubic feet per capita per day, and T, the temperature in ° F, between 50 and 100 only.   *Answer.* (*a*) At 60°, 7.8.

25–7. Determine the volume of a separate sludge-digestion tank under the following conditions: population, 10,000; dry solids in sludge, per capita daily, 0.17 lb; 3.1 per cent dry solids in raw sludge; specific gravity of sludge, 1.015; 2 per cent, by volume, of wet sludge is added to the digesting sludge daily. If the tank is kept full, what is the required digester volume in cubic feet per capita?   *Answer.* 4.3.

25–8. Sludge placed in a digestion tank has the following characteristics: per cent solids, 1.8; per cent of solids that are volatile, 77; flow in gallons per day, 3,960. During a digestion period of 28 days, the volatile matter is reduced to 40 per cent, the rate of digestion being proportional to time in the tank. The moisture in the digested sludge is 94 per cent. (*a*) What should be the volume, in cubic feet, of a single digestion tank to receive this sludge daily? (*b*) Will the volume of liquid drawn from the tank daily be greater, less, or equal to the volume of sludge added? Why?   *Answer.* (*a*) 8,940.

25–9. If the sludge entering a digestion tank contains 77 per cent of volatile matter, and the digested sludge removed from the tank contains 58 per cent of volatile matter in the solids, what is the percentage reduction of volatile solids during digestion?

25–10. (*a*) Which tank, in Fig. 25–2, has a fixed cover? (*b*) If the diameter of the cover of the secondary tank is 50 ft, its maximum rise and fall are 6 ft, and the cover weighs 41,700 lb, what volume of gas can be stored between high and low positions of the cover? Answer in cubic feet at atmospheric pressure of 760 mm of mercury, and a temperature of 60° F.
                                Answers. (*a*) The primary tank; (*b*) 11,900.

25–11. (*a*) What is the total weight of a 30-ft diameter floating cover on a tank similar to the tank shown in Fig. 25–3 to produce a gas pressure equal to 4.08 in. of water? (*b*) If the volume of gas in the digester and gasometer is 500 cu ft when the pressure equals 4.08 in. of water, and the cover sticks in place, how many gallons of sludge must be removed from the tank, without replenishment, to reduce the pressure to atmospheric? Assume atmospheric pressure to be equal to 34 ft of water.   *Answer.* (*b*) 37.5.

25–12. (*a*) At what rate can waste gas properly be burned in the waste burner shown in Fig. 25–6, if the gas flows through the pipe to the burner at the lowest economical velocity mentioned in Sect. 23–17? Answer in cfm. (*b*) If gas is generated at the maximum rate per capita mentioned in Sect. 25–10, what population would properly be served by this burner if all gas generated were passed through the burner, and conditions of part *a* of this problem control?

Answer. (*b*) 194,000.

25–13. If the tank shown in Fig. 25–4 has a sludge-holding capacity of 42,500 gal; the entire volume of sludge is to be circulated through the heat exchanger every 4 hr; the discharge velocity of the centrifugal pump is 8 fps; the velocity of flow in the sludge pipe may not be less than 4.5 fps; the rate of heat exchange through the tubes in the heat exchanger is 234 Btu per hr per sq ft of pipe surface per degree F difference in temperature; sludge enters the heat exchanger at 90° F and leaves at 100° F; and the temperature of the water in the heat exchanger is 215° F: (*a*) What is the nominal size of the centrifugal, sludge-circulating pump, in inch-diameter of the discharge pipe? (*b*) What should be the diameter of the sludge pipe, in inches? (*c*) What should be the length of tubes exposed to the hot water in the heat exchanger, in feet?   *Answers.* (*a*) 3 in.; (*c*) 30 ft.

25–14. If the contents of both tanks *A* and *C* in Fig. 25–7 are recirculated every two hours through heat exchanger *L*, entering at *M* at 95° F, and leaving at *M'* at 101° F; and the temperature of heating water entering through *K* is 182° F, and leaving through *K'* is 110° F; what is rate of flow through pipe *K*, to nearest gpm? The volumes of tanks *A* and *C* combined are 180,000 gal. The specific heats of sludge and of water may be assumed to be equal. Neglect heat losses.

25–15. In a test on the effect on gas production resulting from the heating of the sludge-digestion compartment of an Imhoff tank by using gas from a separate-sludge digestion tank, the temperature of the effluent from the Imhoff tank was found to be 4° F warmer than the influent. The rate of gas production was raised to 0.9 cu ft per capita daily. The rate of flow of sewage was 80 gcd, with a daily flow of one mgd. The heat content of the gas produced was 780 Btu per cu ft. (*a*) How many Btu would be required, in addition to the Btu in the gas produced, to raise the temperature of each million gallons of sewage treated? (*b*) How many additional cubic feet of gas would be required?

Answer. (*b*) 31,500.

25–16. Determine the heat requirements, in Btu per hour, for a concrete, sludge-digestion tank, under the following conditions: (1) Tank is 35 ft in diameter and is 26 ft deep, of which 12 ft is above the ground surface. C_1 above ground is 0.13 and below ground is 0.07. (2) Tank has a floating, steel cover, for which C_1 is 0.020. (3) Tank is fed with 4,200 gal of sludge daily, at a temperature of 58° F. (4) Lowest outside air temperature is −10° F. The lowest average ground temperature is 28° F. (5) Sludge in the tank is maintained at 95° F.

25–17. What should be the diameter of a spherical, pressure, gas holder to make available 50,000 cu ft of gas at 60° F and a pressure of 2 in. of water above atmospheric, if the maximum pressure in the gas holder is to be 50 psi at a temperature of 110° F?   *Answer.* 28.7 ft.

25–18. How many horsepower will be delivered by a gas engine at a sewage-treatment plant which burns 9,000 cu ft of gas a day? The gas contains 740 Btu per cu ft, and the gas engine has a heat efficiency of 23 per cent?

26–1. (*a*) If a sludge contains 98 per cent moisture and it is run onto a drying bed to a depth of 14 in., what will be the approximate percentage of moisture when the depth has reduced to 7 in.? (*b*) What will be the depth of sludge on the bed, in inches, when the sludge contains 93 per cent moisture? Neglect changes in specific gravity of the sludge. *Answer.* (*a*) 96.

26–2. (*a*) How many pounds of 95 per cent moist sludge can be handled daily on a vacuum filter under the conditions at Cleveland, Ohio, shown in Table 26–3? The filter is 20 ft long and 12 ft in diameter. It operates 16 hr daily. (*b*) How many pounds of sludge cake will be produced daily?

Answer. (*a*) 748,000.

26–3. Determine the lowest reasonable number of vacuum filters to be provided in a sewage-treatment plant handling 50 mgd of normal, domestic sewage, each filter unit being 8 ft in diameter and 14 ft long: (*a*) if raw sludge produced by plain sedimentation in a mechanical clarifier is to be treated at a rate similar to that at Minneapolis-St. Paul, Minn., as fast as it is produced, (*b*) if raw, activated sludge is to be filtered at a rate similar to that at Milwaukee, Wis. The maximum rate of sludge production is three times the average. Refer to Tables 24–4 and 26–3.

Answer. (*a*) Use 6 with 2 additional for standby.

26–4. What is the rated capacity of one sludge-drying bed at Vallejo, Calif., shown in Fig. 26–1, for drying primary sludge, according to the standards shown in Table 26–1? Answer in population served.

26–5. If the diameter of the rotor at the larger end of the shaft of the centrifuge shown in Fig. 26–2 is 14 in., and the speed of revolution is 3,250 rpm, what centrifugal force, in terms of gravity, is produced?

Answer. 2,100 times gravity.

26–6. (*a*) What is the purpose of the "cyclone" shown in Fig. 26–5? (*b*) What is the purpose of the "dry divider" conduit?

26–7. (*a*) Does the sludge, after drying in the dryer shown in Fig. 26–4, pass through the fan or around it? (*b*) How is sludge moved through the dryer and in what direction is it moved? *Answer.* (*a*) Through.

26–8. If the vacuum filter shown in Fig. 26–3 is 12 ft in diameter and is 12 ft long: (*a*) what is the approximate, maximum number of square feet of sludge cake discharged per minute during normal operation at the rate mentioned in the text? (*b*) At what speed is the filter revolving at this maximum rate, in revolutions per hour? *Answer.* (*b*) 1.6.

26–9. A vacuum filter 10 ft in diameter and 12 ft long is producing sludge cake at a rate and with a moisture content the same as that shown at Cleveland, Ohio, in Table 26–3. The weight of this sludge cake is 68 lb per cu ft. If the filter is revolving at the peripheral speed mentioned in the text, what is the thickness of the sludge cake, to the nearest 0.1 in.?

26–10. (*a*) At what hearth level, or levels, are raw sludge and sludge cake shown entering in Fig. 26–6? (*b*) At what point, or points, can dried cake or ash be removed? (*c*) How many typical burners are shown in the figure?

Answer. (*c*) One.

28–1. In the treatment plant shown in Fig. 28–1: (*a*) Is separate sludge digestion provided for? (*b*) From and to what tanks is activated sludge recirculated? (*c*) What proportion of packing-house waste is shown mixing with domestic sewage?   *Answer.* (*c*) All.

28–2. In the two treatment plants shown in Fig. 28–1: (*a*) Into what tank is sludge from the final sedimentation tanks normally being recirculated? (*b*) If separate sludge digestion is used, what path does sludge from the final sedimentation tanks follow to pass to the sludge-digestion tanks?

29–1. Prepare an operating report similar to the one shown in Fig. 29–1 but applicable to the trickling-filter plant shown in Fig. 28–1.

Index

Oxidation-reduction potential, 356, 709, 710
Oxidized sludge process, 552
Oxygen, absorbed by water, 379, 382, 383, 532
  absorption by plants, 382, 383
  balance, 377
  consumed, 341, 343, 352, 353, 355, 357
  consumption, per capita, 357
  deficiency, in sewer atmosphere, 307, 308
  in a lake, 379
  demand, in analyses, 343
   chemical (COD) 352
   immediate, 343, 352, 384
  dissolved, *see* Dissolved oxygen
  forms reported, 343
  sag curve, 376, 378–380
  self-purification indices, 370–374
  solubility in water, 343–345
Ozone, metallurgical waste treatment, 647

Paper, in coagulation, 448
  in sludge conditioning, 619
  manufacturing wastes, 631, 633, 658–661
  water used in manufacture, 36
Parbon, 186
Paris, France, sewage farm, 386
Parks, E. W., industrial wastes, 630
Parmely, overflow weir formula, 144, 145
  runoff formula, 54
Parshall flume, 424, 426, 427, 429
Pasadena, Calif., 678
Passaic Valley outfall sewer, New Jersey, 158
Patents, 334, 335
Pathogenic organisms in sewage, 358
Pavement, removal and replacement, 204, 205
Pearl's logistic curve, 26
Pearse, Langdon, sewage-treatment principles, 326
Pearson, E. A., beet sugar wastes, 640
Peat in sludge conditioning, 619
Pekin, Ill., digester loadings, 636

Pennsylvania State Department of Health, 331
Pennsylvania State Sanitary Water Board, 648, 649
Peoria, Ill., digester loadings, 636
  population study, 26, 28
Percolation coefficient, 396
Permeability of air diffusers, 542
Permit for sewer construction, 332
Personnel, operating, 684, 685
Peterson on lipids in sludge, 572
pH, adjustment with activated carbon, 450
  in analyses, 342
  index of acidity, 357, 374
  self-purification index, 374
  of sewage, 356
Phages in sewage, 358
Pharmaceutical manufacturing wastes, 661, 662
Phenol wastes, 661, 662
Phillip's egg-shaped sewer, 71
Phosphorus, in industrial wastes, 650
  in organic matter, 361
Phosphates, self-purification index, 370
Photoelectric cell for solids determination, 343
Photosynthesis, biological effects, 324, 327
  self-purification of streams, 370
Physical analyses, 338, 340
Picrates, manufacturing wastes, 650
Piles, foundation, 257, 258
Pills for cleaning sewers, 313, 314
Pipe, bends, flow measurement, 152, 153
  clay specials, 166
  cradle for laying, 241
  flexible, 190
  galleries, 267, 541
  hook for laying in trench, 241
  lines in buildings, 272
  rigid, 190
Pipes, air, materials for, 540, 541
  bedding in trench, 191, 211
  bell-and-spigot joints, 179
  buried, conditions, 189–200
   ditch condition, 192, 194
   loads on, 188–200